Visual Optics

LECTURES IN OPTICS
Volume 4

By the Author

Visual Optics

LECTURES IN OPTICS
Volume 4

George Asimellis

SPIE PRESS
Bellingham, Washington USA

Library of Congress Cataloging-in-Publication Data

Names: Asimellis, George, 1966- author.
Title: Visual optics / George Asimellis.
Description: Bellingham, Washington : SPIE Press, [2022] | Series: Lectures
    in optics ; Vol. 4 | Includes bibliographical references and index.
Identifiers: LCCN 2020046082 (print) | LCCN 2020046083 (ebook) | ISBN
    9781510622616 (paperback) | ISBN 9781510622623 (pdf)
Subjects: LCSH: Eye--Accommodation and refraction. | Visual acuity. |
    Physiological optics.
Classification: LCC RE925 .A78 2021 (print) | LCC RE925 (ebook) | DDC
    617.7/5--dc23
LC record available at https://lccn.loc.gov/2020046082
LC ebook record available at https://lccn.loc.gov/2020046083

Published by
SPIE
P.O. Box 10
Bellingham, Washington 98227-0010 USA
Phone: +1 360.676.3290
Fax: +1 360.647.1445
Email: books@spie.org
Web: http://spie.org

Printed in the United States of America.
First Printing.
For updates to this book, visit http://spie.org and type "PM291" in the search field.

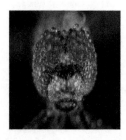

Cover Image:

Macro photography of a fly eye with spherical drops acting as magnifying lenses providing local
detail of the ommatidia.

TABLE OF CONTENTS

FOREWORD

The application of core vision science to clinical practice is universal, yet finding a suitable teaching resource to convey a comprehensive message is difficult. Students may be forced to rely on superficial knowledge gained through Internet sources due to a lack of suitable resources. What is required is a textbook that has a comprehensive discussion on a range of core vision science topics that provides a nexus to understand basic principles essential for clinical practice. The *Visual Optics* text of Dr. Asimellis is such a text, providing sections devoted to the development of the eye, monocular sensory perception that includes visual acuity, contrast sensitivity, color vision, and then an in-depth discussion on refractive errors and optics of the eye and core optics concepts.

The textbook beautifully integrates biological science, physical science, and clinical science to produce a textbook that would be useful to the novice and to those with a keen interest in optics and the eye. Dr. Asimellis' expertise in visual optics is clearly illustrated in the textbook, which challenges those who may be outside their knowledge comfort zone.

The text begins with basic optics and vision principles, including comparative anatomy of the eye. There are introductory examples of image formation and the visual pathways, which are useful in providing a holistic view of vision. Basic optical principles are then integrated with visual perception to integrate this core knowledge. In addition to visual acuity, the perception of color is introduced, including connections to photoreceptor density and type, and how the encoding of chromatic information is achieved. The remaining text is focused on the optics of the eye, including a comprehensive discussion on ametropia and factors affecting image quality. The expertise of the author is clearly evident in this section, which includes excellent biometric measurements that are now essential in clinical practice.

Dr. George Asimellis has written a text from a student's perspective and provides a well-laid-out and well-illustrated format that is comprehensive and highly readable. The integration of theoretical and clinical information contributes to the understanding of monocular sensory and clinical procedures. I congratulate him and have no reservations in recommending this textbook to all of those with an interest in vision science.

Michael Kalloniatis BSc(Optom), MSc(Optom), PhD, FAAO
Director, Centre for Eye Health
Professor of Optometry and Vision Science
University of New South Wales, Sydney, Australia

PREFACE

Visual optics is, in essence, an application of optics for a very important sensory organ: the eye. While rather complicated, the process of vision can be divided into two parts, the optical and the neural. This book extensively and comprehensively covers the optical part, while providing a simple description of the neural part, which is restricted to those aspects that are critical to understanding visual function.

The topic of visual optics can be quite challenging and fascinating. This topic bridges knowledge acquired from more science-oriented, geometrical and wave optics material with the application of this knowledge to the eye, and extends in clinical relevance to optometry and ophthalmology. Optics is the foundation of how the eye works, how we image the eye for diagnosis, and, most recently, how we use many laser-based therapeutic and cosmetic applications. A good understanding of the simple yet powerful relationships that describe the interaction between light and the eye helps to pave the way to a comfortable approach to understanding the operation of traditional examination techniques such as retinoscopy as well as modern ocular diagnostics such as topography and optical coherence tomography. Thus, the first three books in this series provide the scientific foundation for the explorations and applications discussed in this book. The applications of ocular imaging are extensively presented in the final volume of this series, *Ocular Imaging*.

Combining optical science with clinical relevance, this *Visual Optics* volume is written specifically for adult learners in the optometry and ophthalmology professions. It is referenced with the most recent research findings that have been published in peer-reviewed journals—almost 1000 external references are included.

The text follows the didactic principles adopted throughout the series, with adherence to a deductive approach, lots of practical examples, ample illustrations, and clear, concise language. Often my students tell me that the words from the lectures are also the words in my texts. While I see this as an exaggeration, it is true that, despite endeavoring to explain complex concepts and the need to adhere to strict and rigorous definitions, simple language is always sought, with the goal of being thoroughly understood in a clinically meaningful way.

The book is organized based on two broad concepts. The first concept, spanning Chapters 1 to 5, pertains to the well-functioning eye, or the eye that produces retinal images of sufficient quality; let's call this emmetropic visual optics. The second concept spans Chapters 6 to 10 and is called ametropic visual optics. This covers the science of spherocylindrical ametropias, i.e., myopia, hyperopia (Chapter 6), and astigmatism (Chapter 8) for distance- and near-vision accommodation (Chapter 7) and extends to aspects of the aging eye, which include presbyopia and low vision (Chapter 7), optical correction and its considerations (Chapter 9 on ophthalmic lens optics), and prismatic effects (Chapter 10).

Every chapter is followed by an extensive, multiple-choice quiz and a short summary. The quiz questions are in the format followed by the National Board of Examiners in Optometry (NBEO) and aim to be an element of self-evaluation and assessment for the reader.

The contents of this book can be used in a multitude of instructional courses, including core visual optics courses, as well as courses on perception and ophthalmic optics. A recommended structure that adheres best to the flow of this book could be as follows:

Emmetropic Visual Optics; 2-credit course / 30 lecture hours

- Unit 1, 3 hours: Optics of the Eye – Chapter 1 (including some Geometrical Optics review)
- Unit 2: 10 hours: Refractive Elements of the Eye – Chapter 2.
- Unit 3: 5 hours: Visual Acuity – Chapter 3 (including some Wave Optics review) and § 4.5 Digital Signal and Analysis
- Unit 4: 6 hours: Retina / Optics of the Retina – Chapter 4
- Unit 5: 6 hours: Color Science and Color Vision – Chapter 5

Uncorrected & Corrected Ametropic Visual Optics; 4-credit course / 50 lecture hours

- Unit 1, 8 hours: Depth of field, emmetropia, ametropia, myopia, hyperopia – Chapter 6
- Unit 2: 10 hours: Accommodation, near vision, presbyopia, low vision – Chapter 7
- Unit 3: 10 hours: Astigmatism: optical effects, visual effects, nomenclature, effects on vision – Chapter 8
- Unit 4: 14 hours: Ophthalmic Optics: vergence, lens powers, cardinal points, corrected retinal image, lens effects on vision, lens parameters, toric lenses, light transmission properties, neutralization – Chapter 9
- Unit 5: 8 hours: Prismatic effects: prism geometry and optics, prisms in vision correction, combinations of prisms, lens tilt and shift effects – Chapter 10

George Asimellis, PhD
Boston, Massachusetts
October, 2021

Acknowledgments

I am particularly thankful for the advice and guidance that I received from the following colleagues:

Antonio J. del Águila-Carrasco, PhD
Lecturer in Optometry, Faculty of Health,
University of Plymouth,
Plymouth, United Kingdom

David A. Atchison, BScOptom, MScOptom, PhD,
GradCertEd FAAO
Professor of Optometry and Vision Science,
School of Optometry, Queensland University of
Technology,
Queensland, Australia

Ian L. Bailey, OD, PhD
Professor of Optometry and Vision Science,
School of Optometry, University of California,
Berkeley, California

Thomas T.J. van den Berg, PhD
Netherlands Institute for Neuroscience,
Royal Netherlands Academy for Arts and Sciences,
Amsterdam, The Netherlands

Justin Chelette, OD
Assistant Professor, University of Pikeville,
Kentucky College of Optometry,
Pikeville, Kentucky

August Colenbrander, MD, PhD
The Smith-Kettlewell Eye Research Institute and
California Pacific Medical Center,
San Francisco, California

Michael Kalloniatis, BScOptom, MScOptom, PhD
Professor, Centre for Eye Health,
University of New South Wales,
Sydney, Australia

Konstantinos F. Katsoulos, Msc, MCoptom, Med
Ret Cert, FSLS, FBCLA, FEAOO, FAAO
Specsavers Opticians, Norwich, United Kingdom

Vasudevan Lakshminarayanan, PhD
Professor, Optometry and Vision Science,
University of Waterloo,
Waterloo, Canada

Jan Lovie-Kitchin, OD
Associate Professor (retired), School of Optometry
& Vision Science,
Queensland University of Technology,
Brisbane, Australia

Sangeetha Metlapally, BSOpt, PhD, FAAO
Assistant Professor,
New England College of Optometry,
Boston, Massachusetts

Thanasis Panorgias, MSc, PhD, FAAO
Associate Professor,
New England College of Optometry,
Boston, Massachusetts

Corina van de Pol, OD, PhD, FAAO
Assistant Professor, Southern California College of
Optometry,
Marshall B. Ketchum University, Fullerton,
California

Logan Eugene Ritchhart, OD
Kentucky College of Optometry,
Pikeville, Kentucky

Larry N. Thibos, PhD
Professor Emeritus,
Indiana University School of Optometry,
Bloomington, Indiana

Terrace L. Waggoner, OD
Chief Research Officer,
Waggoner Diagnostics LLC,
www.waggonerdiagnostics.com

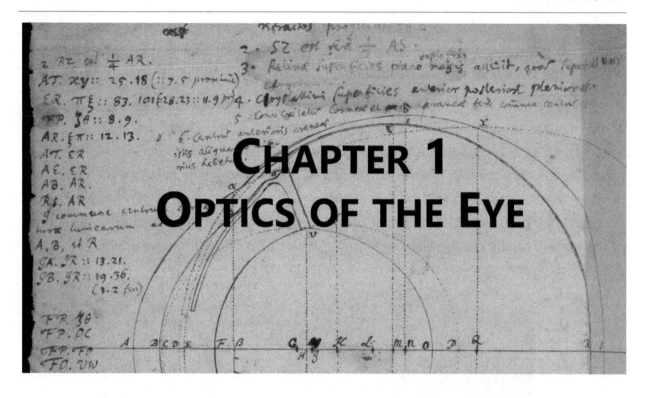

Chapter 1
Optics of the Eye

1.1 The Foundations of Vision

1.1.1 Our Understanding – The First Steps

Any attempt to explain the intricacies of vision in layman's terms is challenging because vision is a highly individualized and extremely complex process. Vision is a process that utilizes the two eyes, engages over forty different parts of the brain, and involves several hundred connection pathways within the brain.

The optics of the eye and the physiology of light transduction within the retina are perhaps essential aspects of vision. However necessary it may be to understand these aspects, it is important to acknowledge that vision is much more than just optics. Throughout this book, we will discuss optics, and although this book is long, it is not the full story.

The German astronomer Johannes Kepler was among the first to describe vision in a way that is close to our current understanding. In his book entitled *Ad Vitellionem Paralipomena, Quibus Astronomiae Pars Optica Traditur* (1604), Kepler describes the dioptrics of the eye using the image formation inside the eye. Just some years later, French philosopher, mathematician, and scientist René Descartes describes in his book *Optics* (1637) the process of retinal image formation in unprecedented detail.

The existence of this image (called retinal because it is formed on the retina) was confirmed with a simple experiment, conducted by the famed Jesuit priest, physicist, and astronomer Christoph Scheiner, who (around the early 17th century) removed a small piece of opaque tissue from the back of an eye, revealing thus the retinal image being minified and inverted, as is much easier to do today in a model eye.[1] Scheiner's book, *Oculus hoc est fundamentum opticum* (1619) is the first known recording of these observations of the anatomy of the eye and can be considered the genesis of visual optics. The Latin word *oculus* has survived in the current use of the adjective *ocular* = of the eye.

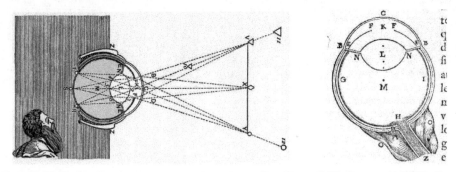

Figure 1-1: (left) Athanasius Kircher's theory of image formation in the human eye, as illustrated in his 1646 book Ars Magna Lucis et Umbrae. *Artwork from Pioneers of Science (Oliver Lodge, 1893). (right) Descartes's eye anatomy showing the pupil, the iris, the cornea, the sclera, the retina, and the optic nerve.*

1.2 RETINAL IMAGE FORMATION

The sense of **vision** (sight) is considered the most important of all senses (the other classical senses being hearing, taste, smell, and touch). The **eye** is the sensory organ of vision. It comes in wondrous varieties among the multitude of species. It is no exaggeration to state that **vision** (sight) is our most important and dominant sense, the other senses being those of smell, taste, hearing, touch, vestibular sensing, proprioception, and interoception. The **eye** is the main sensory organ in vision, and eyes are found in many wonderful and varied types all across the animal kingdom.

Consider the very demanding requirements that an eye must accomplish. The simplest of all is the ability to detect the <u>presence of light</u> (distinguishing light from darkness). Light

---

[1] Daxecker F. Christoph Scheiner's eye studies. Doc Ophthalmol. 1992; 81(1):27-35.

detection leads to an electrical signal being repeatedly processed and computed by the brain. The complexity of the eye only begins to mimic the complexity of vision within the brain. The most fundamental purpose of the eye is to detect light, both its presence and its absence; this feat is performed at the **photoreceptor**, which is at the cellular level. As photoreceptors collect their information and send it to ganglion cells, more advanced features begin to emerge, such as the ability to <u>respond to motion</u> and <u>distinguish shape</u>. As the cells converge in different levels of the visual process, different responses and complex visual computations occur, each generally being more intricate than the previous one.

1.2.1 The Eye versus the Photo Camera

The first visual transformation is the refraction of light, which leads to an image being cast on the retinal photoreceptors. The main refracting elements, the cornea and the crystalline lens, form the optical interface between the world of objects and the encoding of the visual pathway.

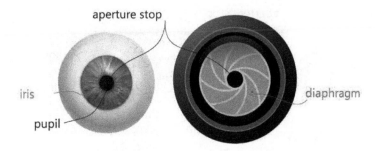

Figure 1-2: Comparison between the eye pupil and the photo camera aperture stop.

The simplest mechanical analog to the eye is the photo camera.[2] We can loosely say that the camera mimics the function of the eye. Both have light-metering mechanisms and mechanical assemblies to control the amount of light (luminous flux) reaching the light-sensitive elements. In the eye, the iris can expand or contract in response to luminance and other neurological stimuli; the opening within the middle of the iris is the pupil. In a camera lens, the operator is able to control the aperture diaphragm in order to take in more or less light.

Both optical instruments collect rays from the object, and with the refractive action of their optical elements, they form real, inverted, and minified images that are perceived by light-sensitive elements and are interpreted. We view the photos taken by the camera as upright by simply flipping the film. In visual sensation, we interpret an upright and 'life-sized' world through cerebral processing. The brain can process spatial information from one eye

---

[2] *Introduction to Optics* Chapter 6. The Photographic Camera.

(monocular processing) using cues such as shadows, interposition, aerial/linear perspective, and diminishing lines. Spatial information from two eyes (binocular processing) uses cues such as retinal disparity. When we have difficulty using both of our eyes effectively, the brain can fill in the world that we see so that it still makes sense, and we can easily navigate within it.

Both the eye and a camera perceive color, thanks to photosensitive elements that are sensitive to specific wavelengths (in this case, the bands of color). In the eye, these are the three types of cone cells (§ 4.3). In the camera, these are the different layers of film or the spectral filters in a digital sensor. To make an analogy to modern times, the eye could be compared (a poor comparison due to its extreme simplicity) to a 120 Megapixel camera (§ 4.5.3), which exceeds even today's most advanced digital cameras.

In addition, the eye focuses by modifying the curvature, and thus the refractive power, of the crystalline lens in a process called accommodation (§ 7.1.3), whereas in the camera, focusing is achieved by moving several lens group elements within a photographic lens.

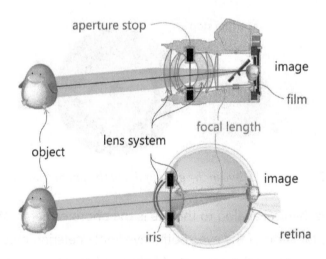

Figure 1-3: Photographic camera versus the eye: simple optical comparison.

The eye resembles a wide-angle camera. Despite the significant operational similarity, there are important differences between the eye and the photo camera, some of which are:

The range of colors (wavelengths) that the eye can sense is limited. Not surprising at all, the eye is only sensitive to visible light, with peak sensitivity in the yellow-green (§ 4.3.2), which is the peak of sunlight emission. Cameras, on the other hand, are sensitive to whatever photographic films or photonic sensors are used, so they can have a sensitivity to light beyond the visible spectrum, such as in the infrared.

The eye is also anatomically limited in physical size—both its axial size and transverse (aperture) size. The anatomy of the eye affects (and can limit) image magnification, the field of view, and the light gathering ability. A camera, on the other hand, has interchangeable parts, so one can easily exchange lenses to change the magnification, the field of view, resolution abilities, etc.

Vision is highly dynamic. The brain processes sequential images at a rate of around 10 images per second. The brain uses its perceptual skills to create the appearance of motion since it compares the last image (which is held in memory for about 1/10th of a second) with what it expects will happen next. The combination of these expectations with what we just saw and mentally processed is how motion is perceived; anything 'filmed' at faster than 1/10th of a second, such as movies at 60 frames per second, moves too quickly for us to process, so it seems steady and continuous. Unlike cameras, we cannot keep the pupil open (the way you would keep a shutter open) to continuously gather light and store it on film; we are limited by the short-term mental storage of images and our frame-processing rate.

Finally, a special differentiation is that the eye has good visual acuity (see § 3.4) only over a central area of about 3° (the angle subtended by two thumbs at arm's length). The sharpness of vision varies with eccentricity,[3, 4] owing to the size and shape of individual cones and the cone packing density (§ 4.2.1), the cone convergence into retinal neurons, and the magnification of retinal-to-cortical connections.[5] The central, sharp vision is called **foveal vision**. Angular subtense of more than 15° corresponds to **peripheral vision**.

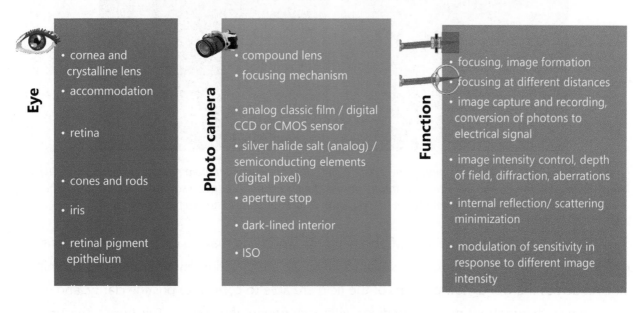

Figure 1-4: Photographic camera versus the eye: simple functional comparison.

[3] Jenninngs JAM, Charman WN. Off-axis image quality in the human eye. Vision Res. 1981; 21(4):445-51.

[4] Escudero-Sanz I, Navarro R. Off-axis aberrations of a wide-angle schematic eye model. J Opt Soc Am A. 1999; 16(8):1881-91.

[5] Tootell RBH, Switkes E, Silverman MS, Hamilton SL. Functional anatomy of macaque striate cortex II. Retinoscopic organization. J Neurosci. 1988; 8(5):1531-68.

Have you ever noticed that we immediately perceive movement in our peripheral visual field? Our eyes are continuously taking in information to send to the brain to process, and even in the eye, there are different neurological pathways, affording different categorization systems. The peripheral retina is sensitive to motion and has a shorter latency than the central retina, which is sensitive to detail. Given that the peripheral retina processes information more quickly, our peripheral vision can be considered the first alerting system, alerting us to both the detection of motion and our orientation in space.[6] We get alerted to motion, which triggers us to turn our eyes toward that position in space to discern the details with our central vision.

Even if we fixate on a single object of interest, the eye does not stay still for long; if it did, the observed image would neurologically fade away. This is known as the Troxler effect, or fading,[7] named after the Swiss physician Ignaz Paul Vital Troxler.[8] Our eyes are constantly making slight movements in order to refresh the image of the spatial world that we see. What is fascinating about this is that <u>only the central</u> part of visual field is observed with clear resolution. If we were to take a snapshot of how the eye sees the visual field, the entire image would not be sharp as seen in Figure 1-5 (left), but rather only the central part would be seen with adequate clarity, as illustrated in Figure 1-5 (right).

Figure 1-5: In a still photo (left), nearly the entire visual field is clearly depicted. In a visual signal (right), only the central field is sharp. The clear image across the entire field is due to saccades, which place the high-resolution foveal region in a position to best evaluate the intended target.

Our brain has a beautiful way of observing the world and making everything visible, but only bringing into the sharpest of focus that to which we are directing our attention. As we shift our eyes across the world, new portions of the field are able to come into pristine clarity, and we can learn new things about our surroundings with each sweep of our eyes. This builds, through

---

[6] Schmolesky MT, Wang Y, Hanes DP, Thompson KG, Leutgeb S, Schall JD, Leventhal AG. Signal timing across the macaque visual system. J Neurophysiol. 1998; 79(6):3272-8.

[7] Barrett JJ, Chatterjee A, Mennemeier MS, Fuhr PS, Novack TA. Influence of reference frames on asymmetries in Troxler's effect. Perceptual and motor skills. 2002; 94(1):29-38.

[8] Troxler DIPV. in: Himly K, Schmidt JA. eds. "Über das Verschwinden gegebener Gegenstände innerhalb unseres Gesichtskreises" [On the disappearance of given objects from our visual field]. Ophthalmologische Bibliothek (in German). 1804; 2(2):1-53.

accumulated information from multiple fixations, a stable **mental model** with high resolution throughout the field.

Saccades are the movements that our eyes make as they dart from one position to the next. They can be characterized as jerk-style, step-like, push–pull conjugate eye movements. Saccades help one to perceive a clear image across the entire field by instantly bringing a different part of the field to the fovea.[9] On the other hand, **pursuits** are the smooth eye movements that we make when observing a moving target, in order to keep that moving target fixated on the fovea. Saccades are freely generated, but pursuits require a moving target in our visual field.

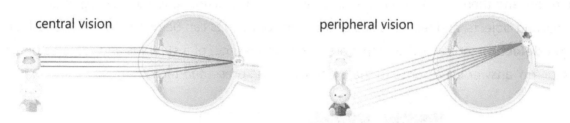

central vision   peripheral vision

Figure 1-6: Central vision versus peripheral vision.

1.3 IMAGE PERCEPTION AND ENCODING

From the initial stimulus of light, the eye must acquire the light photon, register/encode it, and preliminarily process it before sending it to the brain. The main refractive elements, the cornea and the crystalline lens, form a real image of the observed object on the retinal surface, and in particular, on the macular region. This is the first step of vision, the **formation** of an image.

The second step is the **perception** of the light by the light receptors in the retina, a thin layer of neural tissue, located at the back of the eye. This is the simplest, most elementary form of vision. Because it is formed on the retina, the image is called a **retinal image**. Its perception is due to photoreceptor responses that are communicated through several layers of retinal neurons.

The third step involves the **encoding** of the retinal image into a neural response by the photoreceptors, akin to an electrical signal that is sent from the retinal neurons to the cortical neurons. Thus, the photoreceptors are not just detection elements; they are also encoding and initial processing elements. In the human eye, these almost 100 million photoreceptors are

---

[9] Collewijn H, Erkelens CJ, Steinman RM. Binocular co-ordination of human horizontal saccadic eye movements. J Physiol. 1988; 404(1):157-82.

situated in the inner retina. Initial encoding involves compression and transfer through roughly 1 million ganglion cell axons (whose density varies greatly between the central macula and the periphery). This output of ganglion cell axons converges to form the optic nerve, and this nerve leaves the eye and travels through the brain towards the visual cortex. This cortical **representation** involves the retinal information being mapped to the cortex and results from an increasingly complex processing as the signal travels through the visual and the extrastriate cortices.

Vision is the result of a complex succession of processes, starting from the detection of the presence or absence of light. Elements such as color, shape, motion, and location are perceived, and then from those features, details such as discrimination and recognition of targets and objects, and relationships of positions of objects can be understood. The task of **target detection** indicates the simple presence (or absence) of a stimulus and requires only a 'yes' or 'no' answer in response to the existence of the presented target.

Figure 1-7: Input objects for target detection and recognition: (left) bright objects on a dark background and (right) dark objects on a bright background.

More advanced stimuli involve **target discrimination** and **recognition**. Discrimination and recognition of object features are much more involved than just target detection. The target may have two lines instead of one, for example, or it could be a dot or even a square in shape (Figure 1-8). The concept of how densely packed these detected features can be in a complex target, or how close two simple targets can be and still be perceived as two individual stimuli underlies the optical concept of **target resolution**.

Figure 1-8: Stimuli for target resolution: (left) double dot target, (center) acuity grating, and (right) checkerboard.

Successful target resolution is limited by the axial (i.e., how long the eyeball is) and transverse (i.e., how wide the pupil can be) aspects of the eye, as well as how well the optics of the eye (ocular power) are matched to its size. This leads to the concept of emmetropia, or its lack thereof, which is ametropia (§ 6.3). An emmetropic eye is capable of producing a focused retinal image, while an ametropic eye is not. Even within the emmetropic eye, however, there are limitations to how well focused an image can be, which leads to the concept of diffraction, a purely wave effect, as a limit to vision (§ 3.2). Thus, even in the best-case scenario, there is always a limit to how sharp the minute details of the detected image can be. This is clinically associated mainly with **visual acuity** (§ 3.2.1).

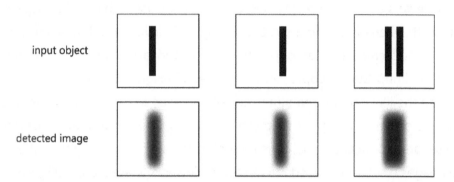

Figure 1-9: (top) An input object (stimulus) and (bottom) the detected image. The first two objects (left and center) comprise a single line. The stimulus in the third case (right) is a superposition of the two lines.

The most drastic and important reason that vision is not the simple analog to a digital camera is the fact that we use two laterally displaced eyes (**binocular vision**). Binocular vision allows for the simultaneous comparison of likes and differences in order to process the spatial relationships of the world in front of us, and the information observed by the two eyes is combined and processed into a single scene that we perceive.

Figure 1-10: Spatial differences in the same scene, as perceived by the right eye (left image) and the left eye (right image). Note the relevant shift of the near objects with respect to the background.

Retinal disparity is the term used to describe the associated differences as initially detected and perceived by each of the two monocular retinal images of the right and the left eye of the same object scene. Conjugate alignment of the eyes and fusion at the visual cortex produces a single sensation of the scene image. The different visual information is processed and fused in the visual cortex, leading to **stereopsis** (στέρεο- for structure, & -ὄψις for sight), which is depth and 3-D structure perception.

Stereo viewers and virtual reality (VR) devices make use of binocular disparity to create the sense of depth when observing a screen. Today's VR devices are the electronic advancement of the stereoscope, an object that was historically popular as a home entertainment medium. Stereoscopic pictures (as seen in Figure 1-11) used two nearly identical images to create the illusion of three dimensionality as seen in nature. These images were taken with stereoscopic cameras (today's 3-D stereo cameras is their modern advancement) that took images from separate optical centers, thus recording the scene from slightly different points of view. These images were then placed into a stereo viewer or stereoscope (Figure 1-12), a viewing 'box' utilizing two lenses of a certain power that were set a particular distance apart, with a sliding rule along which the viewer could move the picture.

 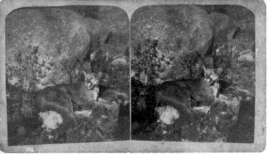

Figure 1-11: Vintage stereoscope cards: (left) the Roman Agora and (right) a cougar. Right image courtesy of D.D. Burnham New York Public Library (public domain).

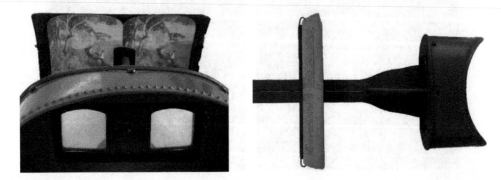

Figure 1-12: Early 20th century stereo viewer (called a telebinocular) by Keystone View (Meadville, Pennsylvania).

Binocular vision requires visual field overlap so that images from this field can be viewed simultaneously by both eyes and thus the visual cortex receives information from both eyes. When the eyes cannot team and align well, or when there is a disturbance in using both eyes simultaneously (such as in a refractive error or in an ocular or neural pathology that affects one or both eyes), the visual processes may fail to properly fuse the two monocular images into a single sensation: this is termed as binocular **diplopia**. When the eyes are inadequately aligned, even if the two monocular images may (or may not) be very clearly formed, their combination may produce a very distorted fused perception [Figure 1-13 (right)]. This perceptual distortion can lead to nausea, dizziness, vertigo, and chronic headaches, amongst other effects.

Figure 1-13: Failure of proper binocular vision due to diplopia. (left) Properly fused image. (right) Even if the fused image can be created, it can be significantly distorted.

Monocular double vision may also occur. This condition may be caused by a dislocated lens, a highly distorted cornea (e.g., keratoconus, in which the cornea changes from its normal round shape to a cone-like shape), or an uncorrected refractive error, usually astigmatism.

Another change resulting from binocular vision is that when the object is a short distance away—between 25 and 50 cm—there are two, not one, aspects to be considered. The first is that at 'rest' the eyes are set to look far away; the optical power of the eye (64.00 D) is tuned to form a sharp image from a distant object. For a nearby object, however, the optical power of 64.00 D is not enough. The eye must change by increasing its optical power (accommodation).

The second aspect is that when looking far away, the lines of sight (presented in § 2.4.3) are almost parallel between the eyes. This is not the case for viewing a near object. To simultaneously fixate both eyes on a near object, the eyes rotate horizontally (and to a lesser degree, vertical as well as cyclorotationally). The cerebral cortex controls the extraocular eye muscles that turn the eyes.

Disjunctive eye movements (**convergence** and **divergence**) align the fovea of each eye with targets at different distances. These movements are usually driven by retinal disparity and elicit eye movements in opposite directions to maintain the image of an object on the fovea at different distances in front of the individual. This permits binocular vision over a range of distances, from close up to far away (§ 10.5.3). Convergence is the nasalward movement of the two eyes, and divergence is the temporalward movement of the two eyes.

| Convergence: | • When fixating on a nearby object, the eyes rotate toward each other. |
| Divergence: | • When fixating on a far object, the eyes rotate away from each other. |

The **visual cortex** is the part of the human brain that processes visual information. It is located in the occipital lobe, toward the back of the head. Approximately one-fifth of the brain function is dedicated to visual processing, which takes place in the occipital lobe and extends into the temporal and parietal regions.[10] When considering only the visual cortex within the occipital lobe, one may mention **cortical magnification**, whereby there is a disproportionate representation of macular information compared to peripheral retinal information.[11]

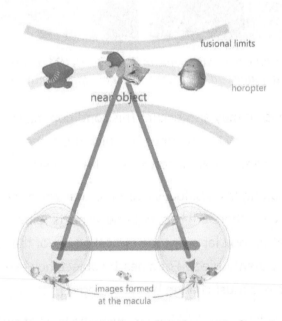

Figure 1-14: Retinal areas in the two eyes with identical oculocentric directions and corresponding retinal points. The locations of objects along the horizontal meridian that are imaged on corresponding points enclose the longitudinal horopter. Image disparity between the two eyes initiates convergence.

Starting at the back of the eye, signals siphoned via the optic nerve (§ 4.3.6) depart the globe and travel through the skull to arrive at what is called the **optic chiasm**, or chiasma

---

[10] Wandell BA, Dumoulin SO, Brewer AA. Visual field maps in human cortex. Neuron. 2007; 56(2):366-83.

[11] Born RT, Trott AR, Hartmann TS. Cortical magnification plus cortical plasticity equals vision? Vision Res. 2015; 111(Pt B):161-9.

(χίασμα, for crossing). The optic chiasm is the first area where the visual streams divert their information (Figure 1-15). Nerve fibers from the nasal retinae (N) of each eye cross over and travel backward on their contralateral side, whereas nerve fibers from the temporal retinae (T) of each eye stay on the same side and travel backward ipsilaterally. This splitting and crossing re-organizes the visual stimuli so that the left hemisphere processes information from the right visual field, and the right hemisphere processes information from the left field. This splitting and crossing over of information become particularly relevant in cases of neuro-ophthalmic disease, as certain visual field defects can be traced back to an issue at this spot within the brain.

The visual pathway after the chiasm is referred to as the **optic tract**. The majority of fibers from the two branches of the optic tract enter the thalamus and synapse at the **lateral geniculate nucleus** (LGN). Note that about 20% of the fibers do not synapse here at the LGN but instead are directed to the superior colliculus.[12]

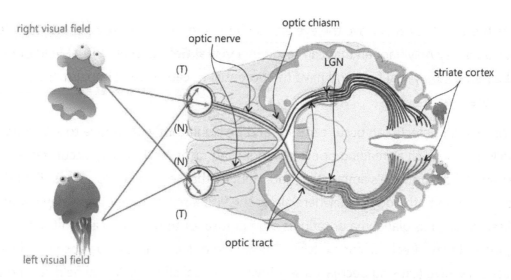

Figure 1-15: Horizontal cross-section schematic of the visual pathways.

After synapsing at the LGN, the optic radiations split into two sets, where one set of nerves travels superiorly within the brain and the other set of nerves travels inferiorly within the brain; both arrive and are reintegrated at the **visual cortex** (see Figure 1-16) (also known as the striate cortex, V1), located within the occipital lobe. Information fed through nerves that originated at the parvocellular ganglion cells is primarily responsible for fine detail and chromatic stimuli, whereas information fed via nerves originating at the magnocellular ganglion cells are more responsible for the detection of motion and achromatic stimuli.[13] The occipital

---

[12] Mize RR. The organization of GABAergic neurons in the mammalian superior colliculus. Prog Brain Res. 1992; 90:219-48.

[13] Davis AR, Sloper JJ, Neveu MM, Hogg CR, Morgan MJ, Holder GE. Differential changes in color and motion-onset visual evoked potentials from both eyes in early- and late-onset strabismic amblyopia. Invest Ophthalmol Vis Sci. 2008; 49:4418-26.

cortex is divided into striations (bands) and columns, and information is fed both backward and forward in order to generate the beginnings of visual information processing.

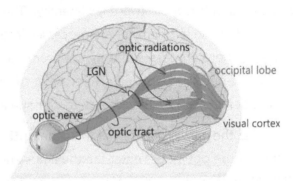

Figure 1-16: Vertical cross-section of the visual pathway from the eye to the visual cortex, illustrating the optic radiations.

As the visual streams leave the eye and arrive at the visual cortex via these complex pathways, an injury may happen that can result in a **visual field defect**. Visual field defects are a loss of a part of the visual field and have the potential to cause visual impairment to either one or both of the eyes.

Visual field defects can occur centrally and be significantly disruptive to attempts to do fine-detailed work, such as reading or even recognizing faces, or they may occur more peripherally and disrupt one's ambulation and mobility through the world. Visual field defects are associated with pathology somewhere along the visual pathway, and they may begin at the eye in diseases such as glaucoma or retinitis pigmentosa, or they may be a result of a stroke or a head injury and may affect the cortex itself. These field defects can also be absolute (leading to blindness) or relative (causing decreased sensitivity to visual stimuli). Visual field testing (§ 4.1.3) is used to identify and map visual field defects and scotomas.

There are different types of defects. A **scotoma** is a localized field defect usually found in the central field, which is surrounded by a normal visual field.

A **hemianopsia** or **hemianopia** is a contralesional-space-related neurological loss of the right or left half of the visual field. Acquired brain injuries (such as strokes, ischemia, or lesions) or trauma in areas that transmit visual information can lead to a partial or complete loss of a side of one's visual field. In general, the type of visual field loss is dependent on where the brain injury occurred and what part of the brain was affected. Most strokes tend to occur in specific places and, as such, produce common field defects. However, when the part of the visual pathway that gets affected is transmitting information from both eyes, then both fields, right and left, are affected. For example, a lesion to the right posterior parietal cortex tends to affect the left hemisphere of vision in both the right and left eyes.

Some terms are used for describing the appearance of visual field defects. **Homonymy** refers to how similar the defects are between the right and left eye, usually mentioned for lesions or injuries that occur posterior to the LGN.[14, 15] A **sectoral defect** describes an incomplete hemianopsia. Lesions that affect both temporal parts of the field create bitemporal field defects (these are usually chiasmal lesions), and lesions that affect both nasal parts of the field create binasal field defects.

Bipolarity refers to the opposite hemisphere (left in one eye and right in the other eye) being nonfunctional, often due to midline chiasmal lesions but also to ocular causes.[16] Chiasmal lesions are usually referred to as bitemporal or binasal. Binasal anopias are very rare, and most are not even chiasmal. **Quadrantanopia** (or quadrant anopia) refers to the loss of vision in one of the quarters of the visual field. It occurs when only the respective superior or inferior quadrant of the visual field is affected, often by a lesion in one geniculocalcarine tract.

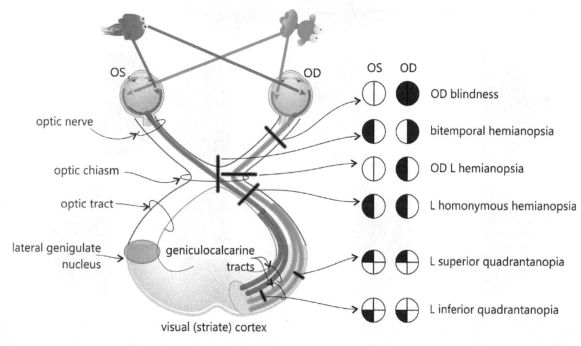

Figure 1-17: Visual field defects associated with lesions of the visual pathway. OD is right eye; OS is left eye.

[14] Purves D, Lotto RB, Williams SM, Nundy S, Yang Z. Why we see things the way we do: evidence for a wholly empirical strategy of vision. Philos Trans R Soc Lond B Biol Sci. 2001; 356(1407):285-97.

[15] Nelson GA, Townsend JC, Ilsen PF, Bright DC. Superior quadrant visual field loss secondary to temporoparietal craniectomy for brain abscess. J Am Optom Assoc. 1993; 64(8):548-56.

[16] Salinas-Garcia RF, Smith JL. Binasal hemianopia. Surgical neurology. 1978; 10(3):187-94.

Classification of hemianopsias:

- **bipolar**, which can be
  - <u>bitemporal</u> when the two halves lost are on the outside of each eye's field, effectively creating a central visual tunnel
  - <u>binasal</u> when the two halves lost are on the inside (nasal side) of each eye's field
- **homonymous** when visual field loss occurs on the same side of both eyes.
  - <u>Right</u> when the two halves lost are on the right of each eye's field
  - <u>Left</u> when the two halves lost are on the leftn of each eye's field.
- **altitudinal** when the dividing line between loss and sight is horizontal, with visual loss either above or below the line

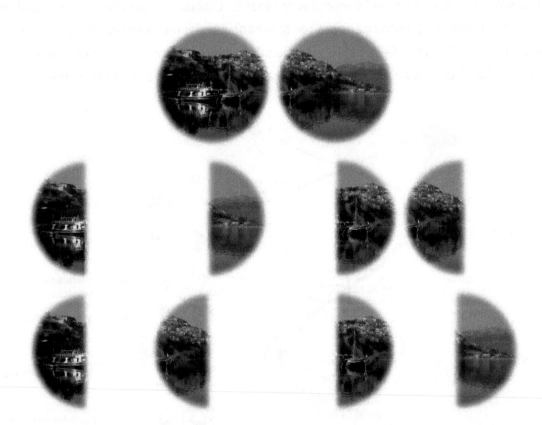

Figure 1-18: (top row) The entire field right in front of a set of healthy eyes. (middle row) Heteronymous (bipolar) hemianopsia: (left) binasal and (right) bitemporal. (bottom row) Homonymous hemianopsia.

1.4 OCULAR REFRACTION

The human eye can be described as a fluid-filled, nearly spherical structure. It is a flexible and robust optical instrument that is fully adapted to serve the needs of the human visual system. Much like any other optical system that we can construct (in the simplest approach, a converging lens), its optical function can be analyzed using the laws of optics. There are, however, two very important differences in comparison to an artificial optical system.

The first difference is that the eye is part of a biological system, a two-eyed system, that is controlled by the brain. The eyes, being biological tissue, are subject to growth and aging, affecting their development and performance, and to disease, affecting their functionality. But as part of a neurological system, their functioning and utilization can be even more intricate. Also, the brain is capable of filling in areas of the visual field to create a steady, continuous scene—something only possible with highly advanced artificial intelligence systems, not simple optical systems.

Optical instruments such as telescopes and microscopes often have rotational symmetry around the optical axis; they are, in other words, coaxial. The observed tolerances during their design and construction result in properly centered optical elements, which make the analysis of the optical system relatively manageable. The system often has a fixed and well-defined aperture stop, and an optical axis can be precisely identified.

The second main difference is that the optical elements of the eye are not exactly centered, symmetrical, and aligned, nor do the optical surfaces have a perfectly symmetrical shape. Also, both the size and the position of the aperture stop, as well as the optical axis in the human eye, can only be approximated.

1.4.1 Cardinal Points

The reduced optical system of the eye is described by six **cardinal points**, all situated on the optical axis (§ 2.4.3). The cardinal points consist of three pairs: the two focal points F and F', the two principal points P and P', and the two nodal points N and N'. The **object space** is outside the eye, while the **image space** is 'inside' the eye, where the images are being formed.

In all three cardinal point pairs, the non-primed notations denote points in object space and the primed notations denote points in image space. The focal point F, nodal point N, and principal point P are also known as object-space, anterior, or front points. The focal F', nodal N', and principal points P' are also known as image-space, posterior, or back points.

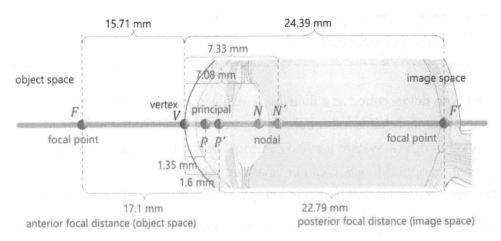

Figure 1-19: Locations of the six cardinal points of the optical system of the human eye.

The average locations of the cardinal points (referenced to vertex point *V*, § 2.4.3) are:

- The focal point *F* (primary) is located at *FV* = 15.71 mm to the left of the vertex, while the focal point *F′* (secondary) is located at *VF′* = 24.39 mm to the right of the vertex.
- The principal points *P* and *P′* are located at *VP* = 1.35 mm and *VP′* = 1.6 mm inside the eye, in the anterior chamber (§ 2.3.2).
- The nodal points *N* and *N′* are located at *VN* = 7.08 mm and *VN′* = 7.33 mm inside the eye. These points are close to the posterior lens/anterior vitreous.

The average locations of the cardinal points, as shown here, apply to the emmetropic eye focused at infinity (§ 6.2). Their locations are dependent on the refractive state of the eye, for example, if the eye is emmetropic, myopic or hyperopic (§ 6.4), and they are even dependent on ametropia being axial or refractive (§ 6.5.1). Their locations change upon refractive intervention such as laser surgery for the correction of ametropia and intraocular lens (IOL) implantation following lens extraction surgery,[17] and with the use of a corrective spectacle lens (§ 6.6.1) or contact lenses. Also, the cardinal point locations shift during accommodation (§ 7.1.3).[18]

The axial (longitudinal, anterio-posterior) distance between the anterior pole of the eye (anterior cornea) and the posterior pole (on the anterior retina) of the eye is the **axial length**. It is called the 'length' of the eye (§ 6.2.1) and <u>should not</u> be confused with the focal length. In Figure 1-19, the axial length is *VF′* = 24.39 mm and the focal length is *P′F′* = 22.79 mm.

Note the use of primed letters to indicate image space variables (such as refractive index, focal length) and reference points (such as focal point, nodal point, principal plane). The same variables in object space use the same, non-primed letter notation.

---

[17] Langenbucher A, Huber S, Nguyen NX, Seitz B, Küchle M. Cardinal points and image-object magnification with an accommodative lens implant (1 CU). Ophthalmic Physiol Opt. 2003; 23(1):61-70.

[18] Pascal JI. Cardinal points in the static and in the dynamic eye. Arch Ophthal. 1945; 34:319.

1.4.1.1 The Cardinal Points: Definitions and Properties

The primary focal point *F* is the unique object point that produces a collimated pencil of rays in image space. The secondary focal point *F'* is the unique image point to which a collimated pencil of rays incident to the lens converges (in other words, the point at which this pencil is imaged). In imaging relationships, we use the secondary focal length, which is referenced from the principal point *P'* to the secondary focal point *F'*.

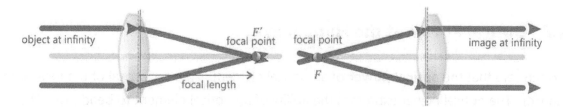

Figure 1-20: Focal points: secondary F' and primary F.

The principal points are the intersections of the principal planes *H* and *H'*, defined as the virtual plane on which a 'sudden' and 'complete' refraction (i.e., application of Snell's law) occurs. The intersection of plane *H* with the optical axis is the principal point *P*. In a thick lens or a lens system, the focal length is termed the equivalent focal length and represents the distance separating the principal points from the focal points, i.e., *P'F'*.

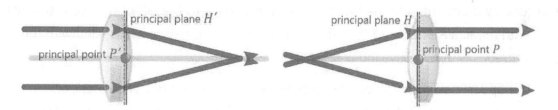

Figure 1-21: Principal points P' and P, and principal planes H' and H.

The nodal points are defined by the angular subtense property: A beam entering the optical system directed at the anterior nodal point *N* exits the optical system as if it originates from the posterior nodal point *N'* with the same inclination ϑ with respect to the optical axis.

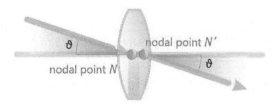

Figure 1-22: Nodal points N' and N.

Focal points	• A diverging beam from the primary focal point exits collimated. • An incident collimated beam is imaged to the secondary focal point.
Principal points	• Principle points preserve ray displacement. Between principal planes, there is unity magnification. There is no change in ray height.
Nodal points	• Nodal points preserve inclination with the optical axis so that rays remain undeviated. There is no change in ray direction.

1.4.2 Optical Power of the Human Eye

It is often said that the **optical power** of an optical element is the reciprocal of the focal length (distance). The optical power expresses the ability of an optical element to bend rays: The greater the optical power, the closer a collimated beam comes to a point, the focal point, and therefore the shorter the focal length. In air, indeed, the optical power F expressed in diopters (D) is simply the reciprocal of the focal length f when expressed in meters (m). If, however, the medium refractive index is other than 1.0, then the optical power is the refractive index (and not the number 1) divided by the respective focal length.

In object space, the equivalent focal length of the eye is f (in air) $= PF = -17.1$ mm, while internally, in the image space, the **focal length** of the eye is f'(in the eye) $= P'F' = 22.79$ mm. This peculiarity is attributed to the fact that the object space to the left of the eye is simply filled with air with refractive index $n \approx 1.0$, while the image space inside the eye is filled with the aqueous/vitreous with refractive index $n' \approx 1.336$.

The optical power F is an optical invariant and therefore is not dependent on image/object space, even if the refractive indices are different in each space. It is a fraction of the respective refractive index divided by the respective focal length:

Optical power of the eye:
$$F = -\frac{1}{f = PF} = \frac{n'}{f' = P'F'} \tag{1.1}$$

Using the values of f (in air) $= PF$ and f'(in the eye) $= P'F'$,

$$F = -\frac{1}{-17.1 \text{ mm} = -0.017 \text{ m}} = \frac{1.336}{+22.79 \text{ mm} = +0.02279 \text{ m}} = +58.5 \text{ D} \tag{1.2}$$

Reciprocal relationships: f (in air) $= -1/F$ and f (in eye) $= +1.33 (= n')/F$ $\tag{1.3}$

We realize therefore that, while the focal lengths of the optical system of the eye are not equal, the ratios of the values of their respective refractive indices equal the optical power of the eye. The asymmetries with respect to the locations of the cardinal points of the eye are mostly due to the different refractive index values in the object space and image space.

Another property of the optical power is that it can be approximated by algebraically adding the optical powers of the elements comprising the optical system. We simply add the corneal (§ 2.1.3) and lenticular (§ 2.2.1) optical powers to approximate the ocular optical power: corneal +40 D and lenticular +20 D combine to an ocular power of ≈ +60 D. This approximation ignores the separation of these two elements, whose clinical equivalent is the anterior chamber depth. The relationship describing the effect of the separation is the **Gullstrand formula**, named after the Swedish ophthalmologist Allvar Gullstrand:

Gullstrand formula: $$F_{equiv} = F_1 + F_2 - \frac{d}{n} F_1 \cdot F_2 \qquad (1.4)$$

where F_{equiv} [D] is the equivalent optical power of the two-lens system, F_1 [D] is the power of the first element, F_2 [D] is the power of the second one, d [m] is their axial separation, and n is the refractive index of the medium between (aqueous). Allvar Gullstrand was awarded the Nobel Prize (1911) for his work on the dioptrics of the eye and is renowned for his schematic eye.

The optical power of the eye is mainly dependent on:	• Cornea power • Lens power • Separation between cornea and lens

Gullstrand's formula can be used for any two optical elements in succession. For a system of two thin lenses separated by a distance d, if the medium between is simply air, we use $n = 1$. If the two lenses are in contact, then $d = 0$, which means that we simply add the individual optical powers.

Optical power of the eye:	• typically ranges between 58 and 64 D, and is the same for object and image space
Focal lengths of the eye:	• anterior (object space) ≈ 17 mm • posterior (image space) ≈ 23 mm
This is due to the different values of the refractive index (object space, air = 1, image space, aqueous = 1.336)	

An alternative approach of specific scientific peculiarity is to space apart all successive optical interfaces that comprise the eye, considering that there is air between them. Gullstrand's relationship can be successively and incrementally applied as we move from left to right. The advantage of this approach is that the in-between spacing always has the value *n* = 1.0.

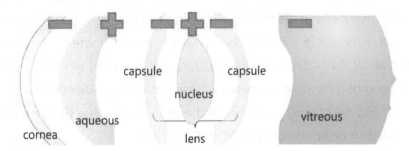

Figure 1-23: The optical power of the eye as the sum of the individual elements separated by air. Here the cornea has a net negative power, the aqueous has a positive power, the lens capsule has a negative power, the lens nucleus has a positive power, and the vitreous has a negative power.

1.5 MODELS OF THE EYE

1.5.1 From the Simplest to the Most Complicated

The evolution of the eye can be appreciated today in a vast variety of eyes found in several species. Insects, for example, have distinctly different eyes compared to the rest of the animals. The insect eye, called the **compound eye**, comprises thousands (3000 to 9000, and up to 25,000) of small eyes, each of which detects light independently. These units are called **ommatidia**, from όμμα = eye. Arthropods (insects) have evolved separately from annelids, cephalopods, and vertebrates. It seems as if this compound eye developed in a backward fashion compared to the rest of the eyes seen today.

Ommatidium { • The element unit of the compound eye, composed of structural elements (such as the lens, typically a crystalline cone, corneagenous cells, and pigment cells) and photoreceptors.

Most other animal eyes are, indeed, different. They have an optical cavity, which evolved through a continued inward, concave bending of the photoreceptors. To the contrary, the insect compound eye does not have a cavity, but a protruding shape, formed by bending in an outward, convex direction. Another difference is that each ommatidium has a primitive, bacterial eyespot. Light incident on the surface of the eye is directed to an opaque surface, and the collected information is then interpreted by the brain as an image.[19] Some elements of light guidance, such single or multiple lenses, were eventually developed.

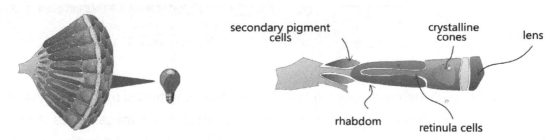

Figure 1-24: (left) The compound eye in which light from a specific angle 'activates' a microscopic eye. (right) Anatomy of an ommatidium.

The compound eye has some advantages, such as directionality and increased field of view. The large compound eyes are immobile; however, because of their spherical protruding shape, they provide an almost 360° view. Thus, instead of the eyes moving, the compound eyes in insects receive information simultaneously from a very large view.

Several aspects of insect vision are fascinating. Pollinating insects, such as bees, possess color vision.[20] These eyes, however, do not have the best resolving power in the animal kingdom. One arcminute of a human eye can make out fine details at just 1 meter away, whereas a corresponding portion of an insect eye at its best resolution, looking from the same distance, can only perceive an outline of the same shape.

In its simplest form, an ommatidium has some form of light-condensing optics, a lens, for example, and guidance, an optical shaft (*rhabdom*), which leads the gathered light to pigment cells that serve as sensors. Each ommatidium has its own nerve fiber connecting to the optic nerve, which relays information to the brain.

The evolutionary process of the eye in various species is particularly interesting. There is a multilayer aspect of eye evolution that involves some or all of these factors: (a) development of efficient photopigments at the photoreceptors, (b) improvement of directionality, and (c) development of the light-gathering and focusing optics. The photoreceptors, in particular, appear to have a common origin among the species. Most eyes that we recognize today can have their origins traced to in the Cambrian explosion, which took place about 550 million years ago, during which a rapid evolutionary progression occurred.

---

[19] Nilsson DE. The evolution of eyes and visually guided behaviour. Philos Trans R Soc Lond B Biol Sci. 2009; 364(1531):2833-47.
[20] Pichaud F, Briscoe A, Desplan C. Evolution of Color Vision. Curr Opin Neurobiol. 1999; 9(5):622-7.

Optical elements:	• provide a mechanism to capture light by either refraction, reflection, wave guidance, etc. • require condensing optics, such as a positive lens.
Receptive elements:	• provide a mechanism to convert the information of 'light' to perception. • Photosensors are typically employed.

Eyes exhibit vastly different optical arrangements, from compound eyes that produce upright images to sophisticated single-chamber eyes that cast inverted images. Eyes can be refractive or reflective. The simplest is light–shadow detection type (types I & II, Figure 1-25).

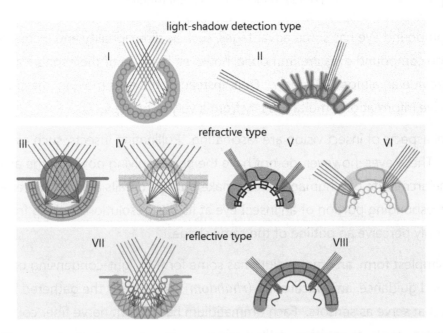

Figure 1-25: Eye types by distinct modes of image formation: (top row) I & II provide simple detection of light or shadow, (middle row) III, IV, V & VI are refractive, and (bottom row) VII & VIII are reflective.

Eyes of types III & IV (Figure 1-25), which are the **refractive types**, evolved in at least three classes of organisms (such as malakia, certain spiders, and vertebrates) that followed independent evolutionary tracks. It is called refractive because this type of eye uses refraction to capture and guide light into the photoreceptors. The human eye is essentially of this type.

Compound eyes of type II and V use one ommatidium for each photosensitive cell or group of cells and are called **apposition type**. The apposition type is, essentially, a compound eye in which the optical apparatus of each ommatidium focuses light into its own photoreceptors. In eyes of type VII and VIII, the photosensitive element receives images from several ommatidia. This type is called **superposition type**, which is a compound eye design, whereby lenses synergistically produce a single upright image.

1.5.2 Schematic Eye Models

Schematic eyes, or eye models, are mathematical tools for studying the optical function of the eye. They geometrically reconstruct the basic optical dimensions and refractive interfaces. The specifics, such as dimensions, radii of curvature, and refractive index values, are derived from anatomical data from a large population of normal eyes studied over the years.[21] Complexities that are not fundamentally important are often ignored.

Schematic eyes are, of course, simplified to facilitate the study of the average eye, since there are significant differences with regard to size among individuals and between any two persons. For example, the average male eye can be approximately 0.5 mm longer than the average female eye, which can have approximately 2.0 D more optical power than the male eye. Schematic eye models have been used extensively over the years for their ray tracing through the optical system, thereby affording retinal image quality evaluation. More advanced models have been created to enable the study of accommodation and optical aberrations.

One of the first schematic eyes was proposed in 1702 by Christiaan Huygens to explain the lens refractive action and the formation of the inverted retinal image. The simplest schematic eye contains only one refractive surface and is called the reduced schematic eye. It is a first approach since this model greatly simplifies the actual anatomy of the eye. There are schematic eyes with three, four, and six refractive surfaces. The simpler the models the easier the working becomes, but this occurs at the price of oversimplifying both the anatomy and functionality of the eye. Other models are much more realistic; depending on the degree of anatomic fidelity, there are **paraxial models**, which are useful for calculations near the optical axis, and **wide-angle**[22] or **finite models**, which serve the study of more advanced modeling.[23]

In many models, the refractive surfaces of the eye are spherical and symmetric, and the visual axis (§ 2.4.3) coincides with the optical axis. It is assumed that the crystalline lens is optically homogeneous with a fixed index of refraction. Improved fidelity can be implemented with the incorporation of aspheric surfaces,[24] certain aberrations,[25] a finite angle between the visual and the optical axis, and a radial gradient of the crystalline lens refractive index.

---

[21] Atchison DA, Thibos LN. Optical models of the human eye. Clin Exp Optom. 2016; 99(2):99-106.

[22] Goncharov AV, Dainty C. Wide-field schematic eye models with gradient-index lens. J Opt Soc Am A. 2007; 24(8):2157-74.

[23] Bakaraju RC, Ehrmann K, Papas E, Ho A. Finite schematic eye models and their accuracy to in-vivo data. Vision Res. 2008; 48(16):1681-94.

[24] Thibos LN, Ye M, Zhang X, Bradley A. Spherical aberration of the reduced schematic eye with elliptical refracting surface. Optom Vis Sci. 1997; 74(7):548-56.

[25] Schwiegerling J. Theoretical limits to visual performance. Surv Ophthalmol. 2000; 45(2):139-46.

1.5.2.1 The Simplified Schematic Models

The simplest **reduced schematic eye** uses a convex <u>single spherical refractive interface</u> (SSRI). The vertex V coincides with the principal point P. The front (anterior) focal point F is −16.67 mm to the left of the principal point, while the back (posterior) focal point F' is +22.22 mm to the right.

The nodal point N is situated 5.6 mm to the right, which is exactly the center of curvature of the first circularly shaped section (defining the SSRI). The radius of curvature of the eyeball, the second circularly shaped section, is 9.22 mm; however, this has only anatomical and not refractive reference. The refractive index inside the eye is uniform and equal to 4/3 = 1.33. There is no lens inside this eye, and the radius of curvature of the cornea is notably smaller than its known mean value. Although this model designates surfaces to eye components that do not exactly relate to anatomy, its simple paraxial imaging properties has a good likeness to that of the human eye.

Reduced-Eye Optical Power: $F = (n' - n)/r = (1.333 - 1.0)/0.0056 \text{ m} = +59.5 \text{ D} \approx +60 \text{ D}$ (1.5)

This simple model was proposed by **Listing/Emsley**, who were influenced by the earlier, Helmholtz–Laurence model.[26] Based on the reduced schematic eye,[27] German physician and physicist Hermann von Helmholtz considered "the whole corneal system ... as a lens like a watch-crystal surrounded by aqueous humor on both sides," ... "consequently, we may just as well consider the aqueous humor as extending clear out to the anterior surface of the cornea."[28]

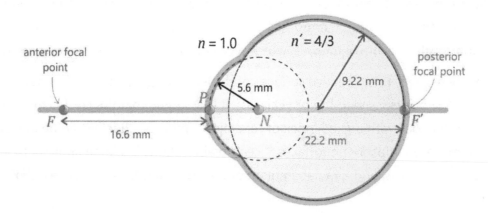

Figure 1-26: The reduced Listing/Emsley eye model.

[26] Listing JB. Beitrag zur physiologischen Optik. Gottinger Studien, Vandenhoeck and Ruprecht (1845).

[27] Listing JB. Mathematische diskussion des ganges der lichtstrahlen im auge. in Wagner R, ed. Handworterbuch der Physiologie. Leipzig, FCW. Vogel, 1853; 451-504.

[28] von Helmholtz H. Über die Akkommodation des Auges. Albrecht von Graefes Archiv fur Ophthalmologie. 1855; 1:1-89.

1.5.2.2 The Le Grand and Gullstrand Eye Models

While the reduced Listing/Emsley schematic eye adequately reproduces the paraxial imaging properties of the eye, it poorly predicts the effects of aberrations other than chromatic aberration; therefore, other models have been proposed. **Le Grand**'s full theoretical eye model incorporates <u>four refractive surfaces</u> (anterior cornea, posterior cornea, anterior lens, and posterior lens), and, in addition, has a relaxed form and an accommodated form.

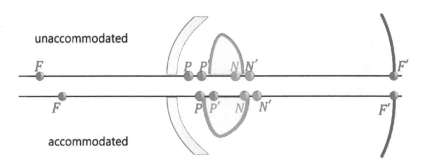

Figure 1-27: Comparison of a relaxed (unaccommodated) and an accommodated eye. Note the displacement of the cardinal points owing to the increased power of the accommodated eye.

The optical power of the relaxed eye is +60.00 D. The accommodated eye (§ 7.1.2) is modeled with a different lens shape and position, which leads to a shift of the cardinal points. For example, to model a +2.50 D accommodative response, the lens anterior/posterior radii decrease from +11 mm and –6.5 mm to +8.6 mm and –5.9 mm, respectively. Also, the anterior lens moves about 0.4 mm outward, and the posterior surface moves about 0.1 mm inward.

The **Gullstrand #1** schematic eye (Figure 1-28) has a total of <u>six refracting surfaces</u>. The additional two surfaces are the anterior and posterior facets of the lenticular nucleus. The crystalline lens has a higher-index nucleus (inner core) of $n = 1.406$, and a lower-index cortex (outer layer) of $n = 1.386$. The **Gullstrand #2** eye, also known as the <u>Gullstrand simplified eye</u>, has <u>three refracting surfaces</u>: the cornea, the anterior, and the posterior lens surfaces. Still, the surfaces are considered spherical, which means that, while the paraxial properties are accurate, aberrations such as spherical aberration cannot be accurately modeled.

In 1997, Hwey-Lan Liou and Noel A. Brennan proposed a schematic eye[29] that is a very close representation of the average normal eye based on anatomical, biometric, and optical data. This model provides spherical aberration values within the limits of empirical results and predicts chromatic aberration[30] for wavelengths between 380 and 750 nm. It provides a model

---

[29] Liou HL, Brennan NA. Anatomically accurate, finite model eye for optical modeling. J Opt Soc Am A Opt Image Sci Vis. 1997; 14(8):1684-95.

[30] *Geometrical Optics* § 8.2 Chromatic Aberration.

for calculating optical transfer functions and predicting the optical performance of the eye under various settings such as refractive surgical procedures, contact lens and spectacle wear, and near-vision conditions.

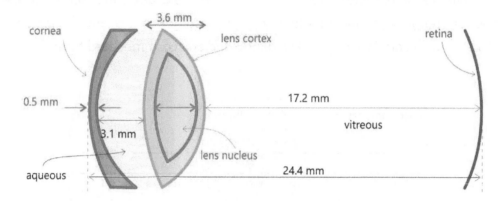

Figure 1-28: The surfaces comprising the Gullstrand # 1 schematic eye.

Table 1–1: Parameters of Gullstrand's exact schematic eye model.

	Thickness	Refractive index	Radii of curvature
Cornea	0.5 mm	1.376	+7.7 mm (anterior) +6.8 mm (posterior)
Aqueous	3.1 mm	1.336	
Crystalline lens	3.6 mm	1.386 (cortex) 1.406 (nucleus)	+10.0 mm (anterior) −6.0 mm (posterior)
Vitreous body	17.2 mm	1.336	
Axial length	24.4 mm		

1.5.3 Ray Tracing

Ray tracing is a valuable tool in the study of optical performance, including that of optical aberrations, in any complex optical system. From an object point, we draw chief rays,[31] whose pathways are determined by applying the laws of refraction/reflection. This helps when one is studying the properties of the formed image. When rays are restricted to the area close to the optical axis, the paraxial image is formed.

A manual implementation of ray tracing in a complex system is rather laborious and, often, is impossible. To study in detail various configurations in the optical system of the eye,

---

[31] *Geometrical Optics* § 7.2.1 The Principal / Chief Ray.

the schematic eye models are introduced in ray-tracing software applications. Such applications are Zemax (Zemax LLC, Kirkland, Washington), Advanced Systems Analysis Program (ASAP, Breault Research, Tucson, Arizona), Optics Software for Layout and Optimization (OSLO, Lambda Research, Littleton, Massachusetts), Code-V (Synopsys Optical Solutions, Pasadena, California), and the Optics Lab Optical Ray Tracing (Science Lab Software, Carlsbad, California).[32, 33]

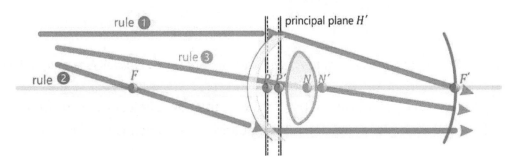

Figure 1-29: Ray tracing (construction rays) in a schematic eye using the cardinal points.

Note 🦉 : Any attempt to establish an equivalent thick lens thickness for the optical system of the eye requires the determination of the vertex points V and V'. Recall that <u>thickness</u> is defined <u>not</u> by the principal or the nodal points, but by the separation of the <u>two vertex points</u>. In a simple thick lens, these are the anterior (V) and posterior (V') extrema of the lens; in a simple system of two thin lenses, these are the optical centers of the two respective lenses.

In a complex system such as the eye, the calculation of the locations of V and V' involves the concept of surface powers, which are rather challenging to define in a complex schematic eye with several refracting surfaces. The eye thickness is <u>not</u> the separation between the two principal (or the two nodal, for that matter) points, as is incorrectly stated in some textbooks.

Through-focus spot diagrams are very helpful in visualizing image formation. These are cross-sections of rays at select planes perpendicular to the optical axis, produced by the intersections of the pencil of image-forming rays and the transverse planes across various longitudinal distances from the paraxial image. A narrow concentration of the through-focus spot diagram indicates a highly condensed pencil of rays—one that focuses nearly ideally. A broad concentration of the through-focus spot diagram indicates a pencil of rays that is not yet focused (before the focal point), a pencil of rays that is diverging (away from the focus point), or a poorly focused pencil of rays. The narrowest expanse of the through-focus spot diagram is ideally at the focus point and relates to the circle of least confusion (Figure 1-30).

[32] Zhu L, Bartsch DU, Freeman WR, Sun PC, Fainman Y. Modeling human eye aberrations and their compensation for high-resolution retinal imaging. Optom Vis Sci. 1998; 75(11):827-39.

[33] Moreno-Barriuso E, Lloves JM, Marcos S, Navarro R, Llorente L, Barbero S. Ocular aberrations before and after myopia corneal refractive surgery: LASIK-induced changes measured with laser ray tracing. Invest Ophthalmol Vis Sci. 2001; 42(6):1396-406.

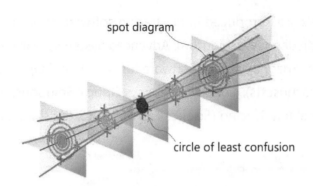

Figure 1-30: Through-focus spot diagrams and the circle of least confusion (see also § 6.1.2).

Using the cardinal points, we can draw the construction rays just as in any other optical system,[34] following the simple ray-tracing rules that apply to geometrical imaging.[176, 35]

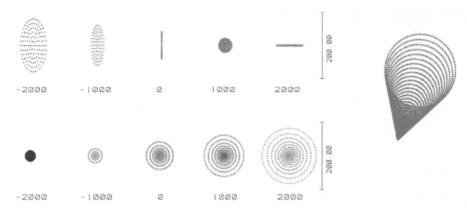

Figure 1-31: (left) Through-focus spot diagrams for astigmatism (top row) and spherical aberration (bottom row). The distance from paraxial focus is indicated in microns. (right) Spot diagram for coma.

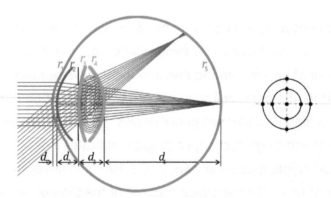

Figure 1-32: Ray tracing in a human schematic eye using the Gullstrand model.[36]

---

[34] *Geometrical Optics* § 6.4.2 Ray Diagrams in a Thick Lens.

[35] Stavroudis ON. A simpler derivation of the formula of generalized ray tracing. J Opt Soc Am. 1976; 66:1330-3.

[36] Goncharov AV, Nowakowski M, Sheehan MT, Dainty C. Reconstruction of the optical system of the human eye with reverse ray-tracing. Opt Express. 2008; 16(3):1692-703.

Example ☞: What are the power and the focal length(s) in a Listing model with r = 6 mm corneal radius of curvature, refractive index n' = 1.33, and length of the eye (axial length) = 25 mm, placed in air (n = 1.0)?

We model this as an SSRI. Power is F_{eye} = $(n' - n)/r$ = (1.33 – 1.0) / 0.006 m = +55.0 D.
Object-space focal length f = $-n/F$ = –1.0 / 55.0 D = –18.18 mm (to the left of the corneal plane).
Image-space focal length f' = n'/F = 1.33 / 55.0 D = +24.18 mm (to the right of the corneal plane).

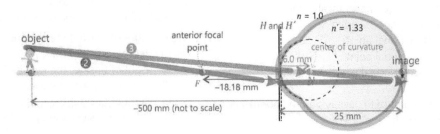

Figure 1-33: Ray tracing in a Listing-type eye model.

Example ☞: In the previous example, if an object h = 5 mm tall is placed half a meter to the left of the corneal plane, what would be the image size and location?

There are two ways to approach this. One is to consider vergence and power considerations,[37] which are

Object location: $x = n/L$;   Image location: $x' = n'/L'$;   Vergence and optical power: $L + F = L'$ (1.6)

The object, placed at –50 cm, has vergence at the corneal plane $L = n/x$ = 1.0/(–0.5 m) = –2.0 D.
This is added to the SSRI power, producing image vergence: L' = $L + F$ = –2.0 + 55.0 = +53.0 D.
Magnification: $m = L/L'$ = –2.0 /+53.0 = –0.037, hence, image size is h' = –0.037·5 mm = –0.185 mm.
The image is formed at $x' = n'/L'$ = 1.33/53.0 = +0.025 m = 25 mm to the right of the corneal plane.

In this simple model, the two principal planes are coincidental at the corneal plane, and the nodal point N is at the center of curvature of the cornea. This enables an <u>alternative way</u> to find image size: The nodal ray (rule # 3 in the ray-tracing example) intersects the cornea perpendicularly and, hence, propagates with no deviation via N to form the image. We now use simple similar-triangle relationships (Figure 1-34):
h/506 mm (orange triangle) = h'/19 mm (green triangle) ⇒ $h'= h·0.0375$ = 5 mm·0.0375 = 0.185 mm.

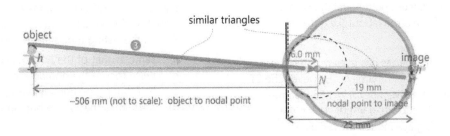

Figure 1-34: Object and image relationships via similar triangles apexed at the nodal point N.

---

[37] *Geometrical Optics* § 4.5 Imaging by an SSRI.

1.6 OPTICS OF THE EYE QUIZ

1) Which cardinal point of the eye is situated about 23 mm inside the eye?

   a) primary (object-space) focal point
   b) secondary (image-space) focal point
   c) object-space principal point
   d) object-space nodal point
   e) image-space nodal point
   f) image-space principal point

2) Which cardinal point of the eye is situated about 17 mm in front of the eye?

   a) primary (object-space) focal point
   b) secondary (image-space) focal point
   c) object-space principal point
   d) the object-space nodal point
   e) image-space nodal point
   f) image-space principal point

3) The nodal points (N, N') in the eye are separated from the principal points (P, P') toward the vitreous (image space). This is because the ...

   a) nodal points always shift toward image space
   b) nodal points are situated at the point of convergence for collimated illumination
   c) eye has positive optical power
   d) image-space (vitreous) refractive index is higher than object-space (air) refractive index

4) The focal points in the eye (F, F') are situated at locations corresponding to different lengths from their principal points (P, P'). This is because ...

   a) their sum needs to add up to about 40 mm
   b) their product needs to be about 400
   c) the ratio of refractive index to focal length has to equal about 60 D
   d) their difference should equal the cornea radius of curvature (about 6.8 mm)

5) An exoplanet ET species has eyes with the same optical power as the human eye. However, the ET aqueous has refractive index $n' = 1.66$. (Same atmospheric air as Earth, $n = 1.0$). Using the simplified Listing eye model, the radius of curvature of the ET eye is ...

   a) half that of the human eye, 2.8 mm
   b) same as that of the human eye, 5.6 mm

   c) twice that of the human eye, 11.2 mm
   d) four times that of the human eye, 22.4 mm

6) Back to Q 5. The anterior (object-space) focal point of the ET eye would be to the...

   a) right of (inside) the eye, 16.6 mm
   b) left of (outside) the eye, 16.6 mm
   c) right of (inside) the eye, 22.2 mm
   d) left of (outside) the eye, 22.2 mm
   e) right of (inside) the eye, 27.7 mm
   f) left of (outside) the eye, 27.7 mm

7) Back to Q 5. The interior (image-space) focal point of the ET eye would be to the...

   a) right of (inside) the eye, 11.1 mm
   b) left of (outside) the eye, 11.1 mm
   c) right of (inside) the eye, 16.6 mm
   d) left of (outside) the eye, 16.6 mm
   e) right of (inside) the eye, 22.2 mm
   f) left of (outside) the eye, 22.2 mm
   g) right of (inside) the eye, 27.7 mm
   h) left of (outside) the eye, 27.7 mm

8) Back to Q 5. The nodal point of the ET eye would be to the...

   a) right of (inside) the eye, 5.6 mm
   b) left of (outside) the eye, 5.6 mm
   c) right of (inside) the eye, 11.2 mm
   d) left of (outside) the eye, 11.2 mm

9) A space mission lands on Planet X to discover that the X-lings have an eye with optical power +120.0 D instead of +60.0 D of the human eye. Everything else is the same: X-planet air has refractive index $n = 1.0$ and the X-Planet eye has aqueous with refractive index $n' = 4/3$. What would be the radius of curvature of the anterior SSRI in the Listing model for the X-ling eye?

   a) same as that of the human eye, 5.6 mm
   b) twice that of the human eye, 11.2 mm
   c) half that of the human eye, 2.8 mm
   d) four times that of the human eye, 22.4 mm

10) Back to Q 9. The interior (image-space) focal point of the X-Planet eye would be to the...

   a) right of (inside) the eye, 11.1 mm

b) right of (inside) the eye, 16.6 mm
c) right of (inside) the eye, 22.2 mm
d) right of (inside) the eye, 27.7 mm

11) In the optical system of the eye, object-space nodal point N is 5.73 mm to the right of object-space principal point P (PN = 5.73 mm). What is the separation between image-space nodal point N' and image-space principal point P' ($P'N'$)?

a) 11.46 mm
b) 5.73 mm
c) 2.865 mm
d) 0 mm

12) According to the Gullstrand eye model, what part of the eye has the highest refractive index?

a) cornea
b) aqueous
c) crystalline lens
d) vitreous

13) According to the Gullstrand eye model, what surface of the eye has a negative radius of curvature?

a) anterior cornea
b) posterior cornea
c) anterior crystalline lens
d) posterior crystalline lens

14) When fixating at a near object, the eyes ...

a) rotate toward each other (nasally)
b) rotate away from each other (temporally)
c) rotate upwards
d) rotate downwards

15) Stereopsis is the result of ... (select two)

a) different spatial information between the two monocular images
b) different light sensitivity between the two monocular images
c) two monocular images being processed at the visual cortex
d) optical misalignment between the two lines of sight

16) In homonymous hemianopsia, the affected individual sees the _____ of the complete field in each eye (two possibilities).

a) right half from right eye, left half from left eye
b) left half from right eye, right half from left eye
c) right half from right eye, right half from left eye
d) left half from right eye, left half from left eye

17) In which two types of hemianopsia is the dividing line between loss and sight vertical?

a) bipolar
b) homonymous
c) altitudinal
d) quadrantanopsia

18) The counterpart of the aperture stop in photography lenses in the eye is the ....

a) cornea
b) retina
c) crystalline lens
d) iris

19) The simplest form of vision in the animal kingdom is ...

a) detection of light
b) image encoding
c) cortical representation
d) target discrimination

20) The optic tract is part of ...

a) the visual pathway before the chiasm
b) the visual pathway after the chiasm
c) the point where the two optic nerves intersect
d) another name for the visual cortex

21) Scotoma is ...

a) a localized defective visual field, surrounded by a non-defective visual field
b) the loss of half of the visual field
c) a localized non-defective visual field, surrounded by a defective visual field
d) the loss of a quarter of the visual field

22) Saccadic eye movements refer to ...

a) smooth eye movements that track foveal fixation of slow-moving objects
b) rapid eye movements that abruptly change the point of fixation
c) disjunctive eye movements that align the foveas with targets at different distances
d) rapid eye movements that track foveal fixation of fast-moving objects

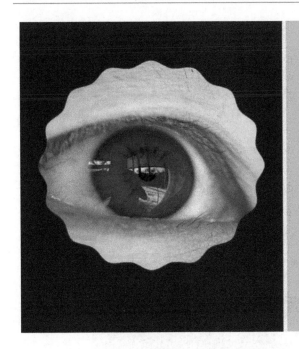

CHAPTER 2
REFRACTIVE ELEMENTS OF THE EYE

The main refractive elements of the eye are the cornea and the crystalline lens; the iris serves as the aperture stop. The transmission of light through the eye is influenced by the transparency of the ocular media, which also include the aqueous and the vitreous.

2.1 CORNEA

2.1.1 Corneal Shape

The **cornea** is the exterior window of the eye and is almost completely transparent to visible light. It is the main refractive element in the optical system: The cornea is responsible for about ⅔ of the optical power of the eye (≈ +40 D out of total ≈ +60 D). Because of this, the cornea is also the main source of refractive errors and high-order aberrations.

The cornea has a dome-like shape, maintained by the intraocular pressure (IOP). The cornea joins the sclera, the 'white' of the eye, at the corneoscleral limbus. The exterior profile of the cornea appears slightly elliptical, with an average diameter of 11.7 mm horizontally and 10.6 mm vertically. This difference is due to, among other factors, the upper eyelid pressure. The interior profile has a circular shape, with an average diameter also of 11.7 mm.[38]

---

[38] Dubbelman M, Sicam VA, van der Heijde GL. The shape of the anterior and posterior surface of the aging human cornea. Vision Res. 2006; 46(6-7):993-1001.

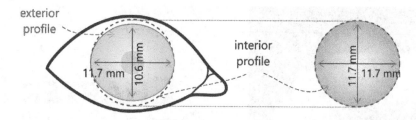

Figure 2-1: (left) Exterior and (right) interior corneal surface en face views.

The cornea can be described by the two surfaces, the anterior (outer) and the posterior (inner) surface. The cornea (its main component is the stroma) has a **refractive index**[39] ≈ 1.376. It is externally surrounded (object space) by air with a refractive index ≈ 1.0 and internally surrounded (image space) by the aqueous humor with a refractive index ≈ 1.336.

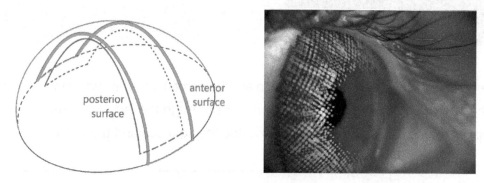

Figure 2-2: (left) The cornea dome shape. (right) Slit-lamp photo of a cornea fitted with a dot-patterned contact lens that helps to demonstrate the dome shape of the cornea.

In a first approach, both corneal surfaces can be considered spherical refracting interfaces with a specific and fixed **radius of curvature**:

- The first interface is formed by the anterior corneal surface with air. The average ± standard deviation is $+7.82 \pm 0.27$ mm.[40] Most models use a value of $+7.7$ mm.[41]

- The second interface is formed by the posterior corneal surface with the aqueous humor. The average radius ± standard deviation is $+6.8 \pm 0.16$ mm.[42]

The two surfaces are normally (perpendicularly) separated by the corneal thickness. Detailed pachymetric measurements[43] show that the thinnest part of the cornea is

---

[39] Olsen T. On the calculation of power from curvature of the cornea. Br J Ophthalmol. 1986; 70(2):152-4.

[40] Jafri B, Li X, Yang H, Rabinowitz YS. Higher order wavefront aberrations and topography in early and suspected keratoconus. J Refract Surg. 2007; 23:774-81.

[41] These values correspond to healthy, normal corneas with measurements taken at the center of the cornea.

[42] Garner LF, Owens H, Yap MKH, Frith MJ, Kinnear RF. Radius of curvature of the posterior surface of the cornea. Optom Vis Sci. 1997; 74(7):496-8.

[43] *Ocular Imaging* Chapter 3 Corneal Pachymetry.

approximately at the pupil center, about $d = 540 \pm 40$ μm thick, while peripherally, the cornea thickness increases by about 50 to 70 μm, and even more so nasally.

The radii of curvature of the posterior and anterior cornea are nearly proportional.[44] The posterior radius of curvature is on average 0.882× the anterior radius of curvature. This reflects that, in healthy adult corneas, the two corneal surface shapes mimic each other.[45] This is <u>not valid</u> if there are conditions such as keratectasia,[46] or, even more clinically relevant, if the eye has been subjected to a laser refractive surgery, which alters the shape of the anterior cornea.

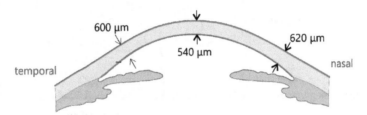

Figure 2-3: Corneal cross-section showing thickness variation (not proportionally drawn).

2.1.2 Corneal Structure and Physiology

The cornea has a distinctive layered (stratified) structure. From the most superficial to the deepest, the five distinct layers/membranes of the cornea are the following: corneal epithelium, Bowman's membrane, stroma, Descemet's membrane, and corneal endothelium.

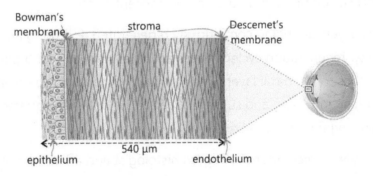

Figure 2-4: Detail of the corneal layered structure.

The corneal **epithelium**, with an average thickness of ≈ 50 to 60 μm, is considered the superficial 'skin' of the cornea. It comprises five to seven nonkeratinized cell layers, populated

---

[44] Lowe RF, Clark BAJ. Posterior corneal curvature; correlations in normal eyes and in eyes involved with primary angle-closure glaucoma. Br J Ophthalmol. 1973; 57(7):464-70.

[45] Edmund C. Posterior corneal curvature and its influence on corneal dioptric power. Acta Ophthalmol (Copenh). 1994; 72(6):715-20.

[46] Kanellopoulos AJ, Asimellis G. Corneal refractive power and symmetry changes following normalization of ectasias treated with partial topography-guided PTK combined with higher-fluence CXL (the Athens Protocol). J Refract Surg. 2014; 30(5):342-46.

by three distinct cell types, which are cells at a different stage of maturity. From outer to inner layers, these are the flatter squamous cells with a cross-section of about 30 μm and a few millimeters of thickness. Directly below them are the wing (suprabasal) cells.[47] The epithelial basement (basal lamina) membrane hosts the cube-like basal cells and is considered the innermost epithelial layer with a thickness of about 25 to 100 nm.

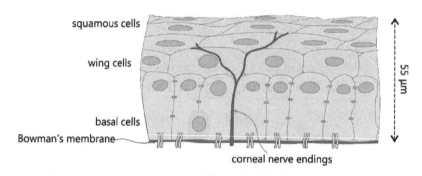

Figure 2-5: Corneal epithelial cell structure.

The epithelium acts as a diffusion barrier that prevents the penetration of substances such as water or ions into the stroma and helps maintain proper stroma oxygenation, transparency, and hydration.[48] The superficial squamous cells' tight peripheral junctions form a tight surface barrier that prevents pathogenic organisms from entering the cornea. The innermost basal membrane operates on two osmotic transport mechanisms that regulate hydration by controlling sodium and potassium ion concentrations.

The epithelial layers are being continuously regenerated, following an, approximately, weekly cycle. This cell-regeneration cycle initiates as limbal stem cell centripetal migration from the corneoscleral limbus to the basal layer. Then, mitosis occurs at the basal layer. The cells move upward, morphing into wing and superficial cells. The stratified squamous cells shed out continuously, terminating the regeneration cycle.

Bowman's layer, named after the English histologist and anatomist William Bowman, also known as the anterior limiting lamina, rests between the epithelium and the stroma. It has a thickness of about 8 to 14 μm. It is an amorphous layer, comprising randomly oriented collagen fibers. Along with the endothelium, Bowman's layer cannot regenerate.

The **stroma** (substantia propria) comprises 90% of the corneal thickness. It consists of about 200 layers (lamellae) of mainly type I and V collagen fibrils, each about 1.5 to 2.5 μm thick.

---

[47] Harrison DA, Joos C, Ambrósio Jr R. Morphology of corneal basal epithelial cells by in vivo slit-scanning confocal microscopy. Cornea. 2003; 22(3):246-8.

[48] Göbbels M, Spitznas M, Oldendoerp J. Impairment of corneal epithelial barrier function in diabetics. Graefes Arch Clin Exp Ophthalmol. 1989; 227(2):142-4.

A distinct structural feature is the patterns of collagen lamellae variability with depth. Within lamellae the fibrils are organized in a parallel fashion, while in adjacent layers they have angled orientations. Anteriorly, the fibril-reinforced lamellae form strongly interwoven, short, randomly directed narrow sheets.[49, 50] Posteriorly, the lamellae structure transitions to long, wide, thick lamellae without significant interlamellar connections. Between the collagen fibrils, there are extracellular matrix components, corneal fibroblasts (keratocytes), and interstitial substances. The keratocyte density is the highest in the anterior stroma.

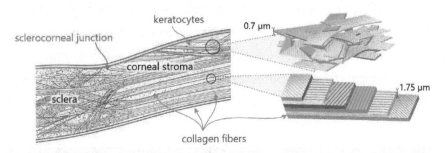

Figure 2-6: Cross-sectional detail of the collagen lamellar structure at the stroma.

This complex corneal structure contributes to corneal biomechanical strength,[51] affording mechanical stability and elasticity that help to maintain the shape of the corneal dome. Also, the remarkable corneal transparency can be attributed to the cornea's avascular structure, the unmyelination of corneal nerve fibers, the number density of the collagen fibrils, the collagen fibril spacing and diameter, the refractive index differential between the interfibrillar substance and the fibrils, and the highly organized fibrillary lamellar spatial array arrangement.[52]

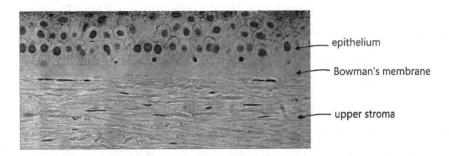

Figure 2-7: Histological anterior corneal section under an electron microscope (× 250). On top is the epithelial layer, beneath that is the homogeneous Bowman's membrane, and beneath that is the upper stroma.

[49] Radner W, Zehetmayer M, Aufreiter R, Mallinger R. Interlacing and cross-angle distribution of collagen lamellae in the human cornea. Cornea. 1998; 17:537-43.

[50] Abahussin M, Hayes S, Knox Cartwright NE, Kamma Lorger CS, Khan Y, Marshall J, Meek KM. 3D collagen orientation study in human cornea using X-ray diffraction and femtosecond laser technology. Invest Ophthalmol Vis Sci. 2009; 50:5159-64.

[51] Bron AJ. The architecture of the corneal stroma. Br J Ophthalmol. 2001; 85(4):379-81.

[52] Jester JV, Moller-Pedersen T, Huang J, Sax CM, Kays WT, Cavangh HD, Petroll WM, Piatigorsky J. The cellular basis of corneal transparency: evidence for 'corneal crystallins'. J Cell Sci. 1999; 112(Pt 5):613-22.

In addition to the anatomical factors, corneal transparency is dependent on stromal hydration, i.e., the water component of the stroma. The cornea has about 78% water content, tolerating with very little fluctuation approximately 5%. Stromal hydration is regulated by factors such as (1) the balance between swelling and intraocular pressure, (2) corneal endothelial and epithelial metabolic pump action, (3) and tear film evaporation.

Corneal transparency can be affected by neovascularization, hypoxia, infection, hydration deregulation, inflammation, or injury. The normally dormant keratocytes, derived from cranial neural crest cells, in addition to being a source for collagen and proteoglycans, play a wound-healing role. Their apoptosis forms scattering centers that contribute to corneal opacity. The stroma normally does not regenerate. However, in response to trauma, injury, or infection, a complex sequence of processes contributes to stromal wound repair and regeneration, which leads to less organized and often opaque tissue. This is known as stromal scarring.[53]

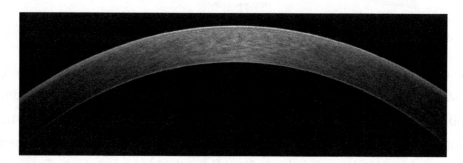

Figure 2-8: Cross-sectional image of the cornea obtained with Fourier-domain OCT (Avanti, Optovue). Anterior-segment OCT can provide an extremely detailed morphological structure of the cornea.[54]

Descemet's membrane, named after the French anatomist Jean Descemet, is an acellular, highly elastic membrane composed of type IV and VIII collagen. It is situated between the stroma and the endothelium. It has regenerative properties and thickens with age from about 5 μm to 10 μm in adults.

The corneal **endothelium** is the innermost layer of the cornea. It comprises a single layer of hexagon/polygon-shaped, highly specialized, squamous (thin flattened) cells laid on a honeycomb-like structure. This layer derives from the neural crest, which is why these cells do not divide and regenerate—and thus cannot replicate.

The primary physiological function of the corneal endothelium is to maintain stromal health, nutrition, and transparency by forming an anatomical and physiological barrier to the

[53] Torricelli AA, Santhanam A, Wu J, Singh V, Wilson SE. The corneal fibrosis response to epithelial–stromal injury. Exp Eye Res. 2016; 142:110-8.

[54] *Ocular Imaging* § 3.3.1 Anterior-Segment Optical Coherence Tomography (OCT).

aqueous. The semi-permeable endothelium, via the tight junctions formed between its cells, provides a diffusive pump function between the aqueous and the stroma. The function regulates the flow of nutrients via diffusion of glucose and other solutes from the aqueous to the avascular stroma, and the reverse osmotic flow from the stroma to the anterior chamber, to maintain the level of corneal hydration (stromal deturgescence). In short, the endothelium maintains stromal transparency by regulating (limiting) fluid flow to and from the aqueous into the stroma.

Failure of the endothelial cell function may bring about a loss of its regulative properties, resulting in non-controlled water content in the stroma, which eventually leads to corneal swelling/edema, loss of stromal transparency, and visual impairment secondary to the above.

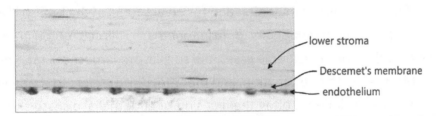

Figure 2-9: Histological posterior cornea section under an electron microscope (× 250). On top is the lower stroma. Between the stroma and the endothelium, we distinguish the homogeneous Descemet's membrane.

In the human eye, the endothelial layer is populated by about 350,000 cells. At infancy, we have the maximum possible number of endothelial cells. In a young healthy cornea, the endothelial cell count (density) ranges from 3500 to 4000 cells/mm^2, with a mean size of 18–20 μm in a somewhat regular cell configuration forming a hexagonal-type mosaic of cells of about the same size and shape for at least 60% of the cell population.[55] Specular endothelial microscopy is used for imaging the endothelium and obtaining feature metrics.[56]

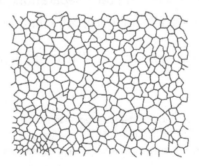

Figure 2-10: Morphology of the endothelial layer cell arrangement. Irregularities in shape among cells indicate polymorphism, and irregularities in size indicate polymegethism.

---

[55] Phillips C, Laing R, Yee R. Specular Microscopy. In: Krachmer JH, Mannis MJ, Holland EJ. eds. Cornea, 2nd ed. Philadelphia: Elsevier Mosby, 2005:261-77.

[56] *Ocular Imaging* § 2.6 Specular Microscopy.

The endothelium is under continuous metabolic stress and thus vulnerability. With advancing age, due to natural attrition, cell density decreases while cell size increases. Until the age of 50, the endothelial cell density remains relatively steady, roughly between 2200 and 3000 cells/mm^2. Endothelial cell loss is either age-related and therefore physiological or is caused by pathological factors. Beyond the age of 50, normal attrition increases, and by the age of 60, the accelerated attrition rate leads to a significant reduction in endothelial cell density.[57] Improper corneal oxygenation (for example, by prolonged use of contact lenses),[58] UV exposure, and trauma, including iatrogenic injury during intraocular procedures such as lens removal surgery,[59] may irrevocably damage this sensitive endothelial layer. Other pathologies that affect the endothelium include ocular conditions, such as glaucoma and Fuchs endothelial dystrophy.

As endothelial cells die, discontinuities are formed in the mosaic that compromise the barrier and pump functions. As cell migration and fusion act to fill in the breach,[60] adjacent cells move, stretch, or slide into the discontinuity, or fuse together. This cell morphing results in a variation in cell size and shape. In extreme cases, the smallest to largest cell ratio may reach 1:20. **Polymegethism** refers to size variation, and **pleomorphism** refers to shape variation. An elevated or abnormal cell variation is often the first sign of endothelial disease and indicates physiological stress to the corneal endothelium and an over-active wound repair mechanism.

Dua's layer was recently proposed by Dr. Harminder S. Dua.[61] This is a highly elastic, acellular collagen layer, 8 to 15 μm thick, situated in the lower stroma, just above Descemet's layer.

2.1.3 Corneal Optical Power

A cross-section of the cornea looks like a negative meniscus lens (thinner at the center). Is this so? To verify this, we have to calculate the optical power of the cornea, assuming the geometry of the two surfaces, the refractive indices, and their separation. The optical power F (also referred to as refractive power) of a single spherical refracting interface (SSRI) is

Single Spherical Refracting Interface Power: F [D] = $(n' - n) / r$ [m]   (2.1)

---

[57] Niederer RL, Perumal D, Sherwin T, McGhee CN. Age-related differences in the normal human cornea: a laser scanning in vivo confocal microscopy study. Br J Ophthalmol. 2007; 91(9):1165-9.

[58] Esgin H, Erda N. Corneal endothelial polymegethism and pleomorphism induced by daily-wear rigid gas-permeable contact lenses. CLAO J. 2002; 28(1):40-3.

[59] Roszkowska AM, Tringali CG, Colosi P, Squeri CA, Ferrreri G. Corneal endothelium evaluation in type I and type II diabetes mellitus. Ophthalmologica. 1999; 213(4):258-61.

[60] Edelhauser HF. The balance between corneal transparency and edema: the Proctor Lecture. Invest Ophthalmol Vis Sci. 2006; 47(5):1754-67.

[61] Dua HS, Faraj LA, Said DG, Gray T, Lowe J. Human corneal anatomy redefined: a novel pre-Descemet's layer (Dua's layer). Ophthalmology. 2013; 120(9):1778-85.

where n and n' are the values of the refractive index <u>before</u> (incident side, object space) and <u>after</u> (refracted side, image space) each surface, and r is the corresponding value of the radius of curvature, expressed in meters (m). In other words, the optical power F is the surface curvature (§ 9.2.1) ($C = 1/r$) multiplied by the difference of the refractive indices around the interface.[62]

Using the numerical data and notation in Figure 2-11, the optical power of the anterior cornea, per the SSRI power relationship, is

$$F_{anterior} = (n_{cornea} - n_{air}) / r_{anterior} = (1.376 - 1.0) / +0.0077 \text{ m} = +48.83 \text{ D} \approx +49.0 \text{ D} \qquad (2.2)$$

and the optical power of the posterior cornea is

$$F_{posterior} = (n_{aqueous} - n_{cornea}) / r_{posterior} = (1.336 - 1.376) / +0.0068 \text{ m} = -5.88 \text{ D} \approx -6.0 \text{ D} \qquad (2.3)$$

If we ignore the separation between the two surfaces (0.540 μm), i.e., we consider the cornea to be infinitesimally thin, then, at first approximation, the optical power of the cornea is simply the sum:

Corneal Refractive Power: $\qquad F_{cornea} \approx F_{anterior} + F_{posterior} \approx +49.0 \text{ D} - 6.0 \text{ D} \approx +43.0 \text{ D} \qquad (2.4)$

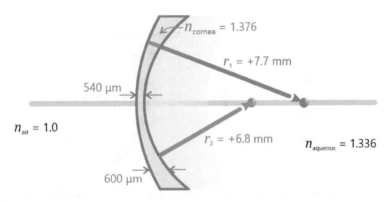

Figure 2-11: Simplified geometrical representation of a corneal cross-section indicating radii of curvature.

This is the corneal **equivalent power**, which corresponds to the refractive power of a single thin lens that optically replaces an equivalent thick lens, in this case, the cornea. The ≈ +43.0 D value obtained indicates that the cornea is <u>a very strong</u> plus lens, not a minus <u>lens</u>, despite the appearance of a negative, thinner-at-the-center meniscus lens. The main reason is that the contribution of the posterior surface to the total corneal power is much smaller than that of the anterior because the refractive index of the medium surrounding the posterior surface, the aqueous, and cornea's refractive index differ only slightly (1.336 versus 1.376).

---

[62] Some optics textbooks use the letters P or D to denote optical power instead of using the letter F.

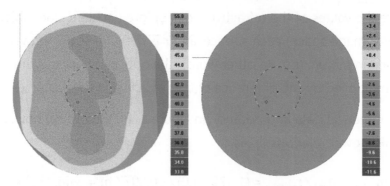

Figure 2-12: Anterior (left) and posterior (right) corneal refractive power. The sum of the two is the corneal equivalent refractive power (the color-coded scale shown to the right of each image reads their values).

Food for thought ✍ : What would the corneal power be if the cornea were surrounded by air?

The optical power of the outer, anterior corneal surface is unaffected.

We use Eq. (2.2): $F_{anterior} = (1.376 - 1.00)/(+0.0077\ m) = +48.83\ D$.

For the inner, posterior surface, we use a version of Eq. (2.3): $F_{posterior} = (1.0 - 1.376)/(+0.0068\ m) = -55.29\ D$.

The two values add to a total of $-6.46\ D \approx -6.50\ D$. In other words, if the cornea were completely surrounded by air, it would, indeed, be a negative lens of about $-6.50\ D$ power.

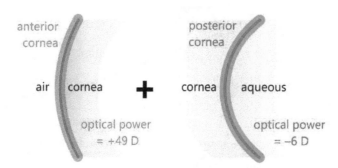

Figure 2-13: The corneal optical power is approximately the sum of the anterior and posterior optical powers. Because the medium to the right of the posterior surface has a refractive index that is almost the same as that of the cornea, the posterior surface optical power is $\approx -6.0\ D$.

We conclude therefore that the main contributor to the corneal refractive power is its anterior surface. This is the reason that the anterior corneal surface properties have such significance in visual and clinical optics.[63]

Corneal refractive power	• Curvature • Refractive index difference with air • Strong plus lens

[63] Ayres BD, Rapuano CJ. Refractive power of the cornea. Compr Ophthalmol Update. 2006; 7(5):243-51.

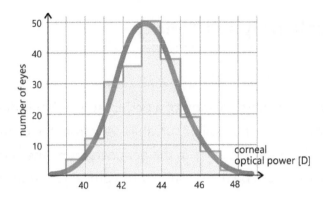

Figure 2-14: Distribution of the equivalent optical power of the human cornea in a healthy population.

In a more rigorous approach, we must recognize that the first actual refractive surface is not the anterior cornea but the **tear film** that covers the cornea (see § 2.1.5). The second parameter is the corneal thickness itself. In general, as in any system comprising two refractive surfaces (such as a thick lens or two thin lenses separated by an optical medium), the equivalent optical power corrective term is provided by the Gullstrand relationship [Eq. (1.4)]: $-(d/n) \cdot (F_1 \cdot F_2)$, where F_1 [D] and F_2 [D] are the individual powers of the cornea and the lens, d [m] is their axial separation, and n is the value of the refractive index of the medium in between, which in this case is the cornea. Using the stated values, this third, corrective term introduced by Gullstrand's formula only contributes -0.11 D of power to the total corneal power.

Cornea:
- Largest contributor to ocular optical power (⅔)
- Mainly attributed to the anterior surface curvature
- Corneal thickness and posterior cornea curvature also contribute, to a lesser degree, to the magnitude of the corneal refractive power.

When reporting corneal optical power, we generally consider the central part of the cornea, or the central zone, which is 3 to 4 mm in diameter. Less often, we report optical power for the mid-peripheral zone, which is up to 7 to 8 mm in diameter. The peripheral/transitional zone and the limbal zone can reach up to 12 mm in diameter.

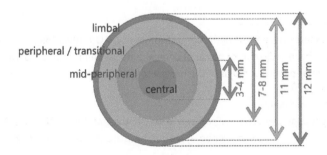

Figure 2-15: Corneal zones arranged from central to limbal.

2.1.4 Corneal Asphericity and Toricity

2.1.4.1 Corneal Asphericity

The corneal surface is only an approximation of a perfect sphere;[64] this deviation from the sphere is called **asphericity**.[65, 66] The radii of curvature vary from the center to the limbus. In the central zone, the radii are shorter, while in the peripheral zone they are longer. They also vary at different meridians, as can be demonstrated by corneal topography.[67, 68, 69]

Among the rotationally symmetrical shapes (sphere, ellipsoid, paraboloid, hyperboloid) and their intersections on a two-dimensional (2-D) plane (circle, ellipse, parabola, hyperbola), only a sphere/circle has zero asphericity. Asphericity is mathematically described by a set of parameters. These are the **asphericity index Q** (Q-value), the **conic parameter** or **shape factor p**, and the **eccentricity e**. For an ideal sphere, $Q = 0$. A hyperboloid has $Q < -1$, and a paraboloid has $Q = -1$ (Figure 2-16). These parameters are related by[70]

$$Q = -e^2 \quad p = 1+Q \quad p = 1 - e^2 \tag{2.5}$$

In an ellipsoid, $-1 < Q < 0$ if the ellipse's long axis is along the y axis. This is a prolate ellipsoid and is steeper at the center and flatter toward the periphery. The ellipsoid can also have $Q > 0$ if the long axis is along the $-x$ axis. This is an oblate ellipsoid and is flatter at the center and steeper toward the periphery. The shape factor values in an ellipsoid are between 0 and 1.

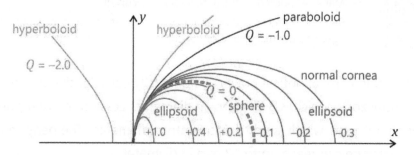

Figure 2-16: Asphericity values for various conical surfaces.

[64] Mandell RB. Everett Kinsey Lecture. The enigma of the corneal contour. CLAO J. 1992; 18(4):267-73.

[65] Patel S, Marshall J, Fitzke FW. Shape and radius of posterior corneal surface. Refract Corneal Surg. 1993; 9:173-81.

[66] Edmund C, Sjøntoft E. The central-peripheral radius of the normal corneal curvature. A photokeratoscopic study. Acta Ophthalmol (Copenh). 1985; 63(6):670-7.

[67] *Ocular Imaging* § 4.3 Corneal Topography.

[68] Dingeldein SA, Klyce SD. The topography of normal corneas. Arch Ophthalmol. 1989; 107(4):512-8.

[69] Carney LG, Mainstone JC, Henderson BA. Corneal topography and myopia: a cross-sectional study. Invest Ophthalmol Vis Sci. 1997; 38(2):311-20.

[70] Kiely PM, Smith G, Carney LG. Meridional variations of corneal shape. Am J Optom Physiol Opt. 1984; 61(10):619-26.

A spherical surface with radius r_o is described on the x-y plane as

Spherical Surface (p=1.0): $y^2 = 2r_o x - x^2$, and Conical Surface ($p \neq 1.0$): $y^2 = 2r_o x - p\,x^2$ (2.6)

which becomes a sphere if $p = 1.0$. The coordinate origin is displaced from the center of the sphere (Figure 2-16). In a perfect sphere, $Q = 0$, and thus $e = 0$ and $p = 1.0$. The indices of asphericity describe the departure of the sphericity from the center toward the periphery.

The aspheric surface that describes the naturally aspheric cornea has a **prolate** profile. The shorter radius of curvature at the center results in a cornea being steeper at the center. Likewise, the longer radius of curvature at the periphery results in a flatter cornea at the periphery. An **oblate** surface is flatter at the center and steeper at the periphery. Myopic laser vision corrections alter the anterior corneal surface from prolate to oblate.

Prolate asphericity is a natural state of the human cornea. The flatter cornea at the periphery can have a curvature of 40.0 D, as opposed to a steeper cornea at the center, with 44.0 D.[71] Typically, the central anterior cornea is about 3.0 D steeper than the peripheral.

Asphericity usually has different values away from the center. The visually significant area is the **optical zone**, which is approximately the corneal area with the same extent as the entrance pupil.[72] Typically, the larger the optical zone, the greater the asphericity, as the deviation from the spherical shape is pronounced (Figure 2-17). For a 6.0 mm optical zone (3 mm away from the center), the average anterior corneal asphericity is $Q = -0.24 \pm 0.18$, and for an 8.0 mm optical zone (4 mm away from the center), $Q = -0.51 \pm 0.08$.[73]

The optical importance of asphericity is the **spherical aberration** (SA). Asphericity is, in a way, the amount of SA that this surface is capable of compensating. It is reported by the root mean square (RMS) of the SA error and is expressed in micrometers (μm), usually computed for a 6.0 mm optical zone (pupil diameter). An average eye has a +0.50 μm RMS of positive longitudinal spherical aberration (LSA). The contributions to spherical aberration can be from the cornea and the lens; collectively, these contributions add to the ocular aberration.

The interesting aspect is that the contributions to ocular SA from the cornea and from the lens often have opposite signs. This is welcome news because partially, at least, corneal SA compensates for lenticular SA, leading to an overall reduced ocular SA. The theoretical corneal Q-value that can eliminate the average LSA in the eye is –0.53. This means that if an eye has a cumulative Q-value of –0.53, then its LSA drops to zero.[74] The average corneal Q-value is about

[71] Calossi A. Corneal asphericity and spherical aberration. J Refract Surg. 2007; 23(5):505-14.

[72] Artal P, Guirao A. Contributions of the cornea and the lens to the aberrations of the human eye. Opt Lett. 1998; 23(21):1713-5.

[73] Kanellopoulos AJ, Asimellis G. Presbyopic PiXL cross-linking. Curr Ophthalmol Rep. 2015; 3(1):1-8.

[74] The lenticular contribution is dynamic, as well. It often depends on subject age and status of accommodation: Smith G, Cox MJ, Calver R, Garner LF. The spherical aberration of the crystalline lens of the human eye. Vision Res. 2001; 41(2):235-43.

–0.27, which indicates that the cornea is typically compensating for approximately one-half of the spherical aberration of the eye. This corresponds to a +0.25 μm RMS of positive SA.

As shown in the clinical example in Figure 2-17, contributions to corneal asphericity are not limited to the anterior surface (shown on the left). The posterior surface (shown on the right) has a significant asphericity as well.[75] The center-zone posterior corneal asphericity has about $Q = -0.50$.[76] However, because the posterior surface has a negative optical power and the difference in the refractive indices between the cornea and the aqueous is very small, the contribution to spherical aberration is smaller, resulting in a total corneal asphericity with an opposite sign.[77]

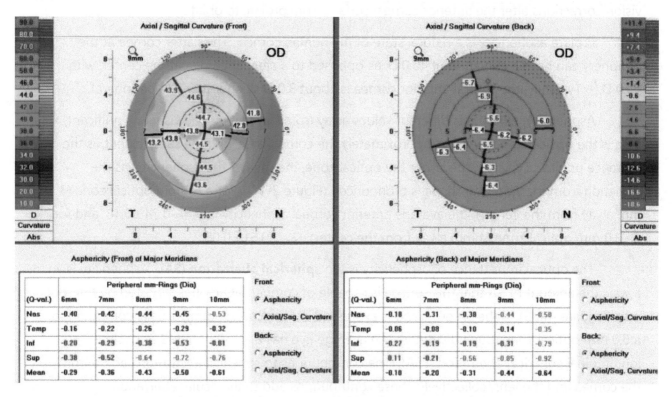

Figure 2-17: Top row shows the distributions of anterior (left) and posterior (right) corneal curvature. Note the naturally occurring drop in corneal curvature toward the periphery. Bottom row shows asphericity Q-values for the anterior cornea and the posterior cornea over various optical zones.

[75] Sicam VA, Dubbelman M, van der Heijde RG. Spherical aberration of the anterior and posterior surfaces of the human cornea. J Opt Soc Am A Opt Image Sci Vis. 2006; 23(3):544-9.

[76] Lam AK, Douthwaite WA. Measurement of posterior corneal asphericity on Hong Kong Chinese: a pilot study. Ophthalmic Physiol Opt. 1997; 17(4):348-56.

[77] Atchison DA, Suheimat M, Mathur A, Lister LJ, Rozema J. Anterior corneal, posterior corneal, and lenticular contributions to ocular aberrations. Invest Ophthalmol Vis Sci. 2016; 57(13):5263-70.

Excluding any potential pathology that may affect the corneal shape, corneal asphericity is fairly stable. This is not true in the aging eye in which several of these parameters change.[78, 79]

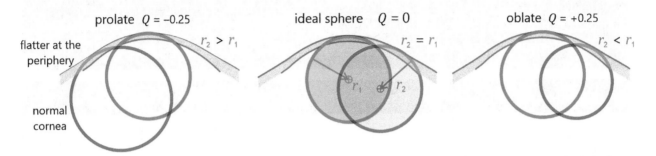

Figure 2-18: (left) Prolate cornea, (center) ideal spherical cornea, and (right) oblate cornea. The normal cornea is prolate, meaning that it is flatter toward the periphery. A more negative Q-value suggests that the cornea becomes even flatter at the periphery.

Corneal Asphericity	The cornea is not an ideally spherical surface, but is aspheric, so is steeper at the center and flatter at the periphery.
	Asphericity can be expressed mathematically by parameters such as the Q-value, shape factor p, and eccentricity e.
	Asphericity compensates for high-order aberrations such as spherical aberration (SA).
	Corneal asphericity must be considered in the design of the profile of a laser-refractive surgery or in the selection of a contact lens.

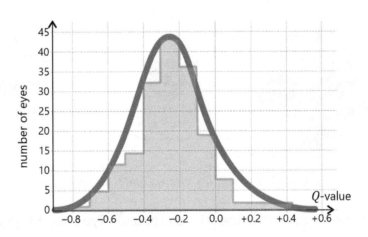

Figure 2-19: Distribution of Q-values in a healthy population of 175 eyes.[78]

[78] Benes P, Synek S, Petrová S. Corneal shape and eccentricity in population. Coll Antropol. 2013; 37(Suppl 1):117-20.
[79] Mandell RB, Helen RS. Stability of the corneal contour. Am J Optom Arch Am Acad Optom. 1968; 45(12):797-806.

Asphericity: What's the point?

A perfectly spherical surface is NOT an ideal refractive shape. It is an approximation, valid for rays confined close to the optical axis (paraxial approximation) forming small angles. Spherical aberration describes image quality degradation due to rays forming large angles with respect to the optical axis.

An aspheric cornea partially compensates for the spherical aberration found in the eye.

2.1.4.2 Corneal Toricity

In Figure 2-20, both the soccer ball and the tennis ball are perfectly spherical. This means that all cross-sections correspond to the same radius of curvature. The only difference is that the soccer ball has a larger radius of curvature (smaller curvature) than the tennis ball. This is not the case for the rugby or US football. In this case, the horizontal cross-section has a larger radius of curvature, while the vertical cross-section has a smaller radius of curvature.

This difference between curvatures is called **toricity**. The surface is no longer an ideal sphere; however, each of the two independent cross-sections is spherical, albeit with a different radius. The mathematical description of a torus involves a surface generated by revolving a circle in three-dimensional (3-D) space about an axis coplanar with the circle. Real-world examples of toroidal objects include inner tubes, swimming rings, and the doughnut or a bagel.

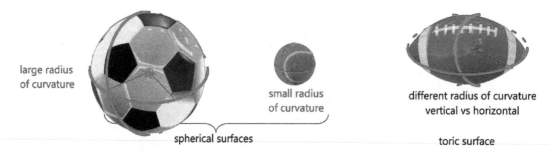

large radius of curvature

small radius of curvature

spherical surfaces

different radius of curvature vertical vs horizontal

toric surface

Figure 2-20: Familiar spherical and toric surfaces.

Corneal toricity is the rule rather than the exception.[80] Typically, the <u>vertical</u> cross-section has a greater curvature (hence, the name <u>steep meridian</u>, § 8.1.1) than the <u>horizontal cross-section</u>, which has less curvature (<u>flat meridian</u>). This toricity is with-the-rule and is the most likely manifestation in most corneas. The opposite is against-the-rule, having the vertical meridian flatter, with the horizontal meridian steeper, which is the least likely manifestation. The two cross-

---

[80] Royston JM, Dunne MCM, Barnes DA. Measurement of posterior corneal surface toricity. Optom Vis Sci. 1990; 67(10):757-63.

sections with the greatest radius (flatter curvature) and smallest radius (steeper curvature) are the **principal meridians** and are usually 90° apart. This results in corneal astigmatism (§ 6.6.), where the magnitude is the difference between the refractive powers of the two meridians.

The posterior corneal surface also exhibits toricity, which, like optical power and asphericity, is often greater than that of the anterior corneal surface.[81] This means that the curvature difference between the principal meridians is greater than that of the anterior surface. However, given the proximity of the posterior surface to the vitreous, much like in the case of optical power, the contribution to corneal astigmatism is less. In addition, the opposite algebraic sign of the posterior corneal power contributes to the compensation of the total corneal astigmatism by the posterior surface, which may be as much as 30%.[38]

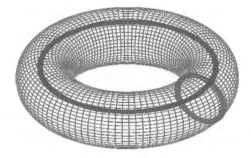

Figure 2-21: Three-dimensional representation of a toric (ring-shaped) surface. The poloidal direction is represented by the purple circle, and the toroidal direction is represented by the blue circle.

When representing posterior corneal toricity, we mind the opposite sign of optical power between the anterior and posterior surfaces. Therefore, the term 'flat' in posterior curvature must be specified when it corresponds to the geometrically flat meridian (largest radius of curvature), which, in most normal corneas, lines up with the largest radius of curvature of the anterior cornea.

This flat meridian corresponds to a less-negative posterior surface refractive power. The example in Figure 2-22 illustrates the correlation between anterior and posterior toricity. The steep meridian is the vertical (90°) one, with +48.2 D / +7.8 mm radius of curvature (corresponding to the deeper yellow color-coded value), and the flat meridian is the horizontal (180°) one, with +43.7 D / +8.6 mm radius of curvature (corresponding to the lighter yellow color-coded value); conversions use the relationship in Eq. (2.2). The difference in meridian power results in anterior corneal astigmatism with a magnitude of –4.5 D (the negative sign is produced when subtracting the steeper power from the flatter power).

---

[81] Dunne MC, Royston J, Barnes DA. Normal variations of the posterior corneal surface. Acta Ophthalmol. 1992; 70(2):255-61.

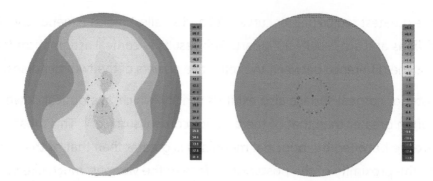

Figure 2-22: Axial curvature of the anterior (left) and the posterior (right) corneal surface. In both maps, the vertical meridian is geometrically steeper.

The interesting aspect is that on the posterior surface, the geometrically steep meridian is the 90° one, with −6.60 D / +6.06 mm radius of curvature (corresponding to the deeper blue color-coded value), and the geometrically flat meridian is the 180° one, with −6.10 D / +6.56 mm radius of curvature (corresponding to the lighter blue color-coded value); the conversions here use the relationship in Eq. (2.3).

Thus, the flat (geometrically flat, meaning that it has a greater radius of curvature) posterior meridian has a less-negative refractive power. This difference in meridional power results in a posterior astigmatism of +0.5 D. This astigmatism is less than the anterior astigmatism and has the opposite sign. The relationship between anterior, posterior, and total corneal astigmatism is also discussed in § 8.3 (The Seat of Astigmatism).

Asphericity	• Difference in curvature between center and periphery. • Typically, the cornea is steeper at the center and flatter at the periphery. • Relates to spherical aberration.
Toricity	• Difference in curvature between the principal meridians. • Typically, the cornea is steeper along the vertical meridian. • Relates to astigmatism.

2.1.5 Tear Film

The anterior eye is covered by the (pre-corneal) tear film. Optically, it serves to provide a high-quality, smooth optical interface. The tear film is the first refractive interface of the eye, with a thickness from about 5 μm to 10 μm.[82] The thickness uniformity of the tear film, at least over the central region, is important in ensuring good visual quality.[83, 84] The tear film is thicker superiorly, is uniformly distributed centrally, and becomes thinner inferiorly.[85]

The main physiological functions of the tear film are to protect[86] and lubricate the eye, to maintain ocular hydration, and to assist in providing nutrition to the epithelium.[87] The tear film is a complex aqueous microenvironment composed of 98.2% water. Other constituents present are mucins, lipids, glucose, sodium, urea, and other organic substances.[88]

The tear film is distinguished in the outermost lipid layer, the main aqueous layer, and the innermost basal, or mucous, layer. The lipid layer is oily in substance; therefore, it helps restrict water (aqueous) evaporation and thus contributes to the stability of the tear film.[89] Lipid layer thickness (LLT) may vary between 20 and 180 nm (a healthy range is 60 to 90 nm)[90] and is considered a measure of the ocular surface regularity and the dynamics of tear spreading. The lipids of this layer are produced by the meibomian glands. Meibomian gland dysfunction (MGD), a common ocular surface disease, manifests as a chronic eyelid condition with occlusion of terminal meibomian gland ducts.[91] In hypersecretory MGD (increased secretions), LLT may be increased, whereas in hyposecretory MGD (reduced secretions), LLT may be reduced.[92]

---

[82] King-Smith PE, Fink BA, Fogt N, Nichols KK, Hill RM, Wilson GS. The thickness of the human precorneal tear film: evidence from reflection spectra. Invest Ophthalmol Vis Sci. 2000; 41(11):3348-59.

[83] Tutt R, Bradley A, Begley C, Thibos LN. Optical and visual impact of tear break-up in human eyes. Invest Ophthalmol Vis Sci. 2000; 41(13):4117-23.

[84] Campbell C. The effect of tear film on higher order corrections applied to the corneal surface during wavefront-guided refractive surgery. J Refract Surg. 2005; 21(5):S519-24.

[85] Benedetto DA, Clinch TE, Laibson PR. In vivo observation of tear dynamics using fluorophotometry. Arch Ophthalmol. 1984; 102(3):410-2.

[86] Govindarajan B, Gipson IK. Membrane-tethered mucins have multiple functions on the ocular surface. Exp Eye Res. 2010; 90(6):655-63.

[87] Bron AJ, Tiffany JM, Gouveia SM, Yokoi N, Voon LW. Functional aspects of the tear film lipid layer. Exp Eye Res. 2004; 78(3):347-60.

[88] Riordan-Eva, P, Cunningham, ET, Jr., Vaughan & Asbury's General Ophthalmology, LANGE Medical Publications, 18th ed. 77-78 2015.

[89] Mishima S, Maurice DM. The oily layer of the tear film and evaporation from the corneal surface. Exp Eye Res. 1961; 1:39-45.

[90] King-Smith PE, Hinel EA, Nichols JJ. Application of a novel interferometric method to investigate the relation between lipid layer thickness and tear film thinning. Invest Ophthalmol Vis Sci. 2010; 51(5):2418-23.

[91] Nelson JD, Shimazaki J, Benitez-del-Castillo JM, Craig JP, McCulley JP, Den S, Foulks GN. The international workshop on meibomian gland dysfunction: report of the definition and classification subcommittee. Invest Ophthalmol Vis Sci. 2011; 52(4):1930-7.

[92] Knop E, Knop N, Millar T, Obata H, Sullivan DA. The international workshop on meibomian gland dysfunction: report of the subcommittee on anatomy, physiology, and pathophysiology of the meibomian gland. Invest Ophthalmol Vis Sci. 2011; 52:1938-78.

The stability of the tear film is often reported according its opposite manifestation, which is the instability of the tear film. The concept primarily relates to <u>the rate at which the aqueous layer evaporates</u>. When the evaporation rate is low, allowing sufficient replenishment, the aqueous layer is not quickly depleted. Lipid layer stability helps keep the evaporation rate low.

Several studies suggest that the tear film does not have an evenly distributed thickness, and that it changes over time.[93] When the tear film evaporates, the low tear film thickness leads to tear break-up.[94] The surface formed by the tear film becomes irregular, which severely disrupts vision.[95, 96] Tear instability may be caused by a thin tear film,[97] an unstable lipid layer, or insufficient aqueous production. Blinking of the eyelids plays an important role in the normal function and physiology of the ocular surface, including the reconstitution of the tear film.[98]

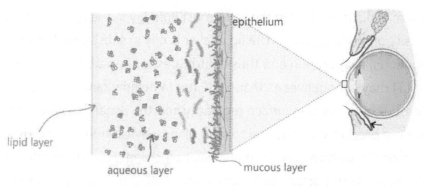

Figure 2-23: The tear film structure illustrated in detail.

The mucous layer helps to attach the tear film to the epithelium. When the mucous layer is contaminated by lipid from the top, it becomes hydrophobic and the tear film ruptures.

Optically, the contribution of the tear film is often ignored if the film is not interrupted. In other words, a uniform tear film with a refractive index almost identical to that of water ($n \approx$ 1.33) can simply be ignored and instead reported as the anterior corneal surface in the calculations of the optical power of the eye. This is because it is very thin, so its two delimiting surfaces have almost the same radii of curvature (equal to that of the anterior cornea),

---

[93] Goto T, Zheng X, Okamoto S. Tear film stability analysis system: introducing a new application for videokeratography. Cornea. 2004; 23(suppl.):S65-S70.

[94] *Ocular Imaging* § 2.7 Optical Techniques for Tear Film Stability.

[95] Cho P, Brown B, Chan I. Reliability of the tear break-up time technique of assessing tear stability and the locations of the tear break-up in Hong Kong Chinese. Optom Vis Sci. 1992; 69(11):879-85.

[96] Cho P, Brown B, Lau C. Effect of fluorescein on the tear stability of Hong Kong-Chinese. Optom Vis Sci. 1996; 73(1):1-7.

[97] McDonald JE, Brubaker S. Meniscus-induced thinning of tear films. Am J Ophthalmol. 1971; 72(1):139-46.

[98] Palakuru JR, Wang J, Aquavella JV. Effect of blinking on tear dynamics. Invest Ophthalmol Vis Sci. 2007; 48(7):3032-7.

2.1.5.1 Dry Eye

Dry eye is a condition in which the eye produces fewer or lower quality tears and is unable to keep its surface lubricated. As such, it may be characterized as a multifactorial, progressive, and chronic 'dysfunctional' disease of the tears and ocular surface,[99] often associated with increased ocular inflammation. Dry eye is responsible for major population morbidity and considerable economic impact in terms of both direct and indirect costs[100] because of the disease's progressive nature and the significant toll on the quality of life.

In addition, dry eye may present major challenges in a refractive surgery candidate assessment. The condition may range from mild/episodic to severe/chronic: It can manifest with many symptoms, including visual disturbance (blurred and fluctuating vision), foreign-body sensation & eye discomfort (patient-reported), irritation, ocular surface inflammation, redness, excess tearing, and photosensitivity.[101]

Contributing factors to dry eye may be classified as ocular, medical, pharmaceutical, iatrogenic, environmental, and related to contact lens wear. Ocular conditions include eyelid (blepharitis) and ocular surface inflammation, and chemical burns. Medical conditions include Sjögren's syndrome,[102] vitamin-A and omega-3 fatty acid deficiency, rheumatoid arthritis and other rheumatologic diseases, as well as diabetes and thyroid problems. Reactions to certain medications, such as antihistamines, diuretics, sleeping pills, decongestants, blood pressure medications and antidepressants, postmenopausal estrogen therapy medications, and isotretinoin-type drugs for acne treatment, may impact tear production and lipid layer composition and integrity.

Iatrogenic conditions include eyelid/facial surgery and corneal refractive surgery.[103] Specific to LASIK, although pre-existing dry eye may be subclinical, a sizable portion of LASIK individuals may develop reduced basal tear flow, attributed to a surgical severing of the nerves by the creation of the LASIK flap, and/or by the excimer laser ablation.[104] Environmental conditions that contribute to dry eye include aridity, cold/windy air, and repetitive occupational tasks that require increased concentration that affect blinking.

---

[99] Shimazaki J. Definition and diagnostic criteria of dry eye disease: historical overview and future directions. Invest Ophthalmol Vis Sci. 2018; 59(14):DES7-12.

[100] Pflugfelder SC. Prevalence, burden, and pharmacoeconomics of dry eye disease. Am J Manag Care. 2008; 14(3 Suppl):S102-6.

[101] Portello JK, Rosenfield M, Bababekova Y, Estrada JM, Leon A. Computer-related visual symptoms in office workers. Ophthalmic Physiol Opt. 2012; 32:375-82.

[102] Foulks GN, Forstot SL, Donshik PC, Forstot JZ, Goldstein MH, Lemp MA, Nelson JD, Nichols KK, Pflugfelder SC, Tanzer JM, Asbell P, Hammitt K, Jacobs DS. Clinical guidelines for management of dry eye associated with Sjögren disease. Ocul Surf. 2015; 13:118-32.

[103] Wilson SE. Laser in situ keratomileusis-induced (presumed) neurotrophic epitheliopathy. Ophthalmology. 2001; 108:1082-7.

[104] Sun CC, Chang CK, Ma DH, Lin YF, Chen KJ, Sun MH, Hsiao CH, Wu PH. Dry eye after LASIK with a femtosecond laser or a mechanical microkeratome. Optom Vis Sci. 2013; 90:1048-56.

2.2 CRYSTALLINE LENS

2.2.1 Crystalline Lens: Shape & Optical Properties

The crystalline lens is about 9 mm in diameter. It is a biconvex lens with a center thickness $t \approx 3.5$ to 3.8 mm. Its optical interfaces are the anterior surface with a radius of curvature $r_{anterior} \approx +10.2$ mm and the posterior with $r_{posterior} \approx -6.0$ mm (a negative sign indicates pointing against the direction of light propagation). The average refractive index is $n_{lens} \approx 1.41$. The lens is surrounded anteriorly by the aqueous ($n_{aqueous} \approx 1.336$) and posteriorly by the vitreous ($n_{vitreous} \approx 1.336$).

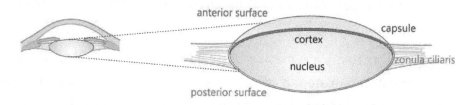

Figure 2-24: Simple anatomy of the crystalline lens.

The lenticular refracting power is approximated by the sum of the anterior and posterior powers: $F_{anterior} = (n_{lens} - n_{aqueous})/r_{anterior} = +7.25$ D and $F_{posterior} = (n_{vitreous} - n_{lens})/r_{posterior} = +12.33$ D.

Crystalline (lenticular) nominal Lens power: $F_{crystalline} = +7.25$ D $+ 12.33$ D $\approx +19.6$ D   (2.7)

which suggests that the crystalline lens is a positive (converging) lens.

Note ⊕ : The lens is not in contact with the vitreous: The vitreous—lens bond is developed through circular adherence of the vitreous to the lens posterior capsule, constituting the Wieger ligament, for which the outer circumference limit is Egger's line, and the central virtual space is known as the Berger space.[105]

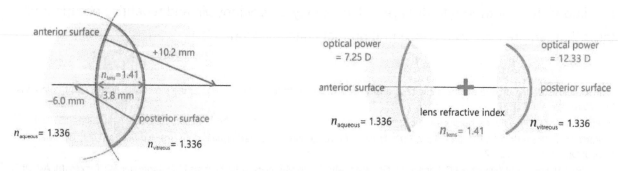

Figure 2-25: (left) Simplified model of the optics of the crystalline lens. (right) The optical power of the crystalline lens can be approximated as the sum of the powers of the two refractive surfaces of the lens.

[105] Santos-Bueso E. Espacio de Berger. Arch Soc Esp Oftalmol. 2019; 94(10):471-7.

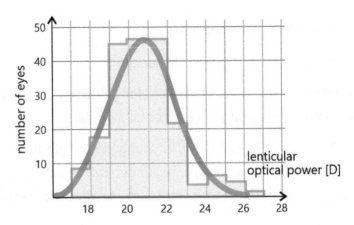

Figure 2-26: Distribution of optical power of the relaxed crystalline lens in a healthy population.

The crystalline lens is a thick lens for which simply adding the two surface powers is an approximation. Lens thickness ranges from ≈ 3.5 to 3.8 mm in a young, relaxed eye, and reaches up to more than 4.0 mm as the eye accommodates or ages. Because of this, the lenticular curvature (and by extension, lenticular power) is not fixed and changes with accommodation (§ 7.1) and age.[106]

Example ☞: For a relaxed, young eye, what is the lenticular power given the following: Lens thickness t = 3.7 mm, refractive index n = 1.422, anterior radius of curvature r_1 = +11.0 mm, posterior r_2 = −6.475 mm?

We first calculate the surface powers: $F_{anterior}$ = +7.82 D, $F_{posterior}$ = +13.28 D. If we simply add the two, we get an approximate nominal power of +21.10 D. We now implement the Gullstrand relationship [Eq. (1.4)] to calculate the exact lenticular power: $F_{crystalline}$ = +20.83 D.

The difference between the approximate (+21.10 D) and the exact lens power (=+20.83 D) is due to the third term in the Gullstrand relationship, i.e., the contribution of lens thickness, which is only minimal, even for such a thick lens.

Example ☞: For an accommodating eye, what is the lenticular power given the following: Lens thickness t = 4.0 mm, refractive index n = 1.422, anterior radius of curvature r_1 = +6.0 mm, posterior r_2 = −5.0 mm?

Surface powers: $F_{anterior}$ = +14.33 D, $F_{posterior}$ = +17.20 D. Approximate nominal power +31.53 D. Exact lenticular power: $F_{crystalline}$ = +30.84 D.

The difference between the accommodating (=+30.84 D) and the relaxed lens power (=+20.83 D) is (mostly) due to the steeper lenticular surfaces.

---

[106] Brown N. The change in lens curvature with age. Exp Eye Res. 1974; 19(2):175-83.

2.2.1.1 Lenticular Toricity and Asphericity

Like the cornea, the lens has both toricity and asphericity.

Toricity: The lenticular optical power varies along different meridians. Typically, the largest optical power in the lens is along the horizontal meridian.[107]

Asphericity: The asphericity of the lens in young people (up to 40 years) has the same magnitude and the opposite sign (it is positive, i.e., under-corrected) compared to the cornea (which is negative, i.e., over-corrected), thus contributing to a reduced ocular spherical aberration.[108]

With increasing age (e.g., 60 years), there is a reversal in the spherical aberration algebraic sign from negative to positive: The lenticular spherical aberration gradually changes to about 0 by the age of 40, then becomes positive (+0.25 µm RMS).[109] Thus, on average, at this age, the total ocular spherical aberration RMS is about +0.50 µm: +0.25 µm from the cornea and +0.25 µm from the crystalline lens.

The clinical relevance of the above is important in the selection of an aspheric intraocular lens (IOL) in cataract surgery and in achieving corneal asphericity via laser vision correction procedures. In the first case, the aim is to maintain crystalline lens asphericity. Aspherical IOLs today such as the Tecnis (Advanced Medical Optics) –0.27 µm, SofPort AO (Bausch + Lomb), and the AcrySof IQ (Alcon) –0.20 µm, offer negative spherical aberration, contributing to zero total ocular spherical aberration. In the second case, the aim is to maintain corneal asphericity, i.e., a custom-designed ablation profile aims to preserve the corneal asphericity, the objective being to preserve total ocular spherical aberration.

The crystalline lens	Is a variable power biconvex lens.
	Is the second refractive element of the ocular system of the eye, with positive refractive power from +20 to +32 D.
	Contrary to the cornea, the lens does not have a fixed curvature. The lens curvature changes in the short term (accommodation) or in the long term (aging eye).

[107] Mutti DO, Mitchell GL, Jones LA, Friedman NE, Frane SL, Lin WK, Moeschberger ML, Zadnik K. Refractive astigmatism and the toricity of ocular components in human infants. Optom Vis Sci. 2004; 81(10):753-61.

[108] Berrio E, Tabernero J, Artal P. Optical aberrations and alignment of the eye with age. J Vis. 2010; 10(14):1-17.

[109] El Hage SG, Berny F. Contribution of the crystalline lens to the spherical aberration of the eye. J Opt Soc Am. 1973; 63(2):205-11.

2.2.1.2 The Lens Paradox

There is substantial evidence that an aging lens gradually changes its shape. The anterior lens surface becomes steeper: The radius of the anterior lens surface decreases from about 15 mm to about 8.5 mm between the ages of 20 and 80. A smaller effect also takes place in the posterior surface: The posterior lens radius decreases from 8.5 mm to about 7 mm.[106]

Using the laws of optical power, it is easy to deduce that these curvature changes relate to increased lenticular power, and, clinically, to a tendency toward myopia (as is shown in § 6.4.1, myopia is associated with increased ocular power). However, what is clinically observed between the ages of 30 and 65 is not a myopic shift, but a hyperopic shift.[110, 111] This is the **lens paradox**.[112] The curvature of the aging lens increases (therefore, its power increases), but the eye not only does not shift toward myopia—the result of increased optical power—but, instead, shifts toward hyperopia.[113]

Some compensating mechanisms explain this paradox. One is the changes in the refractive index distribution inside the lens (the GRIN effect):[114] The refractive index at the nucleus becomes less positive, resulting in a reduced refractive index profile. Changes in lenticular asphericity come with age and with the accommodative state. Finally, the aging lens changes in thickness. These changes eventually lead to an optical power reduction that more than balances, and even exceeds, the optical power increase associated with the increase in lens surface curvature. Thus, gradually with age, the lens shifts to a reduced power, not an increased power.

2.2.2 Refractive Indices in the Eye

Water is the main component of all of the ocular tissue, so the majority of the refractive indices of the different parts of the eye are around 1.33; individual differences in tissue composition account for the different indices. Thus, the value of the refractive index for the tear film is $n \approx 1.333$, for the cornea (mainly, the stroma) is $n \approx 1.376$, for the aqueous is $n \approx 1.336$, and for the vitreous is $n \approx 1.336$.

The crystalline lens refractive index varies from a peripheral (capsule) $n \approx 1.39$ to the center (nucleus) $n \approx 1.42$. This is called a gradient index (gradient index lens – **GRIN**). In the

[110] Slataper FJ. Age norms of refraction and vision. Arch Ophthalmol. 1950; 43:466-81.
[111] Saunders H. Age-dependence of human refractive errors. Ophthalmic Physiol Opt. 1981; 1(3):159-74
[112] Koretz JF, Handelman GH. The lens paradox and image formation in accommodating human eyes. Topics in Aging Research in Europe. 1986; 6:57-64.
[113] Dubbelman M, Van der Heijde GL. The shape of the aging human lens: curvature, equivalent refractive index and the lens paradox. Vision Res. 2001; 41(14):1867-77.
[114] Moffat BA, Atchison DA, Pope JM. Explanation of the lens paradox. Optom Vis Sci. 2002; 79(3):148-50.

Gullstrand model (§ 1.5.2.2) that integrates six refractive surfaces, an additional pair of surfaces represents an added lens 'in the lens' with $n = 1.406$, while the capsule has $n = 1.386$.

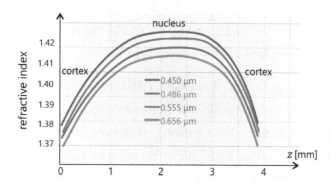

Figure 2-27: Refractive index in the crystalline lens along the optical axis for various wavelengths.[115]

This refractive index variation leads to an increased lens refractive power. In addition, it partially compensates for corneal spherical aberration. The lower peripheral value in refractive index versus the cortex/nucleus contributes to a negative lenticular spherical aberration of about −0.30 μm, which is opposite in sign to that of the corneal spherical aberration.

The values of the refractive index and other lens parameters depend on age and accommodation. Table 2–1 summarizes lens thickness t, radius of curvature r, asphericity (Q-value), and refractive index dependence on age (years, A) and on accommodation amplitude (D).

Table 2–1: Lens parameters dependence on age (A) and accommodation (D).

Parameter	Age (A, years); Accommodation amplitude (D, diopters)
Lens thickness t [116]	$t = 2.93 + 0.0236\,A + D(0.058 - 0.0005\,A)$
Anterior radius of curvature [116]	$r_1 = 1/[1/(12.7 - 0.058\,A) + 0.0077\,D]$
Posterior radius of curvature [116]	$r_2 = -1/[1/(5.9 - 0.013\,A) + 0.0043\,D]$
Anterior asphericity [117]	$Q_1 = -2.8 + 0.025\,A - 0.0013\,A^2 - 0.25\,D$
Posterior asphericity [117]	$Q_2 = -1 - 0.06\,A$
Refractive index [118]	$n = 1.1 \times 10^{-7} A^4 + 2.85$

---

[115] Chen YC, Jiang CJ, Yang TH, Sun CC. Development of a human eye model incorporated with intraocular scattering for visual performance assessment. J Biomed Opt. 2012; 17(7):075009.

[116] Dubbelman M, Van der Heijde GL, Weeber HA. Change in shape of the aging human crystalline lens with accommodation. Vision Res. 2005; 45(1):117-32.

[117] Navarro R, Palos F, González LM. Adaptive model of the gradient index of the human lens. II. Optics of the accommodating aging lens. J Opt Soc Am A Opt Image Sci Vis. 2007; 24(9):2911-20.

[118] Navarro R, Palos F, González LM. Adaptive model of the gradient index of the human lens. I. Formulation and model of aging ex vivo lenses. J Opt Soc Am A Opt Image Sci Vis. 2007; 24(8):2175-85.

The contribution of the GRIN structure is one of the possible explanations for the optical properties that counteract the observed age-related changes in lens curvature that would otherwise create an increasingly myopic eye, in the controversy known as lens paradox.[119]

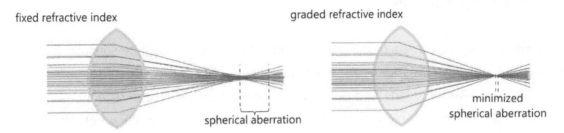

fixed refractive index

graded refractive index

spherical aberration

minimized spherical aberration

Figure 2-28: *The crystalline lens' graded refractive index (gradually increasing toward the nucleus) contributes to spherical aberration minimization.*

Finally, there is the dependence of the refractive index on the wavelength (color), as implied by the data presented in Figure 2-27. This effect, called **dispersion**, is a property of any optical medium, not a peculiarity of the ocular medium. Specifically, most media manifest normal dispersion[120] across the visible: Shorter wavelengths (e.g., blue) have higher values of the refractive index than longer wavelengths (e.g., red).

Dispersion is the basis for the rainbow effect,[121] white-light decomposition by a prism, and chromatic aberration.[30] This dependence is also relevant to the ocular media. Generally, the refractive index is greater for the shorter wavelengths and less for the longer wavelengths. The clinical application of this effect is the duochrome test (see § 6.3.1).

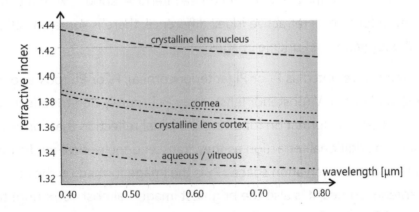

Figure 2-29: *Distribution of refractive index for various elements of the eye.*

[119] Giovanzana S, Evans T, Pierscionek B. Lens internal curvature effects on age-related eye model and lens paradox. Biomed Opt Express. 2017; 8(11):4827-37.

[120] *Wave Optics* § 3.3.1 Dispersion in Thin Media.

[121] *Introduction to Optics* § 3.5.2.1 The Rainbow.

2.3 ANTERIOR CHAMBER OPTICS

2.3.1 Purkinje Images

The **Purkinje images** (reflexes, or Purkinje–Sanson images) are formed by specular (i.e., not diffuse) <u>reflections</u> from the four ocular interfaces: air–anterior cornea, posterior cornea–aqueous, aqueous–anterior lens, and posterior lens–Berger space. These reflection images are named after the Czech physiologist Johannes Evangelista Purkinje (Jan Purkyně), who first identified them,[122] and French physician Louis Joseph Sanson, who further investigated them.

Figure 2-30: Johannes Evangelista Purkinje (1787–1869) and Louis Joseph Sanson (1790–1841).

As light intersects an optical interface, a fraction of light is transmitted, and a fraction is reflected. The larger the difference in the refractive index along the optical interface the more light is reflected (§ 2.5.1). For the air–anterior cornea interface, about 2% of the incident light is reflected. Thus, even for a small refractive index difference, there is some reflection, which is responsible for the formation of Purkinje images.

Purkinje images are noted as P_1 or PI (anterior cornea), P_2 or PII (posterior cornea), P_3 or PIII (anterior lens), and P_4 or PIV (posterior lens). Only P_1 is purely due to reflection because there is no other optical transformation following the initial reflection that forms it. The other reflexes are subject to additional refraction as they transcend the optical media between the point of reflection and the observation space. P_1 is the image formed by the convex 'mirror' defined by the anterior cornea; it is also the brightest image—almost 100× brighter than P_2. P_2 is the image formed by reflection from the inner (posterior) cornea surface and subsequently refracted through the cornea. P_2 is formed slightly anterior to P_1; because of the very small difference in refractive index between the cornea and the aqueous, P_2 is the dimmest of all.

---

[122] Purkyně JE. Beobachtungen und Versuche zur Physiologie der Sinne (Observations and experiments on the physiology of the senses) Prague. 1923; 2:128.

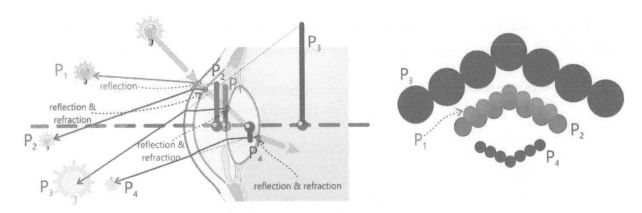

Figure 2-31: (left) Purkinje images. (right) Slightly misaligned, Λ-shape Purkinje reflection patterns. Note that P_3 is twice as large as P_1 and that P_4 is inverted (color coding is only used for simulation purposes).

Image P_3 is formed by light reflected from the outer (anterior) lens surface that is subsequently refracted through the anterior chamber and the cornea, i.e., the cornea. It is the largest image and forms more deeply in the eye, behind the lens. Finally, P_4 is the image formed by light reflected from the inner (posterior) lens surface that is subsequently refracted through the lens, the anterior chamber, and the cornea, forming a very strong plus lens of nearly +60 D.[123] This is why P_4 is an inverted, real image, whereas P_1, P_2, and P_3 are virtual, erect images. The locations of P_3 and P_4 are dependent on the accommodative state of the eye (§ 7.1.3), as the lens surfaces change in curvature. Normally, P_4 is not easily observed in an eye with a natural lens, but it becomes easier to see when the eye has an intraocular lens instead.

Table 2–2: Properties of Purkinje images.

Purkinje image	Reflected from	Image type	size	description
				(relative w/respect to P_1)
I (P_1)	anterior cornea	virtual, erect	base (1)	-
II (P_2)	posterior cornea	virtual, erect	1.25	very dim, obscured by P_1
III (P_3)	anterior lens	virtual, erect	2	broad, spaced away
IV (P_4)	posterior lens	real, inverted	–0.75	flipped

The axial locations of Purkinje images depend on the relative position of the light source from the eye. The easiest to calculate is that of P_1, which is formed by simple reflection off the anterior cornea, which functions as a convex mirror with a radius of curvature $r = -0.0077$ m, (–) meaning against the direction of light propagation following reflection. Unsurprisingly, P_1 is situated at half the anterior cornea radius of curvature, about –3.85 mm, (–) indicating that it is inside the eye.

---

[123] Tabernero J, Benito A, Nourrit V, Artal P. Instrument for measuring the misalignments of ocular surfaces. Opt Express. 2006; 14(22):10945-56.

Example ☞:   What is the axial location of the first Purkinje reflection image if a spotlight source is held far from the eye? (It's time to review mirror optics discussed in *Geometrical Optics*, Chapter 5!)

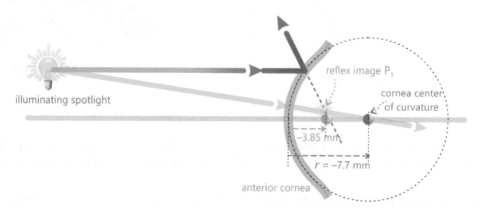

Figure 2-32: Formation of the first Purkinje image by reflection off the anterior cornea for an object (spotlight) at a very far distance (not shown to scale).

The object (light source) is at 'infinity,' so its vergence L equals 0.0 D. The mirror power is $F = 2/r = 2/(-0.0077\ \text{m}) = -260$ D. Thus, image vergence is $L' = -260$ D (–indicating that it is a virtual image), and image location is $x' = 1/L' = -1/260\ \text{D} = -3.85$ mm from the corneal plane (–indicating that the direction of the image is against that of light propagation following reflection). This means that the image appears from a position 3.85 mm inside the eye, which is halfway to the anterior cornea center of curvature.

When computing the first Purkinje image, we ignore all but the anterior corneal surface, as it acts as a convex mirror. In the previous example, the spotlight source was at infinity; realistically, nothing is ever situated at infinity, but for the purpose of creating collimated light, we state that objects are situated at infinity. The location of P_1, however, is only very slightly affected by the object distance in front of the examinee—it remains almost at the same place.

Example ☞:   What are the location and the size of the first Purkinje reflection image if a 4-cm-long light pen is held half a meter in front of the eye?

Object location is $x = -0.5$ m, so vergence $L = 1/x = -2.0$ D. This is added to mirror power, so image vergence is $L' = -262$ D. Image location is $x' = 1/L' = -1/262\ \text{D} = -3.82$ mm. This means that the image appears from a position 3.82 mm inside the eye (note, that this almost equals 3.85 mm when the target source is at infinity). Magnification is $m = x'/x = +0.0076$; image size (height) is 40 mm · 0.0076 = 0.3 mm.

Note ⊕: The Purkinje images, as described, are not the only images that can be formed by ocular surface reflections. They are the ones formed by <u>single</u> (as opposed to multiple) reflections. Images can be formed by multiple reflections, e.g., two, three, etc.; these are the 'higher-order' Purkinje images. They are not clinically relevant because, for an image exiting the eye to be observed in object space (reflection mode), three (in general, an odd number) reflections are needed. Light becomes weaker upon each reflection: If 2% is reflected off a single reflection, 0.04% is reflected off the second, and so on. Thus, the light intensity following multiple reflections is notably reduced.

The Purkinje images are very important in visual optics because they help locate the optical axis and the associated angles in the eye (§ 2.4.3). Clinically, Purkinje reflexes are used to measure corneal curvature (topography),[124] to evaluate lens position and curvature, to evaluate lens changes during accommodation, to evaluate intraocular lens (IOL) alignment,[125, 126] and to monitor eye movements and position. One of the best-known clinical applications of Purkinje images is the **Hirschberg** corneal reflex **test**, named after the German ophthalmologist Julius Hirschberg, who in 1886 used candlelight to observe light reflex in strabismus.[127]

The test can estimate eye deviations by comparing the positions (with respect to pupillary landmarks such as the pupil center) of the first Purkinje reflex formed from a fixed light such as a penlight held at a distance. It is employed both at the bedside and where a poor fixation or lack of cooperation (non-responsive individuals) precludes the use of more accurate methods. In the Hirschberg test, the position of Purkinje reflex image P_1 in one eye is compared to that in the fellow eye: If the two eyes are properly aligned with the fixed light, the two Purkinje reflections are located at a similar position in each eye (negative test, Figure 2-33).

Figure 2-33: Negative Hirschberg test. The two reflexes appear at similar center pupil locations.

However, in the case of ocular misalignment (§ 10.5.3.2), the two reflexes do not appear at the same cornea/pupil reference coordinates. For example, in exodeviation, the eye turns temporally; while the absolute position of the image itself does not shift, as the eye rotates, the

[124] *Ocular Imaging* § 4.2 Principles of Keratometry.

[125] de Castro A, Rosales P, Marcos S. Tilt and decentration of intraocular lenses in vivo from Purkinje and Scheimpflug imaging. J Cataract Refract Surg. 2007; 33(3):418-29.

[126] Nishi Y, Hirnschall N, Crnej A, Gangwani V, Tabernero J, Artal P, Findl O. Reproducibility of intraocular lens decentration and tilt measurement using a clinical Purkinje meter. J Cataract Refract Surg. 2010; 36(9):1529-35.

[127] Hirschberg J. Beitrage zur Lehre vom Schielen und von der Schieloperation. Zentralblatt fur Praktische Augenheilkunde.1886; 10:5.

P₁ reflex of the affected eye appears closer to the nasal side of the pupil [Figure 2-34 (left)]. In esodeviation, the affected eye turns nasally; the P₁ reflex appears closer to the temporal side of that pupil [Figure 2-34 (right)].

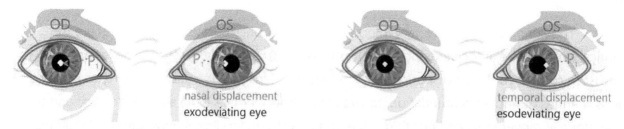

Figure 2-34: (left) P₁ Purkinje reflex image in exodeviating left eye (OS). The reflex of the left eye appears to move nasally with respect to the pupil center. (right) P₁ Purkinje reflex image in esodeviating left eye (OS). The reflex of the left eye appears to be shifted temporally with respect to the pupil center.

Hirschberg test and deviation determination	• nasal displacement; exotropia • temporal displacement; esotropia • superior displacement; hypertropia of the other eye • inferior displacement; hypertropia

Under binocular fixation, the P₁ reflexes are displaced slightly nasally due to being the corneal intercept of the line of sight (§ 2.4.3), which is about 3° (up to 8°) nasally from the pupillary axis, measuring an arc of about 0.5 mm [see Eq. (2.9)]. Thus, the true deviation is confounded by this displacement. To reveal the actual value of the deviation, we need some math: If P₁ is shifted temporally, the true deviation is greater by the amount of 0.5 mm, which must be added to the measured deviation. If P₁ is shifted nasally, the true deviation is less by the amount of 0.5 mm, which must be subtracted from the measured deviation; see examples in § 10.5.3.2.

Hirschberg test P₁ Purkinje true deviation compensation	• nasal P₁ displacement: subtract 0.5 mm from the measured deviation • temporal P₁ displacement: add 0.5 mm to the measured deviation

Clinical note 📖 : Because normally the P₁ reflexes are displaced slightly nasally in both eyes, even in normal eyes, there is no perfect centration in Hirschberg testing. What is evaluated clinically is whether the possible difference from the pupil center to the P₁ reflex is symmetrical and (about) equal. The absence of parity/symmetry indicates the possibility of an abnormal deviation.

2.3.2 Anterior Chamber

The eye can be distinguished by three compartments. The first is the **anterior chamber**, which is defined as the space between the cornea and the iris, and is filled with the aqueous humor. The aqueous has a refractive index of 1.336. Next is the **posterior chamber**, which is the space between the iris, the ciliary body and the lens, and which is also filled with the aqueous. Finally, there is the space between the lens and the retina, which is the **posterior segment** that is filled with the vitreous.

The **anterior chamber depth** (ACD)[128] is the distance from the posterior corneal surface to the center of the anterior lens surface, averaging in a healthy, adult eye between 3.15 and 3.25 mm.[129] The ACD changes over time with age and pathology (such as cataract). It also changes dynamically during accommodation as the lens shifts position.

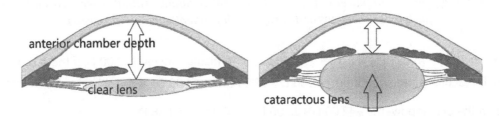

Figure 2-35: The anterior chamber depth in a cataractous lens decreases, affecting the optics of the eye.

The contribution of the ACD to ocular optics is kept indirect, by maintaining a separation between the cornea and the lens. If two +5.0 D lenses are separated in air by d = 0.1 m, the equivalent optical power is +5.0 + 5.0 − (0.1 m·5.0·5.0) = +7.5 D. If the two lenses were in contact, then +5.0 +5.0 = +10.0 D. Therefore, the spacing between the two elements is important for determining the total optical power, and, accordingly, the focal length of the optical system.

This is also true for the optical system of the eye: In this case, the two elements are the cornea and the lens. The medium in between is the aqueous with refractive index n = 1.336. Their spacing d can be approximated by the ACD. Thus, optically, the ACD serves as the spacing in the 'lens system' comprising the cornea and the crystalline lens. This distance affects the optical power of the eye in an indirect way by means of the third term in the Gullstrand Eq. (1.4): $-(d/n)\cdot(F_1\cdot F_2)$, where F_1 and F_2 are the individual powers of the cornea and the lens. Because both powers (cornea and lens) are positive, the third element is always negative. Thus, the effect

---

[128] *Ocular Imaging* § 2.3 Anterior Chamber Depth, Volume, and Angle.

[129] Hashemi H, Yazdani K, Mehravaran S, Fotouhi A. Anterior chamber depth measurement with A-scan ultrasonography, Orbscan II, and IOLMaster. Optom Vis Sci. 2005; 82(10):900-4.

of the ACD is to reduce the total ocular power from the simple sum of the cornea and lens power. A smaller ACD will lead to a smaller optical power change.

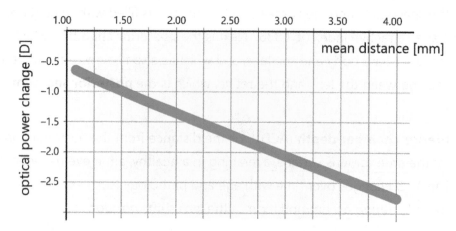

Figure 2-36: Change in optical power of the eye (dependent variable, ordinate) versus a shift in the mean spacing between lens and cornea (independent variable, abscissa).

Example ☞: In an eye with corneal power +42.00 D and lenticular power +22.00 D, if there is no separation, the ocular power would be +42.00 D +22.00 D = +64.00 D. If the spacing d is...

3.5 mm, then the ocular power is +42.00 D +22.00 D − 2.42 D = +61.58 D.
2.0 mm, then the ocular power is +42.00 D +22.00 D − 1.38 D = +62.62 D.

This spacing change can be brought about by a forward lens shift by +1.5 mm, producing an ocular power increase of about +1.0 D. Essentially, this is the mechanism of pseudoaccommodation (§ 7.3.3).

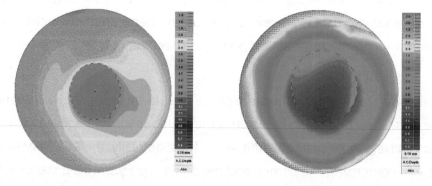

Figure 2-37: Examples of shallow (left) and deep (right) anterior chamber depths measured by Scheimpflug imaging. Different colors show the different depths of the anterior chamber. The data in these 2-D color-coded maps correspond to the color scale shown beside each map.

2.4 OPTICAL APERTURES AND AXES IN THE HUMAN EYE

2.4.1 The Necessity of the Diaphragm

Let's think of an eye with no diaphragm. As rays from each object point propagate in all possible directions, rays arrive at the sensory level from all directions as well, not only from the object on which the eye is fixated, but from every other object in the scene [Figure 2-38 (left)]. Light arrives in a very, very confusing way, to say the least, as if thousands of whales are trying to be imaged. The problem is that this eye receives too much information to handle.

Figure 2-38: (left) Rays from any object point spread in many directions on their way to the eye, forming a multitude of indiscernible images. (right) A diaphragm enables the formation of a clear image.

There is a need to isolate and eliminate redundant information. This can be achieved by the incorporation of a **diaphragm**, a small aperture/stenopic disk [Figure 2-38 (right)] in front of the eye. Now the eye can optically isolate (from all of the overlapping rays) those rays that form a single, clear image. Image formation follows the simple rules of the *camera obscura*.[130]

2.4.2 Iris and Pupil

2.4.2.1 Iris Color

The **iris**, the colorful part of the eye, forms a circular opening, the **pupil**, which controls the amount of light entering the eye. Since most of the light entering the eye does not escape, the pupil appears black. The iris, on the other hand, is the colorful element of the eye. Irises can be brown, hazel, gray, green, or blue. Remarkably, this is due to the varying distribution of a single pigment, **melanin**, which in turn depends on age and genetic factors.[131] The bulk of the iris and

---

[130] *Introduction to Optics* § 4.1 Camera Obscura.

[131] Sturm RA, Larsson M. Genetics of human iris colour and patterns. Pigment Cell Melanoma Res. 2009; 22(5):544-62.

outer layer, the stroma, is composed of pigmented cells, such as melanocytes and clump cells, and non-pigmented cells, such as fibroblasts, lymphocytes, and mast cells.[132] Reduced melanin levels in the iris stroma make the iris appear blue, while increased melanin levels in the iris stroma make the iris appear brown.[133] The back surface of the iris is lined with the heavily pigmented iris pigment epithelium, which strongly absorbs light, making the iris opaque to most of the visible light. The local iris color variations within the eye—often with one dominant color near the pupil edge and another at the scleral edge—are due to different melanin distributions across the iris. Thus, the color of the iris is due to the distribution of melanin in the iris stroma, while the opacity of the iris (strong light absorption) is due to the iris pigment epithelium.

Newborn babies do not have adequate melanin, so they begin life with mostly blue irises.[134] More pigment accumulates in the iris over the first few months of a child's life, and blue eyes can become less blue or even turn completely brown. In most cases, the iris color stops changing after the first year, but it may continue to change for several more years.

Eye color, or more precisely, iris color, is one of the most obvious phenotypic characteristics of an individual.[135] The portrait of the young Afghan refugee by Steve McCurry has captivated the world since it appeared on the *National Geographic* cover in June 1985. As the country descended into the turmoil of war, the refugee was lost. The story of how she was found again in 2002[136] reveals the importance of the biometric properties of iris landmarks.[137, 138]

2.4.2.2 Iris Optics

The iris is the **aperture stop**.[139] The **entrance pupil** is the image of the anatomical iris formed by the cornea, which is the optical element preceding the pupil. Looking at the eye we see not the anatomical pupil, but its image through the cornea, which is then the entrance pupil.

The entrance pupil is a virtual image of the pupil and is closer to the cornea (for a relaxed eye, ≈ 0.6 mm in front of the iris) and larger in diameter compared to the iris. The size of the entrance pupil depends on the cornea–iris separation [approximated by the anterior

---

[132] Mason CW. Blue Eyes. J Phys Chem. 1923; 1924285498-50 doi: 10.1021/j150239a007.

[133] Prota G, Hu DN, Vincensi MR, McCormick SA, Napolitano A. Characterization of melanins in human irides and cultured uveal melanocytes from eyes of different colors. Exp Eye Res. 1998; 67(3):293-9.

[134] Ludwig CA, Callaway NF, Fredrick DR, Blumenkranz MS, Moshfeghi DM. What colour are newborns' eyes? Prevalence of iris colour in the Newborn Eye Screening Test (NEST) study. Acta Ophthalmol. 2016; 94(5):485-8.

[135] Mackey DA, Wilkinson CH, Kearns LS, Hewitt AW. Classification of iris colour: review and refinement of a classification schema. Clin Exp Ophthalmol. 2011; 39(5):462-71.

[136] http://www.nationalgeographic.com/magazine/2002/04/afghan-girl-revealed/ accessed 12/10/2017.

[137] Pillai JK, Puertas M, Chellappa R. Cross-sensor iris recognition through kernel learning. IEEE Trans Pattern Anal Mach Intell. 2014; 36(1):73-85.

[138] Rathgeb C, Uhl A, Wild P. Iris Biometrics: From Segmentation to Template Security. Springer Science & Business Media. 2012.

[139] *Geometrical Optics* § 7.1.1 The Aperture Stop.

chamber depth (ACD)], the refractive indices n of the anterior chamber (aqueous), and the corneal refractive power.[140] In an emmetropic eye of average corneal power +42.0 D, ACD 3.6 mm, and $n_{aqueous}$ 1.336, the apparent pupil is about 12.7% larger than the iris and 0.6 mm closer to the cornea compared to the iris.[141]

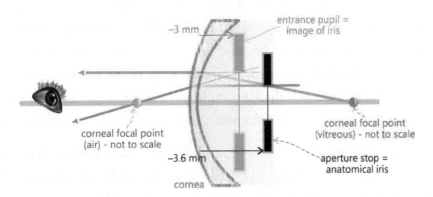

Figure 2-39: The entrance pupil is a virtual image of the anatomical pupil, imaged via the cornea.

Clinical note 📖: In microscopes, telescopes, and the slit lamp or the surgical scope, the exit pupil of the optical instrument must be matched to the entrance pupil of the eye.

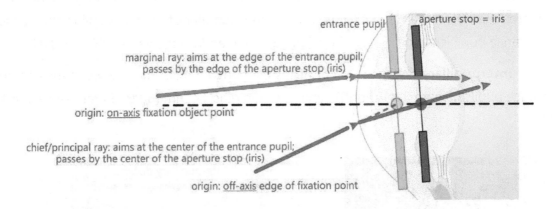

Figure 2-40: Entrance pupil of the human eye, iris, marginal, and chief ray.

The entrance pupil affects the optical zone, the depth of field, and optical aberrations. When selecting a contact lens or planning a laser refractive intervention, the optical zone must cover the diameter of the entrance pupil. The depth of field (discussed in § 6.1.4) and the impact of ocular aberrations in vision[142] are also dependent on the pupil diameter. A larger

[140] Fedtke C, Manns F, Ho A. The entrance pupil of the human eye: a three-dimensional model as a function of viewing angle. Opt Express. 2010; 18(21):22364-76.

[141] *Geometrical Optics* § 7.1.3.5 The Entrance Pupil in the Human Eye.

[142] Westheimer G. Image quality in the human eye. Opt Acta (Lond). 1970; 17:641-58.

pupil results in a shallower depth of field (§ 6.5.3 and Figure 6-50) and an increased geometrical blur. The diffraction-limited spot at the focus is, at the same time, finer.[143] This means that visual acuity is, in principle, better but deteriorates at a faster rate for out-of-focus objects. A smaller pupil results in an increased depth of field and reduced geometrical blur.

The diffraction-limited blur spot exactly on focus is, at the same time, coarser. Visual acuity is, in principle, reduced, but the increased depth of field allows perception with relative clarity of objects that are both near and far, thus requiring less accommodation. This explains why pupils shrink when adjusting for focusing on near objects: Miosis serves to increase the depth of field. This is the principle of the surgical management of presbyopia with special intracorneal implants that limit the pupil diameter, such as KAMRA corneal inlays (§ 7.8.4).

There is an antagonistic effect, however, which is important because the above considerations ignore the effects of aberrations. A smaller pupil helps reduce the effects of refractive errors such as myopia, hyperopia, and astigmatism and high-order aberrations such as spherical aberration. Thus, a balance of about 3 mm in pupil diameter results in an optical compromise for optimal visual acuity (§ 3.2.2).

The **exit pupil** is the image of the pupil via the lens, formed in image space. It is also a virtual image, usually located in front of the pupil and somewhat larger than the pupil but to a lesser degree than the entrance pupil. The ratio of the diameter of the exit pupil to the diameter of the entrance pupil is the pupil magnification ratio with an average value of 0.91 ± 0.04.

The **interpupillary distance** (IPD or PD) is the horizontal distance between the centers of the entrance pupils [(Figure 2-41 (right)], typically averaging 64 mm (60 to 65 mm—see also § 10.5.2.1.)

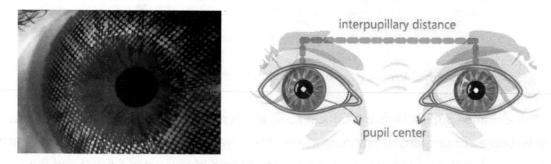

Figure 2-41: (left) Slit lamp photo of the anterior chamber illustrating the cornea and the iris. The cornea is fitted with a dot-pattern contact lens. (right) Interpupillary distance.

---

[143] *Wave Optics* § 5.4 Circular Aperture Diffraction.

Because of binocular vision, IPD is dependent on whether fixation is distant (parallel lines of sight) or near (inward, converging lines of sight). A note must always be made whether IPD is measured when the eyes are fixating at a distant point or a near point.

Clinical note 📇: PD is clinically significant in the diagnosis of craniofacial ailments under hyper- and hypotelorism ($\tau\eta\lambda\varepsilon$- apart, and -$o\rho\dot{\iota}\zeta\omega$, to separate). Normal IPD values are useful in the identification of ocular hyper- and hypotelorism in syndromes that might otherwise be obscured by various somatometric facial traits.[144]

In hypertelorism ($\upsilon\pi\dot{\varepsilon}\rho$- excessive),[145] the separation between the orbits is wider than normal, resulting in an increased IPD. This is different from the increased PD due to exodeviation, which occurs with normal bony orbits.[146] Hence, orbital hypertelorism (ORH) describes the lateralization of the bony orbit where the distance between the lateral canthus and auditory meatus is shortened.[147] Hypertelorism is associated with craniosynostosis[148]/ acrocephalosyndactyly (Apert syndrome),[149,150] craniofacial dystosis (Crouzon's disease),[151] frontonasal dysplasia (median cleft face syndrome),[152] and fetal hydantoin syndrome.[153]

Conversely, in hypotelorism ($\upsilon\pi\dot{o}$- deficient), the separation between the orbits is less than normal,[154] resulting in a decreased IPD. Hypotelorism is associated with mongolism[155] and Waardenburg syndrome.[156]

There are two distinct techniques for measuring PD. The first, physiological PD, measures the distance between the first Purkinje images of the two eyes, while the second, anatomical PD, measures the distance between common points on each eye.[157]

---

[144] Singh JR, Banerjee S. Normal values for interpupillary, inner canthal, and outer canthal distances in an Indian population. Hum Hered. 1983; 33:326–8.

[145] Weinberg SM, Leslie EJ, Hecht JT, Wehby GL, Deleyiannis FW, Moreno LM, Christensen K, Marazita ML. Hypertelorism and orofacial clefting revisited: an anthropometric investigation. Cleft Palate Craniofac J. 2017; 54(6):631-8.

[146] Greig DM. Hypertelorism: A hitherto undifferentiated congenital craniofacial deformity. Edinb Med J. 1924; 31:560.

[147] Tessier P. Orbital hypertelorism. I. Successive surgical attempts. Material and methods. Causes and mechanisms. Scand J Plast Reconstr Surg. 1972; 6(2):135-55.

[148] Sharma RK. Hypertelorism. Indian J Plast Surg. 2014; 47(3):284-92.

[149] Stomnaroska O, Danilovski D, Ivanovska S. Craniosynostosis: Acrocephalosyndactyly (Apert syndrome) diagnosed in a newborn. Prilozi. 2017; 38(3):153-5.

[150] Kabbani H, Raghuveer TS. Craniosynostosis. Am Fam Physician. 2004; 69(12):2863-70.

[151] Dodge HW Jr, Wood MW, Kennedy RL. Craniofacial dysostosis: Crouzon's disease. Pediatrics. 1959; 23(1):98-106.

[152] Sharma S, Sharma V, Bothra M. Frontonasal dysplasia (Median cleft face syndrome). J Neurosci Rural Pract. 2012; 3(1):65-7.

[153] Hanson JW, Smith DW. Fetal hydantoin syndrome. Lancet. 1976; 1(7961):692.

[154] Maltese G, Tarnow P, Tovetjärn R, Kölby L. Correction of hypotelorism in isolated metopic synostosis. J Plast Surg Hand Surg. 2014; 48(1):63-6.

[155] MacLachlan C, Howland HC. Normal values and standard deviations for pupil diameter and interpupillary distance in subjects aged 1 month to 19 years. Ophthalmic Physiol Opt. 2002; 22(3):175-82.

[156] Minami SB, Nara K, Mutai H, Morimoto N, Sakamoto H, Takiguchi T, Kaga K, Matsunaga T. A clinical and genetic study of 16 Japanese families with Waardenburg syndrome. Gene. 2019; 704:86-90.

[157] Osuobeni EP, al-Fahdi M. Differences between anatomical and physiological interpupillary distance. J Am Optom Assoc. 1994; 65(4):265-71.

2.4.2.3 Pupillary Response

Pupillary response or **pupil light reflex** is a physiological response that leads to a change in the pupil diameter (size). While the pupil diameter (PD) is about 3.5 mm, the pupil constricts under a bright light to 1.5 or 2 mm in diameter and expands under dim light up to 8 mm.

Pupil constriction and dilation can be brought about by the contraction of the sphincter and the dilator pupillae, two antagonistic autonomic (reflex) muscles. The sphincter muscle (σφιγκτήρας), innervated by the parasympathetic nervous system, is a circumferential muscle that forms a ring around the iris edge; its contraction leads to pupil constriction. The dilator muscle (διαστολέας), innervated by the sympathetic nerve system, forms radially from the iris edge into the ciliary body; its contraction leads to excitation of the radial fibers of the iris, which leads to an increased pupillary aperture.

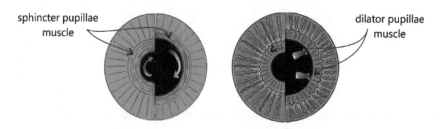

sphincter pupillae muscle

dilator pupillae muscle

Figure 2-42: Pupillae muscles driving pupil response.

Pupil size may be <u>pharmacologically induced</u>: It may constrict (miosis) in response to agents such as opiates/opioids or anti-hypertension medication. The pupil may dilate (mydriasis) by anticholinergic agents and amphetamines that block the responses of the ciliary muscle during accommodation (cycloplegia, § 7.1) and <u>also</u> act on the sphincter muscle, producing mydriasis. A pharmacologically mydriated pupil remains dilated even in bright light. Phenylephrine and pilocarpine, alpha-1 adrenergic agonists, are used as mydriatic agents.

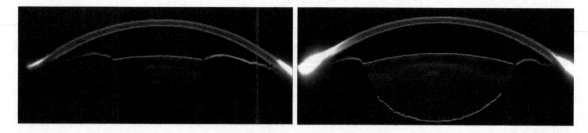

Figure 2-43: Scheimpflug images taken before (left) and after (right) pharmacologic mydriasis.[158]

---

[158] Razeghinejad MR, Lashkarizadeh H, Nowroozzadeh MH, Yazdanmehr M. Changes in ocular biometry and anterior chamber parameters after pharmacologic mydriasis and peripheral iridotomy in primary angle closure suspects. J Optom. 2016; 9(3):189-95.

Pupil size changes may be a result of the pupillary light reflex, initiated in the retina via the optic and oculomotor cranial nerve in response to changing ambient luminance (Figure 2-44). The afferent pupillomotor signal that drives the pupillary light reflex involves a specific class of intrinsically photosensitive (ipRGC) ganglion cells (discussed in § 4.3.3).[159]

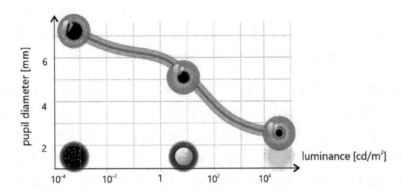

Figure 2-44: Pupil size (diameter) variation with ambient luminance.

Clinical note 👥 : The pupillary response has clinical and research interest because it can be an objective marker of retinal response to light.[160] The amplitude of the pupillary constriction to light stimuli is reduced with increasing age (senile miosis)[161] and iris thickness in subjects with normal ocular health.[162] Interestingly, not only the constriction amplitude, but also the mean pupil diameter, decreases with age.

The dependence of pupil diameter D [mm] on luminance L [cd/m², also called nit] is[163, 164]

$$\underbrace{\log_{10}(D)}_{\text{log of pupil diameter}} = 0.8558 - 4.01 \times 10^{-4} \left(\underbrace{\log_{10}(L)}_{\text{luminocity log}} + 8.6 \right)^3 \qquad (2.8)$$

The range from a miotic (1.00 to 2.00 mm) to a mydriatic (4.00 to 8.00 mm) pupil diameter corresponds to an area increase from 16 (=4²) to 64 (=8²), which is barely one order of magnitude. This pupil constriction in response to increased luminance helps to reduce the luminous flux reaching the retina; a smaller pupil area admits less light. However, this response

[159] Güler AD, Ecker JL, Lall GS, Haq S, Altimus CM, Liao HW, Barnard AR, Cahill H, Badea TC, Zhao H, Hankins MW, Berson DM, Lucas RJ, Yau KW, Hattar S. Melanopsin cells are the principal conduits for rod-cone input to non-image-forming vision. Nature. 2008; 453(7191):102-5.

[160] Kawasaki A. Physiology, assessment, and disorders of the pupil. Curr Opin Ophthalmol. 1999; 10(6):394-400.

[161] Sloane ME, Owsley C, Alvarez SL. Aging, senile miosis and spatial contrast sensitivity at low luminance. Vision Res. 1988; 28(11):1235-46.

[162] Sharma S, Baskaran M, Rukmini AV, Nongpiur ME, Htoon H, Cheng CY, Perera SA, Gooley JJ, Aung T, Milea D. Factors influencing the pupillary light reflex in healthy individuals. Graefes Arch Clin Exp Ophthalmol. 2016; 254(7):1353-9.

[163] Adrian W. Spectral sensitivity of the pupillary system. Clin Exp Optom. 2003; 86(4):235-8.

[164] Definitions of luminance and the unit nit are detailed in: *Introduction to Optics* § 2.2.1 Photometric Quantities.

is not sufficient to fully control and explain the reaction of the eye to the increased light ambience since it can only provide a small compensation by restricting the area (aperture stop) of light collection by one to two orders of magnitude.

The human eye works comfortably over a ×10⁶ luminance range of 0.001 cd/m² in the dim night sky to 1000 cd/m² on a sunny day—this is six orders of magnitude. There are therefore other responses to increased luminance that involve neural adaptation (discussed in § 4.3.3)[165] and, to a lesser degree, reflex response to target proximity.[166]

Another aspect of pupil light reflex is the reaction time (latency) in bright stimulus and the color (wavelength) dependence. Figure 2-45 illustrates dynamic pupil diameter data for OFF and ON light stimulus of 300 cd/m² (room light). The ON-phase duration is 20 seconds. Miosis is almost immediate, within less than 1 second, with pupils becoming the smallest in ≈ 3 to 4 seconds. When the stimulus ceases, the return to mydriasis is slower, requiring ≈ 10 to 15 seconds. We also note the wavelength dependence: The reaction for the red is more direct but weaker than for the blue. The quantification of pupil responses to light stimuli of a specific luminance and wavelength (color) is used to assess retinal function.[167, 168, 169]

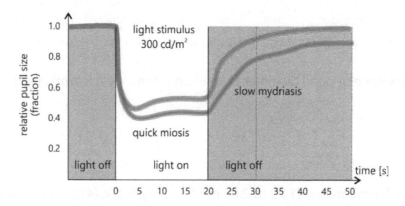

Figure 2-45: Pupil diameter reflex change for two different wavelengths (blue at 470 nm, red at 660 nm) in a normal eye as a function of time.[170]

[165] Woodhouse JM, Campbell FW. The role of the pupil light reflex in aiding adaptation to the dark. Vision Res. 1975; 15:649-53.

[166] Mathôt S, van der Linden L, Grainger J, Vitu F. The pupillary response to light reflects the focus of covert visual attention. PLoS One 2013; 8(10):e78168.

[167] Gamlin PD, McDougal DH, Pokorny J, Smith VC, Yau KW, Dacey DM. Human and macaque pupil responses driven by melanopsin-containing retinal ganglion cells. Vision Res. 2007; 47(7):946-54.

[168] Grozdanic SD, Matic M, Sakaguchi DS, Kardon RH. Evaluation of retinal status using chromatic pupil light reflex activity in healthy and diseased canine eyes. Invest Ophthalmol Vis Sci. 2007; 48(11):5178-83.

[169] Kardon R, Anderson SC, Damarjian TG, Grace EM, Stone E, Kawasaki A. Chromatic pupillometry in patients with retinitis pigmentosa. Ophthalmology. 2011; 118(2):376-81.

[170] Herbst K, Sander B, Milea D, Lund-Andersen H, Kawasaki A. Test-retest repeatability of the pupil light response to blue and red light stimuli in normal human eyes using a novel pupillometer. Front Neurol. 2011; 2:10.

2.4.2.4 Pupil Symmetry Fluctuations

In a perfectly symmetric eye, the pupil center would be on the axis of symmetry, the optical axis. In an actual eye, the pupil center is slightly offset nasally by about 0.5 mm,[142] and the pupil center shifts with pupil diameter variations; this is the centroid shift:[171, 172] The pupil center shifts temporally by up to about 0.6 mm as the pupil dilates (§ 2.4.3).

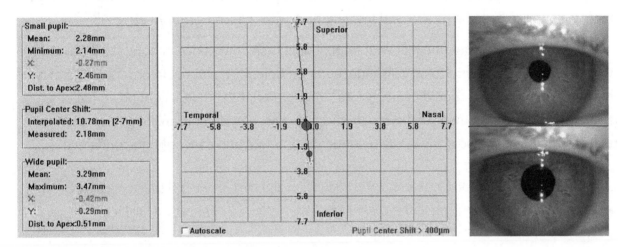

Figure 2-46: Centroid shift changes. Notice that the pupil center shifts with respect to the corneal Purkinje reflex when the pupil dilates.[173]

The acronym PERRLA stands for pupils equal, round, and reactive to light and accommodation. It is a convenient but incomplete description of pupilomotor function, as it does not include the actual size and shape of each pupil, the speed and extent of pupillary constriction, and the possible afferent pupillary defect.

PERRLA acronym for recording pupils	• PE: pupils equal
	• R: round
	• RL: reactive to light (direct and consensual)
	• A: responsive to accommodation (near target)

Often the pupils fail the PE and R parts of the PERRLA test. Many factors can contribute to non-round pupil shapes. These can be trauma, surgical complications, posterior synechia,

---

[171] Wilson MA, Campbell MC, Simonet P. The Julius F. Neumueller Award in Optics, 1989: change of pupil centration with change of illumination and pupil size. Optom Vis Sci. 1992; 69(2):129-36.

[172] *Ocular Imaging* § 2.4 Pupilometry.

[173] Kanellopoulos AJ, Asimellis G, Georgiadou S. Digital pupilometry and centroid shift changes after cataract surgery. J Cataract Refract Surg. 2015; 41(2):408-14.

intraocular inflammation, age-related iris atrophy, or ischemia. The pupil size(s) may be affected by a cataract, possibly in correlation with ACD changes.

It appears that an obtuse cataract crystalline lens has the secondary effect of restricting the iris' free constrictive movement by pushing if forward, thus making the effective pupil size slightly larger and less circularly symmetric. The removal of the lens frees the space previously occupied in the posterior segment, thus re-establishing the free iris movement and enabling the photopic pupil to become smaller and less elliptical, with reduced centroid effects.[174]

Anisocoria (*άνισο-* unequal and *-κόρη*, pupil) is any difference in pupil size between the two eyes. It can be pharmacologically induced or pathologic in nature. In order to determine the cause, the pupil size should be measured[172] in both bright and dark lighting conditions, isolating the parasympathetic and sympathetic pathways. Physiologic anisocoria occurs if the relative amount of anisocoria is the same under both bright and dark lighting conditions.

Clinical note 🖳 : If anisocoria increases under bright light and the larger pupil is not constricting normally, this suggests a parasympathetic pupil problem. Some of the more common 'big pupil' problems include Adie's tonic pupil, cranial nerve III palsy, and pharmacologic dilation.

If anisocoria increases under dark light and the smaller pupil is not dilating normally, it is likely a sympathetic pupil problem. Potential causes of small pupil problems include Horner's syndrome, Argyll Robertson pupils, and pharmacologic constriction.
Whenever anisocoria is suspected, recent medication history should be evaluated.

Pupil abnormalities also include displaced pupil (corectopia), multiple pupils (polycoria), white pupils (leukocoria, suggesting retinoblastoma, a serious ocular form of cancer), or iris heterochromia, a difference in iris colors between the two eyes.

2.4.3 Axes and Reference Points in the Human Eye

In coaxial, rotationally symmetric optical systems, the **optical axis** is the straight line connecting the centers of curvature of all refractive and/or reflective interfaces. In these systems, the optical axis determines the axis of symmetry of each component and is the alignment line for all elements: In other words, the optical axis is the <u>axis of symmetry</u> for the entire optical system.

The eye is not symmetrical; its optical elements are not perfectly centered, and the optical surfaces do not have ideal rotational symmetry due to global eye tilt, lens tilt, and lens

[174] Kanellopoulos AJ, Asimellis G. Clear-cornea cataract surgery: pupil size and shape changes, along with anterior chamber volume and depth changes. A Scheimpflug imaging study. Clin Ophthalmol. 2014; 8:2141-50.

decentration. In addition, the fovea is physiologically displaced temporally and slightly inferiorly to the intersection of the 'optical axis' from the center of the posterior pole (Figure 4-1).

When the eye fixates on an eccentric source, the four **Purkinje images** (§ 2.3.1) are typically seen as misaligned [Figure 2-31 (right)]. To approximate the optical axis, we align the Purkinje images in the best possible way. Because there is no placement of the illuminating source that perfectly aligns all four images, the source is positioned so that it <u>minimizes their lateral spread</u>, usually by achieving a center overlap between P_1 (or P_3) and P_4; then the line connecting the source to the 'centered' images is the best approximation of the optical axis.

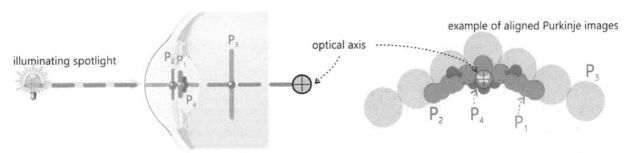

Figure 2-47: Optical axis and aligned Purkinje images. Compare to Figure 2-31.

Clinical note 📊 : If the lens is decentered, then P_3 (and P_4) cannot be aligned with P_1. If the lens is tilted, this manifests as an angular expanse from the centrally aligned fixation point to that fixation when the best overlap is achieved. These aspects become important in the evaluation of lens placement following cataract extraction and intraocular lens (IOL) implantation.

Because the optical axis cannot be determined precisely and is not adequate to describe the visual function, we also use several other axes. Specifically:

The **visual axis** is the line that connects the fixation point and the fovea; it passes through the nodal points N and N' when the eye is fixated on a target. The visual axis (green line in Figure 2-48) is angled nasally (N) from the optical axis by $\approx 5°$ because of the slight temporal displacement of the fovea with respect to the 'optical axis' retinal intersection. The visual axis is, in theory, fixed because the locations of the nodal points do not depend on the pupil size. This axis is drawn as a broken line with a short segment between the two nodal points, maintaining the inclination with respect to the optical axis at N and N'.

The visual axis is a <u>theoretical construct</u> because the nodal points do not correspond to specific anatomic reference landmarks or points of the eye but are determined by optical considerations.[175] Also, the nodal points are not uniquely defined, even in the same eye, if there

---

[175] Mandell RB, Chiang CS, Klein SA. Location of the major corneal reference points. Optom Vis Sci. 1995; 72(11):776-84.

is a lack of spherical symmetry: In astigmatism, for example, there are different sets of nodal points due to different refractive powers along different meridians.

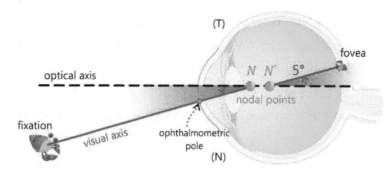

Figure 2-48: Visual axis (angle not shown to scale).

Notes on the visual axis : There are some objections to the use of the term 'visual' axis. This axis does not represent a true path of light through the human eye but a fragmented ray path that corresponds to origin and destination; recall that this is the equivalent of the nodal ray (rule # 3 of the ray-tracing rules).[176] Ronald Rabbetts has proposed the use of the term 'nodal' axis instead.[177]

The **line of sight**, or paraxial principal/chief ray, is the straight line that connects the fixation point to the center of the entrance pupil (object space), the center of the exit pupil (image space), and the fovea (approximately). It is the clinical counterpart of the visual axis and defines the center of the cone of light entering the eye.[175]

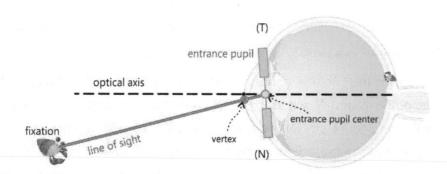

Figure 2-49: Line of sight.

Unlike the visual axis, the line of sight is not fixed because the geometric center of the pupil fluctuates upon pupil size (diameter) and shape changes. Both the visual axis and the line of sight are angled nasally. They are used to determine the location and size of the retinal

---

[176] *Geometrical Optics* § 4.3 Ray Diagrams.
[177] Rabbetts RB. Bennett and Rabbett's Clinical Visual Optics 4th Edition § 12. The Schematic Eye. Butterworth-Heinemann; 2007.

image (see § 6.2.2 and § 6.5.2), and to study optical effects relating to corneal (and, in general, ocular) refraction. According to the standards of the Optical Society of America (OSA), the line of sight is the reference axis for measuring ocular aberrations.[178]

The **pupillary axis** is the line from the center of the entrance pupil that intersects the cornea perpendicularly. Thus, it crosses the center of curvature of the cornea. It is the <u>clinical counterpart of the optical axis</u>. If the center of the entrance pupil was on the optical axis, then the pupillary and the optical axes would coincide; but since the pupil is slightly displaced nasally, these axes do not coincide. The pupillary axis helps define several reference angles in the eye.

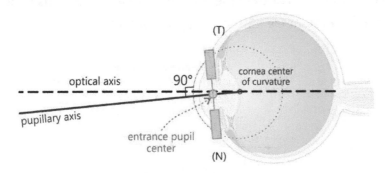

Figure 2-50: Pupillary axis.

The line of sight and the pupillary axis (shown together with the optical and the visual axis in Figure 2-51) are defined by anatomical reference points of the eye; thus, they are neither approximations (such as the optical axis) nor mathematical constructs (such as the visual axis).

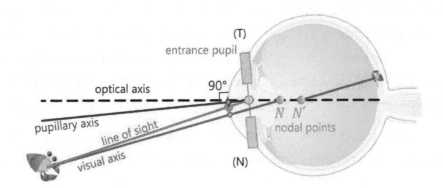

Figure 2-51: Optical axis, visual axis, line of sight, and pupillary axis.

On the flip side, the line of sight and the pupillary axis are not fixed, i.e., they depend on the exact location of the center of the entrance pupil, which both axes intersect. Yet another approximation is that the line of sight, defined in geometrical optics terms from the fixation

---

[178] Thibos LN, Applegate RA, Schwiegerling JT, Webb R; VSIA Standards Taskforce Members. Vision science and its applications. Standards for reporting the optical aberrations of eyes. J Refract Surg. 2002; 18(5):S652-60.

point to the center of the entrance pupil and onwards to the center of the exit pupil, is supposed to terminate at the conjugate image point at the fovea; however, this occurs only if the pupil is properly centered.[179]

The corneal **reference points** are the apex, the anterior pole, and the vertex. The corneal **apex** is defined geometrically as the point of maximum corneal curvature (steepest cornea / shortest radius of curvature). In a normal cornea, the apex is close to the corneal intersect of the pupillary axis[180, 181] and coincides with the **anterior pole of the eye**, defined as the most forward point of the cornea. The apex describes the cornea geometrically and relates to aspects of the cornea shape. For example, the fitting of a contact lens relates to the corneal geometry, so the apex is a reference for the riding position of a contact lens.

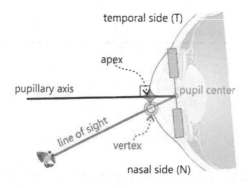

Figure 2-52: Corneal reference points apex and vertex.

The **vertex** or **corneal sighting center** is defined as the intersection of the line of sight with the corneal surface. Being a marker for the line of sight, the vertex is effectively the reference point when describing the optics of the cornea (and the eye, by extension). Other terms used in lieu of the vertex are cornea visual center and ophthalmometric pole (the latter being defined as the visual axis corneal intercept). The apex and vertex are slightly displaced: The vertex is slightly more nasal and, to a lesser degree, slightly inferior with respect to the apex.

The pupil geometrical center is another corneal landmark. While being neither fixed (it shifts with dilation, for example) nor corneal, it is often used to reference other corneal points.

---

[179] In several textbooks, the line of sight is drawn either as a broken line (alas, at the pupil center!) or arbitrarily terminating at a point other than the fovea, a terminus that only the visual axis faithfully observes. The first approach is optically wrong. In fact, because the entrance pupil is a virtual image of the real pupil, the rays directed toward the entrance pupil are refracted by the cornea and pass through the actual pupil, then are refracted again by the lens. The line of sight has a virtual segment for any point past the cornea but does not bend at the pupil center! The second approach, which assumes that the line of sight does not necessarily terminate at the fovea, is rather more truthful (if the pupil is not properly centered). The problem arises is when we need to use this line of sight to approximate the retinal image. Ouch. Hence, we use the visual axis to calculate the retinal image size.

[180] Tomlinson A, Schwartz C. The position of the corneal apex in the normal eye. Am J Optom Physiol Opt. 1979; 56(4):236-40.

[181] Mandell RB, Helen RS. Position and curvature of the corneal apex. Am J Optom Arch Am Acad Optom. 1969; 46(1):25-9.

For example, several ocular imaging devices align the subject's eye (using horizontal and vertical joystick twists) with the centered displayed pupil, often projecting cross or annular light.

Eye rotations are centered at the **center of rotation (CoR) of the eye**, also known as the pivot point.[182] This is the point that remains fixed when the globe rotates in its orbit to switch to a different fixation. The reference axis for eye movements is the **fixation axis**, the line that connects the fixation point to the center of rotation of the eye (Figure 2-53).

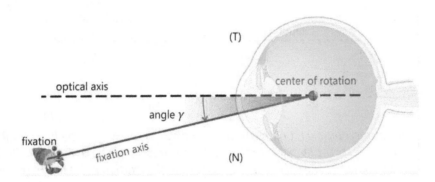

Figure 2-53: Fixation axis, center of rotation, and angle gamma.

The center of rotation of the eye is not precisely fixed, as it is slightly fluctuating.[183] In an average-sized eye, it lies on the optical axis, 13.5 mm in the eye (ranging between 12.95 and 14.73 mm)[183] and 0.1 mm to the nasal side.[184] Its location is dependent on the axial length of the eye; therefore, it is less than 13.5 mm in eyes with shorter axial lengths and more than 13.5 mm in eyes with longer axial lengths (§ 6.4.1.1).[185]

The final set of corneal reference points and axes relates to ocular imaging with a corneal topographer (and other ocular imaging devices with coaxial optics). When a subject's eye is coaxially sighted (illumination and measurement share the same axis),[175] and the subject's eye is fixating on the instrument's centerl light source, the reflection pattern off the cornea is centered at the subject-fixated **coaxially sighted corneal light reflex** (CSCLR).[186] The axis connecting the instrument's center light fixation source and the CSCLR is the **corneal topographic, keratometric**, or **videokeratoscopic axis** (Figure 2-54). In other words, the videokeratoscopic axis connects the center light spot at the axis of the instrument with the first corneal reflex when the subject is fixating on said center light spot.[186]

[182] Donders FC, Doijer D. The location of the pivot point of the eye. Part II. Strabismus. 2016; 24(4):184-8.

[183] Park RS, Park GE. The center of ocular rotation in the horizontal plane. Am J Physiol.-Legacy Content. 1933; 104(3):545-52.

[184] Fry GA, Hill WW. The center of rotation of the eye. Am J Optom Arch Am Acad Optom. 1962; 39:581-95.

[185] Touzeau O, Allouch C, Borderie V, Kopito R, Laroche L. [Correlation between refraction and ocular biometry]. J Fr Ophtalmol. 2003; 26(4):355-63.

[186] Chang DH, Waring GO IV. The subject-fixated coaxially sighted corneal light reflex: a clinical marker for centration of refractive treatments and devices. Am J Ophthalmol. 2014; 158(5):863-74.

Because the eye is both coaxially illuminated <u>and</u> imaged, the reflection off the cornea must occur at a point that is perpendicular to the cornea. Thus, the CSCLR, the center of the reflected pattern (such as topography rings) is the **vertex normal**,[175] and the videokeratoscopic axis also crosses the center of curvature of the cornea (about 7.7 mm in the eye).

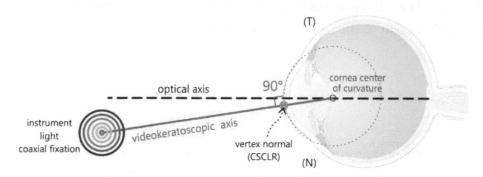

Figure 2-54: The videokeratoscopic axis. Comparison to Figure 2-49 shows that the line of sight is tied to the same fixation point but intersects the pupil center instead. Also, a comparison to Figure 2-50 shows that the pupillary axis is perpendicular to the cornea and is tied not to the fixation point but to the pupil center.

Compared to the other two axes that originate from the fixation point, the line of sight intersects the pupil center about 3 mm inside the eye, and the visual axis intersects the nodal point about 7 mm inside the eye. It thus appears that, coincidentally, the vertex normal is the closest clinical marker of the 'ophthalmometric pole', the corneal intersect of the visual axis[187] and the videokeratoscopic axis is a closer clinical match to the visual axis than the line of sight when using an instrument light coaxial fixation.

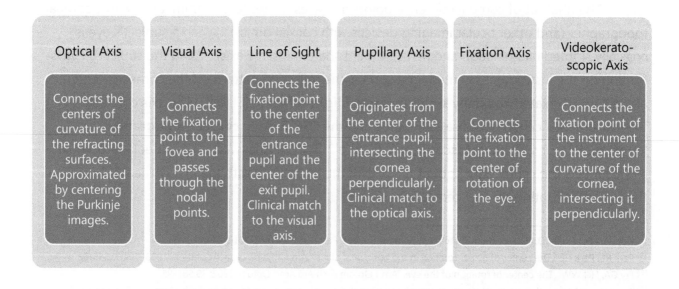

Optical Axis	Visual Axis	Line of Sight	Pupillary Axis	Fixation Axis	Videokerato-scopic Axis
Connects the centers of curvature of the refracting surfaces. Approximated by centering the Purkinje images.	Connects the fixation point to the fovea and passes through the nodal points.	Connects the fixation point to the center of the entrance pupil and the center of the exit pupil. Clinical match to the visual axis.	Originates from the center of the entrance pupil, intersecting the cornea perpendicularly. Clinical match to the optical axis.	Connects the fixation point to the center of rotation of the eye.	Connects the fixation point of the instrument to the center of curvature of the cornea, intersecting it perpendicularly.

[187] Pande M, Hillman JS. Optical zone centration in keratorefractive surgery. Entrance pupil center, visual axis, coaxially sighted corneal reflex, or geometric corneal center? Ophthalmology. 1993; 100(8):1230-7.

2.4.4 Angles in the Human Eye

The angle between the pupillary axis and the line of sight is **angle lambda** λ. Because the line of sight has a nasal inclination with respect to the pupillary axis, angle λ tends to be displaced nasally, with values[188] measuring from 3° to 8°. Positive values indicate a nasal displacement, and negative values indicate a temporal displacement.

Angle lambda λ is the only angle corresponding to eye anatomical landmarks because both of its sides are defined anatomically, lending itself thus to practical clinical measurements: The pupillary axis and the line of sight both pass through the center of the entrance pupil, which is the apex of angle λ. This angle can be observed and measured clinically as follows: The subject's eye fixates on a point light source and the observer traces the corneal reflex of that source by moving the source laterally (typically, nasally) until the reflex is seen overlaid on the subject's pupil center. The line from the observer and the subject's pupil center is the pupillary axis, while the line from the light source and the subject's pupil center is the line of sight.

Angle alpha α is the angle formed between the optical axis and the visual axis and is an optical approximation to angle λ.

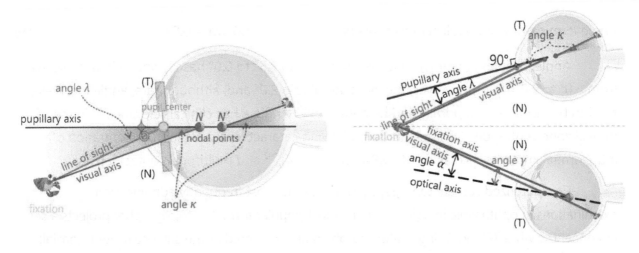

Figure 2-55: (left) Angles kappa κ and lambda λ. (right) Angles alpha α, lambda λ, kappa κ, and gamma γ (typically) tend to be nasally displaced because of the temporal shift of the fovea.

Angle kappa κ is formed by the pupillary axis and the visual axis. Its apex is the object-space nodal point N. Unlike angle λ, angle κ is fixed; i.e., it is not dependent on pupil centration variations. However, it is not possible to clinically measure angle κ because the location of the nodal point is not defined by an eye landmark. Often, the numerical differences between angles κ and λ are very small, so both are sometimes referred to as angle κ.

---

[188] Loper LR. The relationship between angle lambda and the residual astigmatism of the eye. Am J Optom Arch Am Acad Optom. 1959; 36(7):365-77.

Finally, **angle gamma** γ is formed between the fixation axis and the optical axis. Its apex is the eye's center of rotation (Figure 2-53), and its values range from 2° to 8° in a normal eye, with greater values associated with hyperopia.[182]

Angle lambda	Angle kappa	Angle alpha	Angle gamma
Formed between the pupillary axis and the line of sight; its apex is the center of the pupil.	Formed between the pupillary axis and the visual axis.	Formed between the optical axis and the visual axis; its apex is the nodal point. Its clinical counterpart is angle lambda.	Formed between the fixation axis and the optical axis; its apex is the eye's center of rotation.

In eyes with normal to large axial lengths, the arc corresponding to angle κ is 100 to 400 μm (0.1 to 0.4 mm). For short axial lengths, it can be as large as 700 to 800 μm (0.7 to 0.8 mm). This distance can be used to compute angle κ (in degrees), considering that its apex is the nodal point N.[189] For example, for an arc length of 400 μm = 0.4 mm and an (average) distance from the cornea to nodal point N = 7.0 mm, the angle is 0.4/7.0 = 0057 rad = 3.27°.

Angle κ (microns from pupil center) conversion: $\qquad$ 100 μm = 0.82° $\qquad\qquad$ (2.9)

Angle κ values in emmetropic eyes range from 3.5° to 6.0° nasally and in hyperopic eyes from 6.0° to 9.0°. In myopic eyes, the average value is 2.0° and, although rare, angle κ can even tend to be displaced temporally and be negative.[190] Angle κ has clinical relevance[187] in the of optical zone centration, IOL implantation following cataract lens extraction,[191] centration of intracorneal implants such as the KAMRA ring (§ 7.8.4),[192] and multifocal contact lenses.

Computerized corneal topography is one of the most frequently administered examinations in ophthalmic imaging.[193] In its most popular form, the topographer projects a set of concentric white (Placido) rings, reflected off an area centered at the subject-fixated, coaxially sighted CSCLR, which is the vertex normal [Figure 2-56 (left)]. The reflection pattern is called a mires or mire pattern (latin for *mirare*). Often, the instrument also images the pupil edge and

---

[189] Nowakowski M, Sheehan M, Neal D, Goncharov AV. Investigation of the isoplanatic patch and wavefront aberration along the pupillary axis compared to the line of sight in the eye. Biomed Opt Express. 2012; 3(2):240-58.

[190] Damms T, Damms C, Schulz E, Haase W. Pseudoesotropie durch Verlängerung der Makula nach nasal bei Patienten mit infantiler hoher Myopie (Pseudo-esotropia caused by nasal dislocation of the macula in patients with high infantile myopia). Ophthalmologe. 1994; 91:77-80.

[191] Prakash G, Prakash DR, Agarwal A, Kumar DA, Jacob S. Predictive factor and kappa angle analysis for visual satisfactions in patients with multifocal IOL implantation. Eye (Lond). 2011; 25:1187-93.

[192] Langenbucher A, Goebels S, Szentmáry N, Seitz B, Eppig T. Vignetting and field of view with the KAMRA corneal inlay. Biomed Res Int. 2013; 2013:154593.

[193] *Ocular Imaging* § 4.3.1 Computerized Corneal Topography.

marks the pupil center [Figure 2-56 (right) and Figure 2-57]. The pupil center, as it is imaged in this case (with a fixated eye), is the corneal intersect of the line of sight.[67]

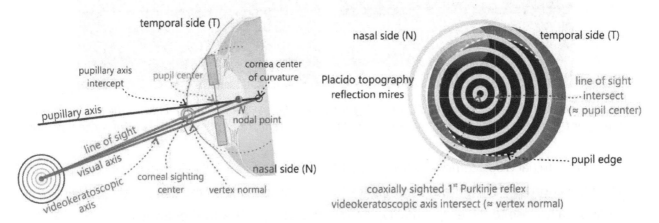

Figure 2-56: (left) Corneal intercepts of the line of sight and the pupillary, visual, and videokeratoscopic axes (differences are shown exaggerated with the fixation point being very close for illustrative purposes). (right) Corneal topography effect simulated for the left eye (OS): The pupil geometrical center does not correspond to the center of the Purkinje reflections (mire pattern).

The CSCLR vertex normal and the pupil center (line of sight intercept) can be clinically identified (Figure 2-57 and Figure 2-58), and their displacement can be measured.[194] Often, this two-point distance, expressed in units of length [microns or millimeters], is referred to as 'angle κ (or λ); however, this is an oversimplification. Common misconceptions are that the CSCLR (vertex normal) is the vertex (the corneal sighting center), or that the CSCLR lies at the lens anterior surface.

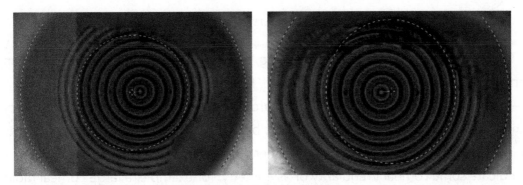

Figure 2-57: Corneal topography pupillary and limbal edge markers shown in dashed white lines. (left) An OD eye showing the mire pattern Placido rings displaced nasally with respect to the pupil center. (right) An OS eye showing, again, nasal displacement of the Placido rings.

[194] Gatinel D, El Danasoury A, Rajchles S, Saad A. Recentration of a small-aperture corneal inlay. J Cataract Refract Surg. 2012; 38(12):2186-91.

Figure 2-58: Details of the patterns shown in Figure 2-57. The cross-like symbol denotes the pupil center, a proxy for the line-of-sight intercept. The CSCLR Placido ring reflections are centered at the corneal vertex.

The arcual displacement between the CSCLR and the coaxially viewed pupil center is called the **chord μ** .[186] (Figure 2-59 amplifies the differences due to the fixation target being unrealistically close to the eye; in reality, the target is at least 10× farther away.)

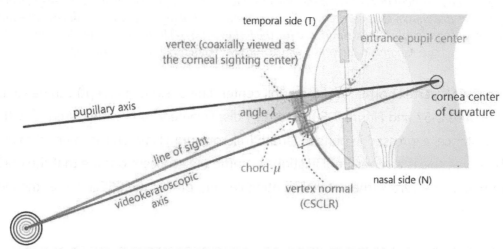

Figure 2-59: Vertex versus CSCLR and angle λ.

Often, in research and in a clinical setting, this arcual displacement is called the angle λ (or even angle κ). This is <u>not accurate</u>, however. First, an arcual displacement—which is length—cannot be 'an angle'; it is also not the arc for which the angle λ intercepts the cornea, but rather a simplified approximation of this arc because the CSCLR and the vertex points in a normal cornea are often fairly close to each other. Notable differences between these two points indicate some corneal irregularity or asymmetry; for example, a large corneal radius of curvature (flat cornea) may shift the videokeratoscopic axis farther from the line of sight. Such differences, if present, may have a bearing on the planning of a corneal laser refractive surgery.

One more difference is that the chord μ is not related to the axial length, unlike angle κ (Figure 2-60). The latter is due to the displacement of the macula from the posterior pole. Consider a right-angle triangle, whose opposite side is the macula-posterior pole distance. In eyes with a long axial length (as in axial myopia § 6.4.1.1), the triangle has a longer adjacent side and thus a smaller angle κ. In eyes with a short axial length (as in axial hyperopia § 6.4.2.1), the triangle has a shorter adjacent side and thus a larger angle κ.

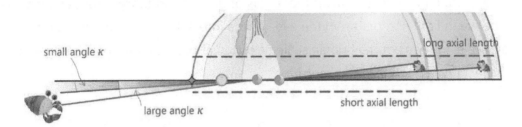

Figure 2-60: A longer (shorter) axial length of the eye correlates to a smaller (larger) angle κ.

Clinical note 🖁 : The proper centration of the laser ablation pattern in laser refractive surgery such as PRK or LASIK[195] is associated with good visual outcomes.[196] An ablation pattern zone that is improperly centered is associated with decreased retinal image quality,[197] manifested as high-order aberrations and decreased contrast, particularly under mesopic or scotopic conditions.[198] The question is, what is 'proper centration'? Where exactly should the pattern be centered?

The two options are for the pupil center[199] or the vertex normal to serve as a proxy for the corneal intersect of the visual axis.[187] Aberrometry measurements, often centered on the pupil, can be introduced into the software planning the laser ablation pattern. If the CSCLR is to be used, it can be determined intraoperatively, or the topographic placement of a coaxial light reflex or corneal topography data can be imported in the software; these data, however, are acquired around the vertex normal.

If the laser treatment is eccentric, in subsequent aberrometry measurements (which, by OSA standards, are centered around the line of sight),[178] any amount of spherical aberration that is deliberately induced symmetrically about the treatment center would be interpreted as coma! This aspect becomes more relevant in hyperopic eyes because the difference between the two, reported as angle κ, is typically larger in eyes with axial hyperopia and smaller in eyes with axial myopia. This can be interpreted with a geometrical approximation (Figure 2-60)[200] because eyes with axial hyperopia have shorter axial lengths (§ 6.4.2.1), while eyes with axial myopia have longer axial lengths (§ 6.4.1.1).

[195] Kanellopoulos AJ, Asimellis G. LASIK ablation centration: an objective digitized assessment and comparison between two generations of an excimer laser. J Refract Surg. 2015; 31(3):164-9.

[196] Mrochen M, Kaemmerer M, Mierdel P, Seiler T. Increased higher-order optical aberrations after laser refractive surgery: a problem of subclinical decentration. J Cataract Refract Surg. 2001; 27:362–369.

[197] Park CY, Oh SY, Chuck RS. Measurement of angle kappa and centration in refractive surgery. Curr Opin Ophthalmol. 2012; 23(4):269-75.

[198] Reinstein DZ, Gobbe M, Archer TJ. Coaxially sighted corneal light reflex versus entrance pupil center centration of moderate to high hyperopic corneal ablations in eyes with small and large angle kappa. J Refract Surg. 2013; 29(8):518-25.

[199] Uozato H, Guyton DL. Centering corneal surgical procedures. Am J Ophthalmol. 1987; 103(3 Pt 1):264-75.

[200] Rynders M, Lidkea B, Chisolm W, Thibos LN. Statistical distribution of foveal transverse chromatic aberration, pupil centration, and angle psi in a population of young adult eyes. J Opt Soc Am A Opt Image Sci Vis. 1995; 12(10):2348-57.

2.5 THE TRANSIT OF LIGHT IN THE HUMAN EYE

Because the eye is a light-detection instrument, it is of great importance to understand the interaction between light and matter in the eye. These interactions are classified on the macroscopic scale, in terms of the human scale of observation, into four main categories: refraction, reflection, scattering, and absorption.

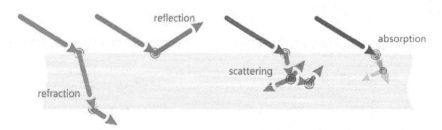

Figure 2-61: Interactions between light and matter.

Reflection and refraction describe <u>macroscopic</u> effects associated with light encountering an interface separating two media with different propagation speeds, which is represented by a change in the index of refraction. Part of the beam returns to the original medium (for example, air); this effect is **reflection**. Part of the beam propagates in the subsequent medium (for example, glass); this effect is **refraction**.

Scattering and **absorption** describe the <u>microscopic</u> interaction of light with matter and result in changes in the propagation path or a transfer of energy.

In scattering (see § 2.5.3), light exits the medium in a random direction without transferring to any other form of energy. The direction of light propagation changes randomly and therefore in all directions, with a strong preference for the forward direction.

On the other hand, in absorption (see § 2.5.3), light energy is converted into another form, usually heat. For example, during thermal absorption, light is converted into molecular oscillations (macroscopically, this is heat). Sunlight warms us precisely via the mechanism of thermal absorption. During electrochemical absorption, which is the main mechanism for light detection in the eye (§ 4.3), light energy is used to break molecular bonds. An effect often following absorption is the re-emission of light to other, longer wavelengths. The associated effects are fluorescence and phosphorescence.

<u>Microscopically</u>, on the molecular scale of observation, there are only two light–matter interactions: scattering (photon collides with an atom or molecule and is re-emitted to a random

direction) and absorption (the energy of the photon is such that the atomic/molecular system completely transforms the photon energy). Both reflection and refraction can be described as a macroscopic manifestation of organized forms of scattering arising from the interface.

When light propagates through a medium, there are losses because part of the light is reflected just before entering the medium and due to either absorption or scattering. Thus, the retinal image is not formed by the full amount of light initially reaching the eye.

Part of light, along its path from the cornea to the retina, is lost to:
- reflection from the four main refractive interfaces,
- absorption by the optical media, and
- scattering.

2.5.1 Losses due to Reflection

Any optical interface reflects part of the light energy incident on it. We are interested in the analytical expressions for the **amplitude reflection coefficient** ρ, the ratio of the reflected amplitude to the incident amplitude of the electric field E, and the **amplitude transmission coefficient** τ, the ratio of the refracted (transmitted) amplitude to the incident amplitude. The subscript indices i, r, and t denote the incident, reflected, and transmitted electric field, respectively:

$$\rho = \frac{E_r}{E_i} \quad \text{and} \quad \tau = \frac{E_t}{E_i} \tag{2.10}$$

A sensor (the eye _is_ a sensor) records intensity, not the electric field. Thus, the directly measurable quantities are **reflectance** or **reflectivity** $R = \rho^2$, the dimensionless ratio of the reflected light intensity to the incident light intensity, and **transmittance** or **transmissivity** $T = \tau^2$, the ratio of the refracted (transmitted) light intensity to the incident light intensity:

Reflectivity: $\qquad R \equiv \dfrac{\text{reflected light intensity } I_r}{\text{incident light intensity } I_i}$ (2.11)

These are the **Fresnel coefficients**,[201] named after the French physicist Augustin-Jean Fresnel. If there are no losses, then $R + T = \rho^2 + \tau^2 = 1$, which means that the total amount of incident light is either reflected or refracted (transmitted).

The amplitude reflection and transmission coefficients are, in general, complex numbers and depend on the state of polarization of the incident light, the angle of incidence, and the

---

[201] _Wave Optics_ § 2.5.2.1 Fresnel Coefficients of Reflection.

values of the refractive indices of the two media separated by the interface. However, there are some situations in which certain simplifications occur. The most notable is when the angle of incidence is relatively small. This is the case of normal incidence ($\vartheta_i = 0°$).

2.5.1.1 Reflection Coefficients for Normal Incidence

Specifically for normal incidence ($\vartheta_i = 0°$), the coefficients ρ and R are dependent only on the value of the relative refractive index (n_2/n_1), which is noted by n_{21}. The coefficients are

$$\rho = \frac{1 - \dfrac{n_2}{n_1}}{1 + \dfrac{n_2}{n_1}} = \frac{1 - n_{21}}{1 + n_{21}} \quad \text{and} \quad R = \left(\frac{1 - n_{21}}{1 + n_{21}}\right)^2 \tag{2.12}$$

Example ☞: For normal incidence from air to glass ($n_{21} = 1.5$), the values for coefficients ρ and R are –0.2 and 0.04 (= 4%), respectively, meaning that the reflected intensity from an air–glass interface is only 4%:
$$\rho_{\vartheta=0} = [1 - (1.5/1.0)]/[(1.5/1.0)] = -0.5/2.0 = -0.2 \quad \text{and} \quad \rho_{\vartheta=0} = (-0.2)^2 = 0.04 = 4\%$$

Note ✖: The value for reflectivity is not dependent on the order of the media: It is the same (%) for reflection from an air–glass (external reflection) or an glass–air interface (internal reflection). The value of reflectivity is only dependent on the ratio of the two refractive indices. In the example above, one may use $n_{21} = 1.5$ or $1/1.5 = 0.66$. The value of R is the same, $0.04 = 4\%$.

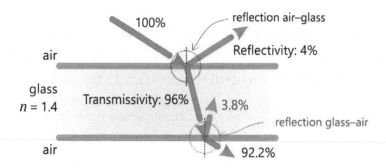

Figure 2-62: Reflectivity in an air-glass interface and a glass-air interface. These values are valid for normal incidence (very small angle of incidence), which, in this illustration, is notably out of proportion for the purpose of separating the various rays.

Note 👥: Reflectivity increases significantly when the ratio of the two refractive indices that straddle the interface is large. A common example is the air–diamond interface. Diamond, with $n \approx 2.4$, is among the materials of relatively high refractive index. When preceded by air, $n_{21} \approx 2.4$ yields a reflectivity in the vicinity of $\approx$ 17%. This explains why diamonds are 'shiny': They <u>reflect</u> strongly. Obviously, they have no light of their own. Diamonds are forever, but they do not shine.

To the contrary, in an air–water interface, with $n_{21} = 1.33$, reflectivity is $\approx$ 2%. This is the case in the tear film of the human cornea. About 2% of the light incident on the eye is reflected back.

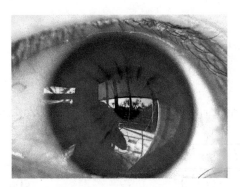

Figure 2-63: About 2% of the light incident on the eye is being reflected back. Photo by Manutsawee Buapet / www.bmanut.com, used with permission.

Light reflected from the cornea and the lens forms Purkinje images (§ 2.3.1). The relative strength of the four images is dependent on the ratio of the refractive indices surrounding each ocular interface. Thus, the weakest reflex of all, P_2, is due to reflection by the posterior cornea–aqueous interface, where the respective refractive indices are 1.376 and 1.336. Using Eq. (2.12) we find that the amount of light reflected by this interface is only 0.0002 = 0.02%.

2.5.2 The Complicated Nature of Reflection Coefficients

As noted, the amplitude reflection and transmission coefficients are, in general, complex numbers and depend on the state of polarization of the incident light, the angle of incidence, and the value of the refractive index of the two media separated by the interface. The computation of these coefficients involves analytical expressions of the continuation of the projection of the electric vector along the interface.[201]

Due to the dependence of the coefficients on the state of linear polarization, there are separate expressions for the two orthogonal states of linear polarization. These states are:

Parallel Eigenstate: The electric field vector is parallel to the plane of incidence (noted as the *x–y* plane), while the magnetic field vector is perpendicular to it, so it is parallel to the surface (*x–z*). This state is also called transverse magnetic (TM) and parallel or *p*-polarization (∥).

Perpendicular Eigenstate: The electric field vector is perpendicular to the plane of incidence (noted as *x–y* plane), and the magnetic field vector is parallel to it, so it is perpendicular to the interface (x–z plane). This state is also called transverse electric (TE) and perpendicular or s- (Senkrecht) polarization ($\perp$).

The coefficients ρ and τ are thus reported with subscripts p and s, respectively: For p- parallel polarization with relative refractive index ratio $n_{21} = n_2/n_1$ and angle of incidence ϑ_i, the coefficient ρ_p and coefficient τ_p are

$$\rho_p(\vartheta_i, n_{21}) = \frac{-n_{21}^2 \cos\vartheta_i + \sqrt{n_{21}^2 - \sin^2\vartheta_i}}{n_{21}^2 \cos\vartheta_i + \sqrt{n_{21}^2 - \sin^2\vartheta_i}} \quad \text{and} \quad \tau_p(\vartheta_i, n_{21}) = \frac{2 \cdot n_{21} \cos\vartheta_i}{n_{21}^2 \cos\vartheta_i + \sqrt{n_{21}^2 - \sin^2\vartheta_i}} \tag{2.13}$$

The corresponding expressions for the perpendicular s-polarization are

$$\rho_s(\vartheta_i, n_{21}) = \frac{\cos\vartheta_i - \sqrt{n_{21}^2 - \sin^2\vartheta_i}}{\cos\vartheta_i + \sqrt{n_{21}^2 - \sin^2\vartheta_i}} \quad \text{and} \quad \tau_s(\vartheta_i, n_{21}) = \frac{2 \cdot \cos\vartheta_i}{\cos\vartheta_i + \sqrt{n_{21}^2 - \sin^2\vartheta_i}} \tag{2.14}$$

The above—rather complicated, indeed—expressions provide the dependence of coefficients ρ_p and ρ_s on the angle of incidence ϑ_i and the relative refractive index n_{21}.

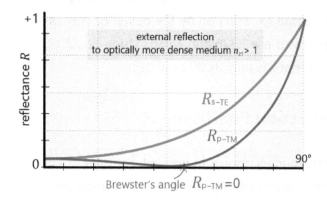 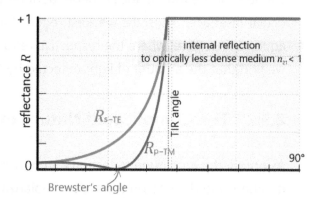

Figure 2-64: Angle of incidence dependence of the coefficients $R_{p\text{-}TM}$ and $R_{s\text{-}TE}$ for external reflection (left) and internal reflection (right).

Figure 2-64 describes the dependence of the reflectance ($R = \rho^2$) coefficients on the angle of incidence and polarization state for reflection from (left) an optically more-dense medium ($n_{21} = n_2/n_1 > 1$), which is the case of external reflection, and (right) for reflection from an optically less-dense medium (internal reflection, $n_{21} = n_2/n_1 < 1$).

Some comments about the data presented in the graphs are provided in the next two subsections.

2.5.2.1 Normal Incidence Reflection

The reflection coefficients are equal for an angle of incidence = 0°. These are the values in Eq. (2.12); they are the same for internal or external reflection (i.e., the same for air–glass and glass–air) and are purely dependent on the ratio of the refractive indices along the reflecting interface.

2.5.2.2 Brewster's Angle Reflection

Generally, the reflection coefficient increases for an increased angle of incidence. This is true, however, only for the perpendicular state of polarization. There is a specific angle, **Brewster's angle**, named after the British scientist Sir David Brewster, for which the parallel polarization reflection coefficient drops to zero: At this angle, the parallel polarization is not reflected at all. This means that all reflected light has the (other) perpendicular state of linear polarization and therefore it is linearly polarized. This is why at oblique angles light is often linearly polarized.

When the angle of incidence ϑ_i is equal to Brewster's angle ϑ_B, the reflected and refracted beams are orthogonal. The angles of incidence ϑ_i, reflection ϑ_r, and refraction ϑ_t are related to the laws of reflection $\vartheta_i = \vartheta_r$ and refraction, $n_1 \cdot \sin(\vartheta_i) = n_2 \cdot \sin(\vartheta_t)$, respectively; therefore, $n_1 \cdot \sin(\vartheta_{i=B}) = n_2 \cdot \sin(\vartheta_t) = n_2 \cdot \sin(90° - \vartheta_B) \Rightarrow n_1 \cdot \sin(\vartheta_B) = n_2 \cdot \cos(\vartheta_B)$, which leads to

Brewster's Angle:
$$\vartheta_B = \tan^{-1}\frac{n_2}{n_1}$$
(2.15)

Figure 2-65: The same storefront without (left) and with (right) a linear polarizer. The strong surface reflections from the verticals and the glass are eliminated once a linear polarizer is used, indicating that the surface reflection light is linearly polarized because the reflection angle is close to Brewster's angle.

When light is incident on a surface at Brewster's angle:

- The reflected light is linearly polarized.
- Its polarization state is parallel to the surface (and simultaneously perpendicular to the plane of incidence).
- This occurs for both internal and external reflection.

2.5.2.3 Grazing Incidence Reflection

The reflection coefficients have again the same values for angle of incidence = 90°. This occurs for almost parallel incidence ($\vartheta_i = 90°$) about the surface of the two media (grazing incidence). Then, coefficients $\rho_{p\text{-TM}}$ and $\rho_{s\text{-TE}}$, as well as the corresponding reflectivities, are equal to 1.0 for the two polarization eigenstates, independent of the value of the refractive index:

$$\rho_{s\,\vartheta=90°} = \rho_{p\,\vartheta=90°} = 1.0 \quad \text{and} \quad R_{s\,\vartheta=90°} = R_{p\,\vartheta=90°} = 1.0$$

A smooth, flat glass (or water) surface acts as a 100% perfect mirror for incidence almost parallel to the surface, regardless of internal or external reflection and the refractive index.

*Figure 2-66: Strong reflection for very large angles of incidence (nearly parallel incidence). Photos by Petros Tsakmakis [great egret/*Casmerodius albus *(left) and* Sterna hirundo/*common stern (right)] taken at the Kalloni Salt Pans, Lesvos Island, Greece (used with permission).*

2.5.2.4 Critical Angle of Reflection

In internal reflection, where $n_2 < n_1$ or $n_{21} < 1.0$, there are angles ϑ_i such that $\sin(\vartheta_i) > n_2/n_1$. This applies to an angle of incidence $\vartheta_i > \vartheta_{CR}$, the angle of incidence for which the angle of refraction is 90°: The refracted ray is tangent (grazing emergence) to the dividing surface. By Snell's law,

$$n_1 \cdot \sin(\vartheta_{CR}) = n_2 \cdot \sin(90°) \;\Rightarrow\; \sin(\vartheta_{CR}) = \frac{n_2}{n_1} \;\Rightarrow\; \vartheta_{CR} = \sin^{-1}\!\left(\frac{n_2}{n_1}\right) = \sin^{-1}(n_{21})$$

Critical Angle:
$$\vartheta_{CR} = \sin^{-1}\frac{n_2}{n_1} \tag{2.16}$$

Any angle of incidence greater than the critical angle results in total internal reflection.[202] In this case, the internal reflection (meaning toward the medium with a higher refractive index) is complete, and reflectivity for both parallel and perpendicular polarization becomes 1.0.

---

[202] *Introduction to Optics* § 3.2.4 Critical Angle of Incidence; Total Internal Reflection.

When light is incident on a surface at just > the critical angle:	• Light is 100% reflected: total internal reflection. • This occurs only for internal reflection, meaning reflection from an optically more dense to an optically less dence medium (such as from glass to air).

Example ☞: Brewster's and the critical angle from air (n_{air} = 1) to glass (n_{glass} = 1.5) and from glass to air.

From air to glass:

Brewster's angle: $\vartheta_B = \tan^{-1}(n_2/n_1) = \tan^{-1}(n_{glass}/n_{air}) = \tan^{-1}(1.5/1.0) = 56.3°$

Critical angle: $\vartheta_{CR} = \sin^{-1}(n_2/n_1) = \sin^{-1}(n_{glass}/n_{air}) = \sin^{-1}(1.5/1.0) = $ ERROR!

The latter is a ...friendly reminder that there is no 'critical' angle when reflecting from a less optically dense medium (such as air) to a more optically dense medium (glass).

From glass to air:

Brewster's angle: $\vartheta_B = \tan^{-1}(n_2/n_1) = \tan^{-1}(n_{air}/n_{glass}) = \tan^{-1}(1.0/1.5) = 33.7°$

Critical angle: $\vartheta_{CR} = \sin^{-1}(n_2/n_1) = \sin^{-1}(n_{air}/n_{glass}) = \sin^{-1}(1.0/1.5) = 41.8°$

The latter is a reminder that the critical angle (when reflecting from a more optically dense medium such as glass to a less optically dense medium such as air), if there is one, is always greater than Brewster's angle.

Brewster's angle (applicable in polarization)	• $\tan^{-1}(n_2/n_1)$ • valid for both more dense to less dense optical media, and vice versa. • is the angle of incidence for which reflection becomes linearly polarized. • angle of reflection ⊥ angle of refraction. • always less than the critical angle for the same pair of media.
Critical angle (applicable in total internal reflection)	• $\sin^{-1}(n_2/n_1)$ • valid only for more dense to less dense optical media. • is the angle of incidence for which there is only internal and total reflection, i.e., no refraction. • angle of reflection = angle of incidence.

2.5.3 Losses Due to Absorption

If the photon energy matches specific atomic/molecular system energy level differences, it is absorbed by the atom/molecule, eventually dissipating in the form of heat. Thus, absorption entails the conversion of photon (light) energy to another form. The effect is energy and is therefore dependent on frequency v and wavelength λ, and, of course, on the material. Material dispersion describes the complex relationship between material parameters and spectral absorption properties.[203] The analytical expression that describes the luminous intensity $I_z(\lambda)$ fall off as light travels within a medium a distance (depth) z is:

---

[203] *Wave Optics* Chapter 3. Dispersion and Absorption.

$$I_z(\lambda) = I_o(\lambda) \times \exp[-(\alpha(\lambda) + b(\lambda)) \cdot z] \qquad (2.17)$$

where $I_o(\lambda)$ is the incident intensity, and $a(\lambda)$ and $b(\lambda)$ are material properties of absorption and scattering. Thus, light <u>attenuates</u> <u>exponentially</u> as it propagates through a medium. This relationship is known as the Beer–Lambert law of absorption.[204]

Transmissivity is the dimensionless ratio of light intensity that is transmitted relative to the light intensity that is incident to an interface or transparent body:

Transmissivity:
$$T \equiv \frac{\text{transmitted light intensity } I_t}{\text{incident light intensity } I_i} \qquad (2.18)$$

Like reflectivity, transmissivity can be expressed as either a fraction (maximum value 1) or as a percentage (%). We want transmissivity close to 1.0 for most of the visible spectrum. However, this is not the case for the entire spectrum. Transmissivity is dependent on wavelength. **Spectral transmissivity** expresses transmissivity for a range between λ and $\lambda+\delta\lambda$:

Spectral Transmissivity:
$$T_{\lambda+\delta\lambda} \equiv \frac{I_t\left(\lambda+\delta\lambda\right)}{I_i\left(\lambda+\delta\lambda\right)} \qquad (2.19)$$

The eye is nearly opaque (0% transmissivity) beyond the blue end of the visible spectrum (ultraviolet, $\lambda < 0.4$ µm) and nearly 100% transparent in the visible 0.4 to 0.7 µm (Figure 2-67).

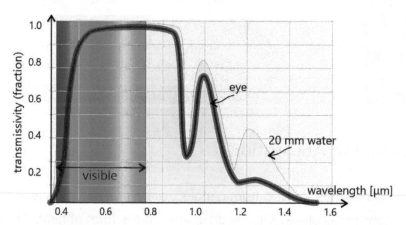

Figure 2-67: Spectral distribution of ocular transmissivity as measured experimentally in relation to a similar-thickness water layer. Created based on published data.[205, 206]

---

[204] *Wave Optics* § 3.2 The Imaginary Part of the Refractive Index.

[205] Johnson CA, Howard DL, Marshall D, Shu H. A non-invasive video-based method of measuring lens transmission properties of the human eye. Optom Vis Sci. 1993; 70(11):944-55.

[206] van de Berg TJ, Tan KEW. Light transmittance of the human cornea from 320 to 700 nm for different ages. Vision Res. 1994; 34(11):1453-6.

On the right end of the visible spectrum (infrared $\lambda > 0.7$ μm), there is a transmissivity window around 1.1 μm, and then, beyond 1.5 μm, the eye becomes again opaque. Thus, the eye has the greatest possible transmissivity for the spectrum that it is designed for, the visible, with a high similarity to water, the major component of optical tissue—this is no surprise.

2.5.4 The Ultraviolet Radiation and the Eye

Transmissivity and (its complement) absorbance in the **ultraviolet** (UV) is important because the particularly damaging UV radiation is strongly absorbed in the eye. The three UV bands are the UV-C ($\lambda < 0.280$ μm), which is nearly 100% absorbed by the cornea, the UV-B ($\lambda = 0.280$ to 0.320 μm, also known as *suprathreshold*), which is absorbed by the cornea and the lens, and the UV-A ($\lambda = 0.320$ to 0.400 μm). The shorter the wavelength the higher the frequency, which is directly related to photon energy, which is reported in electron volts (eV): a 400 nm photon has 3.1 eV energy, while a 280 nm photon has 4.4 eV energy.[207]

Photon energies range from a fraction of an eV at low frequencies to hundreds (and more) of eV at high frequencies. The higher the photon energy the greater the risk of molecular disruptions and ionization. Here lies the importance of UV: The UV photon energies border on the range of ocular tissue destructive ionization, which occurs at about 3.5 eV.[208]

UV-C is the most damaging, having the shortest wavelength / highest frequency. The good news is that the ozone layer and the atmosphere absorb most of the UV-C from the Sun.[209] UV-B is not as strongly absorbed by the atmosphere, so it is more abundant on Earth. UV-B is essential for the natural production of vitamin D3; however, as we cannot have too much of a good thing, UV-B also causes sunburn to unprotected skin, and excessive UV-B exposure may lead to skin melanoma.[210] The effects of UV-A (less damaging than UV-B) are also important.

In the eye, the epithelium bears the brunt of UV exposure by strongly absorbing UV radiation. The toxic effects of acute UV-C and UV-B exposure cause epithelial cell necrosis and shedding, leading to photokeratitis.[211] Mountaineers, skiers (snow blindness), and those actively engaging in water sports are at high risk because ambient UV radiation increases in high altitude (less atmospheric absorption) and/or reflection (white surfaces).

---

[207] *Wave Optics* § 1.4.4 The Particle Theory: The Revenant

[208] Tabrah FL. Human injury from atomic particles and photon exposure: fears, myths, risks, and mortality. Hawaii Med J. 2010; 69(4):93.

[209] Sliney D. Balancing the risk of eye irritation from UV-C with infection from bioaerosols. Photochem Photobiol. 2013; 89(4):770-6.

[210] Sample A, He YY. Mechanisms and prevention of UV-induced melanoma. Photodermatol Photoimmunol Photomed. 2018; 34(1):13-24.

[211] Shimmura S, Suematsu M, Shimoyama M, Tsubota K, Oguchi Y, Ishimura Y. Subthreshold UV light-induced peroxide formation in cultured corneal epithelial cells. Exp Eye Res. 1996; 63(5):519-26.

The clinical presentations of photokeratitis include ocular pain, tearing, conjunctival chemosis, blepharospasm, and deterioration of vision typically several hours after exposure. The presentation can be transient (recessing as the epithelium regenerates)[212] but can also be long term.[213] Chronic UV-B exposure is associated with abnormal cornea conjunctiva growth such as pterygium.[214, 215] UV exposure may lead to the irrevocable loss of corneal endothelial cells,[216] since these non-regenerating cells are very susceptible to UV radiation.[217]

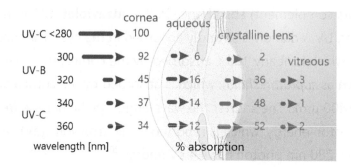

Figure 2-68: Absorption of UV bands by various components of the human eye.

The crystalline lens of the eye strongly absorbs UV, mainly due to its longer optical path (being much thicker than the epithelium). UV absorption by the lens is associated with cataract development: Studies suggest that doubling the lifetime of UV-B exposure increases the risk of cortical and posterior subcapsular cataract by 60%;[218] other studies conclude that individuals with a high, long-term UV-B exposure have over 3× increased chance of developing a cortical cataract.

While the UV radiation is strongly absorbed (1% remaining) before reaching the retina, even this small fraction, if phototoxic, is of concern.[219, 220, 221] Lens removal by cataract surgery leads to an increase in the UV that reaches the retina if the IOL does not effectively block it.[222]

[212] Willmann G. Ultraviolet keratitis: from the pathophysiological basis to prevention and clinical management. High Alt Med Biol. 2015; 16(4):277-82.

[213] Guly HR. Snow blindness and other eye problems during the heroic age of Antarctic exploration. Wilderness Environ Med. 2012; 23(1):77-82.

[214] Taylor HR. Ultraviolet radiation and the eye: an epidemiologic study. Trans Am Ophthalmol Soc. 1989; 87:802-53.

[215] Li X, Dai Y, Xu W, Xu J. Essential role of ultraviolet radiation in the decrease of corneal endothelial cell density caused by pterygium. Eye. 2018; 32(12):1886.

[216] Spoerl E, Mrochen M, Sliney D, Trokel S, Seiler T. Safety of UVA-riboflavin cross-linking of the cornea. Cornea. 2007; 26(4):385-9.

[217] Cullen AP, Chou BR, Hall MG, Jany SE. Ultraviolet-B damages corneal endothelium. Am J Optom Physiol Opt. 1984; 61(7):473-8.

[218] Taylor HR. The biological effects of UV-B on the eye. Photochem Photobiol. 1989; 50(4):489-92.

[219] van Kuijk FJ. Effects of ultraviolet light on the eye: role of protective glasses. Environ Health Perspect. 1991; 96:177-84.

[220] Zuclich JA. Ultraviolet induced damage in the primate cornea and retina. Curr Eye Res. 1984; 3(1):27-34.

[221] Youn HY, McCanna DJ, Sivak JG, Jones LW. In vitro ultraviolet-induced damage in human corneal, lens, and retinal pigment epithelial cells. Mol Vis. 2011; 17:237-46.

[222] Longstreth J, de Gruijl FR, Kripke ML, Abseck S, Arnold F, Slaper HI, Velders G, Takizawa Y, van der Leun JC. Health risks. J Photochem Photobiol B. 1998; 46(1-3):20-39.

2.5.5 Losses due to Scattering

Scattering is a complex effect that relates not to a disappearing photon (as in absorption) but to a photon that is abruptly changing course. In scattering, the photon energy does not match specific atomic/molecular system energy level differences, so it is not being absorbed; when the photon collides with an atom or molecule, it recoils in a random direction. Because there is no energy loss, the effect is called elastic scattering.[223] Macroscopically, scatter is the deflection of light from its straight path that is neither reflection nor refraction.

The properties of scattered light depend on the size of the particles that are responsible for the scatter effect in comparison to the wavelength of the incident light. If the scattering particles have a very small size (e.g., a diameter less than about one-tenth the wavelength), then the scattering is called Rayleigh scattering, named after John William Strutt (3rd Baron Rayleigh). If the scattering particles have a large size (e.g., a diameter larger than the approximate wavelength), then the scattering is described by Mie scattering, named after the German physicist Gustav Mie.

Atmospheric nitrogen or oxygen are small particles of about 160 pm = 0.160 nm in size. Even larger molecules in the atmosphere reach no more than 230 pm, such as the CO_2 molecule, or 270 pm, such as the H_2O molecule, a.k.a. water. The wavelengths of the visible range from four to eight hundred nanometers, so it is fair to say that scattering from atmospheric air molecules or water molecules (as in the eye) is governed predominantly by Rayleigh scattering.

A key property of Rayleigh scattering is that it is significantly dependent on wavelength. Specifically, scatter intensity is inversely proportional to the fourth power of the wavelength[224] and is also strongly dependent on the direction of observation. The formula is somewhat complicated, so we present what appears to be the scattered light intensity along the direction of stronger scatter, which is perpendicular to the initial direction of propagation:

Rayleigh-Scattered Light Intensity: $$I_{scatter} \propto N \cdot \left(\frac{1}{\lambda^4} \right)$$ (2.20)

where N is the density of the scatter centers, and λ the wavelength. Thus, Rayleigh scattering favors the blue (short wavelength) end of the spectrum. For example, the maximum of the Rayleigh-scattered light from sunlight occurs when we observe the sky such that the sun is to our right or left. Although there is no change in the re-emitted wavelength, the sky is blue

---

[223] There is also inelastic, or Raman scattering. In this case, the scattered photon has a lower (Raman Stokes) or higher (Raman anti-Stokes) energy than the incident photon.

[224] *Wave Optics* § 2.5.1 Scattering in the Sky – The Color of Blue.

because the perceived light is mostly blue due to the strong dependence of scatter intensity on wavelength.[225]

| Rayleigh scattering favors short wavelengths. | • Scatter intensity corresponding to the blue is much greater than that for the red because $\lambda_{blue} \approx \frac{1}{2}\,\lambda_{red}$, so $I_{blue} \approx 16 \times I_{red}$. |

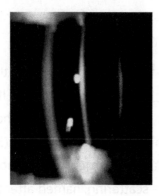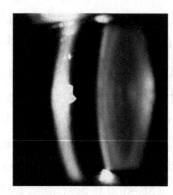

Figure 2-69: (left) Normal slit lamp exposure in a young eye: The lens appears to have a dark interior. (right) Using overexposure, the lens gets a sky-blue overcast, typical of Rayleigh scattering. Image courtesy of Dr. Thomas JTP van den Berg,[226] used with permission.

Example ☞: What is the ratio of scatter intensity for the hydrogen blue emission line (λ_{blue} = 434 nm) relative to the hydrogen red line (λ_{red} = 656 nm)?

$I_{blue} / I_{red} = (\lambda_{red\ 656} / \lambda_{blue\ 434})^4 = (656/434)^4 = (1.511)^4 = 5.22$. Hydrogen blue scatter intensity is stronger than the hydrogen red scatter intensity by a factor greater than 5×.

Mie scattering involves larger particles than Rayleigh scattering and is not as strongly wavelength dependent. Mie scattering is stronger along the direction of propagation of the incident light. For example, sunlight scatters off of white clouds, whose aerosol particles are particle colloids that are much larger than simple molecules. In the eye, scattering from a corneal scar or lens opacification is Mie-type, which explains the white appearance of a posterior capsule opacification in a slit lamp.

In a perfectly clear eye, there should be no scatter. There are, however, cells and tissue parts that form optical discontinuities for specific light wavelengths. Considering this, it is surprising that the eye is so transparent. Even in healthy eyes, <u>there is</u> scatter, which is likely to affect vision in the presence of very bright sources. For example, light from a bright source away from the fixation point may reach the retina, overlapping the retinal image.

---

[225] Strutt JW. On the light from the sky, its polarization and colour. Philos Mag Ser. 1871; 4(41):274-9.

[226] van den Berg TJP. Intraocular light scatter, reflections, fluorescence and absorption: what we see in the slit lamp. Ophthalmic Physiol. Opt. 2018; 38(1):6-25.

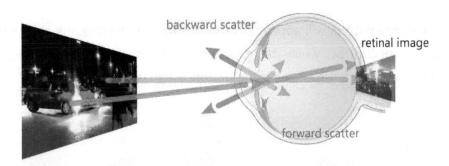

Figure 2-70: Backward and forward scatter resulting in stray light. The optical components of the eye form an image of the outside world (left) on the retina (right). In such a scene, the retinal image is degraded.

Scattered light that is deviated more than 90° is <u>backward scatter</u>. This is what is observed in the slit lamp. Its main visual effect is that it reduces light reaching the retina. Scattered light that is deviated less than 90° is <u>forward scatter</u> or **stray light**.[227]

Forward scatter reaches the retina, resulting in glare, the luminous veil over the retinal image.[228] According to the CIE (Commission Internationale de l'Eclairage) conventions,[229] glare is distinguished as **disability glare**, which affects visual performance, and **discomfort glare**, which causes visual discomfort due to glare that does not directly affect visual function.

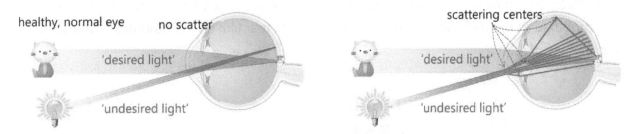

Figure 2-71: Scattering in the human eye from a bright source outside the fixation point. Comparison between a healthy (left) and an eye with significant scatter (right).

Ocular scatter therefore affects vision in two ways. First, backward-scattered light is 'removed' from the ray bundle that is directed toward the image. In a way, this is similar to the effect relating to absorption and reflection—a weaker retinal signal. The more important type of scatter, however, is forward scatter, or the light that reaches the retina but should <u>not be there</u>; e.g., light from a non-fixated light source. This light makes black image areas appear as dark gray instead. Likewise, less light reaching the retina makes the white areas appear as light gray.

---

[227] Jinabhai A, O'Donnell C, Radhakrishnan H, Nourrit V. Forward light scatter and contrast sensitivity in keratoconic patients. Cont Lens Anterior Eye. 2012; 35(1):22-7.

[228] de Waard PW, IJspeert JK, van den Berg TJ, de Jong PT. Intraocular light scattering in age-related cataracts. Invest Ophthalmol Vis Sci. 1992; 33(3):618-25.

[229] Vos JJ. Disability glare-a state of the art report. Commission International de l'Eclairage Journal. 1984; 3/2:39–53.

Thus, a black-and-white pattern will appear as gray-on-gray. Therefore, the chief visual effect of scatter is a reduction of contrast, which decreases vision at dusk and nighttime, increases the difficulty in night driving, and introduces some diurnal fluctuation in vision.

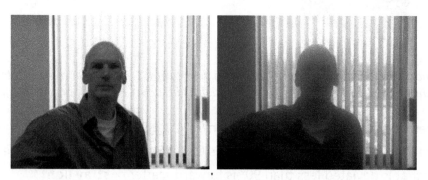

Figure 2-72: Dr. Thomas JTP van den Berg shown with minimal (left) and significant (right) disability glare. Note the reduction in contrast. Images courtesy of Dr. Thomas JTP van den Berg, used with permission.

Scatter distribution and magnitude are different in each eye, and even differ between the eyes of the same individual.[230] This difference depends on age, iris color, pathologies such as cataract or diabetes, and possible previous ocular surgery. Although low in a young, healthy eye, scattering is mainly attributed to centers in the cornea and the lens, while smaller amounts are attributed to the iris[231] and the fundus. An unstable tear film also contributes to transient fluctuations of scatter.

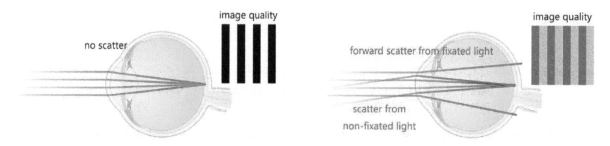

Figure 2-73: Forward scatter mainly affects the contrast in the retinal image.

backward scatter
• reduces the light forming the retinal image
• observed in a slit lamp
• quantified by Scheimpflug imaging

forward scatter
• affects vision
• disability glare
• discomforting glare

---

[230] Van den Berg TJ. Importance of pathological intraocular light scatter for visual disability. Doc Ophthalmol. 1986; 61(3-4):327-33.
[231] van den Berg TJP, IJspeert JK, de Waard PW. Dependence of intraocular straylight on pigmentation and light transmission through the ocular wall. Vision Res. 1991; 31(7-8):1361-7.

The distribution and magnitude of ocular scatter also strongly depend on the angle of incidence. By rule, scatter is strong for forward directions and is not very dependent on wavelength.[232] The explanation is that straylight contains a blue dominant component (small-particle Rayleigh type) as well as a red dominant component (reflectance from the fundus, and eyewall transmittance).

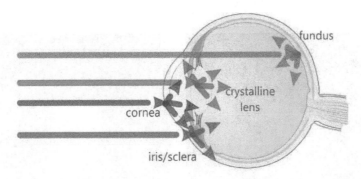

Figure 2-74: Primary sources of intraocular stray light: corneal scatter, iris and sclera transparency, lens scatter, and fundus scatter.

Ocular scatter typically increases with age.[233, 234] In a young eye, the cornea and the lens have a near-perfect optical transparency, which is related to a highly organized collagen fibril structure.[235] When this complex configuration is altered, light scatter increases.

This increase can be because of trauma, edema, depositions from contact lens use, and any form of optical media opacity and associated diseases. One of the leading pathological causes of ocular scatter is diabetes mellitus, which affects corneal and, uniquely, lenticular clarity. The lens' clarity is affected by chronic diabetes because of is its composition, which is protein-based crystalline fibers.[236] These fibers are affected by blood glucose level fluctuations, leading to the development of localized-fiber-size distortions and orientation distortions that are detrimental to the clarity of the crystalline lens.[237, 238]

Certain ocular surgical interventions may lead to a transient increase in disability glare. These include laser refractive corneal surgeries that affect corneal clarity[239] and intraocular

---

[232] Coppens JE, Franssen L, van den Berg TJ. Wavelength dependence of intraocular straylight. Exp Eye Res. 2006; 82(4):688-92.

[233] Allen MJ, Vos JJ. Ocular scattered light and visual performance as a function of age. Am J Optom Arch Am Acad Optom. 1967; 44(11):717-27.

[234] Shahidi M, Yang Y. Measurements of ocular aberrations and light scatter in healthy subjects. Optom Vis Sci. 2004; 81(11):853-7.

[235] Farrell RA, McCally RL. On corneal transparency and its loss with swelling. J Opt Soc Am. 1976; 66(4):342.

[236] Gwinup G, Villareal A. Relationship of serum glucose concentration to changes in refraction. Diabetes. 1976; 25(1):29-31.

[237] Calvo-Maroto AM, Perez-Cambrodí RJ, Albarán-Diego C, Pons A, Cerviño A. Optical quality of the diabetic eye: a review. Eye (Lond). 2014; 28(11):1271-80.

[238] Asimellis G. Diabetes screening in rural Appalachian population by ocular scatter measurement. JOJ Ophthal. 2017; 4(2).

[239] Ackermann R, Kammel R, Merker M, Kamm A, Tünnermann A, Nolte S. Optical side-effects of fs-laser treatment in refractive surgery investigated by means of a model eye. Biomedical Optics Express. 2013; 4(2):220-9.

surgery, including cataract removal and the secondary lens capsule opacification that develops.[240, 241]

The iris and sclera are not completely opaque and thus contribute to ocular scatter. Especially for eyes with low melanin, some light incident on the iris or the sclera eventually enters the eye, bringing undesired light to the retina.

Figure 2-75: Glare perception with normal scatter (left) and with a high level of scatter (right). This is a simulation of cataract vision. Image courtesy of Dr. Thomas JTP van den Berg, used with permission.

The fundus contributes to ocular scatter because it does not fully absorb light (at the melanin pigment epithelium), so a small part of the incident light is locally reflected and scattered. The contribution of scatter by the iris and the fundus is more pronounced in people with blue eyes or low amounts of melanin. The aqueous and the vitreous are much more homogenous, causing less scattering, with the exception of the scattering associated with floaters.[242, 243]

The main effect of ocular scatter is a reduction of perceived contrast.[244] This is different from the effects of a refractive error, such as myopia/hyperopia/astigmatism, or high-order aberrations, such as spherical aberration or coma. Scatter only affects contrast.

It is important therefore to <u>distinguish scatter from refractive errors or aberrations</u>. Scatter affects retinal image luminance via two distinct modes. The first mode relates to backward scatter and results in less (otherwise desired) light being directed toward the image. In essence, it is a subtraction from the retinal image-forming illumination. The second mode

---

[240] Applegate RA, Ballentine C, Gross H, Sarver EJ, Sarver CA. Visual acuity as a function of Zernike mode and level or root mean square error. Optom Vis Sci. 2003; 80(2):97-105.

[241] Artal P, Ferro M, Miranda I, Navarro R. Effects of aging in retinal image quality. J Opt Soc Am A. 1993; 10(7):1656-62.

[242] Spadea L, Maraone G, Verboschi F, Vingolo EM, Tognetto D. Effect of corneal light scatter on vision: a review of the literature. Int J Ophthalmol. 2016; 9(3):459-64.

[243] Castilla-Marti M, van de Berg TJ, de Smet MD. Effect of vitreous opacities on straylight measurements. Retina. 2015; 35(6):1240-6.

[244] Abrahamsson M, Sjostrand J. Impairment of contrast sensitivity function (CSF) as a measure of disability glare. Invest Ophthalmol Vis Sci. 1986; 27(7):1131-6.

relates to forward scatter and results in more (otherwise undesired) light being directed toward the image. In essence, it is an addition of rays whose origin is often from a background light source. This addition forms a veil of light 'noise' that is superimposed over the image. These two effects cause a reduction of contrast in the image, which, however, remains sharp—scatter does not alter the refractive state and/or vergence of the image-forming rays.

In emmetropia (§ 6.2), these image-forming rays are focused on the retina, and the retinal image is sharp. If refractive errors such as myopia/hyperopia/astigmatism (§ 6.4) or high-order aberrations such as spherical aberration are present, the retinal image is far from perfect. Some rays are deflected away, focusing in front of or behind the retina. Aberrations may cause peripheral rays to be deflected away from the retinal image. Thus, the retinal image is blurry (§ 6.5.3), with reduced sharpness and contrast.[245]

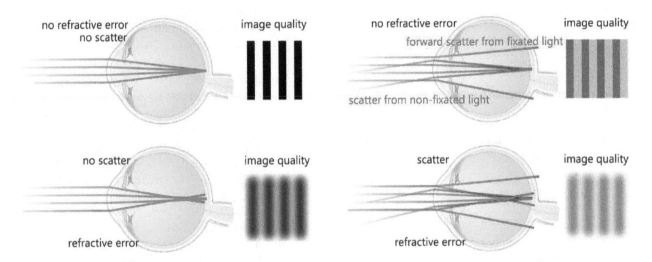

Figure 2-76: Retinal image quality in an eye with (top left) no scatter and no refractive error, (top right) scatter and no refractive error, (bottom left) no scatter and refractive error, and (bottom right) scatter and refractive error.

---

[245] *Ocular Imaging* § 5.4.1 Contrast Sensitivity Measurement.

2.6 REFRACTIVE ELEMENTS OF THE EYE QUIZ

Cornea

1) When measuring corneal thickness, which part of the cornea is expected to yield the thinnest measurement?

   a) inner peripheral (nasal)
   b) outer peripheral (temporal)
   c) upper peripheral (superior)
   d) lower peripheral (inferior)
   e) central

2) Which part (layer) of the cornea can regenerate itself in about one week?

   a) tear film
   b) epithelial layer
   c) Bowman's layer
   d) stroma
   e) Descemet's membrane
   f) endothelium

3) Which part (layer) of the cornea can be affected by lipid layer deficiency?

   a) tear film
   b) epithelial layer
   c) Bowman's layer
   d) stroma
   e) Descemet's membrane
   f) endothelium

4) Which part (layer) of the cornea largely determines the corneal thickness?
   a) lipid layer
   b) epithelial layer
   c) Bowman's layer
   d) stroma
   e) Descemet's membrane
   f) endothelium

5) Which two layers of the cornea contribute to maintaining proper stroma hydration?

   a) lipid layer
   b) epithelial layer
   c) Bowman's' layer
   d) stroma
   e) Descemet's membrane
   f) endothelium

6) Collagen type I & V fibrils are found in ...
   a) the lipid layer
   b) the epithelial layer
   c) Bowman's layer
   d) the stroma
   e) Descemet's membrane
   f) the endothelium

7) Stromal scarring occurs as a result of ...
   a) keratocyte response to stromal infection
   b) endothelial cell damage
   c) epithelial layer removal
   d) exposure to infrared radiation

8) Endothelial cell density measurements by specular microscopy report that Mr. Silver, a 65-year-old candidate for cataract-removal surgery, has 1050 cells/mm^2 on average. Most likely, this is ...

   a) a better than average endothelial cell density. Well done, Mr. Silver!
   b) an average endothelial cell density for this age group. No worries.
   c) a slightly below average cell density. We should be on alert.
   d) a notably below-average cell density. Further examination for endothelial cell integrity is warranted.

9) Indicate the (average) radii of curvature for the two corneal surfaces:

   a) anterior 7.7 mm; posterior 6.8 mm
   b) anterior 7.7 mm; posterior 8.6 mm
   c) anterior 6.8 mm; posterior 8.6 mm
   d) anterior 8.6 mm; posterior 7.7 mm

10) The most reasonable value for average corneal thickness is ...

    a) central 540 μm; peripheral 600 μm
    b) central 450 μm; peripheral 600 μm
    c) central 600 μm; peripheral 600 μm
    d) central 640 μm; peripheral 540 μm

11) The contributions to corneal power, in order of significance (most to least), are ...

a) correction due to thickness, posterior surface power, anterior surface power
b) correction due to thickness, anterior surface power, posterior surface power
c) anterior surface power, correction due to thickness, posterior surface power
d) posterior surface power, correction due to thickness, anterior surface power
e) anterior surface power, posterior surface power, correction due to thickness

12) Considering single spherical refractive interface (SSRI) power relationships, the anterior surface power of the cornea (radius of curvature 7.7 mm) is about 49.0 D, while the posterior surface power (radius of curvature 6.8 mm) is only about –6.0 D. This is due to ...

a) the fact that this is the rule for the back surfaces of meniscus lenses
b) the very small central corneal thickness
c) the presence of the tear film
d) the very small difference in refractive index between the cornea and the aqueous

13) If the cornea were to be surrounded by (both sides!) air, which surface powers would be different, if any (two correct answers)?

a) the anterior power would be nearly 5.0 D
b) the anterior power would be no different
c) the posterior power would be nearly –55.0 D
d) the posterior power would be no different

14) Which type of surface would have a fixed value of refractive power across its expanse (near the optical axis)?

a) spherical
b) toric
c) aspherical
d) parabolic

15) The statement that the cornea has some degree of asphericity indicates that there is a variance in the _____ from the center to the limbus.

a) radii of curvature
b) thickness
c) intraocular pressure
d) refractive index

16) If a surface has an asphericity index $Q = 0$, then ...

a) shape factor $p = -1$, eccentricity $e = 1$
b) shape factor $p = +1$, eccentricity $e = 0$
c) shape factor $p = 0$, eccentricity $e = -1$

d) shape factor $p = +1$, eccentricity $e = 1$
e) shape factor $p = +1$, eccentricity $e = -1$

17) Assume a perfectly spherical corneal surface. This surface has _____ longitudinal spherical aberration.
a) negative (–0.5 μm RMS)
b) zero (0.0 μm RMS)
c) positive (0.5 μm RMS)
d) positive (5.0 μm RMS)

18) If a cornea anterior surface has asphericity index $Q = -0.25$, then ...

a) shape factor $p = -1$, eccentricity $e = -0.5$
b) shape factor $p = +0.75$, eccentricity $e = -0.5$
c) shape factor $p = -0.75$, eccentricity $e = +0.5$
d) shape factor $p = +1.25$, eccentricity $e = -0.5$
e) shape factor $p = +0.75$, eccentricity $e = +0.5$

19) An eye with asphericity index $Q = -0.50$ has _____ spherical aberration.

a) negative (–0.5 μm RMS)
b) zero (0.0 μm RMS)
c) positive (0.5 μm RMS)
d) positive (5.0 μm RMS)

20) Central measurement of corneal power reports +44.5 D, while peripheral measurement (at 8 mm diameter) reports nasal +42.5 D and temporal +42.5 D. This cornea has ...

a) fixed, spherical distribution of corneal power, as expected for most corneas
b) aspheric power distribution, as expected for most corneas
c) aspheric power distribution, contrary to what is expected for most corneas
d) against-the-rule toric power distribution, as expected for most corneas
e) with-the-rule toric distribution, contrary to what is expected for most corneas

21) Corneal asphericity, if within normal values, serves the purpose of ...

a) augmenting spherical aberration of the eye by about 2×
b) augmenting spherical aberration of the eye by about 1×
c) countering the spherical aberration of the eye by about 0.5×
d) countering the spherical aberration of the eye by about 2×

22) The average ocular spherical aberration is about _____ μm RMS, while the average corneal spherical aberration is about _____ μm RMS.

a) ocular +0.50; corneal +0.05
b) ocular +0.25; corneal −0.25
c) ocular −0.50; corneal +0.25
d) ocular +0.25; corneal +0.50
e) ocular +0.50; corneal −0.25

23) Measurement of corneal power reports +44.5 D along the vertical meridian and +42.5 D along the horizontal meridian. This cornea has ...

a) fixed, spherical distribution of corneal power, as expected for most corneas
b) aspheric power distribution, as expected for most corneas
c) aspheric power distribution, contrary to what is expected for most corneas
d) against-the-rule power distribution, contrary to what is expected for most corneas
e) with-the-rule toric distribution, as expected for most corneas

24) A report of anterior corneal surface power mentions +47.0 D of refractive power. Considering that the refractive index of the cornea is 1.376, the radius of curvature of the anterior cornea is ...

a) +7.125 mm
b) +7.7 mm
c) +8.0 mm
d) +8.125 mm

25) The power along the horizontal meridian of the anterior cornea is +50.0 D, while the power along the vertical meridian is +45.0 D. In this cornea, ...

a) the flatter surface is the horizontal, and the steeper surface is the vertical
b) the flatter surface is the vertical, and the steeper is the horizontal

c) the flatter surface is central, and the steeper is peripheral
d) the flatter surface is peripheral, and the steeper is central

26) Considering that the refractive index of the cornea is 1.376, the radii of curvature of the anterior surface as described in Q 25 are...

a) horizontal 8.35 mm; vertical 7.97 mm
b) horizontal 7.97 mm; vertical 8.35 mm
c) horizontal 7.52 mm; vertical 8.35 mm
d) horizontal 8.35 mm; vertical 7.52 mm

27) The average cornea has a posterior radius of curvature of +6.8 mm and a posterior optical power of −5.88 D. What is the measure of the posterior surface optical power if the radius of curvature increases to +7.26 mm?

a) a change to −5.26 D
b) a change to −5.50 D
c) a change to −5.62 D
d) no change: −5.88 D
e) a change to −5.92 D

28) George swims underwater with open eyes. What element would be optically affected and how?

a) the corneal power, which would decrease
b) the corneal power, which would increase
c) the lenticular power, which would increase
d) the lenticular power, which would decrease

29) Given that water has refractive index $n = 1.333$ and the cornea has refractive index $n = 1.376$, what is the anterior cornea power under water ($r_{anterior} = +7.7$ mm)?

a) −5.58 D
b) +5.58 D
c) +42.8 D
d) +48 .8 D

Lenticular and Ocular Optics

30) The crystalline lens is best described by a ...

a) strong plus meniscus lens
b) weak plus meniscus lens
c) fixed-power biconvex lens
d) variable-power biconvex lens
e) variable-power planoconvex lens

31) The power of the crystalline lens increases when the ...

a) curvature of the surfaces increases
b) lens moves closer to the cornea
c) lens becomes more transparent
d) refractive index of the aqueous decreases

32) The refractive index of the lens is ...

a) fixed through the volume of the lens, ≈1.40
b) variable; increases at the periphery, ≈1.40

c) variable; increases when the lens accommodates
d) variable; increases at the nucleus to ≈ 1.40

33) The variable refractive index of the lens helps reduce the lens ...

a) spherical aberration
b) optical power
c) toricity
d) opacity

34) According to the Bennett–Rabbett schematic eye, the lens radii of curvature in an accommodating eye are $r_{anterior} = +7.0$ mm and $r_{posterior} = -5.5$ mm. Given the refractive indices of the lens (1.42) and the aqueous/vitreous (1.336), the lens surface powers are ...

a) $F_{anterior} = +7.25$ D and $F_{posterior} = +12.00$ D
b) $F_{anterior} = +15.25$ D and $F_{posterior} = +12.00$ D
c) $F_{anterior} = +7.25$ D and $F_{posterior} = +12.00$ D
d) $F_{anterior} = +12.00$ D and $F_{posterior} = +15.25$ D

35) Back to Q 34. Given a lens thickness of $t = 4$ mm, the nominal (approximate) and exact lenticular powers are ...

a) nominal $F = +27.25$ D, exact $= +26.75$ D
b) nominal $F = +26.75$ D, exact $= +27.25$ D
c) nominal $F = +26.75$ D, exact $= +27.25$ D
d) nominal $F = +26.75$ D, exact $= +27.25$ D

36) Back to Q 34. The same eye, when returning to the relaxed (non-accommodating) form, will have a lenticular power of about ...

a) +19.00 D
b) +23.00 D
c) +27.00 D
d) +31.00 D

37) The axial length of the eye can be described as the separation between ...

a) object-space principal point P and image-space focal point F'
b) object-space vertex point V and image-space focal point F'
c) object-space focal point F and image-space focal point F'
d) object-space nodal point N and image-space focal point F'

38) The spacing between the object-space principal point P and the image-space principal point P' equals the ...

a) equivalent thickness of the eye as a thick lens

b) spacing between the anterior and posterior poles of the eye
c) spacing between the two nodal points
d) spacing between the anterior focal point and the vertex
e) equivalent thickness of the lens as a thick lens

39) Purkinje images are formed by ...

a) reflections off four different surfaces of the cornea and the lens
b) reflections off the retina and then refraction by the lens and cornea
c) refractions off the cornea and the lens
d) double-pass imaging off the cornea and the fundus

40) The (relative) light intensity of each Purkinje image is dependent on ...

a) their order of formation, i.e., the sequential number
b) the difference in the refractive indices along each surface forming them
c) their order of appearance, i.e., the axial displacement of the images
d) whether they are real or virtual

41) The first Purkinje reflex P_1 is a virtual and erect image of the ...

a) cornea center
b) anterior cornea
c) lens surface center
d) fundus posterior pole
e) light source in front of the eye

42) The axial location of the first Purkinje image is about 3.85 mm to the right of the corneal plane because this is ...

a) half the anterior corneal radius of curvature
b) half the distance of the first nodal point
c) the distance of the object-space principal point
d) half the distance of P_4 formation

43) A vertical pen light that is 10 cm long is held 25 cm against (in front of) the subject's eye. How long is the image of this pen, as formed by reflection off the anterior cornea?

a) 10 cm
b) 1 cm
c) 0.385 cm
d) 0.15 cm

44) Back to Q 43. The examiner rotates the pen from vertical to horizontal. The pen image, as formed by reflection off the anterior cornea, ...

   a) remains fixed
   b) enlarges horizontally
   c) shrinks horizontally
   d) rotates along the direction of the pen

45) Where is the first Purkinje image formed, and what is its size if a 10-cm-side-square white screen is held 25 cm in front of the eye?

   a) 3.79 cm inside the eye; size 1.5 cm
   b) 3.79 mm inside the eye; size 1.5 cm
   c) 3.79 mm inside the eye; size 1.5 mm
   d) 3.79 mm outside the eye; size 1.5 mm
   e) 25 cm outside the eye; size 1.5 mm

46) Which Purkinje reflex image changes in size when the target moves from infinity to closer to the eye, for example, held 25 cm in front of the eye?

   a) P_1 because of reduced object vergence
   b) P_2 because of the different corneal powers
   c) P_3 because of the different anterior chamber depths
   d) P_4 because of increased lenticular power

47) An examiner holds a bright penlight half a meter away from the subject's eyes. The reflection on the right (OD) eye appears to be shifted just

slightly nasally, while the reflection on the left (OS) eye appears to be shifted temporally. This suggests (select two) ...

   a) exodeviation OS eye
   b) esodeviation OS eye
   c) probably normal OS eye
   d) exodeviation OD eye
   e) esodeviation OD eye
   f) probably normal OD eye

48) Back to Q 47. For a different subject's eye, the Purkinje reflex is shifted nasally in both eyes by about 0.4 mm. This suggests (select two) ...

   a) exodeviation OS eye
   b) esodeviation OS eye
   c) probably normal OS eye
   d) exodeviation OD eye
   e) esodeviation OD eye
   f) probably normal OD eye

49) When the ambient light decreases from photopic to scotopic, John's pupil increases from 3 to 6 mm in diameter. This corresponds to _____ x more pupil area?

   a) 1.5×
   b) 2×
   c) 4×
   d) 8×
   e) the same size because John has fallen in love.

Eye Axes, Angles, and Reference Points

50) The two axes that pass via the center of the pupil are ...

   a) the optical axis and the pupillary axis
   b) the visual axis and the fixation axis
   c) the visual axis and the optical axis
   d) the visual axis and the line of sight
   e) the pupillary axis and the line of sight

51) The two axes that pass via the fixation point are ...

   a) the optical axis and the pupillary axis
   b) the visual axis and the fixation axis
   c) the visual axis and the optical axis
   d) the visual axis and the line of sight
   e) the pupillary axis and the line of sight

52) The three points that the visual axis intersects are the ...

   a) fixation point
   b) vertex

   c) pupil center
   d) nodal point
   e) fovea
   f) first Purkinje image

53) The three points that the line of sight intersects are the ...

   a) fixation point
   b) vertex
   c) pupil center
   d) nodal point
   e) fovea
   f) first Purkinje image

54) The two axes perpendicular to the cornea are the...

   a) optical axis
   b) visual axis
   c) line of sight
   d) pupillary axis

e) fixation axis

f) videokeratoscopic axis

55) The <u>two axes</u> that pass by the center of curvature of the cornea are the ...

a) optical axis

b) visual axis

c) line of sight

d) pupillary axis

e) fixation axis

f) videokeratoscopic axis

56) The <u>two axes</u> that <u>do not</u> pass by the fixation point are the ...

a) optical axis

b) visual axis

c) line of sight

d) pupillary axis

e) fixation axis

f) videokeratoscopic axis

57) The <u>two axes</u> used for evaluating the retinal image size (approximations OK) are the ...

a) optical axis

b) visual axis

c) line of sight

d) pupillary axis

e) fixation axis

f) videokeratoscopic axis

58) The axis that best describes the pathway of light entering the optical system of the eye is the ...

a) optical axis

b) visual axis

c) line of sight

d) pupillary axis

e) fixation axis

f) videokeratoscopic axis

59) The axis that best approximates the visual axis in a clinical setting is the ...

a) optical axis

b) visual axis

c) line of sight

d) pupillary axis

e) fixation axis

f) videokeratoscopic axis

60) From the corneal plane, the correct order of points is...

a) vertex, pupil center, nodal point, corneal curvature center, center of rotation of the eye

b) vertex, pupil center, corneal curvature center, nodal point, center of rotation of the eye

c) pupil center, vertex normal, corneal curvature center, nodal point, center of rotation of the eye

d) pupil center, vertex normal, center of rotation of the eye, corneal curvature center, nodal point

61) Which of the following corneal points is situated more nasally?

a) apex

b) vertex

c) vertex normal

d) pupillary axis intercept

62) Which angle has its apex at the pupil center?

a) angle α

b) angle λ

c) angle γ

d) angle κ

63) Angle κ has its apex at the ...

a) center of rotation of the eye

b) center of curvature of the cornea

c) nodal point

d) pupil center

64) Which angle depends entirely on eye anatomical landmarks?

a) angle α

b) angle λ

c) angle γ

d) angle κ

65) If the arc length corresponding to the displacement between the corneal vertex normal and the pupillary axis intercept is 0.5 mm, angle κ is ...

a) 8°

b) 5°

c) 4°

d) 1°

66) Large angle κ values are expected in eyes with ...

a) axial myopia

b) refractive myopia

c) axial hyperopia

d) refractive hyperopia

67) The reason that the line of sight and the pupillary axis are non-coincidental is the ...

a) fovea location being temporal

b) cornea being aspheric

c) cornea being toric

d) lens being decentered from the axis

68) The clinician is challenged to properly overlap the P_3 and P_4 Purkinje images with P_1 and P_2. This is an indication of ...

a) lens tilt

b) lens decentration

c) pupil decentration

d) fovea temporal placement

69) From the corneal plane, the eye's nodal point is about 7 mm, and the corneal center of curvature is 7.7 mm. This is the reason that the following two axes are nearly identical:

a) visual axis and videokeratoscopic axis

b) line of sight and visual axis

c) optical axis and pupillary axis

d) line of sight and videokeratoscopic axis

70) In a screenshot of a Placido imaging topography mire pattern, the centers of the mire reflection and the apparent pupil center are non-coincidental. Select two correct statements.

a) The pupil center is the corneal intercept of the line of sight.

b) The pupil center is the apex.

c) The mire reflection center is the vertex normal.

d) The mire reflection center is the vertex.

e) The displacement between the two points is angle k.

f) The displacement between the two points is angle λ.

Interaction of Light with Ocular Media

71) When light is reflected off an interface, such as air and tear film, the reflected light intensity is ...

a) complete, 100%

b) partial, 50%

c) little, about 10%

d) very little, about 4%

72) If the light intensity reflected off an air–water interface is 5%, then the amount of light reflected off a water–air interface (same interface, reverse propagation) is ...

a) 5%

b) 25%

c) 75%

d) 95%

73) If we have a single surface with reflectivity equal to 5%, the, transmissivity should be ...

a) 5%

b) 25%

c) 75%

d) 95%

74) Light transmissivity though the eye is greater at which part of the electromagnetic spectrum?

a) the ultraviolet

b) the visible

c) the near infrared

d) the far infrared

75) UV radiation absorption by which layer of the eye may lead to photokeratitis?

a) the epithelium

b) the stroma

c) the endothelium

d) the lens

e) the retina

76) UV radiation absorption by which layer of the eye may lead to irrevocable loss of cells in that layer?

a) the epithelium

b) the stroma

c) the endothelium

d) the lens

e) the retina

77) UV radiation absorption by which layer of the eye may lead to cataract development?

a) the epithelium

b) the stroma

c) the endothelium

d) the lens

e) the retina

78) Which interface has the strongest reflectivity when light is striking at a normal angle to that interface?

a) medium 1 $n_1 = 1.0$; medium 2 $n_2 = 1.333$

b) medium 1 $n_1 = 1.0$; medium 2 $n_2 = 1.5$

c) medium 1 $n_1 = 1.333$; medium 2 $n_2 = 1.5$

d) medium 1 $n_1 = 1.333$; medium 2 $n_2 = 1.7$

79) Which interface has the weakest reflectivity when light is striking normal to that interface?

   a) medium 1 n_1 = 1.0; medium 2 n_2 = 1.333
   b) medium 1 n_1 = 1.0; medium 2 n_2 = 1.5
   c) medium 1 n_1 = 1.333; medium 2 n_2 = 1.5
   d) medium 1 n_1 = 1.333; medium 2 n_2 = 1.7

80) Light striking a thin glass slab with parallel surfaces is reflected by 5% upon the first air–glass interface. Assuming zero absorption, what percent of the original light intensity leaves the slab upon refraction at the second, glass–air interface?

   a) 15.00%
   b) 77.00%
   c) 85.50%
   d) 90.00%
   e) 90.25%
   f) 95.00%

81) An underwater snorkel diver is looking up at the sea–air surface and sees a shark reflected on that surface. Scared to death, he dives in deeper, when suddenly the reflection is gone. This happens at what angle of incidence (n_{water} = 1.33, n_{air} = 1.0)?

   a) the critical angle, ϑ_{CR} = 36.8°
   b) the critical angle, ϑ_{CR} = 48.6°
   c) the critical angle, ϑ_{CR} = 53.1°
   d) Brewster's angle, ϑ_B = 53.1°

82) When light is reflected at Brewster's angle, reflection is ...

   a) 100% reflected, i.e., all is reflected
   b) slightly reflected but 100% polarized
   c) 0%, i.e., nothing is reflected
   d) 50% reflected, 50% polarized

83) To observe 100% polarized light from an air–glass interface (n_{air} = 1.0, n_{glass} = 1.6), one has to be observing light reflected at what angle?

   a) Brewster's angle = 32.00°
   b) Brewster's angle = 38.68°
   c) critical angle, ϑ_{CR} = 38.68°
   d) Brewster's angle, ϑ_B = 58.00°

84) Light can be 'lost' due to (select three) ...

   a) reflection off a single surface
   b) refraction at a single surface
   c) absorption along the optical path length
   d) scatter during the transit in a medium

85) Light striking a 1-cm-thick glass slab with parallel surfaces is 5% reflected by the first air–glass interface. With absorption of 10% per 1 cm of path length, what percent of the original light intensity reaches the second, glass–air interface?

   a) 15.00%
   b) 77.00%
   c) 85.50%
   d) 90.00%
   e) 90.25%
   f) 95.00%

86) Back to Q 85. The glass slab thickness doubles. Approximately what percent of the initial intensity reaches the second glass–air interface?

   a) 15.00%
   b) 77.00%
   c) 85.50%
   d) 90.00%
   e) 90.25%
   f) 95.00%

87) An R-G-B source has red (λ_R = 0.633 μm), green (λ_G = 0.525 μm), and blue (λ_G = 0.4345 μm) light components. By about how much more is a component scattered (select three correct)?

   a) green scatters about 2× more than red
   b) red scatters about 2× more than green
   c) green scatters about 2× more than blue
   d) blue scatters about 2× more than green
   e) red scatters about 4.5× more than blue
   f) blue scatters about 4.5× more than red

88) A light component with wavelength λ_A scatters 2× more than light with wavelength λ_B. This means that wavelength λ_A is ...

   a) half that of λ_B
   b) double that of λ_B
   c) about 0.84 that of λ_B
   d) about 1.20 that of λ_B

89) In the eye, forward scatter results in ...

   a) glare superimposed on the retinal image
   b) reduced lightness for the retinal image
   c) the image becoming more blurry
   d) the image becoming brighter

90) In the eye, backward scatter results in ...

   a) glare superimposed on the retinal image
   b) reduced lightness for the retinal image
   c) the image becoming more blurry
   d) the image becoming brighter

2.7 OCULAR REFRACTION & EYE ELEMENTS SUMMARY

Schematic Eyes & Eye Power

Schematic eyes are optical models that summarize the key optical (more accurately) and anatomical (less accurately) elements of the eye, and help to model the optical function of the eye.

The Listing/Emsley model uses a single spherical refracting interface, comprising a 5.6 mm radius of curvature surface separating air from a medium with 4/3 refractive index. Other models include more anatomically correct representations, such as the Le Grand model. The Gullstrand #1 schematic eye describes six surfaces, including a lens nucleus that describes the variable refractive index of the crystalline lens.

Regardless of the degree of anatomical simplification, these models always describe the six cardinal points of the eye: the two focal points, the two principal points, and the two nodal points. The key to understanding the cardinal point locations in the eye is the different refractive indices in object space (air, n = 1.0) and image space (aqueous/vitreous n' = 1.336).

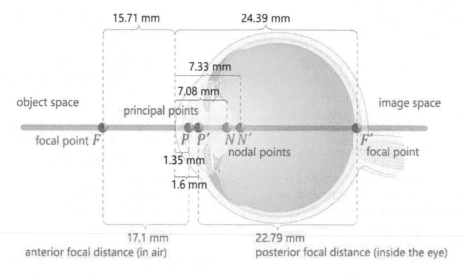

Figure 2-77: Examples of cardinal points of the optical system of the eye.

The power F is an optical invariant and therefore is not dependent on image/object space, even if the refractive indices are different in each space. Optical power is the ratio of the refractive index to the respective focal lengths:

Optical Power of the Eye:

$$F = -\frac{1}{f=PF} = \frac{n'}{f'=P'F'}$$

(2.21)

Using the values of f (in air) = PF and f'(in eye) = $P'F'$,

$$F = -\frac{1}{-17.1 \text{ mm} = -0.017 \text{ m}} = \frac{1.336}{+22.79 \text{ mm} = +0.02279 \text{ m}} = +58.5 \text{ D} \qquad (2.22)$$

Reciprocal relationships: f (air) = $-1/F \approx -17$ mm and f'(eye) = $1.336/F \approx +23$ mm   (2.23)

Recall that the object-space focal length f (in air) is measured from the object-space principal point P and the image-space focal length f'(in eye) is measured from the image-space principal point P'. The two nodal points N and N' are displaced to the right of their respective principal points P and P' by the quantity $f + f'$ = -17 mm + 23 mm $\approx$ 6 mm.

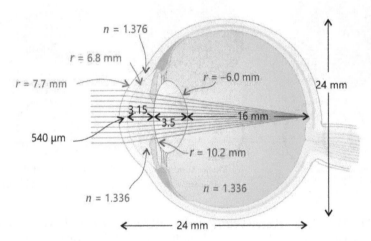

Figure 2-78: Mean values for the most essential ocular dimensions that correspond to the average anatomy of the relaxed emmetropic eye.

Cornea and Lens

The cornea is described by two surfaces with radii of curvature r_1 = +7.7 mm (anterior) and r_2 = +6.8 mm (posterior), separated by about 0.5 mm of central corneal thickness. The refractive index of the cornea is n = 1.376. The reason that the anterior surface provides most of the corneal power ($\approx$ +48.0 D) is the relatively large difference between the refractive index of air to the left and that of the cornea to the right of the first interface. The reason that the posterior surface provides little corneal power ($\approx$ −6.0 D) is the very small difference between the refractive index of the cornea and that of the aqueous (1.367 versus 1.336).

The crystalline lens is described by two convex surfaces with radii of curvature r_1 = +10.0 mm (anterior) and r_2 = −6.0 mm (posterior), separated by about 3.5 mm of central lenticular thickness. The lenticular shape is a biconvex lens with a power of about +20.0 when the lens is relaxed. During accommodation, the radii of curvature become steeper (about 5 mm radius of curvature) and the lenticular power increases, up to +30.0 D (§ 7.1.3). Unlike the cornea, the lens has a locally variable refractive index, reaching a maximum of 1.42 at its core from 1.38 at the periphery.

The corneal (and to a lesser degree, the lenticular) surfaces are aspheric and toric. **Asphericity** describes a deviation from being spherical. The surface has different radii of curvature (hence, different refractive powers) <u>between the center and the periphery</u>. In a normal cornea, the steepest radius of curvature is near the center, while the flattest (increased) radius of curvature is toward the periphery.

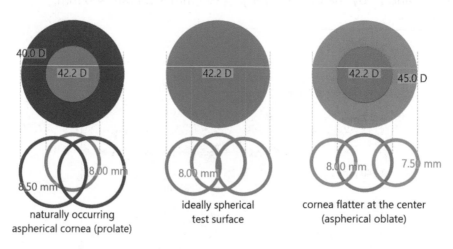

Figure 2-79: Corneal asphericity and curvature maps. All three corneas have the same central radius of curvature of 8.00 mm, corresponding to 42.2 D of corneal power.

The asphericity index Q value describes the departure of sphericity from the center to the periphery of the cornea. A perfect sphere has $Q = 0$ (so $e = 0$ and $p = 1$). A prolate ellipse (flatter toward the periphery) has a negative Q value; the average Q value for the cornea is –0.25. A naturally occurring prolate aspheric cornea partially compensates for the spherical aberration in the optical system of the eye.

Eccentricity e is an expression of the rate of corneal flattening from the apex to the periphery. The more spherical the cornea the lower the e-value, which approaches zero for a perfect sphere. The shape factor may have positive value for a prolate cornea.

Toricity describes another type of deviation from being spherical. The surface has different radii of curvature (hence, different refractive powers) <u>along different meridians</u>. Usually, the vertical meridian is steeper (higher curvature) than the horizontal meridian (lower curvature). This produces with-the-rule astigmatism. The two meridians with the steepest and flattest curvatures are usually 90° apart.

Anterior Eye Optics

The Purkinje corneal reflexes are four distinct images produced by reflection off the four surfaces, namely, the anterior cornea, posterior cornea, anterior lens, and posterior lens. The first corneal reflex (image P_1) is the brightest. P_1 relates to the intersection of the line of sight with the cornea, a landmark known as the vertex.

The Hirschberg test compares the positions of the P_1 Purkinje reflex (with respect to pupillary landmarks such as the pupil center) from the two eyes, as formed from a fixation light such as a penlight held at a distance. The asymmetry between the two reflex positions with regard to the pupil center indicates the presence of ocular deviation.

The anterior chamber depth (ACD), with normal values up to 3.5 mm, is the distance between the posterior corneal surface to the anterior lens surface. As the age advances, the ACD shrinks, mainly due to a thickening cataractous lens.

Eye Apertures, Axes, and Angles

The anatomical iris of the eye forms a clear opening, the pupil, which serves as the aperture stop of the optical system of the eye. The image of this pupil, as seen looking at the eye, is the entrance pupil. The entrance pupil is a virtual image of the anatomical pupil formed by the cornea. The clinical relevance of the entrance pupil lies in the optical zone, the depth of field, and the impact of optical aberrations.

Several axes are needed to describe the eye. This is because the eye is not symmetrical, and the fovea is displaced temporally and slightly inferiorly from the center of the posterior pole. The main axes are (Figure 2-80):

- **optical axis**, approximated by the centers of the four Purkinje images,
- **visual axis**, the line connecting the fixation point and the fovea via the nodal points (theoretical construct),
- **line of sight**, the line connecting the fixation point to the center of the entrance pupil and the center of the exit pupil (and eventually, the fovea),
- **pupillary axis**, the line from the center of the entrance pupil that is perpendicular to the cornea,
- **fixation axis**, the line from the fixation point to the center of rotation of the eye, and the
- **videokeratoscopic (keratometric) axis**, the optical axis of the instrument that becomes perpendicular to the cornea when the coaxially illuminated eye fixates on the center light source of the instrument.

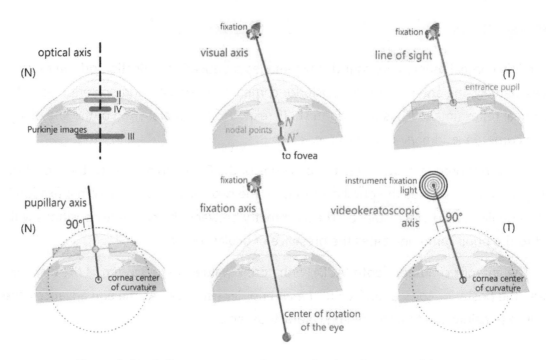

Figure 2-80: Reference axes in relation to landmark points of the eye.

The most frequently used landmark points in the eye are:

- **vertex**, the corneal intersect of the line of sight,
- **apex**, the point of maximum corneal curvature,
- **anterior pole**, the most forward corneal point,
- **coaxially sighted corneal light reflex** (vertex normal), the corneal intersection of the videokeratoscopic axis when the eye is coaxially sighted, and the
- **center of rotation** of the eye, the fixed pivot point upon fixation, usually about 13.5 mm inside the eye.

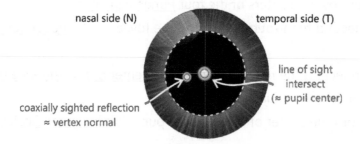

Figure 2-81: Differences between the center of the coaxially sighted reflex and the geometrical pupil center.

The main angles that relate to the axes are the following:

- angle **lambda** λ, the angle between the pupillary axis and the line of sight,
- angle **alpha** α, the angle between the optical axis and the visual axis,

- angle **kappa** κ, the angle between the pupillary axis and the visual axis, and
- angle **gamma** γ, the angle between the fixation axis and the optical axis.

Angle λ is clinically estimated (approximated as angle κ) by the arcuate difference between the corneal intersects of the pupillary axis and the keratometric axis, a proxy for the vertex. This arc 'naturally' tends to be displaced nasally, about 3° to 5°, or about 0.4 mm. In practice, the measures of angles κ and λ are very close.

Transit of Light in the Eye

When light interacts with any transparent medium (the eye is not an exception), there are four major interactions.

- **Reflection** describes the effects associated with the part of the beam returning to the original medium (for example, air).
- **Refraction** describes the effects associated with part of the beam propagating in the subsequent medium (for example, the cornea).
- **Scattering** and **absorption** describe the <u>microscopic</u> interactions of light with matter, and they result in changes in the propagation path or a transfer of energy. In scattering, light exits the medium in a random direction without transforming to another form of energy—its direction changes randomly, i.e., in all directions, with strong preference for the forward directions. In absorption, light energy is converted into another form, usually heat.

The fraction of light reflected off an interface of two media is dependent on angle of incidence, the state of polarization, and the two refractive indices n_1 and n_2. It is reported by the reflection coefficients ρ (wave amplitude) and R (reflectivity, reporting reflected light intensity).

When viewing a surface normally (angle of incidence $\vartheta_i = 0°$), the coefficients depend only on the values of the relative refractive indices (n_2/n_1), which is noted by n_{21}. Then, reflectivity R, the dimensionless ratio of the reflected light intensity to the incident intensity, becomes

Reflectivity for normal incidence:
$$R \equiv \frac{\text{reflected light intensity } I_r}{\text{incident light intensity } I_i} = \left(\frac{1 - \dfrac{n_2}{n_1}}{1 + \dfrac{n_2}{n_1}} \right)^2 \qquad (2.24)$$

Reflection is strong if the difference between the two refractive indices is large. Between air $n_1 = 1.0$ and glass $n_2 = 1.5$ ($n_2/n_1 = 1.5$), $R = 0.04$, or 4%. Between air and diamond $n_2 = 2.4$ ($n_2/n_1 = 2.4$), $R = 0.17$, or 17%. When viewing a surface almost parallelly (angle of incidence

ϑ_i = 90°), the reflectivity coefficient R becomes nearly 1.0, or 100% (grazing incidence reflection). These two effects occur regardless of whether the light is traveling from an optically more-dense (high n) medium to an optically less-dense (smaller n) medium, or vice versa.

When light travels from an optically more-dense medium to an optically less-dense medium, such as from glass to air (internal reflection), there is an angle of incidence, the critical angle, beyond which there is no refraction, only total internal reflection. For any angle of incidence greater than the critical angle, light is reflected 100%. The condition for the critical angle is

Critical Angle (producing TIR): $$\vartheta_{CR} = \sin^{-1}\frac{n_2}{n_1} \qquad (2.25)$$

When light is incident on a surface at Brewster's angle, the reflected light is linearly polarized; i.e., its polarization state is parallel to the surface. This occurs for both internal and external reflection.

Brewster's Angle (producing polarized light): $$\vartheta_B = \tan^{-1}\frac{n_2}{n_1} \qquad (2.26)$$

Transmissivity is the dimensionless ratio of the light intensity that is transmitted relative to the light intensity that is incident to an interface or transparent body.

Transmissivity: $$T \equiv \frac{\text{transmitted light intensity } I_t}{\text{incident light intensity } I_i} \qquad (2.27)$$

Light can be 'lost' due to:

- Reflection off a single surface—such the cornea, which, when normal, follows Eq. (2.24).
- Absorption during the transit in a transparent medium (such as the eye). Absorption losses increase exponentially with the optical path traveled within that medium.
- Scatter during the transit in a medium. Scatter intensity by very small particles in a transparent medium is strongly favored for short wavelengths, such as the blue [Eq. (2.20)].

In the eye, light scatter can present a problem that degrades the retinal image quality. Light may scatter off the cornea, the lens, or even the iris. Scattered light that is deviated more than 90° is backward scatter. This is what is observed in the slit lamp. The main visual effect of backscattered light is that it reduces the amount of light reaching the retina. Scattered light that is deviated less than 90° is forward scatter or stray light; its main effect is that it overlays as undesired light over the retinal image, degrading its quality.

CHAPTER 3
VISUAL ACUITY

Visual acuity is, in simple words, a measure of the clarity of vision, or how well a person sees. According to international standards, **visual acuity** is a numerical variable that characterizes the ability of the visual system to recognize optotypes.[246]

Often, erroneously, the terms 'visual acuity' and 'vision' are used interchangeably. Visual acuity is one of the standard parameters by which vision is evaluated. It directly relates to the ability of the optical system of the eye to resolve detail, depending on the clarity of the focused image. Visual sensation involves an intricate set of steps and relies on factors such as visual innervation and the cerebral interpretive faculty. Vision, in essence, is the ability of the brain to recognize the objects that form the retinal image.

Visual acuity relates to optical resolution, which can be expressed by the closest angular spacing of the two finest/closest targets that can be seen as two. The measurement of visual acuity often involves charts; hence, it relates the eye's ability to either resolve targets, called optotypes, on a chart placed a large distance away from the subject, or to read text on a chart placed very close to the subject. Reading, however, involves, interpretation and recognition, in addition to resolution. Near vision and low vision, which are broader in perspective, are presented in the chapter on accommodation and presbyopia (§ 7.9 and § 7.10).

---

[246] http://standards.globalspec.com/std/10052053/din-en-iso-8596 and www.iso.org/obp/ui/#iso:std:iso:8596:ed-3:v1:en

3.1 ANGULAR EXPRESSIONS

To avoid the use of expressions involving two lengths, it is easier to use an angle. Thus, visual acuity can be expressed in terms of the smallest angular spacing between two targets or features in a complex target (such as a set of closely spaced lines, a grating, or a letter) that can be distinguished. Specifically, visual acuity is the reciprocal of this angular spacing, which is the angular resolving power of the visual system.

An angle (often called ϑ) is formed between two intersecting lines, the spokes, or sides. These lines intersect at the apex of the angle. Consider the circle in which the angle is inscribed; the center of the circle is the apex, while the two spokes subtend an arc. The measure of the angle is the ratio of the length of the subtended arc to the length of the radius of the circle. If the circle has a radius equal to unity (the unit circle), then the measure of the angle is simply the length of the subtended arc.

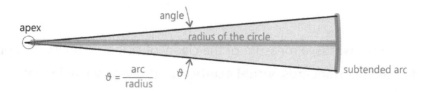

Figure 3-1: The angle measure is a ratio of two lengths.

The angle is, essentially, dimensionless (length ÷ length); there are, however, units. The fundamental unit is the **radian** (rad), the angle whose arc length s equals the radius r of the circle. Any angle produced by a ratio of length to length is expressed in radians. Since the circumference of a circle is $2\pi \cdot r$, the angle attending to a full circle is 2π rad, and one (1) radian attends to $1/2\pi$ of the circle. The decimal divisions of the radian are the rarely used hundredth or centrad,[247] the millirad (1 mrad $= 10^{-3}$ rad), and the microrad (1 μrad $= 10^{-6}$ rad).

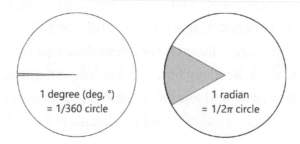

Figure 3-2: Fundamental angle units: the degree and the radian.

---

[247] Dennett WS. A new method of numbering prisms. Trans Amer Ophth Soc. 1889.

To convert from radians to degrees:	→	multiply by 360/2π (≈ 57.3°)

To convert from degrees to minutes:	→	multiply by 60

The **degree** (deg, °) is the angle attending to 1/360 of the circle. Thus, one radian equals 360/2π ≈ 57.3°. The degree is divided into 60 minutes (1 arcmin = 1′ = 1°/60 ≈ 0.29 mrad). This is the angle often encountered in optometry, particularly with respect to visual acuity. The arcmin is further divided into 60 seconds (1 arcsec = 1″ = 1′/60 ≈ 4.85 μrad). An arcsec is thus 1/3600 of a degree and is mostly used in astronomy.

Note ☀: Both the sun and the moon are seen from Earth by ϑ ≈ 0.0087 rad ≈ 0.5° = 30 arcmin. The fact that this angle is almost the same for both of these celestial objects is a pure and fascinating coincidence. In fact, the sun diameter is almost 400 times larger than the diameter of the moon. At the same time, the sun is also 400 times farther from Earth than the moon, whose angular subtense, however, varies from a maximum of 33 arcmin and 45 arcsec for a full moon at perigee to 29 arcmin and 40 arcsec at apogee.

Table 3-1: Conversion between radians, degrees, and arcminutes.

Radian (rad)	Degree (°)	Arcminute (′)
π/180 = 1/57.3 = 0.0175 ≈ 0.02	1	60
1	57.3 = 360/2π = 180/π	3438
3.1416 (π)	180	10,800
6.2832 (2π)	360	21,600

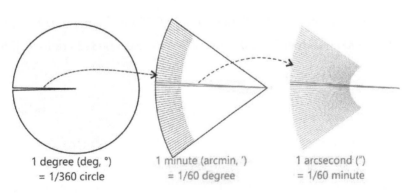

1 degree (deg, °) = 1/360 circle

1 minute (arcmin, ′) = 1/60 degree

1 arcsecond (″) = 1/60 minute

Figure 3-3: The degree and its subdivisions.

Example ☞: The arcmin is approximately the angle subtended by a quarter-dollar coin (about 2.5 cm in diameter) at a distance of 100 m or a thick sheet of paper, such as a business card (0.25 mm), held at arm's length. One arcsec is a very fine angle. It is approximately the angle subtended by a quarter (a 25-cent coin, about 2.5 cm in diameter) at a distance of 5 km away, or a pair of car headlights (assuming that they are spaced by about 2 m) at 256 miles away. A person on the moon would form an angle no larger than 0.001 arcsec as seen from Earth.

For small angles, the angle (expressed in radians) is well approximated by the ratio of the opposite to the adjacent; in this case, the angle [rad] is the **small-angle approximation**:

Small-Angle Approximation (ϑ in radians):
$$\vartheta \, [\text{rad}] \approx \frac{\text{opposite}}{\text{adjacent}} \qquad (3.1)$$

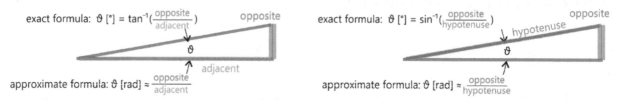

Figure 3-4: For small angles, the angle (expressed in radians) is satisfactorily approximated by the ratio of the opposite to the adjacent. More precise formulas involve the ratio of the tangent of the opposite to the hypotenuse (left) or the ratio of the sine of the opposite to the hypotenuse (right).

Example ☞: What is the angle subtended by two points spaced 1 cm apart when viewed from 8 m away?

For this small angle, the angle is simply the ratio of the opposite side (1 cm) to the radius (800 cm), or 0.01 m to 8 m; the two lengths must be expressed by the same units. The ratio of these two lengths is the angle ϑ expressed in radians: ϑ = 1 cm / 800 cm = 0.00125 rad ≈ 0.07162° = 4.3 arcmin.

Example ☞: What is the angle ϑ subtended by a quarter-dollar coin (about 2.5 cm in diameter) at a distance of (a) 100 m and (b) 5 miles?

(a) 2.5 cm converts to 0.025 m. Then ϑ = 0.025 m / 100 m = 0.25×10^{-3} rad ≈ 0.014° = 0.859 arcmin.

(b) 5 miles converts to ≈ 8000 m. Then ϑ = 0.025 m / 8000 m = 0.000003125 rad = 3.125×10^{-6} rad = 0.01 arcmin = 0.64 arcsec.

Note ◉ : What if the angles are not small? Is there an accurate formula?

The precise formula states that the angle ϑ is the <u>inverse tangent</u> ($^{-1}$), also known as the arc of the function, of the opposite to the adjacent. (Now expressed in degrees—Auntie Trigonometry loves degrees, while grumpy Uncle Physics loves radians.) Alternatively, the angle ϑ can be given as the inverse sine of the opposite to the hypotenuse, if this is known:

Precise angle formulas (ϑ in °):
$$\vartheta \, [°] = \tan^{-1}\left(\frac{\text{opposite}}{\text{adjacent}} \right) \quad \text{or} \quad \vartheta \, [°] = \sin^{-1}\left(\frac{\text{opposite}}{\text{hypotenuse}} \right) \qquad (3.2)$$

Once we calculate the trigonometric value, e.g., tan(ϑ) = opposite to adjacent = 0.5, we then find the angle ϑ using the inverse function, e.g., ϑ = $\tan^{-1}$(0.5) = arctan(0.5) = 26.56°.

Example ☞: What is the angle ϑ if the ratio of the opposite to adjacent equals 0.1?

The ratio is the tangent: $\tan(\vartheta)$ = 0.1. Using Eq. (3.2), the actual value of angle ϑ is $\tan^{-1}(0.1)$ = arctan(0.1) = 5.71°.

This is a small angle. If we use the small-angle approximation [Eq. (3.1)], then the angle itself is the ratio of the opposite to adjacent: ϑ = 0.1 rad ≈ 5.73°. No need to use a calculator for the inverse tangent! The small-angle approximation (5.73°) is very close to the actual value (5.71°). The essence of the small-angle approximation is that for small angles, the ratio itself (the tangent) is the angle, expressed in radians.

3.1.1 Viewing Angle

Visual acuity is typically measured by reading a standardized test pattern (letters or a target) at a certain distance (§ 3.3). The examinee identifies the smallest of the features (as in random letters of the alphabet or details on a target) that are recognizable from a certain distance.

As many people may have experienced while driving on a highway, when a passing car speeds ahead, its license plate appears progressively smaller to our eyes. At a certain point, the plate becomes too small for us to read. Did the license plate become smaller? No. It is only the angle that the plate subtends at the eye that becomes smaller. Because of this decrease in angle, the retinal image is too small—its lines are too closely spaced—to be clearly seen.

Figure 3-5: As a passing car speeds away, the letters and numbers on its license plate become increasingly difficult to resolve.

The **viewing angle** or **apparent angle** can be used to express the angle formed at the nodal point of the eye between the two lines of sight drawn from the edges of the target, or between two targets or features in that target. The suitability of this term is that, for a sufficiently large distance from the eye, an object 10× larger but located 10× farther away forms the same apparent angle, so the retinal image (§ 6.2.2) has the same size.

The tangent of the angle ϑ equals the ratio of the height to the distance in the right-angle triangle in Figure 3-6. If small, the angle ϑ, expressed in radians, is well approximated by the simple ratio of the two lengths, target size to target distance:

Viewing or Apparent Angle (in radians): $$\vartheta\,[\text{rad}] = \frac{\text{target size }(h)}{\text{target distance }(d)} \tag{3.3}$$

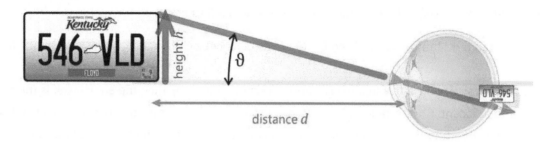

Figure 3-6: Apparent (viewing) angle for a single target (the license plate).

3.1.2 Resolution Limit and Resolving Power

Angular resolution refers to the minimum resolvable <u>angular separation</u> in a spatial pattern. When resolved, two black dots are seen as two, not one. When we move farther away, the two black dots subtend a smaller angle. At some point, we can barely tell if they are one or two.

The angular **resolution limit** refers to the **minimum angle of resolution** (MAR), the smallest angular separation formed by two discernible points. The smaller the MAR the better. However, defining 'better' with a smaller number is not the preferred way. The reciprocal of the resolution limit is the **resolving power** or **resolving ability**. Using this concept, the smaller the MAR the larger the resolving power. Now 'better' is associated with a larger number.

Resolution Limit

✔ The **separation** (expressed either angularly or spatially) between the closest distinguishable image points.

✔ The smaller the better.

✔ Expressed in units of angle (e.g., arcmin, mrad) or length (e.g., mm).

Resolving Power (Ability)

✔ The **reciprocal of the separation** between the closest distinguishable points imaged through an optical instrument.

✔ The larger the better.

✔ Expressed in units of inverse angle (e.g., arcmin⁻¹) or inverse length (e.g., line pairs/mm, cycles/deg).

In <u>optics terms</u>, we <u>define visual acuity</u> as the resolving power of the eye, or the reciprocal of the minimum angle of resolution (MAR). The smaller the MAR the greater (better) the visual acuity. The MAR is expressed in arcmin; therefore, <u>visual acuity has units of arcmin⁻¹</u>:

Visual Acuity:

$$\frac{1}{MAR \ [\text{arcmin}]}$$

(3.4)

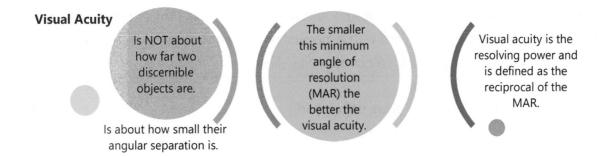

3.2 DIFFRACTION, A LIMIT TO VISION

Naturally, for sharper vision, we want an increased resolving power. This is not as easy as it may sound. Two small point-objects at an infinitesimally small (angular) separation are not seen as two. The reason is that a single point-object does not form a point image, but a blurry version of it with a finite light-intensity distribution on the image-forming plane. Even in well-focused systems, aberrations and diffraction effects contribute to this effect. Diffraction effects relate to the wave nature of light,[248] which is often ignored in geometrical optics.

Figure 3-7: Input object versus detected image. The image of a line object is not a line but a blurry version of the object.

The term **diffraction-limited** describes an imaging system that produces fine images of the same quality as the instrument's theoretical limit, set by diffraction.[143] This system is, in practice, aberration-free. In a diffraction-limited optical system whose pupil has a circular shape (such as the eye), the smallest extent of an image from a distant point-object has an intensity distribution pattern known as the **Airy disk**. The angular radius of the first zero ring (first dark minimum) of the Airy disk is

Angular Radius of First Zero in air [rad]: $1.22\dfrac{\lambda}{D}$ (3.5)

---

[248] *Wave Optics* Chapter 5. Diffraction.

where λ is the wavelength of light in vacuum, and D is the pupil diameter. The result is reported in radians. If the image space is filled with a medium with a refractive index n, then the wavelength changes to λ/n, and the Airy disk radius (first minimum) appears at

Angular Radius of First Zero in medium with n [rad]: $1.22\dfrac{\lambda}{n\cdot D}$ (3.6)

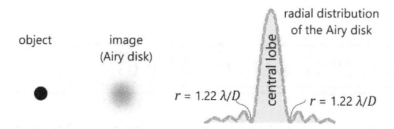

Figure 3-8: Diffraction is a limiting factor that determines how small the image can be formed by a point object through a diffraction-limited optical system of pupil diameter D.

3.2.1 The Rayleigh Criterion

Assume two neighboring, independent radiating points S_1 and S_2 such as two stars imaged through a diffraction-limited telescope. At the image-forming plane, the images are two neighboring, independent Airy disks. If they overlap, the two images cannot be resolved, and they are perceived as one larger image.

John William Strutt (3rd Baron Rayleigh), the English scientist credited with fundamental discoveries in acoustics and optics (including scattering § 2.5.3) and 1904 Nobel prize laureate in Physics, declared that, at the limit of resolution, the center (bright maximum) of one Airy disk must coincide with the first minimum (dark minimum) of the other. In this marginally resolved case, the peak-to-peak separation of the two Airy disk formations is at least equal to the radius of the central Airy lobe.

The **Rayleigh criterion** states that the minimum angular separation of two objects that are marginally resolved is their Airy disk radius:

Angular Resolution Limit [rad]: $\text{MAR} = \vartheta_{\text{MIN}} = 1.22\dfrac{\lambda}{n\cdot D}$ (3.7)

which is exactly the expression in Eq. (3.6). We realize therefore that the resolution limit in an aberration-free optical system is, *ceteris paribus*, governed by diffraction.

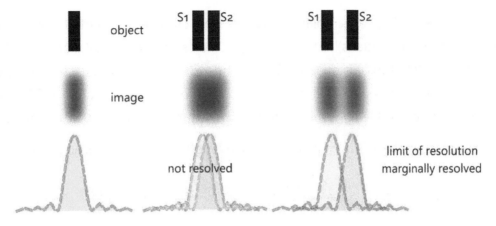

Figure 3-9: (left) A single object imaged to an Airy disk, (center) two unresolvable spots, and (right) two marginally distinguishable spots (the Rayleigh criterion).

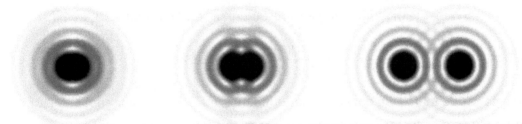

Figure 3-10: (Left) Unresolved Airy pattern, (center) marginally (just) resolved Airy pattern, and (right) fully resolved Airy pattern. Intensity is represented in black.

Can we magnify the image to get better resolution?

When two image spots overlap, it does not help to further magnify the formed image. The two points will still be overlapping! The spots are either resolved or not.

To calculate the resolution limit of the human eye set by diffraction, we use Eq. (3.7), where $n = 1.336$ is the refractive index of the aqueous, the liquid that fills the eye (the vitreous, the substance in the eye past the crystalline lens, has almost the same refractive index). The pupil of the human eye is approximately 2 mm in diameter in daylight. Thus, for $\lambda = 0.55$ μm, the human eye can discern objects separated by a minimum angle of 0.25 millirad (milli = 10^{-3}):

$$\text{MAR}_{2\text{ mm}} = \vartheta_{\text{MIN}} = 1.22\frac{\lambda}{n \cdot D} = 1.22\frac{0.55 \text{ μm}}{1.336 \cdot 2 \text{ mm}} = 0.25 \times 10^{-3} \text{ rad} = 0.25 \text{ mrad} \approx 0.86 \text{ arcmin} \quad (3.8)$$

The value of 0.25 mrad is converted to 0.86 arcmin, which is rounded up to 1 arcmin.

Human eye's minimum angle of resolution (diffraction limit)

≈ 1 arcmin (1/60 of the degree).

There are several implied simplifications here. We consider the central vision in a diffraction-limited (no aberrations) emmetropic eye. We use a 2 mm pupil diameter, which is accurate for daylight/photopic vision (§ 4.3.2), but under dim light/scotopic vision, the pupil may be 8 mm. Finally, we use the mean wavelength value of the visible spectrum ($\lambda = 0.55$ µm yellow-green); however, visible light ranges from $\lambda = 0.40$ µm (blue) to $\lambda = 0.80$ µm (red).

For a pupil diameter $D = 8$ mm, the minimum angle of resolution is about 0.215 arcmin:

$$\text{MAR}_{8\text{ mm}}\,(\vartheta_{\text{MIN}}) = 1.22\frac{\lambda}{n\cdot D} = 1.22\frac{0.55\ \mu m}{1.336\cdot 8\ mm} = 0.0625\times10^{-3}\ \text{rad} \approx 0.215\ \text{arcmin} \qquad (3.9)$$

This suggests that the eye in dim light (8 mm pupil) can have 4× better resolution compared to the eye in daylight (2 mm pupil diameter). If we consider a smaller pupil with a diameter $D = 1.5$ mm, the minimum angle of resolution is larger, about 1.15 arcmin:

$$\text{MAR}_{1.5\text{ mm}}\,(\vartheta_{\text{MIN}}) = 1.22\frac{\lambda}{n\cdot D} = 1.22\frac{0.55\ \mu m}{1.336\cdot 1.5\ mm} = 0.335\times10^{-3}\ \text{rad} \approx 1.15\ \text{arcmin} \qquad (3.10)$$

We conclude that, if we only consider diffraction effects, the minimum angle of resolution decreases as the pupil diameter increases; this implies that a larger pupil affords better visual acuity (smaller MAR → better visual acuity!).

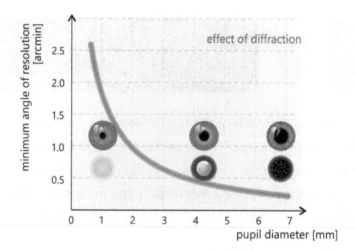

Figure 3-11: *Dependence of the minimum angle of resolution (MAR) on the pupil diameter. Only the effect of diffraction is illustrated in this graph.*

Note ⑧: The calculation of the MAR (ϑ_{MIN}) considers the image-space separation between two adjacent Airy function formations that result from diffraction within the eye, which is filled with a liquid medium with refractive index $n = 1.336$. However, we measure MAR (ϑ_{MIN}) in object space. The question is what is the relationship between the object-space and the image-space MAR? Should we consider the refractive index $n = 1.0$ in object space instead of calculations involving the MAR?

First of all, these angles are small and represent a diffraction-limited case. Actual MAR values are, by rule, larger. Second, even if we drop the value of the refractive index in the calculations such as those carried in Eq. (3.8), the result would be 1.14 arcmin instead of 0.86 arcmin; we would still round this to 1 arcmin. Therefore, in image space, the refractive index slightly raises the calculated value of the MAR. However, there is a reduction in apparent depth by a factor proportional to the refractive index;[249] thus, the concurrent increase in the MAR by $1/n$ and reduction in apparent depth by n balance this change in spacing so that the Airy disk radius in the eye (image space) is the same as it would be in the air (object space).[250]

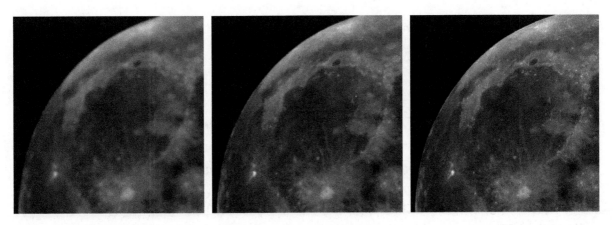

Figure 3-12: Simulated lunar image using a 2 mm exit pupil (left), a 4.5 mm exit pupil (center), and a 9 mm exit pupil (right). Original image by Luc Viatour https://Lucnix.be, used with permission.

3.2.2 Aberrations and Visual Acuity

We just stated that a larger pupil affords a better visual acuity. Does this really happen? Not at all. There are other competing mechanisms, which, in effect, degrade image quality. These include myopia, hyperopia, and astigmatism, which are collectively known as defocus errors or low-order aberrations. But these can be well corrected with a spherocylindrical spectacle prescription (§ 6.6). Even in a corrected (emmetropic) eye, the other parameters that affect the limit to vision are the high-order aberrations, such as spherical aberration and coma.[251]

To include the effects of aberrations, we need a more general expression for the Airy disk. This is the **point spread function** (PSF). In the diffraction-limited case, the PSF has the shape of an Airy disk. Aberrations severely affect light distribution at the image plane. The image spot corresponding to a single object-point is the point spread function.[252] The PSF is, in

[249] *Introduction to Optics* § 3.4.2 Apparent Depth.

[250] Thibos LN. Optical limitations of the Maxwellian view interferometer. Appl Opt. 1990; 29(10):1411-9.

[251] *Ocular Imaging* § 5.2 Classification of Aberrations and § 5.6 Wave Functions and Their Effect on Vision.

[252] Rovamo J, Kukkonen H, Mustonen J. Foveal optical modulation transfer function of the human eye at various pupil sizes. J Opt Soc Am A Opt Image Sci Vis. 1998; 15(9):2504-13.

general, a 3-D function. The –*z* dimension is intensity, while the –*x* and –*y* dimensions correspond to the cross-sectional shape at the image-forming plane.

The **line spread function** (LSF) is an alternative function that corresponds to the image of a line (a narrow slit). While the PSF describes the image formed by an infinitesimally small point, the shape of the LSF (Figure 3-13) describes the image formed by an infinitesimally narrow line and can be mathematically derived by slit-diffraction properties.[253]

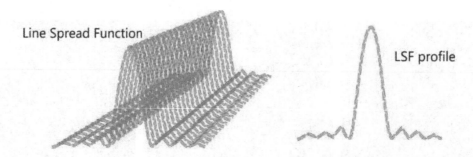

Figure 3-13: The cross-section of the LSF has a shape similar to (a bit narrower) the PSF profile.

At the image plane, the cross-section perpendicular to the slit (the one-dimensional profile of the LSF) corresponds to the Fourier-transform image along the infinitesimally small line width, so it has a shape similar to (essentially without the 1.22 factor and therefore slightly narrower) the PSF radial profile from a point with the same radius as that of the width of the slit.

Both the PSF and the LSF are functions that help quantify the resolution limit by describing the light intensity distribution that corresponds to the image (on the retina or any other image-forming plane) formed from a point object placed at infinity.

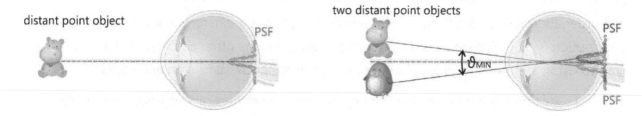

Figure 3-14: (left) The retinal image light distribution from a point object forms the PSF. In the ideal, diffraction-limited case, the PSF has the shape of the Airy disk. (right) Two point sources and their point spread functions. The two points are just resolved if they satisfy the Rayleigh criterion.

Note ✐: The case presented in Figure 3-14 involves a diffraction-limited, emmetropic eye. Several other simplifications are assumed. The rays lie along the visual axis, whose clinical counterpart is the line of

---

[253] *Wave Optics* § 5.3 Single Slit Diffraction.

sight. The object-space MAR ϑ_{MIN}, which we can measure, equals the image-space MAR ϑ_{MIN} determined by the Rayleigh criterion only along a nodal line (visual axis). Finally, the angles between the two marginally resolved targets are significantly smaller than the one shown, the PSF is much smaller than the one shown. and the targets themselves are just lines or points, not illustrative figurines.

Diffraction-limited imaging is the best-case scenario. The Rayleigh criterion, as applied so far, determines the minimum angular separation of two ideally shaped images, which have the shape of an Airy disk [Figure 3-15 (left)]. The central lobe of this PSF is confined on the x-y image plane by a narrow disk, while its central peak maximum is intense. Since the most restricted form of the PSF is encountered in the diffraction-limited case, it follows that the maximum resolution can only be realized in a diffraction-limited system.

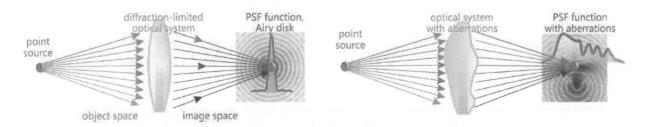

Figure 3-15: The PSF can be perceived as the image corresponding to an object point. In a diffraction-limited optical system, it can be an Airy disk (left). In a real system with aberrations, the PSF has reduced peak intensity and a larger cross-sectional extent (right).

The presence of aberrations only serves to degrade the PSF, thus increasing the MAR and decreasing the resolving power. In an optical system with aberrations [Figure 3-15 (right)], the PSF—no longer an ideal Airy disk—is spread over the x-y image plane, and the central peak maximum is neither well defined nor as intense as in an Airy disk.

The Rayleigh criterion applies to PSFs with aberrations as well, in this case, stated as follows: Resolution is possible if the two targets are angularly separated by at least the angular half-width at full maximum of their PSF. Any realistic ocular system carries aberrations; even the emmetropic eye (presented in § 6.2), which, by definition, has no low-order aberrations (defocus/astigmatism), carries small amounts of high-order aberrations.

Rayleigh criterion (generalized) Resolution is possible if the two targets are angularly separated by at least the angular half-width at full maximum of their corresponding PSF.

A key aspect of high-order aberrations is that an increase in pupil diameter results in a significant increase in their contributions that degrade image quality:[254, 255] The PSF cross-section increases dramatically [Figure 3-16 (bottom)] even in the case of an emmetropic, or spherocylindrically corrected, eye (§ 8.5.1). Thus, the high-order aberrations are the limiting factor for large pupils, particularly those of more than 4 mm in diameter.

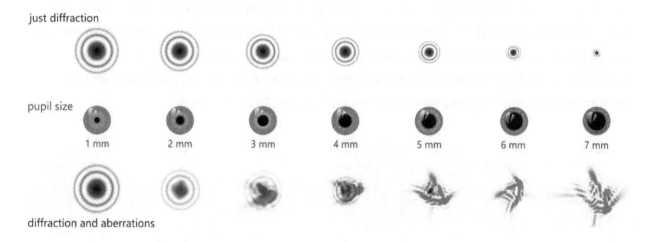

Figure 3-16: Simulation of the point-spread function of (top) a diffraction-limited system and (bottom) an optical system with approximately the same amount of aberration as a typical human eye.

With small pupil diameters, the effect of high-order aberrations is relatively small and can be ignored. In these small pupils, the limiting factor is diffraction: A smaller pupil makes the PSF broader [Figure 3-16 (top)]; the smaller the pupil the worse the attainable resolution and visual acuity. This is true for a pupil diameter of less than about 3.0 mm.

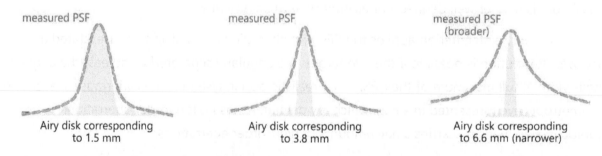

Figure 3-17: Theoretical (Airy disk) and actual/measured eye PSF cross-sections for various pupil diameters. Each curve represents the normalized distribution of retinal illuminance for a thin-slit light source. Created based on published data.[256]

---

[254] *Ocular Imaging* § 5.6.1 Pupil Size and its Effect on High Order Aberrations.

[255] Applegate RA, Gansel KA. The importance of pupil size in optical quality measurements following radial keratotomy. Refract Corneal Surg. 1990; 6(1):47-54.

[256] Campbell FW, Gubish RW. Optical quality of the human eye. J Physiol. 1966; 186(3):558-78.

The 'sweet spot' occurs for pupil diameters of about 2.5 mm to 4.0 mm, in which the net effect of both diffraction and aberrations results in a minimum PSF size; hence, the smallest minimum angle of resolution is 1 arcmin [the green line in Figure 3-18 (right)]. This is good news for visual acuity: This is where we expect the standard eye to attain 20/20, logMAR = 0.0 visual acuity (§ 3.4.5). Therefore, a mid-size pupil is optimal, as it is a compromise between the opposing effects of diffraction and aberrations.[257]

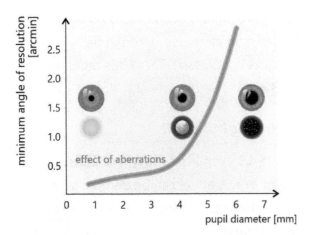 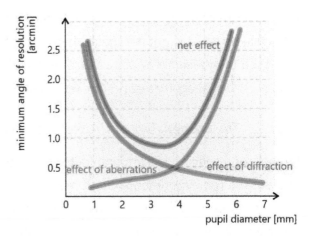

Figure 3-18: Dependence of the minimum angle of resolution on pupil diameter when only the effect aberrations is considered (left) and when the effects of both aberrations and diffraction are considered (right). Compare with Figure 3-11.

3.2.3 Other Factors Affecting Visual Acuity

A variety of factors affect visual acuity; these include the physiological health and integrity of the eye. In a cataractous eye, for example, scatter from a cloudy crystalline lens impairs not only visual acuity, but the overall visual performance because of the significantly increased disability glare (§ 2.5.3). The same is true for an eye with a corneal scar, particularly if the opacity is within the optical zone. Regardless of its refractive status, an eye with compromised retinal health, such as one presenting with macular degeneration, cannot have good visual performance.

3.2.3.1 Pinhole Effect

The pupil size is an important factor affecting visual acuity. So far, we have presented the influence from two opposing effects, aberrations and diffraction. Two additional, also opposing, effects related to pupil size also affect visual acuity. These are the Gaussian beam profile and

---

[257] Atchison DA, Smith G, Efron N. The effect of pupil size on visual acuity in uncorrected and corrected myopia. Am J Optom Physiol Opt. 1979; 56(5):315-23.

the depth of field. A detailed description of the Gaussian beam profile can be quite complicated; the simplest conclusion is that a small pupil results in an increase in the size of the circle of least confusion,[283] which increases the MAR and, subsequently, reduces visual acuity.

At the same time, however, there is the concept of depth of field. If an optical system has a shallow depth of field, a slight deviation from the location of the sharply formed image makes the image very blurry. Conversely, a large depth of field affords more deviations from the exact image locations since there is not much geometrical blur. A small pupil leads to a longer depth of field. This means that there is increased perceptual tolerance of a possible refractive error—a slight myope (or hyperope) benefits from an increased depth of field. The increased tolerance for refractive error is exactly what a small pupil can offer and is the principle of pinhole visual acuity testing (presented in detail in § 3.4.2).

3.2.3.2 The Dimension of the Retinal Mosaic – the Digital Limit

Retinal cone spacing is a limiting factor of central vision (§ 4.5.1), at least within the central 2 degrees.[258] The experimental and objective measurement of this effect can be demonstrated with a grating pattern, which consists of alternating dark/white stripes; such a grating can be resolved if there is a row of unstimulated cones (a 'No' response to black) between the rows of stimulated cones (a 'Yes' response to white). Then, a stripe is identified if the photoreceptor mosaic (§ 4.2.1) produces a 'No-Yes-No' response.

Hence, for two lines to be resolved, a sensor array needs to be fine enough to detect a gap between the two lines; this is the Nyquist resolution limit (§ 4.5.2). A limit on the order of 0.5 arcmin is, approximately, the reasonable limit on visual acuity set by the spatial digital (neural) photoreceptor sampling.

Limit imposed by pupil size	• diffraction-related resolution limit: 1 arcmin • daylight, mid-visible, 2 mm pupil • aberrations balanced at 3 mm pupil diameter
Limit imposed by digital photoreceptor sampling	• 0.5 arcmin • foveal, paraxial

---

[258] Green DG. Regional variations in the visual acuity for interference fringes on the retina. J Physiol. 1970; 207(2):351-6.

3.2.3.3 Eye Chart and Retinal Luminance

Visual acuity (VA) is affected by the amount of light reaching the retina, which involves the eye chart luminance, background luminance, and pupil diameter. The photometric quantity **luminance** L is the luminous flux emanating from a surface, per unit of solid angle of observation and unit of projection area. Luminance expresses the mean energy incident in any direction ϑ with respect to the normal to the surface unit per unit of time (projection area). Its units are cd/m^2, also called nit (1 nit = 1 cd/m^2), from the Latin *nitere*, to shine.

Example ☞: A typical computer screen has luminance of 300 nit ($\log L \approx 2.5$), while an overcast sky has luminance of 1000 = 1×10^3 nit ($\log L = 3.0$). (Explanations of the logarithm math are offered in § 3.4.5.)

To facilitate the comparison of visual acuity data across different studies, the US National Academy of Sciences – National Research Council (NAS-NRC) recommends a standard for eye chart background luminance of $L = 85$ nit ($\log L \approx 1.9$).[259] However, this is not universally followed; luminance for the original ETDRS (Early Treatment Diabetic Retinopathy Study) was 200 nit; in Germany, the standard is 300 nit; while in the United Kingdom, it is 120 nit ($\log L \approx 2.0$).[260] Additionally, the NAS-NRC recommends avoiding VA measurement in a room that is either dark or too bright: The ambient luminance should <u>not exceed</u> one-half of the chart luminance, and should not include glare or distraction.[259] Other bodies, such as the International Council of Ophthalmology (ICO) Visual Functions Committee, suggest that visual acuity chart luminance should be uniform and no less than 160 nit ($\log L \approx 2.2$),[261] which is the average indoor luminance of a reflecting or self-illuminating white surface.

The use of a standard eye chart luminance offers two advantages: First, it reduces the effects of modest variations in target luminance. Second and more importantly, the suggested eye chart luminance values ensure that the eye operates under photopic vision, as opposed to operating under low luminance, which results in the initiation of scotopic vision.

While photopic and scotopic vision are presented in § 4.3.2, here is a brief summary: Depending on the luminance, vision can be either rod-initiated (low-level, scotopic) or cone-initiated (high-level, photopic). Because of the different rod and cone photoreceptor distributions in the retina (§ 4.2.1)—but mainly owing to the different physical sizes, densities, and inner-retinal circuitries (§ 4.2.2) of these photoreceptors—photopic and scotopic vision have

---

[259] National Academy of Sciences – National Research Council NAS-NRC. Recommended standard procedures for the clinical measurement and specification of visual acuity. Report of Working Group 39. Committee on Vision. Assembly of Behavioral and Social Sciences, National Research Council, National Academy of Sciences, Washington, DC. Adv Ophthalmol. 1980; 41:103-48.

[260] Colenbrander A. Visual Acuity Measurement Standard. Section X. Light Adaptation, Luminance and Contrast. Retrieved from www.icoph.org/dynamic/attachments/resources/icovisualacuity1984.pdf

[261] Sheedy JE, Bailey IL, Raasch TW. Visual acuity and chart luminance. Am J Optom Physiol Opt. 1984; 61(9):595-600.

different VA limits. Photopic vision affords a high level (high resolution) of VA but has low sensitivity to dim light; scotopic vision is associated with a lower level of VA (lower resolution).[262]

Eye chart luminance relates to the retinal illuminance via the size of the pupil area. The **troland** (Td), a unit of conventional retinal illuminance named after Leonard T. Troland, is used to report retinal illuminance in a fashion independent of the object (here, an eye chart) distance. A troland represents the retinal illuminance produced by a surface whose luminance is one (1) nit when the area of the eye pupil is one (1) mm^2:

Troland (Td):   Eye Chart Luminance [nit] × Pupil Area [mm^2]   (3.11)

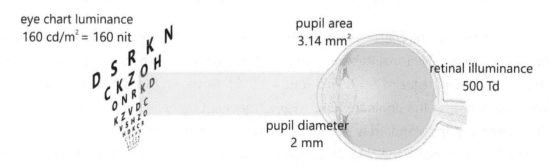

Figure 3-19: Retinal illuminance and the troland unit (Td).

Note 👀: The human visual system reaches photopic operation at around 100 Td. For a visual acuity chart with a 160 nit luminance and a pupil with a diameter of 2 mm (pupil area 3.14 mm²), the retinal illuminance is about 500 Td, which is well into the photopic range.

Example ☞: When viewing a visual acuity chart with luminance at 100 nit, what is the retinal illuminance if the eye pupil diameter is 2.0 mm?

Pupil radius r = 1.0 mm, area $\pi r^2 = \pi \cdot (1.0)^2$ = 3.14 mm², retinal illuminance (100 nit)·(3.14 mm²) = 314 Td.

Finally, it should be noted that visual acuity peaks at the center of macular fixation—moving progressively toward the foveal perimeter, there is a notable acuity drop. The main factor in this VA drop involves the rods' receptive fields (§ 4.3.5) and spatial summation: A larger receptive field results in more-light-sensitive but less-fine peripheral vision. The fact that we normally do not perceive a reduced peripheral VA even as our eyes fixate on a single object is due to saccadic motions (§ 1.2.1). Additionally, due to the Stiles–Crawford effect (§ 4.4.2), retinal illuminance is slightly reduced because of the relative directional efficiency of the retina, which is more sensitive to rays striking it perpendicularly than to those that are slightly oblique.

---

[262] Graham CH. Vision and visual perception. New York: John Wiley and Sons, Inc. 1965.

3.3 VISUAL ACUITY CHARTS

The quantification of VA involves the measurement of a fine angle on the order of an arcminute. Acuity derives from the Latin *acuitas*, for sharpness. This 'normal vision' resolution limit was known, empirically, to astronomers, such as Robert Hooke, who noticed that the human eye can resolve double stars subtending an angle of at least one arcmin. An objective measurement (i.e., one without the subject's participation) of such a small angle is almost impossible. This explains why we use subjective techniques that evaluate the subject's perception and response.

3.3.1 Historical Background

Spectacle correction dates back to medieval times in Italy; lens makers have worked industriously for centuries to improve lens quality. To evaluate their effectiveness, a test of visual acuity was sought. Benito Daza de Valdés, a Spanish Jacobin priest (1591–1634), was the first to state the need for a technique to measure visual acuity.[263]

The need for a standardized visual acuity technique became relevant with the emergence of ophthalmology as a (the first!) medical specialization in the mid-19th century. The first visual acuity measurement (1862) is credited to the German ophthalmologist Hermann von Helmholtz, who used a rod grating composed of black wires separated by intervals equal to the wire diameter; Helmholtz calculated a minimum angle of resolution of just slightly more than 1 arcmin (63.82 arcsec) by measuring the sum of the width of the two bars[264] divided by the distance between the grating and the examinee when the grating was resolved.[265]

Then came the first **eye chart** by the German ophthalmologist Heinrich Georg Küchler. His chart consisted of various symbols of diminishing size. It used shapes such as birds, farm animals, and equipment, cut from various prints and then glued to a sheet of paper. This primitive-symbol eye chart was not optimized, as it lacked consistency in size as well as uniformity in legibility and discriminability. As we now know, without legibility consistency, some characters on different parts of the chart, or even on the same line, might be easier to

---

[263] de Valdés BD. The Use of Eye Glasses (El Uso de Anteojos) [Spanish, 1623]. English translation of the 1923 translation into Spanish by Runge PE is published as part of the series: Hischberg J, ed. History of Ophthalmology. Belgium: G Schmidt, 2004.

[264] e Cruz AAV. Historical roots of 20/20 as a (wrong) standard value of normal visual acuity. Optom Vis Sci. 1990; 67(8):661.

[265] By measuring the sum of two wire widths, not just the width of one, Helmholtz reported a MAR value that was 2× the actual value of the 'minimum' angle of resolution. Thus, the 'standard' VA relating to this (erroneously calculated) MAR is off by a factor of 2. This is why the 20/20 vision, initially adopted by Donders and Snellen on the premise that MAR ≈ 1 arcmin, is not the upper limit of human vision. Effectively but unknowingly, Helmholtz measured the limit imposed on vision by the cone spacing (§ 4.5.2), which is, in fact, MAR ≈ 0.5 arcmin. This was first reported in Tscherning M. Le Sens des Formes. In: *Optique Physiologique*, Paris, 1898.

distinguish or even guess at. Küchler later introduced (in 1843) Blackletter / Old English letters (which formed words) arranged in twelve lines of diminishing size toward the bottom.

Figure 3-20: Küchler's eye charts using words.

In 1854, Austrian ophthalmologist Eduard Jäger (Jaeger) von Jaxtthal published a series of reading test cards called Schrift-Scalen that were originally an addendum to a book on cataract surgery to be used for near-vision testing (§ 7.10). The design of these cards was focused on determining an individual's ability to function following cataract surgery, as part of an activity of daily life (ADL) assessment. Reading complete words is related to, but is not exactly, visual acuity testing (see low-vision testing, § 7.9) since words might be guessed from the passage.

Jaeger's eye charts were the first successful charts of all kinds. They were published in many languages and had excellent print quality, as he used typefaces from the Vienna State Printing House, with well-specified linear print sizes. Jaeger never developed a distance test chart, as he did not prescribe a fixed reading distance.

The founding fathers of what we today call clinical measurement of (distance) visual acuity are two Dutch ophthalmologists, Fransicus (Franz) Cornelis Donders, who is credited with coining the term visual acuity, and Herman Snellen, who is credited with the first successful standardization of visual acuity measurement.[266]

Donders was interested in distance vision tests as a means to determine refractive error; his focus was on how the eyes function, as he was a pioneer of determining ocular refraction on a scientific basis. Initially, he used the larger Jaeger samples, but he needed a more scientific technique. In 1861, at the annual ophthalmology meeting in Heidelberg, Germany, Donders proposed a formula and a reference standard, defining, for the first time, sharpness of vision in terms of the ratio of letter size to specific viewing distance—an <u>angular measure</u>. His proposal was well-received.

---

[266] Colenbrander A. The historical evolution of visual acuity measurement. Vis Impair Res. 2008; 10(2-3):57-66.

Figure 3-21: (left to right) Hermann von Helmholtz (1821–1894), Fransicus (Franz) Cornelis Donders (1818–1889), and Herman Snellen (1834–1908).

Donders subsequently assigned his colleague and, later, successor, Herman Snellen, to devise a standardized measurement tool. He also assigned one of his doctoral students, Jan Vroesom de Haan, Jr., to study the effect of age on visual acuity. This study led to the first doctoral dissertation to employ prototypes of eye charts introduced by Snellen in 1862. It was perhaps the first publication about the most often-used metric in visual function.[267]

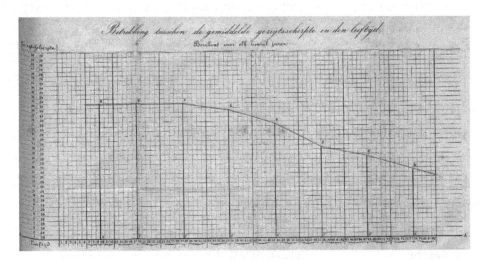

Figure 3-22: Data plot from de Haan's thesis presenting visual acuity of healthy individuals as a function of age. The horizontal scale is age in years, and the vertical scale is visual acuity in Snellen fractions.[267]

Snellen designed special characters, which he called **optotypes**, for the specific purpose of visual acuity measurement. In his work entitled *Optotypi ad Visum Determinandu*, Snellen described how the optotypes should be arranged in a chart format to be used as a test of distance vision (Figure 3-23). Instead of a word, multiple characters (abstract shapes, initially, and later numbers or letters) on each line provided several independent acuity estimates for that line. The examinee had to read each alphanumeric character individually.

---

[267] de Haan JV. Onderzoekingen naar den invloed van den leeftijd op de gezigtsscherpte (Investigations into the effect of age on the visual acuity). Doctoral Dissertation, Utrecht University, The Netherlands, 1862.

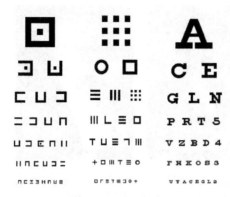

Figure 3-23: Snellen experimented with abstract shapes (left) before using alphanumeric characters. The original charts are on display at the Museum of the University of Utrecht.[266] (right) Vintage eye chart including Snellen optotypes and a dial to measure astigmatism known as the 'Orthops' test chart.

In reality, just one optotype, a single letter/character, would be sufficient to measure visual acuity if it could be gradually moved away, thus making the angle of the minimum detail progressively smaller. This is not efficient in clinical practice, nor is it reliable, as the transition from 'seen' to 'not seen' is not abrupt. The eye charts are designed to be observed from a fixed distance. As mentioned, the lines of optotypes of progressively smaller sizes represent decreasing values of angular separation to resolve; these decreasing values indicate increasing visual acuity. The finest row that can be read by an eye corresponds to the VA of that eye.

To implement Donders' formula, Snellen defined 'standard vision' as the ability to recognize an optotype when its detail (lines or gaps) subtended 1 arcmin. The minimum optotype detail seen by the examinee, divided by the minimum detail seen by the 'standard vision' eye is the **magnification requirement** (MAR) needed to bring the examinee eye to the same performance as the standard eye. Visual acuity is the reciprocal of the MAR:[268]

Donder's Visual Acuity:
$$\text{Visual Acuity} = \frac{1}{\text{MAgnification Requirement}}$$
(3.12)

An examinee who can read details of 1 arcmin needs no magnification (noted as 1×) and has **standard visual acuity**; the individual with that visual acuity is called the **standard observer**. It follows that, if 2× magnification is required to compensate for less than standard vision, then visual acuity is one-half of the standard, and so on.

Important Note 👓: 'Standard observer' and 'standard vision' (20/20) should <u>not be confused with the</u> <u>'best achievable' vision</u> for most individuals. A young emmetrope may typically have vision better than that,

[268] Snyder C. Herman Snellen and V=d/D. Arch Ophthalmol. 1962; 68:571-3.

by perhaps at least one more line (this is why eyecharts often have two lines finer than 20/20: 20/15 and 20/10). Standard vision is not the average, either; it is just a reference standard.[269] Average visual acuity, in general, does not drop to the 20/20 level until later in age.[270]

Today, MAR denotes the minimum angle of resolution (§ 3.1.1). Resolution refers to the finesse of vision, while the magnification requirement described chart letter measurement in terms of how much larger the letters had to be to achieve standard vision performance. This requirement can also express the magnification needed to remediate reduced vision.

The semantics here play a mind game: The same acronym (MAR) is used for two different terms that happen to produce the same numerical metric of vision but were derived from different functional perspectives.

3.3.2 The Snellen Optotype Geometry

The technical details of the optotypes used in eye charts trace their origins to the pioneering work by Snellen in early 1862. The optotypes—numerals, letter-like characters, or symbols—are black on a white background. The critical detail is the angular size of the spacings/gaps (white) and the lines/strokes (black). An optotype has up to five spacing–line pairs, oriented vertically or horizontally. For example, the letters E, F, and P have three black lines spaced vertically by two white gaps. The optotype at the 'standard vision' line has critical detail of $\vartheta_{MAR} = 1$ arcmin and overall angular size $\vartheta_{TOT} = 5$ arcmin. This line is usually placed near the bottom of the chart.

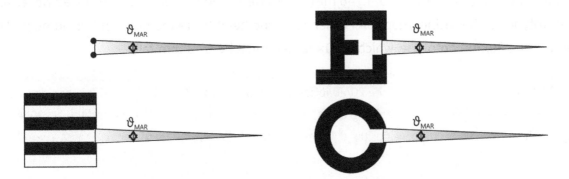

Figure 3-24: Simple observation targets (left) and visual acuity optotypes (right). If an optotype is to be used at the standard visual acuity line, the subtended angle of the detail is 1 arcmin. See Figure 3-26 for more detail regarding the optotype geometry.

[269] Frisén L, Frisén M. How good is normal visual acuity? A study of letter acuity thresholds as a function of age. Albrecht Von Graefes Arch Klin Exp Ophthalmol. 1981; 215(3):149-57.

[270] Elliott DB, Yang KCH, Whitaker D. Visual acuity changes throughout adulthood in normal, healthy eyes: seeing beyond 6/6. Optom Vis Sci. 1995; 72:186-91.

The top line in an eye chart typically corresponds to MAR 10×. This is one-tenth of the standard visual acuity, which resolves ϑ_{MAR} = 10 arcmin, and corresponds to reduced vision. Thus, the details in the top-line optotypes have an angular separation of 10 arcmin, for a total of 50 arcmin. Between the MAR 10 and the MAR 1 arcmin lines, the optotypes have progressively smaller angular detail as they approach the 'standard' vision line.

The physical size h_{opt} of the optotype (= $5 \cdot h_{detail}$) depends on the viewing distance. For a distance of d = 6 m ≈ 20 ft, which is the typical size of an examination lane, the angular subtense is h/6 m, so the <u>critical detail linear size h_{detail} for standard-vision optotype</u> is:

$$h_{detail} = 6\ m \cdot \tan(1') = 6\ m \cdot 0.000291 = 1.746\ mm \qquad (3.13)$$

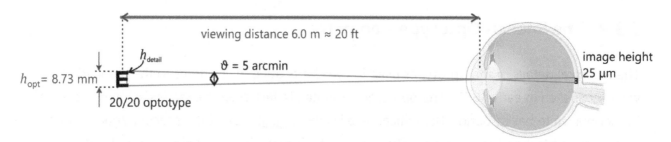

Figure 3-25: The standard-visual-acuity letter E at a 6 m (≈ 20 ft) viewing distance. To subtend a detail of angular size of 1 arcmin (total angular size 5 arcmin), the optotype must be 8.73 mm tall.

The overall <u>optotype size</u> of the standard vision, 20/20 eye should be if viewed from d = 6 m ≈ 20 ft, h_{opt} = $5 \cdot h_{detail}$ = $5 \cdot 1.746$ mm = 8.73 mm. The number 5 is introduced because the optotype has 5 spacings/gaps. All other optotype heights are multiples of this number. For example, the 20/200 optotype, which is 10× larger, must be 87.3 mm tall.

Note ⚲ : Because 20 ft = 6.096 m, the 20/20 letter height is 8.87 mm (= 3/8" or 11/32"). Thus, there is a small, but notable, difference between the exact 6/6 letter height, which is 8.73 mm, and the 20/20 letter height. For simplification, we consider the 8.73 mm linear size for both 20 ft and 6 m.

Comment 🛢 : Why should the viewing distance in the exam lane be 6 m / 20 ft?

This distance is large enough to approximate optical infinity for the optical system of the eye. Distance vision does not depend on distance but rather on the angular subtense of the target. However, the eye should be kept 'relaxed' (minimum accommodation).

A longer viewing distance might not be practically realizable in many exam lanes. A shorter viewing distance might not provide true 'distance' vision because accommodation is elicited.

When the eye is refracted at a shorter viewing distance (for example, if the exam lane is short), object vergence, the reciprocal of object distance, should also be considered. Even at 6 m (≈ 20 ft), object vergence is negligible but not zero = 1/(–6 m) = –0.167 D.

With a 3 m (≈ 10 ft) viewing distance, the examinee is effectively gaining an extra –0.33 D of refracting power because the vergence of the object is now closer. With this in mind, if an eye is refracting at a shorter viewing distance, additional minus power needs to be added to what is found in the phoropter; for example, –0.50 D for a 2 m (6.5 ft) viewing distance.

The best-known optotype is the block letter E, which consists of five spacings that provide details such as black stripes (strokes) and white gaps. A letter E in the standard visual acuity line has a detail of increments of 1 arcmin and a total angular subtense, from bottom to top, of 5 arcmin.

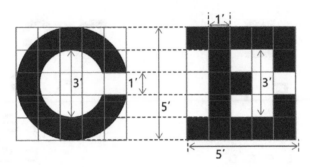

Figure 3-26: Snellen optotype geometry laid over a 5x5 grid. In the standard visual acuity line, bars (strokes) and white gaps subtend angular increments of 1 arcmin, for a total angular subtense of 5 arcmin. In the optotype resembling the letter C, the stroke width is ⅕ of the diameter (⅕ × 5 = 1 arcmin), which also equals the gap width. The letter E has strokes and gaps that subtend 1 arcmin.

By definition, the standard observer can marginally resolve (see) an optotype whose detail is 1 arcmin. This means that if the optotype has a stroke (line) detail that is 1.746 mm, the standard observer needs to be 20 ft away to 'see' it. If, however, the optotype has detail that is 2·1.746 mm = 3.492 mm, the standard observer can see it 40 ft away; if the optotype has detail that is 0.5·1.746 mm = 0.873 mm, the standard observer can see it 10 ft away.

Visual acuity is (most often) reported in clinical practice using Snellen notation. To do this, we determine the smallest (line of) optotypes that the examinee can resolve. Then we calculate the distance at which the standard observer should be seated to recognize the (same) smallest optotype as the examinee. The result is reported as a fraction:

Snellen Fraction: $$\frac{\text{testing distance (assumed to be 20 ft or 6 m)}}{\text{distance (ft) at which the standard observer recognizes the optotype}}$$ (3.14)

Um dies in einer allgemeinen Formel auszudrücken, so ist, wenn

$$S = \frac{d}{D}$$

S = Sehschärfe.

d = kleinste Entfernung, in der die Buchstaben erkannt werden.

D = Entfernung in welcher sich die Buchstaben unter einem Winkel von 5' zeigen.

Figure 3-27: Snellen's fractions explained by Snellen (Probebuchstaben zur Bestimmung der Sehschärfe [Letters for the Determination of Visual Acuity], Berlin, 1963).

The examination distance is <u>assumed</u> to be 20 ft; therefore, the numerator is always 20. At this distance, a person with standard visual acuity can read the smallest letter forming a total angle of 5 arcmin. This is the 20/20 visual acuity standard.

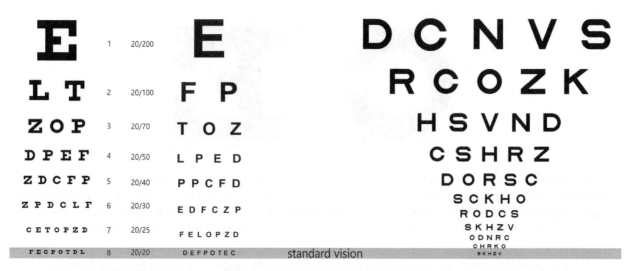

Figure 3-28: Snellen-type charts with a serif font and a sans-serif font (left) and an ETDRS chart (right). Regardless of the chart type, on the standard-vision (20/20) line, optotypes have a total angular subtense of 5 arcmin.

Example ☞: What is the visual acuity of a person who discerns an optotype 17.46 mm tall from 20 ft?

The height of the Snellen 20/20 optotype subtending an angle of 5 arcmin at 20 ft is 8.73 mm. The 17.46 mm optotype is 2× larger than the 20/20 optotype. This can be read by the standard eye at a distance of 40 ft, which means that the person's Snellen visual acuity is 20/40.

Example ☞: Donald has a less-than-standard (reduced) vision. The smallest optotype he can read is a large one, which can be read by a standard vision eye at, say, 100 ft. Donald, then, has 20/100 vision, which is poor. He will probably fail to get a driver's license in most of the United States, since the minimum required visual acuity for driving is 20/40.

Example ☞: Vivian has better-than-standard vision and can read a small optotype, one that a standard observer could only read closer, say, 10 ft away. She therefore has 20/10 vision. We conclude that the smaller the denominator in Snellen fractions the better the measured visual acuity.

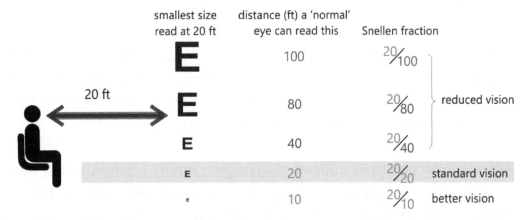

Figure 3-29: Snellen fractions.

Snellen fractions may use the numeral 6 as the numerator, denoting the examination distance as 6 meters. Then the standard vision is 6/6, and 6/12 corresponds to 20/40, and so on. The 6/ notation is used mostly in countries of the (British) Commonwealth of Nations.

The development of test charts has partially been driven by the physical constraints and the nature of the available space in consulting rooms. In shorter exam lanes, the examinee may sit with the chart behind him/her and view the lines through a mirror, which has the effect of doubling the distance at which the letters appear. Then the eye chart is reversed horizontally.

Often, illuminated/transparent test charts are used. These were originally intended to be attached to the surface of a window and required sufficient daylight. Some eye charts had internal illumination as early as the age of gaslight sources. These charts suffered from bleaching and degradation by the heat from the lamp light source.

Back in the days before computer-assisted printing when no standard fonts were available, the construction of optotypes required hand drawing of all optotypes and manual arrangement in rows. The composition could then be photographed and enlarged to the proper size. Slide projectors using 35 mm slides were often used to project the eye charts onto screens.

The examination lane is often not 20 ft long, but shorter. In a 15 ft lane, the true Snellen fractions would be 15/X. Instead, Snellen acuity is recorded as 20/X. Thus, the presence of 20 in the numerator rarely represents an actual measurement made at 20 ft. In this case, the physical optotype size should be adjusted proportionally. This is important when using a projector or electronic eye charts (§ 3.4.8) with adjustable magnification for shorter viewing distances.

Example ☞: We want to use a Snellen chart at 10 ft. What is the necessary optotype size adjustment? At 10 ft, the optotypes form larger angles. For example, a 20/80 optotype viewed at 10 ft subtends the same angle at the subject's eye as a 20/40 standard optotype viewed at a distance of 20 ft. Therefore, a 20 ft calibrated eye chart at 10 ft needs to be reduced in size by half.

Example ☞: We want to use a Snellen chart at 32 ft. What is the necessary optotype size adjustment? At 32 ft, the optotypes form smaller angles. For example, a 20/80 optotype viewed at 32 ft subtends the same angle at the examinee's eye as a 20/50 standard optotype viewed at a distance of 20 ft. Therefore, to use a 20 ft calibrated eye chart at 32 ft, the entire chart needs to be enlarged by 160%.

Snellen's original optotypes purposely <u>did not use a specific typeface</u>, as they were designed based on arcminute geometry. The optotypes were laid over a 5×5 grid and comprised a limited character set of 9 to10 letters. The weight of the black lines was equal to the white space between the lines; the height and width of an optotype were 5× the thickness of the line. These design constraints created oddly proportioned letters. For example, in a typical typeface, C and D may appear wider than Z, but in the optotype, the opposite is true. The letter E sits rather awkwardly on this template, so a 5×4 version was later developed, for which the strokes (serifs) to the left were removed.

While no standard typeface (called a font in today's computer graphics applications) can reproduce the original Snellen optotypes, the Egyptian, or slab-serif, typeface is a close match. The descriptor 'serif' includes a family of fonts/typefaces with ornamental strokes at the ends of each limb, called serifs. The other big family of fonts is the sans-serif, which do not have these ornamental features at the end of strokes—hence, they are simpler.

Efforts were made to introduce sans-serif fonts in eye charts. One of these early efforts was made in 1868 by John Green (College of Physicians and Surgeons, St. Louis, Missouri).[271] Green proposed sans-serif style letters (similar to today's Gothic font) and designed a more structured grid with a consistent logarithmic geometric progression of 25% between successive lines and with proportional spacing.[272] Green's developed sequence, which became known as the Preferred Numbers series, was ahead of its time: The typefaces were deemed of 'unfinished appearance,' and Green reverted to serif letters. His ideas, however, were re-established much later in the design of the Sloan letters (§ 3.4.4).

[271] The school claimed to be the oldest medical school in Missouri, operating between 1869 and 1927.
[272] Green J. On a new series of test-letters for determining the acuteness of vision. Trans Am Opth Soc. 4th Meeting 1868; 68.

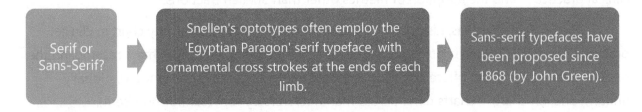

Figure 3-30: Examples of early serif Snellen optotypes.

Serif or Sans-Serif?	Snellen's optotypes often employ the 'Egyptian Paragon' serif typeface, with ornamental cross strokes at the ends of each limb.	Sans-serif typefaces have been proposed since 1868 (by John Green).

Another innovative attempt to create new optotypes around that time, credited to ophthalmologist O. M. Pray, from Brooklyn, New York, resulted in what Pray called "astigmatic letters." Dr. Pray's idea was to measure the power and axis of astigmatism using Snellen-type geometry serif letters that were filled with a texture of black-and-white stripes drawn in increments of 15°. However, the reduced contrast in the letters meant a decreased ability to see the very fine texture (about ⅕ of 1 arcmin). That decreased ability extended below any 'normal' vision, so these astigmatic letters were not effective.

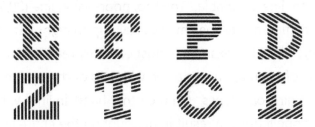

Figure 3-31: Dr. Pray's astigmatic letters.

Figure 3-32: (left to right) Early 20th century Visometer eye test cabinet, antique revolving eye chart, illuminated eye chart cabinet, and Bausch+Lomb Ferree–Rand projector.

3.3.3 Snellen Chart Limitations

Visual acuity testing is the gold standard for primary outcomes of clinical trials worldwide. The US Food and Drug Administration (FDA) requires all vision-related registration and clinical trials to report the outcome in visual acuity or a surrogate that correlates with visual acuity.[273] There are several arguments relating to the need for standardization of visual acuity testing in the clinical practice[274] and the adoption of metrics other than Snellen fractions.[275]

The Snellen chart has, historically, been the most popular visual acuity chart in clinical practice. The term 'Snellen chart' is an umbrella term for several letter eye charts resembling the original Snellen eye chart, offered by various manufacturers. There is no standard, globally uniform Snellen chart;[276] charts differ across manufacturers by font (serif or non-serif), letters/numbers used, and vertical line spacing ratios and size progression.[277] Clinicians often refer to 'Snellen acuity' even without using a common, standard testing procedure or chart.[278]

Other shortcomings/deficiencies of Snellen charts are:

- The scoring method used is line counting when the majority of letters in a line (row) are read. Credit is given to the entire line if the majority of characters on that line are read. A difference of at least two lines is required in order to confidently report that there has been a change.

- Certain letters (e.g., C, D, E, O) are easier to recognize than others (e.g., P, F).[277]

- The number of letters per line is variable: The top, poor-vision line (20/200) usually contains only one letter, while the fine-acuity lines may contain up to eight letters. This introduces several sources of error. Since the examinee must correctly read the majority of optotypes on a line, the identification of the majority on a line with two or three optotypes is less difficult than for lines with six to nine optotypes. On the other hand, in lines with two or three optotypes, missing just one letter can result in discounting the entire line; this brings poorer vision accuracy determination. In lines with letters spaced too closely, adjacent contours result

---

[273] Kaiser PK. Prospective evaluation of visual acuity assessment: a comparison of Snellen versus ETDRS charts in clinical practice (An AOS Thesis). Trans Am Ophthalmol Soc. 2009; 107:311-24.

[274] Ferris FL, Bailey I. Standardizing the measurement of visual acuity for clinical research studies. Ophthalmology. 1996; 103:181-2.

[275] Hofstetter HW. From 20-20 to 6-6 or 4-4? Am J Optom Arch Am Acad Optom. 1973; 50(3):212-21.

[276] Leinonen J, Laakkonen E, Laatikainen L. Random measurement error in visual acuity measurement in clinical settings. Acta Ophthalmol Scand. 2005; 83(3):328-32.

[277] Bennett AG. Ophthalmic test types. A review of previous work and discussion on some controversial questions. Br J Physiol Opt. 1965; 22:238-71.

[278] Williams MA, Moutray TN, Jackson AJ. Uniformity of visual acuity measures in published studies. Invest Ophthalmol Vis Sci. 2008; 49:4321-27.

in crowding effects (overlapping blur), which affect visual acuity.[279] Because of the variable number (and horizontal spacing) of letters per line, contour interactions vary throughout the Snellen chart: The poor-vision lines have minimal crowding, while the fine-acuity lines have greater crowding.

- This irregular progression of letter size and density between the seven steps has statistical consequences, as data based on an uneven scale creates problems in any subsequent parametric analysis. For example, because of the equal-denominator increments in the fractional notation, the difference between 20/100 and 20/200 is too large of a loss and its determination is often dependent on identifying (or not) just one letter.

- There is no specific typeface or font used for Snellen eye charts. Some Snellen charts use serif characters and others use sans-serif characters, and the letters themselves present varying difficulty in being identified properly.[280]

- The progression of letter sizes between steps is not consistent. Changing the viewing distance and thus changing the scale accordingly can introduce under- or over-estimation errors. Also, the inconsistent line spacing and size progression can result in the loss or gain of a line not having the same effect in different parts of the chart.

Comment 🗼: Is the test ... rigged?

Testing with optotype eye charts is considered to be subjective: It requires input from the examinee, whose response might be offered as a matter of opinion. Seeking the last line that can be read clearly may not lead to a definitive answer.

There are some limitations in the use of known characters as optotypes. Cerebral processing helps one to verify that something that looks like a letter E is, indeed, a letter E. Thus, it is the minimum recognizable resolution that is measured, not the minimum separable resolution.

Finally, it should be stressed that the ability to see detail is not a complete description of vision. A comprehensive eye examination should balance subjective and objective tests that extend beyond simply measuring visual acuity. These may include tests of fields of view, contrast sensitivity, binocular perception, aspects of convergence, and so on.

---

[279] Flom MC, Heath GG, Takahashi E. Contour interaction and visual resolution: Contralateral effects. Science. 1963; 142(3594):979-80.

[280] Mathew JA, Shah SA, Simon JW. Varying difficulty of Snellen letters and common errors in amblyopic and fellow eyes. Arch Ophthalmol. 2011; 129(2):184-7.

3.4 THE MEASUREMENT OF VISUAL ACUITY

3.4.1 Visual Acuity Notation

A typical task in visual acuity measurement involves monocular distance vision assessment. In ocular optics, 'distance' corresponds to optical infinity, which is approximated by any distance beyond 6 m. The term 'uncorrected' or 'unaided' means not wearing any spectacles or contact lenses, even if the examinee is typically wearing such vision correction devices. This is called **uncorrected distance visual acuity** (UDVA). The term 'entrance' acuity is also used to indicate uncorrected visual acuity. A shorthand notation often used is *sc* (Latin: *sine correctore*).

In the monocular examination, the eye that is examined (the opposite eye is occluded) must be noted; i.e., whether it is the right OD (Latin: *Oculus Dexter*) or the left OS (Latin: *Oculus Sinister*) eye. Vision assessed with both eyes open is noted as OU (Latin: *Oculus Uterque*).

If the examinee wears the proper/optimal prescription, then VA is recorded as corrected (shorthand *cc*, Latin: *cum correctore*), along with the refraction worn at the time of the examination. This acuity can also be noted as best-spectacle **corrected distance visual acuity** (CDVA),[281] implying best-spectacle correction. In optometry, the term **best corrected visual acuity** (BCVA) is used instead.[282] Often, we may examine intermediate vision (typically at arm's length), noted as UIVA and CIVA, and near vision, noted as UNVA (uncorrected) and CNVA (corrected). Near vision is typically measured between 25 and 40 cm. When reporting either intermediate or near vision, the distance at which the measurement was made must be specified.

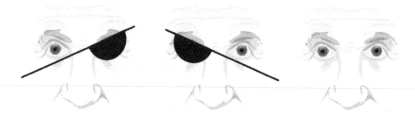

Figure 3-33: (left to right) Measurement of OD, OS, and OU (both eyes viewing) visual acuity.

---

[281] These terms are adopted from Dupps WJ Jr, Kohnen T, Mamalis N, Rosen ES, Koch DD, Obstbaum SA, Waring GO 3rd, Reinstein DZ, Stulting RD. Standardized graphs and terms for refractive surgery results. J Cataract Refract Surg. 2011; 37(1):1-3.

[282] Collin HB. Is BCVA an invention of ophthalmology? Clin Exp Optom. 2008; 91:425-6. In this editorial, Dr. Collin states that visual acuity is, by definition, the best spatial resolution of the eye, and the words 'best corrected' are redundant. He advocates for the use of 'presenting vision' and 'unaided vision.'

In many textbooks, and in the profession of optometry, corrected vision is reported using B for best and S for spectacle. However, both of these modifiers are (or should be) implied. The terms outlined in Table 3-2 are adopted by leading peer-reviewed journals in ophthalmology, including *Cornea*, *Journal of Refractive Surgery*, and *Journal of Cataract and Refractive Surgery*.

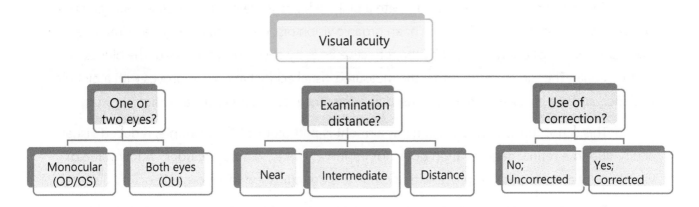

Figure 3-34: The visual acuity tree.

Table 3-2: Visual acuity terms and abbreviations corresponding to monocular measurements.

UDVA	Uncorrected distance visual acuity
UIVA	Uncorrected intermediate visual acuity
UNVA	Uncorrected near visual acuity
CDVA	Corrected distance visual acuity
CIVA	Corrected intermediate visual acuity
DCIVA	Distance-corrected intermediate visual acuity
CNVA	Corrected near visual acuity
DCNVA	Distance-corrected near visual acuity

3.4.2 Pinhole Visual Acuity

The **pinhole occluder** (or stenopic disk) is an eye-shield that allows a view through a small aperture (of about 1.2 mm diameter). The examinee observes the eye chart through a pinhole at the center of the occluder, or through any pinhole if there are multiple. When visual acuity is measured with a pinhole occluder, it should be noted accordingly; the abbreviation used is PH.

Figure 3-35: (left) Pinhole occluder with multiple pinholes and (right) trial lens occluder with pinhole.

The measurement of visual acuity with a pinhole helps to determine whether reduced visual acuity is attributed to a refractive error or an organic vision disorder. A pinhole usually improves the measured visual acuity affected by the refractive error by decreasing the size of the blur circle on the retina. The clinical result is that the measured visual acuity typically improves with a pinhole occluder, and the measurement can be used as a reference for potential visual acuity.

This is not the case when vision impairment is pathological; for example, reduced visual acuity due to a retinal degeneration does not improve with a pinhole occluder. A low value of visual acuity that does not improve with a pinhole is an indication of an organic ocular disease.

This topic is often presented with overwhelming simplifications and sometimes with incorrect scientific explanations. We start by acknowledging the optical effect of the pinhole occluder: It effectively reduces the diameter of the entrance pupil of the eye. Two main effects depend on pupil size (§ 3.2.3): a wave-optics-related effect (diffraction) and a geometrical-optics-related effect. The former, presented in § 3.2, is the diffraction effect associated with a circular aperture. The latter is associated with the depth of field, and, to a certain degree, with the effect of high-order aberrations.

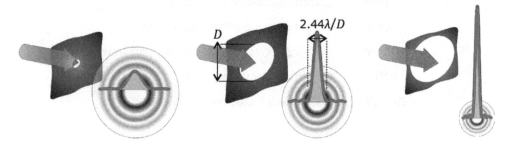

Figure 3-36: Effect of pupil diameter on PSF shape. (left) A small pupil results in a broader PSF, and (right) a large pupil results in a confined PSF.

The diffraction-related effect is that a small pupil results in a broad, smaller PSF, which, in turn, results in less resolving power and therefore reduced visual acuity.

In addition, the Gaussian-optics laws relating to the formation of the beam profile (cross-section of the circle of least confusion; see Figure 3-37)[283] at the focus suggest that, in principle, the size of the circle of least confusion increases as the pupil becomes smaller. Finally, a small pinhole reduces retinal illuminance.

---

[283] *Wave Optics* § 6.3.4 The Gaussian Beam.

larger pupil

smaller pupil

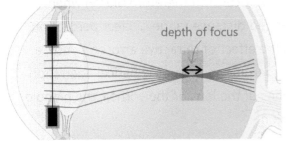
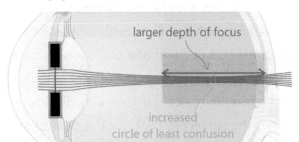

Figure 3-37: A smaller pupil results in an increased depth of focus. Additionally, due to Gaussian imaging, the minimum cross-section, representing the size of the circle of least confusion, increases. The smaller pupil allows a greater tolerance (i.e., no noticeable perceptual blur) for an appreciably longer depth of focus. This is noted as improved visual acuity in individuals with refractive error. See also Figure 6-13.

These considerations suggest that, in principle, visual acuity is expected to drop, not increase, with a pinhole. However, diffraction and Gaussian effects become a factor only when the pinhole is very small. The chief effect is, as we now present, that a pinhole increases the depth of field.

Figure 3-38: Depth of field: The proximal foreground and the distal background of the image are outside the depth of field, while the center is within the depth of field. Photo courtesy of Henryk Niestrój, taken with a 100 mm lens at f/3.5 (used with permission).

The depth of field and, consequently, the depth of focus in the eye (§ 6.1.4) depend chiefly on the pupil size (§ 2.4.2.4), which means that the eye's depth of focus is variable. The key concept is that the <u>depth of focus increases with a small pupil</u>, affording a larger range of acceptable vision. As the depth of focus increases, the range of distances of objects that can be seen with the same perceived clarity also increases.[284, 285]

---

[284] Typically, individuals with very good vision have a shallow depth of focus; a pinhole might not improve—and can even deteriorate—their visual acuity.

[285] *Geometrical Optics* § 7.4 Depth of Field and Depth of Focus.

Objects that cannot be clearly seen (being out of focus and therefore blurry) when viewed through a pinhole probably fall into this extended distance range of clear perception. Thus, the main benefit of a pinhole is that it reduces the effect of refractive errors.[286] Also, a smaller aperture reduces the effects of higher-order aberrations, such as spherical aberration and coma. In the case of unevenly distributed opacities of the lens or the cornea, the pinhole allows the subject to seek out the clearest area of vision.

Because of the reduction of high-order aberrations, the use of a pinhole results in a smaller circle of least confusion and therefore improved visual acuity, particularly in eyes with significant refractive errors. On the other hand, visual acuity is not expected to improve in individuals with very low or insignificant refractive errors.

Therefore, a proper pinhole aperture diameter is chosen (1.2 mm)[287] to balance these counteracting effects. This size is effective for refractive errors of up to ± 5.00 D. With an aperture that is too small, vision will be dominated by diffraction, resulting in reduced visual acuity. With too large an aperture, vision will be dominated by refractive errors and aberrations.

Diffraction: A small pinhole is associated with increased diffraction effects, leading to a decrease in visual acuity.

Depth of focus: A small pinhole results in an increase in the range of acceptable vision, affording more tolerance of refractive error.

Gaussian Propagation: A small pinhole results in an increase in the size of the circle of least confusion, thus decreasing visual acuity.

Aberrations: A small pinhole reduces the effects of aberrations, thus increasing visual acuity.

Pinhole occluders with a 1.2 mm aperture are used during routine ocular examinations to benchmark the potential for best refractive visual correction.

The pinhole allows individuals with a refractive error of up to 5 D to see up to 0.18 logMAR (Snellen equivalent 20/30).

Because of diffraction, a smaller aperture (0.50 or 0.75 mm) results in a decrease in visual acuity in fully corrected ametropes and emmetropes.

[286] Green DG, Powers MK, Banks MS. Depth of focus, eye size and visual acuity. Vision Res. 1980; 20(10):827-35.
[287] Whitney MT, O'Connor P. The ideal pinhole. Invest Ophthalmol Vis Sci. 2009; 50(13):3990.

3.4.3 Expressions of Visual Acuity

Currently, three major different scaling systems are used to describe visual acuity. These are decimal visual acuity, Snellen fraction, and LogMAR acuity (§ 3.4.5).

3.4.3.1 The 6/6 Snellen Fraction - Metric Fractional Notation

In the US, visual acuity is recorded with Snellen fractions using the 20/ fractions, while in the UK and several member states of the Commonwealth of Nations, it is recorded using 6/ fractions, as the reference distance is 6 meters instead of 20 feet.

Example ☞: The Snellen 6/24 acuity means that the examinee can identify at 6 m what the standard observer can identify at 24 m. It is the equivalent of 20/80.

3.4.3.2 Decimal Visual Acuity

The **decimal scale**, proposed by French ophthalmologist Ferdinand Monoyer[288] (the 'Father' of the diopter, the unit of optical power), was introduced in 1875, around the time of the signing of the Metre Convention (Convention du Mètre), which aimed to address the profusion of varying length and weight units. At the time, there were more than 20 different foot standards, such as the Parisian feet. The decimal scale is the reciprocal of the MAR, the 'physical' definition of visual acuity. It is expressed as a fraction of 10 (X/10), or as a decimal 0.X:

Decimal Scale (Monoyer Acuity):
$$\text{Visual Acuity} = \frac{1}{\text{MAR}\,[\text{arcmin}]} \tag{3.15}$$

Example ☞: For a minimum angle of resolution (MAR) of 1 arcmin in a Landolt optotype, which is Snellen VA 20/20, decimal VA is 1/1 = 10/10 or 1.0. Snellen 20/40 (MAR = 2 arcmin) becomes decimal VA 1/2 = 5/10 or 0.5. Snellen 20/100 (MAR = 5 arcmin) becomes decimal VA 1/5 = 2/10 or 0.2.

Decimal-scale VA is used in Japan and many European countries. Its use in the United States was proposed (unsuccessfully) by Dr. Hofstetter nearly 50 years ago.[275, 289] This scale has many advantages, mainly numeric: The decimal 0.X notation is easy to process because no denominator is needed—it relates to a percent of visual ability, which is easier to communicate.

To convert from decimal (Monoyer) VA to Snellen fraction, we first find the denominator by multiplying the reciprocal of the decimal VA ×20 (or 6), using 20 (or 6) as the numerator:

---

[288] Monoyer F. Echelle typographique décimale pour mesurer l'acuité visuelle. Gaz Med Paris. 1875; 21:258.

[289] Rosenfield M. It's time to stop using 20/20 in the clinic. Optom Vis Sci. 2012; 89(10):e27.

Snellen Fraction from Monoyer Acuity: $\dfrac{20}{20 \times \dfrac{1}{\text{decimal acuity}}}$ (3.16)

Example ☞ : The equivalent Snellen fraction for a decimal Monoyer acuity of 0.5 is $\dfrac{20}{20 \times \dfrac{1}{0.5}} = \dfrac{20}{40}$.

3.4.3.3 Spatial Frequency and Cycles per Degree

Often in research, as well as in conjunction with contrast sensitivity measurements,[290] we use the **spatial frequency** unit of **cycles per degree** (cycles/degree, cpd) to express the ability of grating detection. The unit is defined if we consider a grating in which one cycle (= 2 lines) of one bright (white) and one dark (black) bar fits into one degree.

The task of detecting a grating relates to visual acuity if we consider the optical aspect of resolution. The 20/20 standard eye (diffraction-limited 2-mm diameter pupil), which resolves one 'spacing' increment per MAR of 1 arcmin, can see a cycle, one white and one black stripe, whose angular subtense at the eye is 2 arcmin. Therefore, the corresponding spatial frequency is one cycle per 2 arcmin. Since there are 60 arcmin in one degree, one degree has 30 of such cycles. Hence, the spatial frequency corresponding to 20/20 visual acuity is 30 cycles/degree.

Figure 3-39: *Resolution that corresponds to 20/20 visual acuity detects a grating of one cycle per 2 arcmin.*

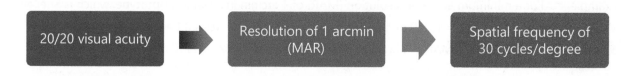

An eye with finer vision resolves better: A 20/10 eye that resolves a MAR of 0.5 arcmin can see a cycle of 1 arcmin angular subtense, which means that 60 resolvable cycles fit in a degree. Thus, 20/10 vision corresponds to a spatial frequency of 60 cycles/degree. An eye with poorer vision, for example, 20/40, resolves a MAR of 2 arcmin; this eye can see a cycle of 4 arcmin, which means that only 15 cycles fit into a degree; the spatial frequency is 15 cycles/degree.

We understand therefore that fewer cycles/degree means reduced vision: As the cycles have to be larger to be distinguished, fewer of such cycles fit into a degree of angular subtense.

---

[290] *Ocular Imaging* § 5.4.1 Contrast Sensitivity Measurement.

Conversely, more cycles/degree means better vision. The conversion between MAR and spatial frequency is

MAR to Spatial Frequency: $$\left(\frac{1\ \text{cycle}}{2\times\text{MAR}\,[\text{arcmin}]}\right)\times\left(\frac{60\ \text{arcmin}}{1\ \text{degree}}\right)$$ (3.17)

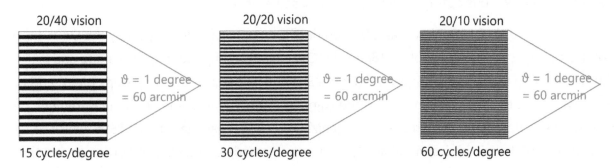

Figure 3-40: Visual acuity and spatial frequency (angles are not drawn to scale). Lower spatial frequency (left) represents coarser detail, and higher spatial frequency (middle and right) represents finer detail.

Examples ☞:

For 20/40 Snellen vision with MAR = 2 arcmin, spatial frequency becomes

$$\left(\frac{1\ \text{cycle}}{2\times2\ \text{arcmin}}\right)\times\left(\frac{60\ \text{arcmin}}{1\ \text{degree}}\right)=\frac{60}{4}=15\ \text{cycles/degree}$$

For 20/10 Snellen vision with MAR = 0.5 arcmin, spatial frequency becomes

$$\left(\frac{1\ \text{cycle}}{2\times0.5\ \text{arcmin}}\right)\times\left(\frac{60\ \text{arcmin}}{1\ \text{degree}}\right)=\frac{60}{1}=60\ \text{cycles/degree}$$

In optics, we also use the unit of **line pairs/mm**.[291] This unit is defined as a pair comprising a black stripe and a white stripe (1 cycle = 2 lines = 1 line pair) in 1°. For the average-axial-length, emmetropic human eye (in which the image-space nodal point to focal point distance is 17 mm, § 6.2.2), an image of 1 mm across corresponds to 3.345°. Thus,

$$1\ \frac{\text{cycle}}{\text{degree}}\ =\ \frac{1\ \text{line pair (2 lines)}}{\dfrac{1}{3.345}\ \text{mm}}\ =\ 6.69\ \frac{\text{lines}}{\text{mm}}=\ 3.345\ \frac{\text{line pairs}}{\text{mm}}$$ (3.18)

---

[291] *Wave Optics* § 5.5.4 Quantification of Image Quality: the PSF and MTF Functions.

3.4.4 Advanced Optotypes and Eye Charts

The test of visual acuity using familiar letters or numbers is based on alphanumeric characters. For this reason, it may be influenced by human subjective perception. The effort to disassociate this subjective aspect and further improve and standardize visual acuity testing has led to the development of various optotypes and eye charts, some of which are as follows:

The **Landolt C**, also known as a broken ring, is an optotype developed by the Swiss-born ophthalmologist Edmund Landolt in 1888. The C is a nearly complete ring with a gap and is thus identical to the sans-serif Snellen C (Figure 3-26). The gap is rotated by steps of 90° and in some variations by 45°. The Landolt C is the standard optotype, together with measurement procedures as described in International Organization for Standardization ISO 8596, which pertains to ophthalmic optics, visual acuity testing, and standard and clinical optotypes and their presentation.[246]

The **tumbling E** 5×5 grid consists of rows of a letter-E-like sans-serif optotype rotated by increments of 90°. Rather than being a letter E, it is more like a vertical line with three horizontal lines (bars) attached; the three bars approximate part of a square-wave grating.[292] The tumbling E chart is suitable for populations not native to the Latin (or any similar) alphabet as well as those who are illiterate very young. When the chart comprises either the Landolt C or the tumbling E, the examinee is asked to show the orientation of the C gap or the E lines.

Figure 3-41: The Landolt C and tumbling E eye optotypes. When used at the 20/20 line, the angular extent of the diameter of the C character and the height of the E character are each 5 arcmin.

The **LEA Vision Test System** is a series of vision charts and tests designed specifically for children, using pictorial optotypes—outlines of an apple, a circle, a house, and a square. The LEA test was introduced in 1976 by Finnish pediatric ophthalmologist Lea Hyvärinen.[293] It allows pediatric low vision to be diagnosed at much younger ages than standard vision tests allow.

---

[292] Alexander KR, Xie W, Derlacki DJ. Spatial frequency characteristics of letter identification. J Opt Soc Am A Opt Image Sci Vis. 1994; 11(9):2375-82.

[293] Hyvärinen L, Näsänen R, Laurinen P. New visual acuity test for pre-school children. Acta Ophthalmol (Copenh).1980; 58(4):507-11.

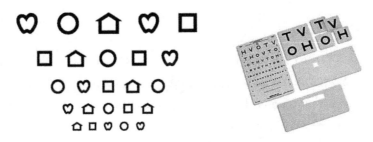

Figure 3-42: (left) Eye chart with LEA symbols and (right) HOTV chart with matching cards.

The **HOTV vision test** uses the sans-serif letters H, O, T, and V, with all letters mirror reversible and laterally symmetrical. These letters allow children having difficulty with right/left distinction to be tested. The test is often presented using four-choice flash cards. The children need not name the letter, they just need to point to one on a matching card.

In 1959, Louise L. Sloan of the low-vision center at the Wilmer Eye Institute, Johns Hopkins University, Baltimore created ten new optotypes based on sans-serif letters (C, D, H, K, N, O, R, S, V, and Z—note, <u>there is no E</u>) based on the principles suggested by John Green nearly 80 years earlier.[294] Like the Snellen letters, each **Sloan letter** optotype is formed within a 5×5 grid, with stroke widths equal to ⅕ of the letter height and with equal visual weight. The original eye chart proposed by Sloan used up to ten letters in some rows.

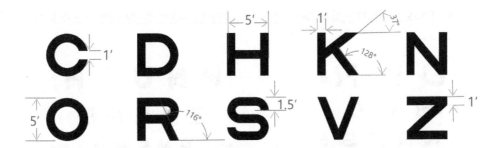

Figure 3-43: Design of the Sloan letters for the 20/20 line. All letters fit into a 5x5 grid.

The Sloan optotypes (letters) allow for the identification of verticals, horizontals, and diagonals, with equal legibility.[295] They can be used as visual acuity and contrast sensitivity charts.[296] The Sloan typeface might, at first glance, resemble Microgramma/Eurostile fonts, but the grid format imposed on these optotypes produces some oddly proportioned letters. The Sloan design has been designated as the US Standard for visual acuity testing by the National Academy of Sciences, National Research Council, Committee on Vision.[259]

---

[294] Sloan LL. New test charts for the measurement of visual acuity at far and near distances. Am J Ophthalmol. 1959; 48(6):807-13.

[295] Sloan LL, Rowland WM, Altman A. Comparison of three types of test target for the measurement of visual acuity. Q Rev Ophthalmol. 1952; 8:4–16.

[296] Alexander KR, Xie W, Derlacki DJ. Visual acuity and contrast sensitivity for individual Sloan letters. Vision Res. 1997; 37(6):813-9.

Comment ▤ : Where did the E go?

The Sloan letter system was the first to implement "E-xit": The letter E is (should) no longer used in eye charts. The reason is none other than the need to provide results that are comparable with the visual acuity test results using the Landolt Rings. It appears that the letter E has increased legibility compared to the other letters, so it does not perform as well as the other letters. [297]

In an effort to develop a scientifically accurate tool for measuring visual acuity, in a 1974 study entitled "Vision in senile macular degeneration," Drs. Ian Bailey and Jan E. Lovie, then at the National Vision Research Institute in Melbourne, Australia, designed a series of visual acuity charts called the **Bailey–Lovie eye charts**.

These charts incorporated several innovations, such as placement of the same number of optotypes on each line, use of the 10 sans-serif letters (on a 5×4 grid) from the 1968 British Standard,[298] consistent spacing between letters and between lines, and a logarithmic progression of sizes with an increment of 0.1 log arcmin between lines.[299]

This layout provides consistency in the crowding effect and the number of errors to be made per line. Instead of the traditional vertical rectangular layout with a variable number of letters per line, the new chart had an inverted-triangular layout with five proportionally spaced letters on each line. The inverted triangle was, of course, wider at the top than the top rows of traditional charts. Thus, <u>the letter size became the only variable between the acuity levels</u>.[298]

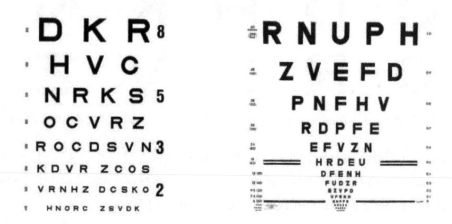

Figure 3-44: (left) The original Sloan eye chart, in which all 10 Sloan letters were used in some rows. However, it lacked line and letter arrangement consistency. (right) The original Bailey–Lovie chart with the British Standard 5×4 grid format letters. Images courtesy of Dr. Bailey, used with permission.

[297] McMonnies CW, Ho A. Letter legibility and chart equivalence. Ophthalmic Physiol Opt. 2000; 20(2):142-52.
[298] Bailey IL, Lovie JE. New design principles for visual acuity letter charts. Am J Optom Physiol Opt. 1976; 53(11):740-5.
[299] Bailey IL, Lovie-Kitchin JE. Visual acuity testing. From the laboratory to the clinic. Vision Res. 2013; 90:2-9.

The Bailey–Lovie chart was calibrated for 6 meters and had 14 rows that covered a range of 1.0 to –0.3 on the logMAR scale (20/200 to 20/10 Snellen equivalent). The design principles of the Bailey–Lovie eye charts are as follows:

- The optotypes were chosen from the British Standard set of characters, meaning that they have comparable legibility.
- Each line has the same number of optotypes (typically, five).
- The horizontal between-letter spacing equals the optotype width on that line, and the vertical spacing between successive rows equals the width of the letters in the larger of the rows, or, practically, is the same as the height of the letters in the smaller of the rows.
- Optotype size progression is geometrical (exponential) in 0.1 log units. Thus, the optotypes double in size every three lines up. An entire line of vision loss (line up) or gain (line down) is the same, irrespective of the initial vision. Most importantly, the chart can be easily scored in logMAR (logarithm of the minimum angle of resolution) units (see § 3.4.5).

3.4.5 The logMAR Metric and the ETDRS Charts

In eye test charts, to cover an anticipated range of visual acuity, the top line tests the 10 arcmin detail (i.e., 20/200), while the fine bottom line tests detail close to the 1 arcmin (i.e., 20/20). However, the size progression between successive lines (and their total number) has been arbitrary for a long time. Traditional mathematical progressions are either linear (arithmetic) or exponential (geometric). In a linear progression, there is a fixed additive constant between two lines; the next line down (or up) is smaller or larger by a fixed amount of type size.

In an exponential progression, there is a fixed multiplicative constant; the type size on the next line down (or up) is a fixed percentage less (or more), for example, 10%, 20%, etc., less (or more) than the type size of reference. The problem with the fixed variation is that a chart using a fixed size progression would end up with too many lines when a small increment is used, or with inadequate fine-line discrimination when a large increment is used. The Snellen line-size progression is based on a multiple of the 20 denominator, so it is not a true linear or multiplicative sequence.

An alternative progression is logarithmic, in which the type size in the next line down (or up) is derived from a <u>fixed progression ratio</u> as opposed to fixed step: The type size in the next line up is derived by raising the previous line size to the power of a fixed ratio instead of multiplying by that ratio. A carefully chosen ratio can give relatively small but practical size increments with adequate sensitivity. The use of logarithmic progression in visual acuity charts was first proposed by John Green,[300] with a ratio of $\sqrt[3]{2}$ ($2^{1/3}$ = 1.2599), and almost a century later by Louise Sloan,[294] with a virtually identical ratio of $\sqrt[10]{10}$ ($10^{1/10}$ = 1.2589), essentially a base-10 logarithm. The progression is denoted by log10, in which log stands for the base 10 logarithm.

The log10 (logarithm base 10) sequence is mathematically convenient and fits a pattern that adheres to the psychophysical concept of just-noticeable perceptual difference.[301] The log10 progression was used in the Bailey–Lovie and the ETDRS charts, thus establishing a new visual acuity metric, the **logarithm of the minimum angle of resolution** (logMAR):

$$\log MAR = \log_{10}\left(\text{Minimum Angle of Resolution}\right) = \log_{10}\left(\frac{1}{\text{decimal VA}}\right) \qquad (3.19)$$

Visual acuity of 20/20 has a minimum angle of resolution (MAR) = 1 arcmin, so logMAR = 0.0 because 10^0 = 0. The advantage of the logMAR metric is that it converts the geometric sequence of letter sizes to a linear scale of vision loss.[302] The converse relationships are

Conversion from logMAR to Decimal Visual Acuity: VA (decimal) = $10^{(-\log\text{MAR acuity})}$ $\qquad$ (3.20)

$$\log_{10}(10)=1 \qquad \log_{10}(1)=0$$

the exponent that 10 must be raised...   ...to get 10   is 1   the exponent that 10 must be raised...   ...to get 1   is 0

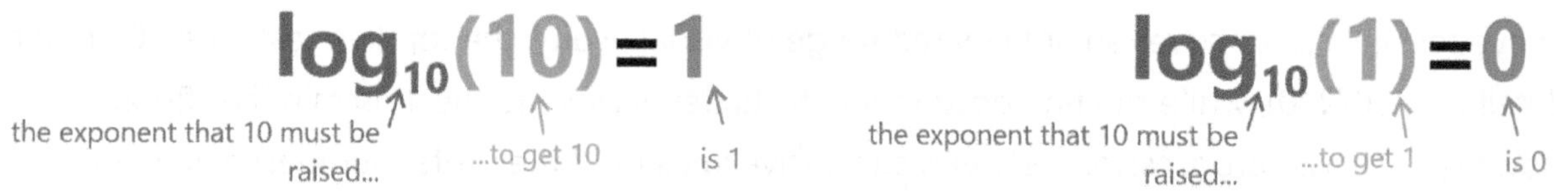

Figure 3-45: Log math: The base 10 logarithm of 10 is 1, and the base 10 logarithm of 1 is 0.

Visual acuity better than 20/20, for example, 20/10, which has MAR = 0.5 arcmin, has logMAR = –0.3 (yes, it is a negative number!). Visual acuity worse than 20/20; for example, 20/40, with MAR = 2 arcmin, has logMAR = +0.3. Very low visual acuity of, 20/200, with MAR = 10 arcmin, has logMAR = +1.0 because 10^1 = 1. Therefore, the logMAR scale measures the loss of vision. The higher the logMAR value the poorer the visual acuity: In the chart shown in Figure 3-46, the finer lines correspond to lower logMAR values.

In 1979, Drs. Aaron Kassoff and Frederick L. Ferris, at the National Eye Institute (NEI, Bethesda) modified the Bailey–Lovie chart using five Sloan letters per line instead of the British Standard letters.[303] The chart had no U, F, or P, in addition to no E. It was calibrated for 4

[300] Green J. On a new series of test letters for determining the acuteness of vision. Trans Am Ophthalmol Soc. 1868; 4:68-71.

[301] Westheimer G. Scaling of visual acuity measurements. Arch Ophthalmol. 1979; 97(2):327-30.

[302] Holladay JT. Visual acuity measurements. J Cataract Refract Surg. 2004; 30(2):287-90.

[303] Kassoff A, and the Diabetic Retinopathy Study Research Group. Design of a new visual acuity chart (modified Bailey–Lovie). Invest Ophthalmol Vis Sci. 1979; 18:S219.

meters. This chart established a standardized method for visual acuity measurement to be used in the Early Treatment of Diabetic Retinopathy Study (ETDRS).[304] ETDRS data were later used to select letter combinations that provide each line the same average perceptual difficulty.

The **ETDRS chart** format (Figure 3-46) has been accepted by the National Eye Institute (NEI) and the US FDA, and is mandated for clinical trials.[273] ETDRS charts can be constructed with the Landolt C or the tumbling E optotypes, as well as the Sloan letters, following exactly the same design principles. An ETRDS chart employing the tumbling E was used by Hugh R. Taylor of the Centre for Eye Research Australia (CERA) in 1978 to test vision in Australian Aborigines presenting with trachoma disorder.[305] An unexpected finding of Taylor's work was that, as a group, healthy indigenous Australians had appreciably better visual acuity than Europeans.[306]

On a chart that follows the log10 progression, such as a Bailey–Lovie or an ETDRS chart (Figure 3-46), the top 20/200 line corresponds to logMAR = 1.00. Each letter corresponds to 0.02 logMAR, so there is a total of 5·0.02 = 0.10 logMAR per 5 letters (one line). Since one line represents 0.10 logMAR, a change of +0.30 logMAR means that one can read 3 lines up (+ : worsening vision), and a change of −1.00 logMAR means that one can see 10 lines down (− : improving vision).

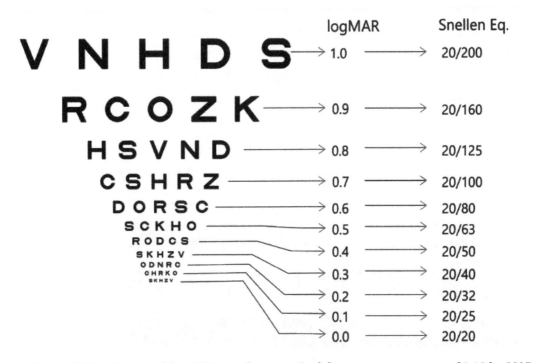

Figure 3-46: ETDRS chart and logMAR visual acuity. Each line represents a step of 0.10 logMAR.

---

[304] Ferris FL, Kassov A, Bresnick GH, Bailey IL. New visual acuity charts for clinical research. Am J Ophthalmol. 1982; 94(1):91-6.
[305] Taylor HR. Applying new design principles to the construction of an illiterate E chart. Am J Optom Physiol Opt. 1978; 55(5):348-51.
[306] Taylor HR. Racial variations in vision. Am J Epidemiol. 1981; 113(1):62-80.

Snellen 'lines' are often reported in clinical practice, assuming that full rows are being read in a Snellen chart. With traditional Snellen-type eye charts, credit for reading a row is given if more than 50% of the letters are correctly identified. With the logMAR-based charts, one can be very specific about fractional line scoring, providing improved precision and sensitivity to change.[307]

If one reads all letters in the logMAR 0.4 line and two letters in the logMAR 0.3 line, the logMAR visual acuity value is between 0.30 and 0.40.[308] The logMAR gives exact credit in these cases, with the **letter count** or **fractional line score**, which counts each letter to 0.02 logMAR. If one more letter is read, this reduces the logMAR visual acuity score by 0.02.

Thus, the logMAR score, when used with the ETDRS charts, provides a more precise measurement compared to the traditional Snellen 'lines lost' or 'lines gained,' which is valid only when all steps between lines are equal. This is particularly important for lower visual acuity.

Practice examples with fractional line score and answers ⚒:

All letters read on the 0.4 line → logMAR visual acuity score = 0.40

All letters read on the 0.4 line (which is our baseline) and
- one (more) letter read on the 0.3 line → logMAR = 0.4 – 0.02 = 0.38
- two letters read on the 0.3 line → logMAR = 0.4 – 2·0.02 = 0.36
- three letters read on the 0.3 line → logMAR = 0.4 – 3·0.02 = 0.34
- four letters read on the 0.3 line → logMAR = 0.4 – 4·0.02 = 0.32
- all five letters read on the 0.3 line → logMAR = 0.4 – 5·0.02 = 0.30

Most letters read on the 0.4 line (which is our baseline) but
- missed one letter on the 0.4 line → logMAR = 0.4 + 0.02 = 0.42
- missed two letters on the 0.4 line → logMAR = 0.4 + 2·0.02 = 0.44

| One more letter read: logMAR decreases by 0.02 |

| One letter missed: logMAR increases by 0.02 |

| One more line read: logMAR decreases by 0.10 |

[307] Brown B, Lovie-Kitchin J. Repeated visual acuity measurement: establishing the patient's own criterion for change. Optom Vis Sci. 1993; 70(1):45-53.

[308] Bailey IL, Bullimore MA, Raasch TW, Taylor HR. Clinical grading and the effects of scaling. Invest Ophthalmol Vis Sci. 1991; 32(2):422-32.

The fractional score can also use the count of the total number of letters read, starting from the top 20/200 (logMAR 1.0) line. The examiner notes the finest read line (as in the Snellen charts) and the total number of letters read in that line. In this case, the logMAR visual acuity is

$$\text{logMAR VA} = 0.10 + \text{logMAR of the finest read line} - 0.02 \cdot (\text{\# of letters read in that line}) \quad (3.21)$$

Alternatively, this relationship can be written using the total number of letters read in the chart:

$$\text{logMAR VA} = 1.10 - 0.02 \cdot (\text{total \# letters read in the chart}) \quad (3.22)$$

Examples ☞:

Finest line read (completely) is the 10th (0.1 logMAR), missed one letter (49 letters read in total).
Using Eq. (3.21): logMAR = 0.10 + 0.10 − 0.02·4 = 0.10 + 0.10 − 0.08 = 0.12.
Using Eq. (3.22): logMAR = 1.10 − 0.02·49 = 1.10 − 0.98 = 0.12.
Alternatively: One letter missed in the 0.10 line means that logMAR increases by 0.02 → 0.12.

Finest line read is the 5th (0.6 logMAR), but only 2 letters were read in this line (22 letters read in total).
Using Eq. (3.21): logMAR = 0.10 + 0.60 − 0.02·2 = 0.10 + 0.60 − 0.04 = 0.66.
Using Eq. (3.22): logMAR = 1.10 − 0.02·22 = 1.10 − 0.44 = 0.66.
Alternatively: Three letters missed in the 0.60 line means that logMAR increases by 3·0.02 → 0.66.

Finest line read is the 1st (top, 1.0 logMAR); all 5 letters were read, plus one in the line below (6 letters total).
Using Eq. (3.21): logMAR = 0.10 + 0.90 − 0.02·1 = 0.10 + 0.90 − 0.02 = 0.98 (finest line is actually the 0.90).
Using Eq. (3.22): logMAR = 1.10 − 0.02·6 = 1.10 − 0.12 = 0.98.
Alternatively: One letter gained in the 1.00 line means that logMAR decreases by 0.02 → 0.98.

Note 🖳 : The measurement of visual acuity using ETRDS eye charts and the reporting of visual acuity with logMAR units is mandatory in most clinical trials.[309] Studies must report whether the VA measurements were monocular or binocular, the measurement of distance, and eye chart luminance. Several studies use Snellen visual acuity charts and report visual acuity measurements that have been converted to logMAR, negating the benefits of the specificity afforded by the ETRDS charts and logMAR units.[310]

The use of Snellen fractions should be strongly discouraged for reporting visual and refractive outcomes; studies collecting Snellen visual acuity should not convert to logMAR for reporting, as doing so may give the false perception that logMAR was collected. In these studies, there is often considerable variation in

[309] Wolffsohn JS, Kollbaum PS, Berntsen DA, Atchison DA, Benavente A, Bradley A, Buckhurst H, Collins M, Fujikado T, Hiraoka T, Hirota M. IMI–Clinical myopia control trials and instrumentation report. Invest Ophthalmol Vis Sci. 2019; 60(3):M132-60.
[310] Yu X, Zhang B, Bao J, Zhang J, Wu G, Xu J, Zheng J, Drobe B, Chen H. Design, methodology, and baseline data of the Personalized Addition Lenses Clinical Trial (PACT). Medicine (Baltimore). 2017; 96(11):e6069.

the expression of VA measurements, visual acuity charts are not standardized, and the procedures used for visual acuity testing are not properly described.[311]

It is imperative that studies follow proper methodology to allow other researchers to verify, replicate, and benchmark against the presented work.

3.4.6 The Visual Acuity Rating

To overcome this rather awkward outcome, in which larger numbers correspond to lower visual acuity, and negative numbers correspond to better-than-standard visual acuity, two other scales have been proposed, the **Visual Acuity Rating** (VAR)[312] and **Visual Acuity Score** (VAS).[313] The VAS is a letter score that is part of a broader system for evaluating vision disability that includes a visual field assessment as well. VAS and VAR measure visual acuity in exactly the same way, i.e., as a transform of the logMAR scale:

VAR Scale: $$VAR = [100 - (50 \cdot logMAR)] \tag{3.23}$$

The VAR is far more intuitive while maintaining, at the same time, all of the advantages of the logMAR scoring system. For example, if all letters are read on the 20/20 line (logMAR = 0), the VAR score is 100, written with square brackets as [100]. For each letter not read, we subtract the value of 1, and for each row not read entirely, we subtract the value of 5. At the 20/200 line (decimal = 0.1, logMAR = 1.0), the VAR score is [50].

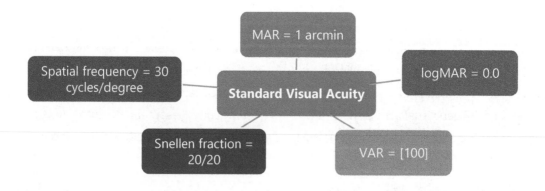

---

[311] Bailey IL. Perspective: visual acuity – keeping it clear. Optom Vis Sci. 2012; 89:1247-8.

[312] Bailey IL. Measurement of visual acuity-towards standardization. In: Vision Science Symposium: A tribute to Gordon G. Heath. Indiana University, 1988.

[313] Colenbrander A. The functional vision score: A coordinated scoring system for visual impairments, disabilities and handicaps. In: Kooijman A. et al., eds. Low Vision: Research and New Developments in Rehabilitation. Studies in Health Technology and Informatics. Amsterdam: IOS Press, 1994:552.

A VAR score larger than [100] indicates better than the standard 20/20 visual acuity. The VAR score extends down to [0] for the 20/2000 (decimal 0.01) acuity. The VAS, VAR, and logMAR scales convert the geometric sequence of visual acuity values into a linear sequence. In conjunction with the precision afforded by the fractional line score (letter count), the statistical averaging of multiple measurements on one subject or one group of subjects can be used for research and comparison purposes. This is impossible to do with Snellen fractions.[314]

Example ☞: What is the average of 20/20 and 20/200?

On the Snellen scale, the average of 20/20 and 20/200 is 20/110, a value too close to 20/200.

On the decimal scale, the average of 1.0 and 0.1 is 0.55, a value close to, but not exactly, halfway.

On the VAR scale, the average of 100 and 50 is 75, which is exactly halfway. This average converts to 20/63 or 0.32 decimal (rounded to 20/60 or 0.3 decimal).

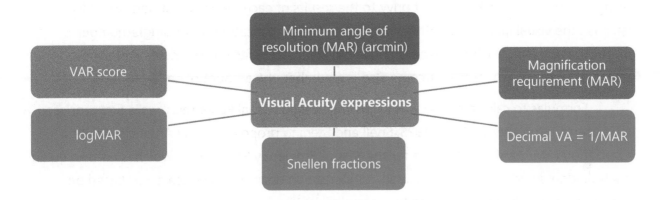

3.4.7 Other Vision Assessment Metrics

While it is true that the measurement of visual acuity is the most often used metric for the quality of vision, it is, by no means, the only one. It is only a measurement of the central, **foveal vision**, not the peripheral vision. We only see at high resolution over a small central area (fovea centralis), where the cone density is largest (§ 4.2.1).

Visual functions are not limited to visual acuity and visual field, but also include functions such as contrast sensitivity, color vision, dark adaptation (§ 4.3.3), binocular vision, etc. Therefore, a comprehensive vision assessment must include, besides visual acuity, the evaluation of contrast sensitivity,[290] ocular scatter (§ 2.5.3), stereoscopic vision, visual fields (§ 4.1.3), peripheral vision, color vision deficiency (§ 5.4), and so on. Binocular vision involves aspects

---

[314] Holladay JT. Proper method for calculating average visual acuity. J Refract Surg. 1997; 13(4):388-91.

such as ocular motility and convergence, which should be evaluated. In short, visual acuity measures only the smallest detail we can see; it does not represent the quality of vision in general. It is true, though, that visual acuity tests a significant aspect of vision quality.

In addition, there are distinctions as to what exactly we are measuring. There are various ways to measure and specify visual acuity, depending on the type of VA test used.

Vision loss is a complex phenomenon that cannot be fully evaluated objectively unless many aspects are considered. A concept that relates to the quality of vision is **functional vision**. Functional vision can only be described qualitatively, for example, in relation to performances such as reading, mobility, and daily living skills.

In some applications, it may be desirable to reduce the complexity of assessing visual function to a single number because, often, these metrics have litigious or insurance-related use. An arbitrator or a social administrator who must assign a disability compensation package owing to vision loss is probably not privy to the results of each detailed test performed to establish the visual impairment of the individual. The simplification of the single-number approach is preferable when a decision on eligibility for benefits for a worker's compensation case is to be made, where the outcome also is a number, the amount of compensation.

Formulas to calculate what was at the time called 'Visual Economics' were first proposed in Germany in the late 1800s. In 1925, Snell and Sterling proposed to the American Medical Association (AMA) a simple formula for the **Visual Efficiency Scale** (VES), which is used to guide legal-blindness and employment-related compensation decisions. The scale was based on statistical employability studies, and the formula is[315, 316]

Visual Efficiency Scale:
$$VES = 0.2^{(MAR - 1)/9}$$
(3.24)

This formula served until the year 2000. According to this scale, a 20/20 Snellen fraction corresponds to 100% visual efficiency. A frequent misconception is that there exists a direct proportionality between visual acuity and visual efficiency; for example, half visual acuity corresponds to half visual efficiency. While a correlation does exist, it is not linear. For example, 20/40, which is half visual acuity, does not correspond to 50% visual efficiency, but to about 80%; 20/100 corresponds to 50% visual efficiency, and 20/200 corresponds to 20% visual efficiency.

[315] Snell AC, Sterling S. The percentage evaluation of macular vision. Arch Ophthalmol. 1925; 54:443-61.
[316] [no authors listed] Guides to the evaluation of permanent impairment; the visual system. J Am Med Assoc. 1958; 168(4):475-88.

The AMA Guides to the Evaluation of Permanent Impairment have adopted the **Functional Vision Score** (FVS), which reflects an estimate of a person's ability to perform Activities of Daily Living (ADLs).[317]

On the new scale, using the FVS, 20/200 acuity is rated as an estimated 50% loss of ADL ability, rather than as an 80% loss of employability. Other changes include no longer considering the two eyes as separate organs since vision with both eyes open is the normal condition. The new scale has been shown to correlate well with other measures of visual ability, although it is still based on statistical estimates: Individuals may score much better or much worse than the statistical average.

3.4.8 Digital / Electronic Charts

Traditionally, the measurement of visual acuity involved printed (paper) charts usually mounted on the wall. As technology and automation progressed, projected charts became the norm in several practices. One drawback relating to the use of projected charts is the inability to properly maintain optotype contrast, a parameter that is sensitive to the amount of ambient illumination and the reflectivity of the projection surface.

The emerging trend in visual acuity testing is the use of computer screens for electronic charts. This mode offers efficient and adaptive measurement;[318] for example, this way the examiner has the option to change letter sequence so that the letters/optotypes cannot be memorized by the examinee. [319]

In addition, due to the variable exam lane lengths (which are rarely 20 ft), the scaling and calibration of the optotype size can be implemented more effectively using electronic eye charts. The Test Chart 2000, designed by Professor David Thomson of the Department of Optometry at The City University, London, UK, was the first Microsoft® Windows®-based computerized test chart that used Sloan-based typefaces.[320]

The use of a computer screen monitor can be more desirable from a contrast perspective since it provides its own illumination. However, to display a full-range ETDRS (20/200 to 20/10) chart on a computer screen requires a large and very high-resolution screen and precise

---

[317] Fuhr PSW, Holmes LD, Fletcher DC, Swanson M, Kuyk T. The AMA Guides Functional Vision Score is a better predictor of vision-targeted quality of life than traditional measures of visual acuity or visual field extent. Vis Impairment Res. 2003; 5(3):137-46.

[318] Bailey IL, Lovie-Kitchin JE. Visual acuity testing: from laboratory to the clinic. Vision Res. 2013; 90:2-9.

[319] Beck RW, Moke PS, Turpin AH, Ferris FL 3rd, SanGiovanni JP, Johnson CA, Birch EE, Chandler DL, Cox TA, Blair RC, Kraker RT. A computerized method of visual acuity testing: adaptation of the early treatment of diabetic retinopathy study testing protocol. Am J Ophthalmol. 2003; 135(2):194-205.

[320] Thayaparan K, Crossland MD, Rubin GS. Clinical assessment of two new contrast sensitivity charts. Br J Ophthalmol. 2007; 91(6):749-52.

illumination uniformity. To circumvent some of the resolution limitations, certain screens display electronic charts (E-ETDRS) one line at a time or even one letter at a time, sometimes surrounded by bars of contour interaction. It has been shown that, a one-at-a-time letter computer chart with flanking bars correlates well with the standard ETDRS chart.[321]

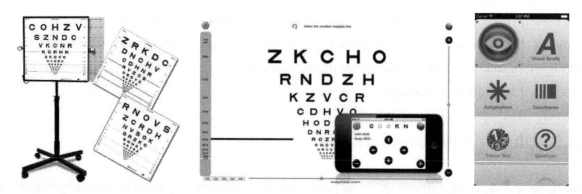

Figure 3-47: (left) The ESV-3000 display of an ETDRS chart offers testing of the full range of ETDRS (20/200 to 20/10) at a distance of 4 m. (center and right) Mobile phone apps for visual acuity testing.

An approach that balances the above considerations can be implemented with a backlit (fluorescent or LED) screen illuminating an ETDRS chart transparency. Illumination is controlled to levels of approximately log $L \approx 2$ (85 cd/m²), per NAS-NRC recommendations.[259] Several versions of illumination screens exist, including self-illuminating computer screens and screens that are backlit with either fluorescent sources or, more recently, light-emitting diodes (LEDs).

Today, a multitude of 'apps' for visual acuity measurement is available. The risk with the new age of electronic applications here is the possible loss of standardization. A measurement of visual acuity on one app may not be reproducible with another; besides, one wonders how distance vision measurement from an arm's length is even possible!

[321] Jolly JK, Juenemann K, Boagey H, Nadsady M, Bridge H, Maclaren RE. Validation of electronic visual acuity (EVA) measurement against standardised ETDRS charts in patients with visual field loss from inherited retinal degenerations. Br J Ophthalmol. 2019. doi: 10.1136/bjophthalmol-2019-315124.

3.5 VISUAL ACUITY QUIZ

Angle Measurement

1) Which of the following angles is the greatest? (notation: radian = rad, degree = °, arcmin = ´)

   a) 30´
   b) 0.2 rad
   c) 90°
   d) π rad
   e) 360 °

2) What is the measure of an angle inscribed in a circle of 10 cm radius that subtends 0.1 cm?

   a) 0.01 rad
   b) 0.10 rad
   c) 0.01°
   d) 0.10°
   e) 1.00°

3) What is the equivalent to $\pi/4$ rad in degrees (°)?

   a) 45°
   b) 90°
   c) 180°
   d) 270°
   e) 360°

4) An onion is an opinion without (two correct answers) ...

   a) a radian
   b) a degree
   c) 180°
   d) 3.14159
   e) Ἀεὶ ὁ Θεὸς ὁ Μέγας Γεωμετρεῖ

5) What is the angle ϑ subtended by a full-face dime (1 cm in diameter) held at a distance of 5 m?

   a) ϑ = 0.01 m/5 m = 0.002 rad ≈ 0.115°
   b) ϑ = 0.01 m/5 m = 0.002° ≈ 0.035 mrad
   c) ϑ = 1 cm/5 m = 0.2 rad ≈ 11.5°
   d) ϑ = 1 cm/5 m = 0.2° ≈ 0.0035 rad

6) In a small angle ϑ, what ratio best describes the measure of the angle?

   a) ϑ [rad] = opposite side / adjacent side
   b) ϑ [rad] = adjacent side / opposite side
   c) ϑ [°] = opposite side / adjacent side
   d) ϑ [°] = adjacent side / opposite side

7) You just calculated an angle in radians. You need to quickly convert to degrees but have no access to a calculator. Your best chance to get the measure of the angle in degrees ϑ [°] is to ...

   a) multiply ϑ [rad] by 10
   b) multiply ϑ [rad] by 60
   c) divide ϑ [rad] by 10
   d) divide ϑ [rad] by 60

8) An optotype has detail (stroke width) of 17.46 mm. When seen from 6 m away, what would be the angle subtended from the observer's eye?

   a) ϑ = 0.03°
   b) ϑ = 0.1°
   c) ϑ = 0.1 rad
   d) ϑ = 10 arcmin (´)

9) The resolution limit of the standard-vision human eye is 1´ = °/60 ≈ 0.29 mrad. At a viewing distance of 6 m, what would be the line stroke width of a letter for that visual acuity?

   a) 1.746 cm
   b) 0.01746 mm
   c) 1.746 mm
   d) 17.46 mm

10) During a full moon, you attempt to block the lunar disk with your index finger (width of 1.0 cm). If the moon subtends on the celestial sphere an angle of 30 arcmin, how far should you extend your finger?

   a) 0.3 m
   b) 1.0 m
   c) 1.15 m
   d) 1.51 m

11) Two (consecutive) vertical bars are spaced by 29 cm. At approximately what distance should you be standing to observe the spacing between the two bars with an angle of 1 arcmin?

   a) 1 m
   b) 3.14 m
   c) 100 m
   d) 1000 m

Visual Acuity

12) If the minimum angle of resolution (MAR) = 4 arcmin, visual acuity is (arcmin^{-1} = 1/arcmin) ...

   a) 0.25 arcmin^{-1}
   b) 0.5 arcmin^{-1}
   c) 2.0 arcmin^{-1}
   d) 4.0 arcmin^{-1}
   e) 20 arcmin^{-1}

13) What is the minimum angle of resolution (MAR) in an eye with visual acuity 0.5 arcmin^{-1}?

   a) 0.25 arcmin
   b) 0.5 arcmin
   c) 2.0 arcmin
   d) 4.0 arcmin
   e) 20 arcmin

14) A spectacle-corrected eye under the influence of a strong miotic agent has 1-mm pupil diameter. The resolution of this eye is mostly limited by ...

   a) astigmatism
   b) myopia
   c) hyperopia
   d) high-order aberrations
   e) diffraction
   f) depth of focus

15) A spectacle-corrected eye under the influence of a strong mydriatic agent has 7-mm pupil diameter. The resolution of this eye is mostly limited by ...

   a) astigmatism
   b) myopia
   c) hyperopia
   d) high-order aberrations
   e) diffraction
   f) depth of focus

16) Which three of the following can be expressions of resolving power?

   a) arcmin
   b) rad
   c) mm
   d) arcmin^{-1}
   e) line pairs/mm
   f) cycles/degree

17) If the resolution limit (MAR) of the human eye is about 1 arcmin, then the resolving power is ...

   a) 0.1 arcmin

   b) 1 arcmin
   c) 1 arcmin^{-1}
   d) 10 arcmin^{-1}

18) Which resolving power is the best?

   a) 0.02 arcmin^{-1}
   b) 0.2 arcmin^{-1}
   c) 2.0 arcmin^{-1}
   d) 20.0 arcmin^{-1}

19) Which limit of resolution is the best?

   a) 0.05 arcmin
   b) 0.5 arcmin
   c) 5.0 arcmin
   d) 50 arcmin
   e) 500 arcmin

20) What is the MAR set by diffraction for the human eye if λ = 0.40 µm and pupil diameter = 2 mm? Use n = 1.336 for the refractive index in the eye.

   a) 0.063 arcmin
   b) 0.63 arcmin
   c) 6.3 arcmin
   d) 63 arcmin

21) If an eye with 2-mm pupil diameter has a minimum angle of resolution (MAR) of 1 arcmin, what would be the MAR for the same eye, with same illumination and an 8 mm pupil if there are (magically) no aberrations?

   a) 0.25 arcmin
   b) 0.5 arcmin
   c) 1 arcmin
   d) 2 arcmin
   e) 4 arcmin

22) For an optical system to be able to just resolve two closely spaced lines, the Rayleigh criterion states that their angular separation is ...

   a) at least half their width
   b) at least their width
   c) about half the width of their PSF functions
   d) about the width of their PSF functions

23) The PSF function is a distribution of light in ...

   a) object space, if the object is a broad light source
   b) image space, if the object is a broad light source
   c) object space, if the object is a fine point
   d) image space, if the object is a fine point

24) PSF stands for...

a) point special function
b) purpose special function
c) point spread function
d) point special formulation
e) Graecum est; non legitur

25) A system is described as diffraction-limited when ...

a) imaging is governed by diffractive optics
b) its resolution is limited by factors other than diffraction

c) high-order aberrations and diffraction have equal effect on resolution
d) its resolution is limited mainly by diffraction

26) If the angular separation between the two lines is about half the width of their corresponding PSF functions, then the two lines are ...

a) completely overlapping
b) not resolved
c) barely (just) resolved
d) adequately resolved

Eye Charts

27) Overcast sky has luminance L of 1×10^3 nit. The logarithmic form of L becomes ...

a) $\log L = 0.1$
b) $\log L = 0.3$
c) $\log L = 1.0$
d) $\log L = 2.0$
e) $\log L = 3.0$

28) An indoor room illumination of $\log L = 2.0$ can be expressed as ...

a) $L = 2.0$ nit
b) $L = 20$ nit
c) $L = 100$ nit
d) $L = 200$ nit

29) According to the US National Academy of Sciences, the standard eye chart luminance L is ...

a) 85 nit
b) 1000 nit
c) depends on the manufacturer
d) depends on type of eye chart

30) What is the (approximate) retinal luminance (in trolands, Td) using a chart illuminated with 85 nit if the subject has a pupil diameter of 2 mm?

a) 85 Td
b) 170 Td
c) 270 Td
d) 340 Td
e) 1070 Td

31) What pupil radius achieves 1070 Td retinal luminance with 85 nit eyechart luminance?

a) 1 mm
b) 2 mm
c) 4 mm
d) 8 mm

32) A detail (dark line or white gap) on the 20/20 optotype in a Snellen chart subtends an angle of ...

a) 0.1 arcmin
b) 0.5 arcmin
c) 1.0 arcmin
d) 5.0 arcmin
e) 10 arcmin

33) An entire optotype letter on the 20/40 line in a Snellen chart subtends an angle of ...

a) 1 arcmin
b) 5 arcmin
c) 10 arcmin
d) 20 arcmin
e) 40 arcmin

34) What Snellen line has a stroke width (detail) of 2 arcmin?

a) 20/200
b) 20/100
c) 20/40
d) 20/20
e) 20/10

35) The Snellen optotype that subtends an angle of 50 arcmin is on the s_____ line.

a) 20/200
b) 20/100
c) 20/40
d) 20/20
e) 20/10

36) What line should be an optotype that subtends a (total) angle of 20 arcmin?

a) 20/10 line
b) 20/20 line

c) 20/40 line
d) 20/80 line

37) Select the two scientifically acceptable statements regarding 20/20 visual acuity:

a) 20/20 indicates a standard value of reference.
b) 20/20 is perfect visual acuity.
c) 6/6 is the metric equivalent to 20/20.
d) 20/20 is only measured at 20 ft exam lanes.

38) Select the two scientifically acceptable statements regarding 20/20 visual acuity:

a) 20/20 visual acuity is the best possible human visual acuity.
b) In a corrected or emmetropic eye, it is expected that vision will be 20/20 or better.
c) 20/20 visual acuity corresponds to 20 arcmin of resolution.
d) While the numerator is 20, often, the exam lane is not 20 ft.

39) Joe is asked to read the Snellen chart (scaled for 20 ft) from the (wrong) distance of 10 ft. At this distance, Joe can read only the 20/10 line. His visual acuity, expressed in Snellen fraction, is

a) 20/40
b) 20/20
c) 20/10
d) 10/20

40) Maria is asked to read the Snellen chart (scaled for 20 ft) from the (wrong) distance of 10 ft. At this distance, Maria can read only the 20/40 line. Her visual acuity, expressed in Snellen fraction, is

a) 20/80
b) 20/40
c) 20/20
d) 40/20

41) In a visual acuity testing chart, an optotype has a detail (vertical or horizontal line width) size of 1.746 mm. This optotype has a total height of

a) 0.873 mm
b) 1.746 mm
c) 3.492 mm
d) 8.73 mm
e) 17.46 mm

42) In a visual acuity testing chart, an optotype has a total height of 8.73 mm. Each detail (vertical or horizontal line) has a width of

a) 0.873 mm

b) 1.746 mm
c) 3.492 mm
d) 8.73 mm
e) 17.46 mm

43) The viewing distance (exam lane) is 4 m. You are given a standard (unscaled) eye exam chart, and you have access to a photocopier. What would you do?

a) nothing, I would post the eye chart as is
b) scale up, 6/4 = 1.5× (150%)
c) scale down, 4/6 = 0.66× (66.6%)
d) increase contrast by 150%

44) Which value of visual acuity, when expressed in logMAR units, is the best?

a) −0.30 logMAR
b) 0.00 logMAR
c) 0.30 logMAR
d) 1.00 logMAR

45) On an ETDRS chart, if the ability to read decreases by one less letter, the logMAR VA ...

a) decreases by 0.02 logMAR
b) decreases by 0.10 logMAR
c) decreases by 1.00 logMAR
d) increases by 0.02 logMAR
e) increases by 0.10 logMAR
f) increases by 1.00 logMAR

46) On an ETDRS chart, if an examinee can read one additional line (down, finer), the logMAR VA ...

a) decreases by 0.02 logMAR
b) decreases by 0.10 logMAR
c) decreases by 1.00 logMAR
d) increases by 0.02 logMAR
e) increases by 0.10 logMAR
f) increases by 1.00 logMAR

47) Which value of visual acuity, when expressed in logMAR units, is the worst?

a) −0.30 logMAR
b) 0.00 logMAR
c) 0.30 logMAR
d) 1.00 logMAR

48) On an ETDRS chart, if one additional letter can be read, the logMAR value of visual acuity ...

a) decreases by 0.02 logMAR
b) decreases by 0.10 logMAR
c) decreases by 1.00 logMAR
d) increases by 0.02 logMAR

e) increases by 0.10 logMAR
f) increases by 1.00 logMAR

49) On an ETDRS chart, if the ability to read decreases by one line (up, bigger), the logMAR value of visual acuity ...

a) decreases by 0.02 logMAR
b) decreases by 0.10 logMAR
c) decreases by 1.00 logMAR
d) increases by 0.02 logMAR
e) increases by 0.10 logMAR
f) increases by 1.00 logMAR

50) The top line in the standard ETDRS eye chart corresponds to what logMAR visual acuity?

a) −0.30 logMAR
b) 0.00 logMAR
c) 0.30 logMAR
d) 1.00 logMAR

51) The standard vision line in the ETDRS eye chart corresponds to what logMAR visual acuity?

a) −0.30 logMAR
b) 0.00 logMAR
c) 0.30 logMAR
d) 1.00 logMAR

52) The finest line in ETRDR visual acuity testing is the 0.5 logMAR line; one more letter is read on the 0.4 line. What is the logMAR value of visual acuity?

a) 0.52
b) 0.50
c) 0.48
d) 0.42
e) 0.40

53) On ETDRS eye chart, all letters are read on the 0.10 line, and two letters are read on the 0.00 line. What is the logMAR value of visual acuity?

a) 0.14
b) 0.12
c) 0.10
d) 0.08
e) 0.06
f) 0.04

54) Visual acuity −0.26 logMAR means that the examinee has read _____ the standard vision (logMAR = 0.0) line.

a) 26 additional letters below
b) 13 additional letters below
c) 13 fewer letters above

d) 26 fewer letters
e) above

55) Visual acuity of −0.30 logMAR means that the examinee has read _____ the standard vision line.

a) three more lines below
b) one and one-half more lines below
c) one-third more lines below
d) one and one-half fewer lines above
e) three fewer lines above

56) When measuring visual acuity with a pinhole occluder, the following optical effects take place (select 2 correct answers):

a) aberrations decrease; the depth of field decreases
b) aberrations increase; the depth of field decreases
c) aberrations decrease; the depth of field increases
d) perceptual tolerance to error increases; diffraction effects increase
e) perceptual tolerance to error decreases; diffraction effects increase
f) refractive (spherocylindrical) error decreases; the retina becomes conjugate to infinity

57) Which of the following is NOT part of Sloan letters?

a) C
b) O
c) R
d) E
e) N

58) The reason for not including the E letter in the Sloan letter optotypes is ...

a) We got tired of paying Edgar royalties.
b) The letter E provides results that are not equivalent to the results of other letters.
c) There is no typeface that can properly reproduce this letter.
d) What, there is no E? You're kidding, right?

59) Which of the following is not an innovation introduced by the Bailey–Lovie eye charts?

a) Each line has the same number of optotypes.
b) The size progression between rows follows the 0.1 log unit.
c) The logMAR unit can be used for scoring.
d) The angular subtense of the standard vision optotype detail is 1 arcmin.

3.6 VISUAL ACUITY SUMMARY

Angular Expressions

An angle ϑ is formed by two spokes, the sides, which share a common origin, the apex. The measure of the angle is the ratio of the length s of the subtended arc to the length of the radius r of the circle in which the angle is inscribed.

The unit of the angle in physics is the radian: 1 radian (rad) is the measure of the angle whose arc length s equals the length of the radius r of the circle. Every time we compute angle as a ratio of length to length, the unit is the radian.

The degree (°) is a convenient measure of the angle that is most often used in trigonometry. 1° (degree) is defined as 1/360th of a circle. Because one circle is 2π radians,

$$2\pi \text{ rad} = 360° \quad \text{and} \quad 1 \text{ rad} \approx 57.3° \tag{3.25}$$

Divisions of the degree are the minute of the arc (′, arcmin), which is 1/60th of a degree. Additionally, there is the second of the arc (″, arcsec), which is 1/60th of a minute.

Frequently used formulas

Small angle approximation: $\qquad \vartheta$ [rad] $\approx$ opposite side/adjacent $\qquad\qquad$ (3.26)

Precise angle: $\quad \vartheta$ [°] $= \tan^{-1}$(opposite/adjacent) $\quad$ or $\quad \vartheta$ [°] $= \sin^{-1}$(opposite/hypotenuse)

Visual Acuity

Visual acuity is an expression of the resolving power of the eye. Because vision is a perceptual sense, other factors influence the way the eye can perceive, discriminate, and recognize certain targets. These include retinal factors, the Stiles–Crawford effect, cognitive factors, and the depth of field, i.e., the perceptual tolerance of the eye.

Optics definition of VA = Reciprocal of the minimum angle of resolution (MAR) = 1/MAR $\quad$ (3.27)

The MAR cannot be infinitesimally small. Factors detrimental to MAR (resulting in an increase) are: refractive error, high-order aberrations, and diffraction. In an emmetropic or properly (spherocylindrically) corrected eye, the two effects that remain are aberrations and diffraction. These are opposing factors because, when the pupil diameter increases, the effects of aberrations increase, resulting in a larger (worse) MAR. At the same time, when the pupil diameter increases, the decreasing effects of diffraction result in a smaller (better) MAR.

Diffraction-limited is the ideal case of an imaging system with no aberrations. In this case, with a circular pupil of diameter D, wavelength λ, and refractive index n, the MAR is given by

Minimum Angle of Resolution [rad]:
$$\text{MAR} = \vartheta_{\text{MIN}} = 1.22\frac{\lambda}{n \cdot D} \qquad (3.28)$$

To calculate the resolution limit of the human eye, we use the refractive index of the aqueous $n = 1.336$, the approximate pupil diameter of the human eye $D = 2$ mm for daylight, and the mean wavelength of visible $\lambda = 0.55$ μm:

$$\text{MAR}_{2\,\text{mm}} = \vartheta_{\text{MIN}} = 1.22\frac{\lambda}{n \cdot D} = 1.22\frac{0.55\ \mu\text{m}}{1.336 \cdot 2\ \text{mm}} = 0.25\times10^{-3}\ \text{rad} = 0.25\ \text{mrad} \approx 0.86\ \text{arcmin} \quad (3.29)$$

This result is usually rounded up to 1 arcmin to indicate the resolution limit imposed in the human eye by diffraction. The standard observer has visual acuity that resolves 1 arcmin.

Eye Charts and Optotypes

Optotypes are letter-like symbols. At the standard vision line, they are composed of increments of 1 arcmin. An eye chart contains a collection of optotypes of varying sizes, ranging from small (standard or better vision) to large (poor vision). The detail (a black stroke or white line) of the optotype used in the standard-vision line is 1 arcmin; the full letter size is 5 arcmin.

When viewed at a distance of 6 m ($\approx$ 20 ft), a standard-vision, 1 arcmin optotype detail (used in the 20/20 and logMAR 0.0 lines) has a linear size $h_{\text{detail}} = 6$ m$\cdot$(tan 1$'$) = 6 m$\cdot$ 0.000291 = 1.746 mm. The entire optotype has a total dimension of 5$\times$detail, or 5$\cdot$1.746 = 8.73 mm.

If the viewing distance (exam lane) is shorter than 6 m / 20 ft, the entire eye chart should be scaled down proportionally: For a 4 m viewing distance, the 1 arcmin optotype detail has size (4/6)$\cdot$1.746 mm = 1.164 mm.

Snellen visual acuity is a fraction: the testing distance (20 ft or 6 m) over the distance at which a standard observer can recognize the smallest optotype that the examinee can see.

- 20/20: The examinee sees what the standard observer can see at 20 ft, which is 1.0 arcmin.
- 20/10 (better): The examinee 'sees' a smaller optotype from 20 ft, subtending 0.5 arcmin. To see that optotype, the standard observer should be at 10 ft.
- 20/40 (worse): The examinee 'sees' a bigger optotype from 20 ft, subtending 2.0 arcmin. To 'see' that optotype, the standard observer should be at 40 ft.

Other expressions of visual acuity

Decimal scale (Monoyer) defined as: $\qquad$ $\text{Visual Acuity} = \dfrac{1}{\text{MAR}\,[\text{arcmin}]}$ $\qquad$ (3.30)

Logarithm of the Minimum Angle of Resolution (logMAR):

$$\text{logMAR} = \log_{10}\big(\text{Minimum Angle of Resolution}\big) = \log_{10}\left(\dfrac{1}{\text{decimal VA}}\right) \qquad (3.31)$$

For the standard observer, MAR = 1 arcmin, logMAR = 0.0. Negative values of logMAR indicate better than standard vision, while positive values of logMAR indicate worse than standard vision. logMAR = 1.0 indicates MAR = 10 arcmin, which is the 20/200 equivalent.

The ETDRS charts are the most scientific versions of visual acuity charts. They follow the log10 progression, and each line has five Sloan letters. The top line (20/200 equivalent) corresponds to logMAR = 1.00. Each letter corresponds to 0.02 logMAR, so there is a total of 5·0.02 = 0.10 logMAR per 5 letters (one line). Since one line represents 0.10 logMAR, a change of +0.30 logMAR means that one can only see 3 fewer lines (+ : worsening vision), and a change of −0.20 logMAR means one can see 2 more lines (− : improving vision).

ETDRS charts can be used to accurately report fractional line scores using the total count of the number of letters read, starting from the top 20/200 (logMAR 1.0) line:

$$\text{logMAR VA} = 1.10 - 0.02 \cdot (\text{total \# letters read in the chart})$$

A simpler approach is to navigate around the base line and add 0.02 for each letter missed or subtract 0.02 for each letter gained: If four letters are read on the 0.10 logMAR line, then the baseline is 0.10, and one letter missed makes logMAR VA = 0.12; if all letters are read on the 0.00 logMAR line, and one additional letter is read (gained) in the line below, then logMAR decreases by 0.02, becoming −0.02.

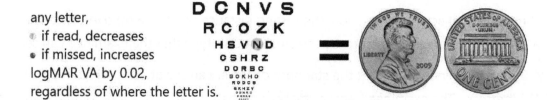

Figure 3-48: Contribution of letters read or missed in the calculation of logMAR VA on a ETDRS chart. The two pennies stand for the loss or gain by a value of 0.02 when one letter is read or missed, respectively.

Table 3–3: Conversion table for different representations (notation) of visual acuity.

MAR detail (arcmin)	Total optotype angular extent (arcmin)	Decimal visual acuity (arcmin⁻¹)	logMAR acuity	VAR acuity	Snellen equivalent ft 20/	m 6/	Vision
0.25	1.25	4.00	−0.60	130	5	1.5	
0.4	2	2.50	−0.40	120	8	2.4	Better-than-normal vision
0.5	2.5	2.00	−0.30	115	10	3	
0.63	3.15	1.59	−0.20	110	12.5	3.8	
0.8	4	1.25	−0.10	105	16	4.8	
1	5	1.00 (10/10)	0.00	100	20	6	Typical range of normal vision
1.25	6.25	0.80	0.10	95	25	7.5	
1.5	7.5	0.67	0.18	91	30	9	
1.6	8	0.63	0.20	90	32	9.6	
2	10	0.50	0.30	85	40	12	Near-normal vision
2.5	12.5	0.40	0.40	80	50	15	
3	15	0.33	0.48	76	60	18	
3.15	15.75	0.32	0.50	75	63	18.9	
4	20	0.25	0.60	70	80	24	
5	25	0.20	0.70	65	100	30	Moderate vision
6.25	31.25	0.16	0.80	60	125	37.5	
8	40	0.13	0.90	55	160	48	
10	50	0.10	1.00	50	200	60	Severe low vision
20	100	0.05	1.30	35	400	120	Legal blindness

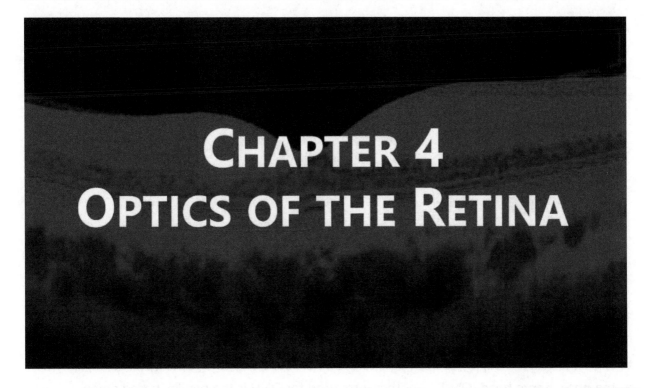

CHAPTER 4
OPTICS OF THE RETINA

Many similarities and differences exist in the way an artificial optical system, such as a photo camera, and the human eye record and perceive (or process) images. In a camera, this role is undertaken by the film or the digital sensor. In the eye, this role is carried out by the retina.

4.1 RETINAL STRUCTURE, GEOMETRY, AND OPTICS

The retina is the photosensitive part of the eye. It is a complex, semitransparent multilayer tissue located at the back of the eye (fundus), covering the choroid. The retina surface spans about 65% of the eye's interior and is centered about the posterior pole (central retina). The outer periphery of the retina reaches about 9 mm temporally and 15 mm nasally along the horizontal meridian. The junction between the retina and the ciliary body is known as the *ora serrata*. The ciliary body covers the remaining 35% of the eye's inner lining surface area.

The main landmarks in the human retina are the **area centralis**, the **optic disk**, and the retinal blood vessels. The area centralis is the most sensitive part of the retina, consisting of the **macula**, its central part the **fovea,** and its most central part, the **foveola**. The retinal blood vessels, particularly the central retinal vein and the central retinal artery, converge to the optic disk and are visible fundus landmarks.

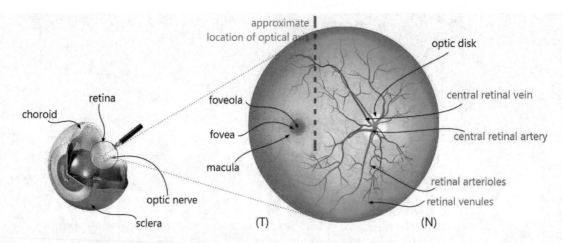

Figure 4-1: Anatomical details of the central retina in the right eye.

The optic disk is circular to slightly oval with diameters of about 1.88 mm vertically and 1.77 mm horizontally (this is 6° measured in angle). It is centered nasally about 5 mm (18°) and 0.45 mm (1.5°) superiorly from the macula.[322] It has two very important physiological functions: to allow the vascular supply to both pass to the inner retina and to exit the optic nerve, known as the **optic nerve head** (ONH). Another term used for ONH is the papilla, based on an erroneous impression that the normal ONH was elevated like a small tissue projection.[323]

Often, the OHN area is a depression rather than a protrusion and is known as the physiological cup. There are significant variations in the structure of this cup among individuals, which may be influenced by ocular diseases as well.[324] For example, being complementary to the visual field (§ 4.1.3), the shape of the optical cup bears clinical relevance in the detection of glaucoma. Because the nerve fiber layer is positioned atop of the photoreceptors (as we will see in Figure 4-12), the optic disk, packed with nerve fibers, cannot accommodate photoreceptors. This explains why the optic disk corresponds to the blind spot in the visual field (Figure 4-14).

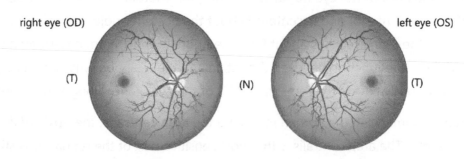

Figure 4-2: Fundus view of the right (OD) eye and the left (OS) eye.

[322] Quigley HA, Brown AE, Morrison JD, Drance SM. The size and shape of the optic disc in normal human eyes. Arch Ophthalmol. 1990; 108(1):51-7.

[323] Briggs G. Ophthalmographia, sive Oculi ejusque partium descriptio Anatomica. Foan Hayes, Celeberrimae, Cantab. 1676:28.

[324] Jonas JB, Budde WM, Panda-Jonas S. Ophthalmoscopic evaluation of the optic nerve head. Surv Ophthalmol. 1999; 43(4):293-320.

Fundus photography has been the primary method of documenting retinal structure. Its key advantage is that the retina can be photographed directly since the pupil is used as both the entrance (illuminating) and the exit (imaging) paths. Fundus photography allows for evaluation of the fine details of the anatomy and monitoring of the longitudinal health status of the retina.

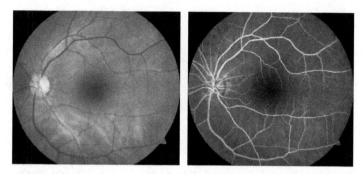

Figure 4-3: (left) Color fundus photography of a left eye extending perimetrically to 30°. (right) Fundus photo using specialized dyes, including fluorescein and indocyanine green, which emphasize the retinal vessel structure (fluorescein angiography).

Computerized imaging techniques, such as optical coherence tomography (OCT) and confocal scanning laser ophthalmoscopy (CSLO) further enhance retinal imaging possibilities. OCT imaging[54] produces quantitative data about macular or retinal thickness and qualitative features relating to retinal and subretinal morphology.[325] Owing to the high-speed imaging capability of Fourier-domain OCT, current devices can reconstruct an *in vivo* 3-D representation of the subretinal morphology with an axial resolution of a few microns.[326, 327]

Figure 4-4: (left) Three-dimensional rendering of the optic nerve head (ONH). (right) Shape- and sublayer-revealing cross-section of the ONH with optical coherence tomography (OCT). A wider and deeper physiological cup is an indication of ONH degeneration and apoptosis of nerve fibers.

---

[325] Swanson EA, Izatt JA, Hee MR, Huang D, Lin CP, Schuman JS, Puliafito CA, Fujimoto JG. In vivo retinal imaging by optical coherence tomography. Opt Lett. 1993; 18(21):1864-6.

[326] Wojtkowski M, Srinivasan VJ, Ko TH, Fujimoto JG, Kowalczyk A, Duker JS. Ultrahigh-resolution high-speed Fourier-domain optical coherence tomography and methods for dispersion compensation. Opt Express. 2004; 12(11):2404-22.

[327] Nassif NA, Cense B, Park H, Pierce MC, Yun SH, Bouma BE, Tearney GJ, Chen TC, de Boer JF. In vivo high-resolution video-rate spectral-domain optical coherence tomography of the human retina and optic nerve. Opt Express. 2004; 12(3):367-76.

Confocal microscopy offers several advantages over conventional optical microscopy, such as tight control of depth of field, elimination of image-degrading out-of-focus light, and imaging of serial optical sections of thick tissue. CSLO can reconstruct a high-resolution 3-D image of the papilla using a series of axial scans through the ONH and parapapillary tissue.

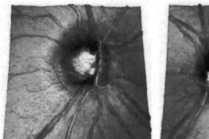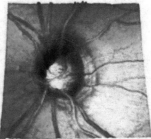

Figure 4-5: Three-dimensional representation of the optic nerve head with CSLO using the Heidelberg retinal tomography (HRT) system, which identifies ring segments. OD and OS eyes are shown.

4.1.1 Retinal Shape

Unlike the flat surface of a camera sensor, the retina is nearly spherical, with a radius of curvature of about 12 mm. In geometrical optics, we apply an approximation when the object extends perpendicular to the optical axis: The paraxial image is formed on a plane, the focal plane, which is also perpendicular to the optical axis.[328] In reality, however, the surface joining the image points of a perpendicularly extended object is curved. This is called **field curvature**. Introduced by Joseph Petzval, field curvature explains why a flat object extending perpendicular to the optical axis cannot be brought properly into focus on a flat image plane.[329]

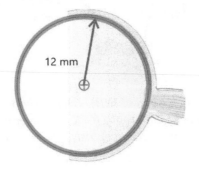

Figure 4-6: (left) Simplified geometry of the retina. Its curvature contributes to an improved recording of the retinal image by compensating for field curvature. (right) A flat-surface detector, such as a CCD array.

---

[328] *Geometrical Optics* § 2.3.3 Focal Planes and Optical Axis.
[329] *Geometrical Optics* § 8.3.4 Field Curvature and Distortion.

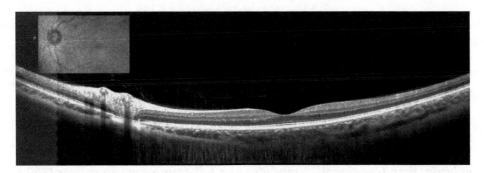

Figure 4-7: Cross-section of a left eye retina using optical coherence tomography (Avanti, Optovue). The very wide (12 mm / 40°) cross-section allows for the simultaneous rendering of both the macula (center-right) and a region close to the optic disk (left). Note the curvature of the overall structure.

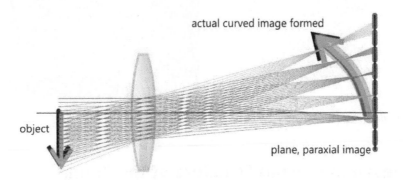

Figure 4-8: Field curvature.

The optical effect of this aberration is that a flat-surface sensor (such as a film or a digital photosensor) cannot simultaneously capture a clear image of both the central image field and the peripheral image field. The problem seems to be addressed if the curvature of the sensor itself matches the field curvature of the optical system. This is exactly the optical advantage resulting from the curved shape of the retina.

 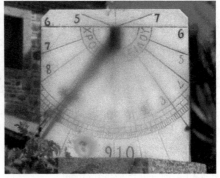

Figure 4-9: In field curvature, a flat-surface sensor cannot record with equal sharpness both the central field and the peripheral field. (left) A clear recording of the central field. (right) When the detector is shifted from the image plane, it may be able to clearly record the peripheral field, but not the center field.

The 12 mm radius of the retina curvature refers to the average eye with an axial length of 24.4 mm.[330] In reality, the retina has an oblate ellipsoid surface.[331] In eyes with a large axial length due to the deep orbit, the shape of the posterior retina is no longer spherical or elliptical, but caves in, forming a staphyloma,[332] and the retina locally assumes a deep, hollow shape.[333]

The retina has an average diagonal of 22 mm, just a bit larger than an M4/3 digital micro sensor. However, the spherical shape of the retina results in a surface area of about 1100 mm², which is a bit larger than traditional 35 mm film or a full-frame camera sensor (860 mm²).

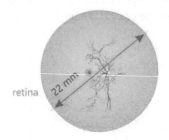 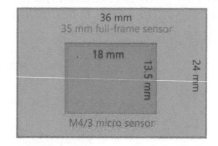

Figure 4-10: Physical size of the retina (left) and a 35 mm full-frame sensor and M4/3 microsensor (right).

4.1.2 Thickness and Layered Structure of the Retina

The retinal thickness varies significantly, particularly at the macula. Morphologically, the macula section resembles a pit structure [Figure 4-11 (left)]. The thinnest part (0.10 to 0.15 mm) is the foveola, shown in blue, and the thickest part (0.23 to 0.32 mm) is next to the foveolar, shown as slightly yellow. The retina progressively becomes thinner (0.080 mm) toward the periphery.

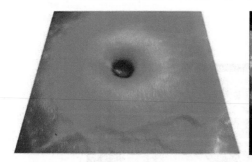 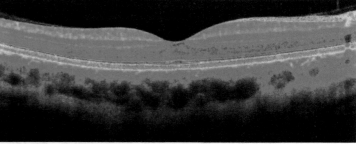

Figure 4-11: (left) Three-dimensional pseudo-chromatic rendering of the 3×3 mm macular region of a right eye obtained with Cirrus HD-OCT (Carl Zeiss Meditec). (right) OCT-derived retinal layered cross-section.

---

[330] *Ocular Imaging* § 2.1 Axial Length Measurement.

[331] Atchison DA, Pritchard N, Schmid KL, Scott DH, Jones CE, Pope JM. Shape of the retinal surface in emmetropia and myopia. Invest Ophthalmol Vis Sci. 2005; 46(8):2698-707.

[332] Pruett RC. Complications associated with posterior staphyloma. Curr Opin Ophthalmol. 1998; 9(3):16-22.

[333] Ohno-Matsui K. Pathologic myopia. Asia Pac J Ophthalmol (Phila). 2016; 5(6):415-23.

The retina has a distinct layered (stratified) structure. Its most superficial part (toward the vitreous) contains the layers of neural cells and blood vessels that are not photosensitive. The sensory layer, among the deepest layers of the retina, is located near the choroid, which is the farthest from the direction of the incident light. From the most superficial layer to the deepest, the ten distinct retinal layers of the human (in general, the vertebrate) retina are:

- Inner limiting membrane (ILM, basement membrane), which contains the endpoints of the Müller glial cells, serving key functions in reprogramming and retinal regeneration.[334, 335]

- Retinal nerve fiber layer (RNFL, *stratum opticum*), which contains the axons of the ganglion cells.

- Ganglion cell layer, which contains the nuclei of ganglion cells and displaced amacrine cells.

- Inner plexiform layer, which contains the synapse between the bipolar cell axons and the dendrites of the ganglion and amacrine cells.

- Inner nuclear layer, which contains the nuclei and surrounding cell bodies (perikarya) of the amacrine cells, bipolar cells, horizontal cells, and Müller glial cells.

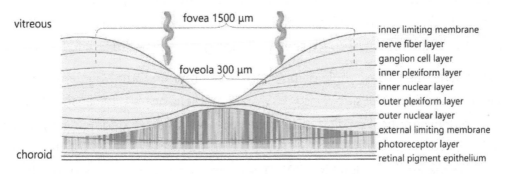

Figure 4-12: Retinal-layer cross-section in the vicinity of the macula.

- Outer plexiform layer, which contains the projections of rods and cones ending in the rod spherule and cone pedicle, respectively, where they synapse with dendrites of bipolar and horizontal cells. In the macular region, this layer is also known as the Henle fiber layer, as the axons of the photoreceptors must travel laterally to synapse with bipolar cells.

- Outer nuclear layer, which contains the cell bodies of the photoreceptors (rods and cones).

- External limiting membrane (ELM), or outer limiting membrane (OLM), which is the layer that separates the inner segment portions of the photoreceptors from their cell nuclei. Because it does not contain cells, the ELM is not considered a membrane, but rather a barrier/band of desmosomal attachments between Müller cells and the inner segments of the photoreceptors. The ELM plays a role in maintaining the retinal structure.

---

[334] Goldman D. Müller glial cell reprogramming and retina regeneration. Nat Rev Neurosci. 2014; 15:431-42.

[335] Giannelli SG, Demontis GC, Pertile G, Rama P, Broccoli V. Adult human Müller glia cells are a highly efficient source of rod photoreceptors. Stem Cells. 2011; 29:344-56.

- Photoreceptor or sensory layer populated by rods and cones (inner and outer segments).
- Retinal pigment epithelium (RPE), the outermost retinal layer, is a single layer of cuboidal cells closest to the choroid. Some consider the RPE as part of Bruch's membrane, which is the innermost layer of the choroid.

The retinal stratification and thickness change significantly in the vicinity of the optic disk as well. For example, the thickness of the RNFL increases toward the optic disk. When imaging the retinal thickness with OCT, the RNFL is often presented along with the retinal thickness. Being a sensitive structure, a compromised RNFL thickness may be associated with natural apoptosis. Certain pathologies that affect RNFL thickness include chronic increased intraocular pressure (IOP), fluctuating IOP, inflammation, vascular disease, and hypoxia.

4.1.3 Field of View / Visual Field Mapping

The visual **field of view** or simply, **visual field**, expresses the still angular extent of the area that can be visualized; still indicating without head movement or eye rotation. The visual field encompasses the entire region of space seen while the gaze is directed at a fixed, central object.

Monocularly, the largest angle of incidence that a ray can form when entering the eye horizontally from the temporal side (T) is ≈ 105°. This angle is not 90° because light is being refracted into a denser optical medium. The nasal side (N) is limited geometrically by the presence of the nose, so the largest angle is 60°. Along the vertical dimension, the superior (S) limit is ≈ 60° and the inferior (I) limit is ≈ 70°. These limitations are associated with the orbit socket. Most US State driving laws require a visual field of at least 130°, which can be provided by a single healthy eye. Thus, a one-sighted individual can legally drive under these regulations.

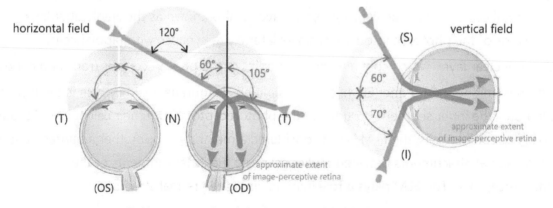

Figure 4-13: (left) Horizontal and (right) vertical field of view in the human eye.

Binocular vision combines the two monocular fields. The term binocular visual field is used in the case where both eyes are open, which, horizontally, is just under 180°. This field is important for detecting sudden appearances or movements of objects, which can be warnings of danger. The **field of binocular vision** encompasses the field in which both eyes contribute information to be cerebrally fused. While the vertical field remains unaffected, the horizontal field of binocular vision is about 120°.

Note 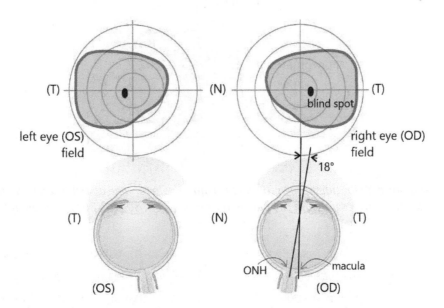: The sharpest view is obtained only in a very narrow area in the foveal region (0.5 to 2°) within the macula. The perception of sharp vision across the entire field is achieved by saccades, which are oculomotor movements characterized by rapid—lasting less than a 1 s (typical 200 msec)—and small eye rotations that extend 0.5°. Saccadic motion brings one part of the target at a time into the foveal region, allowing for high-resolution sampling. Cerebral processing integrates these high-resolution images into a single image, which comprises a mental model in the cone of visual attention.

Mapping the angular extent of the binocular visual field (Figure 4-14) illustrates the asymmetry along the horizontal and the vertical directions, indicating a temporal bend. Also, there is a **blind spot**, a physiologic absolute scotoma, because there are no photoreceptors in the area of the optical nerve head (ONH).[336] The average blind spot is about 7.5° in diameter, 1.5° inferiorly (below the horizontal meridian) and about 15° to 18° temporally.

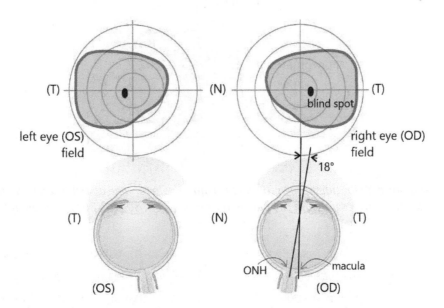

Figure 4-14: Visual field from both eyes. The blind spot is situated temporally because the ONH is situated nasally.

---

[336] Sadun AA, Dao J. Annual review in neuro-ophthalmology. The anterior visual pathways. J Neuroophthalmol. 1994; 14(3):141-54.

Visual field mapping provides a subjective (i.e., what the examinee sees) measure of central and peripheral vision. This is important for many pathologies, particularly disorders of the retina such as macular degeneration and dystrophy, optic nerve-related ailments such as glaucoma, and those related to visual structures in the brain, resulting from cerebral strokes and brain tumors.

Visual field testing can be simply tested by **confrontation visual field evaluation**, which involves the presentation of a stimulus at various lateral or vertical positions. With the other eye covered, the test eye fixates on a target object; the examinee is asked to describe objects (such as two fingers) presented peripherally. Initially, visual field testing (such as detecting hand movements or a small flash of light) was kinetic, i.e., used a moving target.

Clinically, the visual field is tested monocularly with a small flashing light (flicker) inside a dome that is repeatedly and randomly presented with various intensities in different areas of the field. The examinee, fixating straight at a central target, clicks a button when he notes (detects) the appearance of the flicker. This is called **static perimetry** or **threshold testing**, standardized in the mid-1950s by Hans Goldmann.[337] The Goldmann bowl perimeter required highly trained technicians, which led to the development of a standard automated perimetry (SAP). The main SAP devices today are the Humphrey Field Analyzer (HFA, Carl Zeiss Meditec, Jena, Germany) and the Octopus 600 and 900 Perimeter models (Haag-Streit, Köniz, Switzerland).

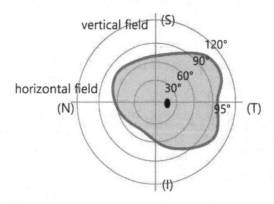

Figure 4-15: Angular distribution of the monocular right eye field. The distribution is centered on the macula. Concentric circles indicate the perimeter angle (from 30° to 120° in increments of 30°).

Note 👁 : Visual field measurement with the Humphrey Field Analyzer (HFA) uses illuminance of 10 nit = 10 cd/m² versus the Octopus in the regular mode, which operates at about 3 nit = 3 cd/m². The human visual system reaches photopic operation at about 100 Td (see § 3.2.3.3). For an average test pupil diameter of 7 mm, the pupil area is about 10 mm², which means that the HFA operates at nearly photopic vision (10 nit · 10 mm² = 100 Td), while the Octopus operates at scotopic vision (3 nit · 10 mm² = 30 Td).

---

337 Johnson CA, Wall M, Thompson HS. A history of perimetry and visual field testing. Optom Vis Sci. 2011; 88(1):E8-15.

Static perimetry results are plotted on a visual field map that depicts the angular distribution of the examinee's responses.[338] This test identifies visual field defects, such as areas of decreased vision (scotoma) surrounded by a normal visual field, and monitors visual field loss. The size and shape of a scotoma offer important clinical clues about the presence and severity of certain vision loss pathologies such as glaucoma.

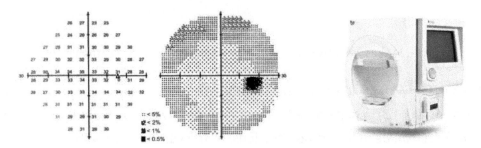

Figure 4-16: (left) Standard automated perimetry (visual field) mapping of the right eye of the center 30°. Darker areas signify reduced sensitivity to light stimulus. (right) The Humphrey Field Analyzer (HFA).

Often with young individuals, there is a need for a differential diagnosis that indicates whether a disease affects the peripheral boundary of the visual field. Since the 'hill of vision' is steeper in the periphery, a technique that is more sensitive than static perimetry testing is needed for mapping visual field sensitivity boundaries.[339] This is **kinetic perimetry** or **kinetic visual field testing**. The examinee is presented with targets of varying sizes that move from the periphery to the center of vision. While looking straight ahead at a central fixation target, the examinee clicks a button upon noticing the moving target appear in the field.

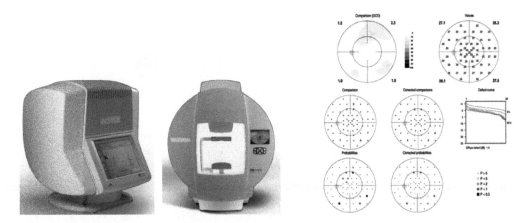

Figure 4-17: (left) The Octopus 600 and Octopus 900 perimeter devices. (right) Layout of the report, showing various probability and comparison results.

[338] Sample PA, Dannheim F, Artes PH, Dietzsch J, Henson D, Johnson CA, Ng M, Schiefer U, Wall M; IPS Standards Group. Imaging and Perimetry Society Standards and Guidelines. Optom Vis Sci. 2011; 88(1):4-7.

[339] Niederhauser S, Mojon DS. Normal isopter position in the peripheral visual field in Goldmann kinetic perimetry. Ophthalmologica. 2002; 216(6):406-8.

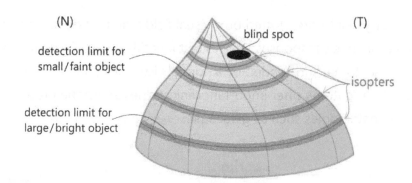

Figure 4-18: A 3-D representation of right-eye sensitivity across the visual field.

Findings in the visual field often have valuable diagnostic utility. For example, hemifields indicate hemianopsia (§ 1.3); a generalized decrease in sensitivity may be indicative of ocular media opacity, which can be in the cornea, the lens, or the vitreous, or can be neurophysiological in origin. A constricted visual field may be associated with a retinal or optic nerve condition, or small pupils. A ring scotoma is often suggestive of retina degeneration, while a central scotoma is associated with macular or optic nerve degeneration. An enlarged blind spot may suggest optic nerve conditions.

Apart from pathology and angular restriction, it is important to stress that within the visual field the light sensitivity of the eye is physiologically not uniform. Maximum sensitivity is at the center of the macula and gradually decreases toward the edges. In the 3-D representation of visual field sensitivity shown in Figure 4-18, the contour lines that connect points with equal sensitivity are called **isopters**.

Figure 4-19: Blind spot and 'filling in' phenomena: Close your left eye and fixate on the cross with your right eye, adjusting the viewing distance until (top) the spot or (bottom) the gap in the line falls in your blind spot, becoming unnoticeable.

4.2 PHOTORECEPTORS

The main task of the retina is to detect the light that forms the retinal image and convert it into an (electrical in nature) signal, called the stimulus, that is transmitted through the optic nerve to the brain. Detection is achieved with dedicated light-sensitive cells, the **photoreceptors**, which are concentrated in the sensory layer of the retina.

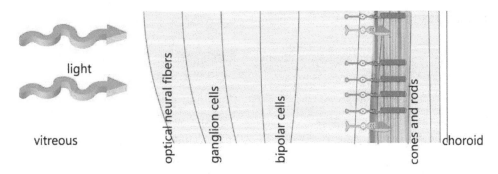

Figure 4-20: The passage of light from the vitreous to the photoreceptor layer.

4.2.1 Cones and Rods

There are two fundamentally different types of photoreceptor cells in the human eye: the **rods** and the **cones**. These are modified neurons, which share the task of transducing light into neural signals. Their structure involves a synaptic terminal, an inner segment, and an outer segment. Their cells contain light-absorbing pigments packaged in membrane-bound disks within their outer segments.

Among the similarities between rods and cones is their spatial orientation.[340] Their synaptic terminals, which offer connectivity to the horizontal and the bipolar cell axons, are oriented toward the inner eye (neighboring the vitreous), closer to the external limiting membrane. The light-absorbing pigments, because they are in the outer segments, are closer to the retinal pigment epithelium (closer to the choroid).

The photosensitive area is <u>away</u> from the direction of the incident light. Light, to be detected, has to not only transcend several overlaying retinal layers; even when it reaches a photoreceptor cell, it is funneled to the cell's outer segment, passing through most of the cell body—through its synaptic terminal and inner segment. There are differences between cones and rods in terms of shape, sensitivity to light, size and packing density, and pattern of synaptic

---

[340] Here, 'inner' means being toward the inside (the vitreous) and 'outer' means being toward the outside (the choroid) of the eye.

connections. These properties reflect the fact that rod and cone photoreceptors are specialized for different aspects of vision and complement each other.

Traditionally, compared to rods, cones are described as being shorter,[341] about 30 to 40 μm in overall length, and most have a rather conical shape when viewed from atop.[342] Their outer segment consists of folding membrane disks containing the light-absorbing pigment.[343] The disks are folded inward or sheathed, meaning that they are continuously connected to the cilium membrane folds that extend over the length of the outer segment. These folds and the coupling of the photoreceptor pigments to cellular membranes magnify the surface area available for light absorption.

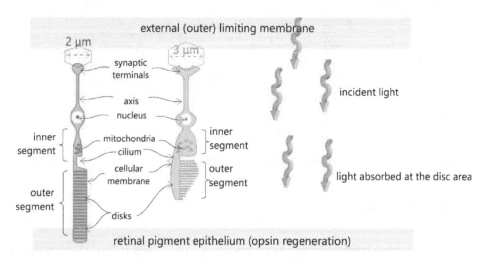

Figure 4-21: Rod (left) and cone (right) cell structures.

Rods, being about 40 to 60 μm in overall length, are longer than cones and have a pencil-like shape. Rods have individual, stacked disks, and more of them compared to cones; however, unlike the disks in the cones, these disks are unconnected to the ciliary plasma membrane. Because of this arrangement, rods can store larger quantities of rhodopsin, the photosensitive pigment primarily responsible for the detection of light (§ 4.3).

Retinal Structure Paradox:
• The photoreceptors are located in the deepest retina layer. • They face away from the incoming light.

---

[341] This holds true in the periphery, but foveal cones are very similar to rods in their shape: long and thin. Their long(-er) axons distinguish them from rods.

[342] Mustafi D, Engel AH, Palczewski K. Structure of cone photoreceptors. Prog Retin Eye Res. 2009; 28(4):289-302.

[343] As discussed in § 5.2, there are three different light-absorbing pigments in the cones, which have different spectral absorption properties, resulting in color vision.

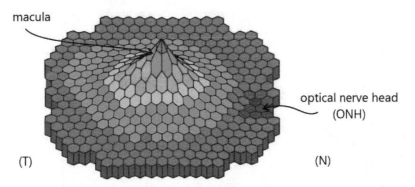

Figure 4-22: Central cone density distribution of the right eye correlated by a multifocal electroretinography (mfERG) plot, in which many local ERG responses are recorded quasi-simultaneously from the cone-driven retina under light-adapted conditions. In this plot, warm colors indicate increased density, peaking at the macula; cool colors indicate reduced density—note the near-zero cell density at the optical nerve head. The cell cross-section from the direction of incoming light has a hexagonal honeycomb shape.

Rods are far more abundant than cones by a 20:1 ratio.[344] There are about 100 million rods and 5 million cones. Their distribution varies significantly across the retina. For example, in the fovea alone, there are about 50,000 cones, in a density exceeding 180,000 per mm^2, but no rods at all.[345] Rods attain their highest packing density about 20° peripherally to the fovea. There are no photoreceptors at the optic disk, which is about 18° nasally.

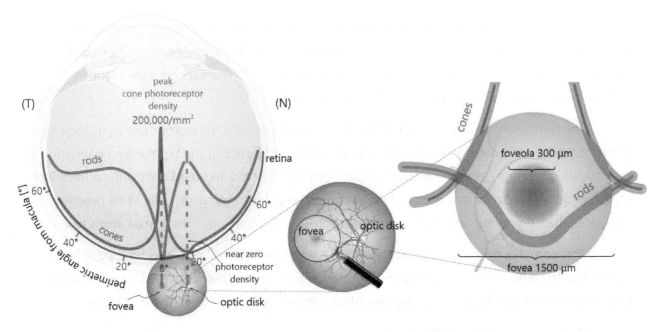

Figure 4-23: (left) Spatial distribution of the cone and rod photoreceptors. (right) Detail of the cone and rod relative distributions in the fovea and the foveola.

---

[344] Ahnelt PK. The photoreceptor mosaic. Eye. 1998; 12(3):531-40.

[345] Österberg G. Topography of the layer of rods and cones in the human retina. Acta Ophthal Suppl. 1935; 6:1-103.

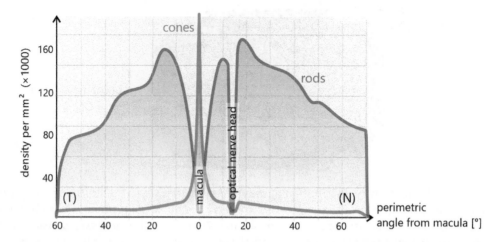

Figure 4-24: Perimetric distribution of cone and rod cell densities across the retina.[346, 347]

4.2.2 Photoreceptor Pathways

To describe how the signal from cones and rods is 'sent' to the optic nerve is far from simple. This is where visual optics meets sensory neuroscience. The rod and cone signals reach the optic nerve via complex pathways via local neural connections that are very precise and not at all random.

There are three different levels of interconnections in these pathways. Cones and rods are connected through their synaptic terminals, initially, with the dendrites of the **horizontal cells** that primarily connect cones to cones and rods to rods.[348] The second layer involves **bipolar cells**, which have synaptic terminals at both ends.

The third layer involves the **ganglion cells**, which produce the output signal, as their axons converge to become the optic nerve fibers. Situated between the bipolar and ganglion cells are the amacrine cells, which obtain input from bipolar cells and feed their output back into other bipolar cells. Some amacrine cells may connect bipolar to ganglion cells. This process reinforces the original signal from the photoreceptors, which becomes the **visual stimulus**.

This complex pathway appears to facilitate high central resolution and high peripheral sensitivity. Because cones and rods serve different visual needs, the pathways to the ganglion cells are characterized by different degrees of convergence. In the fovea, there is a nearly 1:1

---

[346] Peak cone density in the human averages 199,000 cones/mm² with a range of 100,000 to 324,000. Curcio et al. calculated 77 cycles/degree or 0.78 arcmin/cycle of retinal resolution in: Curcio CA, Sloan KR, Kalina RE, Hendrickson AE. Human photoreceptor topography. J Comp Neurol. 1990; 292(4):497-523.

[347] In many adaptations of this plot, the location of the optical nerve head is reported as the 'blind spot.' This not an anatomically proper description. The near-zero photosensor cell density occurs in the area of the optical nerve head, which is nasally displaced from the macula by about 18°. The counterpart in visual fields is the blind spot, which is located peripherally from the macula by about 18°.

[348] There are also connections between photoreceptor and bipolar cells and between horizontal cells.

ratio between cones and ganglion cells.[349] Thus, each ganglion cell in the fovea receives input from just one cone bipolar cell, which in turn, is contacted, often, by just a single cone. The cone system, in other words, is <u>not convergent</u>. This almost 1:1 relationship of cones to ganglion cells serves to maximize visual acuity (high central resolution) at the center of the macula.

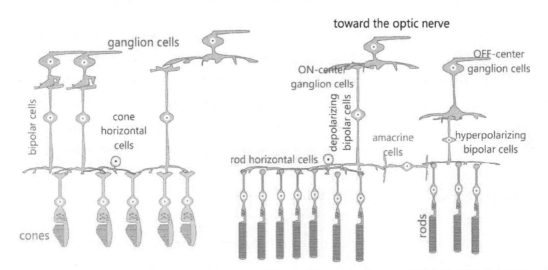

Figure 4-25: Simplified illustration of photoreceptor pathways.[350]

The way rods converge is strikingly different; here, the ratio between rods and ganglion cells is likely to be on the order of 100:1 or more. Each rod bipolar cell is contacted by several rods, and many rod bipolar cells contact a ganglion cell. Thus, there is a many:one relationship between rods and optic nerve fiber neurons, which can even reach 100:1. The response of the ganglion cell depends on the responses of the cells that feed into it, including the rods, the bipolar cells, and various lateral interconnections via horizontal cells and amacrine cells.

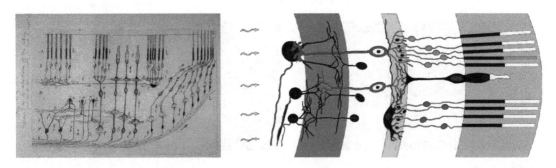

Figure 4-26: Cone and rod pathways (non-mammalian retina) drawn by Santiago Ramón y Cajal (1901).

---

[349] Curcio CA, Allen KA. Topography of ganglion cells in human retina. J Comp Neurol. 1990; 300(1):5-25.

[350] As we shall see in § 4.3.6, the pathways have a far more complicated structure that involves amacrine cells and ON and OFF types of rod bipolar cells. Rod ON signals flow from rod bipolar cell to AII amacrine cells to ON cone bipolar cells, while rod OFF signals are generated at synapses between AII amacrine cells and OFF cone bipolar cells.

The **photoreceptor convergence ratio** is a measure of information convergence that relates the degree of convergence from photoreceptors to bipolar cells and bipolar cells to ganglion cells. <u>Cones have a low convergence ratio</u>: Diffuse bipolar cells connect with a few cones in the central retina and with about 10 cones in the peripheral retina. In the fovea, there is a 1:1 ratio, meaning one cone is effectively connected to just one ganglion cell.

The rod system, on the other hand, has a significantly higher convergence ratio, which can be 100:1 in the periphery. The <u>high rod convergence ratio</u> serves to maximize peripheral light sensitivity: The pooled response of the convergent rods increases light sensitivity, as faint signals from many rods are pooled to generate a strong response. However, this high convergence reduces spatial resolution; peripheral vision is not as sharp as central vision. These features explain the differences between scotopic (rod) and photopic (cone) vision (§ 4.3.2).[351]

4.2.3 Fovea: the Center of Vision

The fovea, the most light-sensitive part of the retina, corresponds to the highest possible optical resolution and, therefore, visual acuity. This is due to several factors, which include:

- the largest pack density of cone cells and the absence of rods;
- the reduction, or practical absence of the inner retinal layers of the retina (which appear to make way for light to pass), which reduces the losses to scattering and absorption;
- the 1:1 convergence ratio of cone cells, which ensures high resolution;
- the small range of the receptive field, which enhances spatial discrimination; and,
- finally, neurophysiology: The fovea corresponds to a large area in the center of the occipital lobe, far more than other parts of the retina.[352] About 50% of cells in the visual cortex are devoted to processing the central 5° of vision.[353]

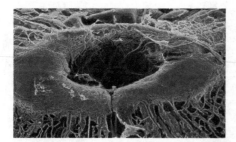 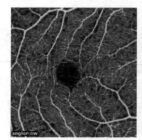 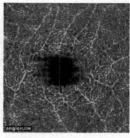

Figure 4-27: (left) A 3-D image of the central fovea. (right) Macula capillary imaging by OCT angiography: upper and deeper layers. The central, foveal area is devoid of blood vessels.

---

[351] Wässle H. Parallel processing in the mammalian retina. Nat Rev Neurosci. 2004; 5(10):747-57.

[352] Dow BM, Snyder AZ, Vautin RG, Bauer R. Magnification factor and receptive field size in foveal striate cortex of the monkey. Exp Brain Res. 1981; 44(2):213-28.

[353] Rovamo J. Receptive field density of retinal ganglion cells and cortical magnification factor in man. Med Biol. 1978; 56(2):97-102.

4.3 THE PHOTONIC SENSATION

Have you ever wondered exactly how the screen of an old-style TV works? These screens are called cathode-ray tubes (CRTs) and were originally used in oscilloscopes. Accelerated electrons are directed toward a screen coated with a fluorescent material. Wherever the electrons hit, the screen lights up. In other words, stimulation by electrons is causing light emission.

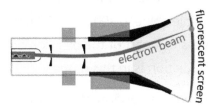 

Figure 4-28: In a cathode ray tube electronic stimulation is causing light emission.

A reverse mechanism takes place in the photonic sensation by the photoreceptors of the eye: Light absorption results in an electrical signal. Photons[354] reach the disks, where they are absorbed by **rhodopsin**, an organic, photosensitive pigment.[355] Rhodopsin consists of a protein part, the opsin, covalently bound to a non-protein part, the chromophore 11-*cis* retinal. Retinal is the aldehyde of vitamin A and derives from it.

Light absorption by a rhodopsin molecule triggers a biochemical cascade that leads to isomerization of the 11-*cis* retinal into all-*trans* retinal that thrusts the opsin into an active state.[356] This initiates a biochemical photo-degradation that leads to closure of photoreceptor cation channels and hyperpolarization.[357] The resulting osmotic ion flow change causes a small electrical charge buildup in the cell membrane (electric potential change/depolarization). The charge buildup is converted into a frequency-modulated signal at the ganglion-cell and higher levels: The ganglion cells fire action potentials, which can be conceptualized as discrete electrical spikes. The signal magnitude is represented in terms of the firing rate (spikes per second). The ganglions fire continuously: The presence or absence of light merely changes their firing rate, which is further processed as information about stimulus intensity.

---

[354] There are always losses of, on average, about 50% due to scattering and absorption by other parts of the eye, even within the retinal layers. Of these 50 photons reaching the retina, about 7, on average, are actually detected.

[355] As will be discussed in § 5.2, rhodopsin is the type of photosensitive pigment encountered in rods. Cones have slightly different L, M, and S cone photopigments, which contribute to color perception.

[356] This means that light absorption can alter the ganglion cell spike-firing rate.

[357] Surprisingly, in the dark (which means at rest), the photoreceptors are quite active, constantly releasing neurotransmitter signals. The resulting hyperpolarization decreases the amount of neurotransmitter released. This means that light actually turns receptors off by reducing their spike-firing rate.

4.3.1 Spectral Sensitivity

The expression 'the eye is sensitive to light' has been used up to this point in a very simplified manner. To specify sensitivity to light, we must state (a) the wavelength, (b) the brightness (luminance, unit nit or, formally, cd/m^2), and, finally, (c) the spatial content, i.e., the area of the retina and the angle formed by the rays.

The notion of **spectral sensitivity** describes the relationship between the sensitivity of the eye and the wavelength. Obviously, the eye is sensitive only to the visible part of the electromagnetic spectrum that extends from the violet/blue, 0.390 µm (390 nm) to the red, 0.780 µm (780 nm). In other words, we 'see' only a small part of the electromagnetic spectrum, but 83% of the amount of solar electromagnetic radiation is in this range.

What's even more important is that the human perception of brightness depends on the color (wavelength). Spectral sensitivity describes how sensitive the eye is to different wavelengths, which is not the same throughout the visible spectrum. The largest response of the eye to light in bright daylight conditions occurs at 0.555 µm (555 nm). At this wavelength (yellow-green color), the eye is more responsive than, for example, in the blue or the red. This means that, if we display the same two quantities of energy but of a different color (for example, a red and a green diode laser rated at exactly the same 'wall power'), the human eye will perceive the green as the brightest.[358]

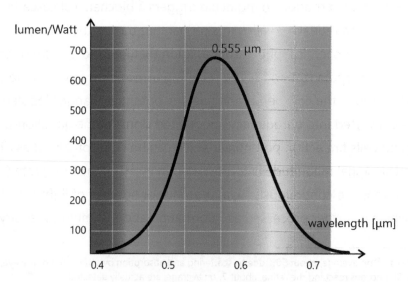

Figure 4-29: Photopic luminosity function (daylight conditions). This is the spectral luminous efficiency function V(λ), which is based on the 1924-CIE established standard photopic observer.

---

[358] Have you ever wondered why road-side workers often wear chartreuse vests?

4.3.2 Response to Luminance

Photometry employs the concept of the luminous flux leaving a surface, per unit of solid angle of observation, and per unit of viewing surface area. This quantity is **luminance**, defined as the light energy per time and unit area along a specific direction. It is the amount of light that passes through, is emitted from, or is reflected off a particular area and falls within a given solid angle. It is expressed in candelas per square meter (cd/m^2), informally known as a nit.

Table 4–1: Typical values of luminance.

| 5×10^{-5} cd/m^2 night sky, no stars | 1×10^{-3} cd/m^2 starry sky | 1×10^{-1} cd/m^2 moonlit sky | 1×10^{2} cd/m^2 indoor lighting | 6×10^{4} cd/m^2 daylight | 1×10^{6} cd/m^2 noon sky |

Under different luminance levels, different types of photoreceptor initiate vision. There are three distinct levels of eye sensitivity.

• **Photopic vision** for luminance above 3 cd/m^2 (log L = +0.5). Vision is initiated by cones. Photopic vision is highly color sensitive and of high resolution.

• **Mesopic vision** for luminance between 0.001 and 3 cd/m^2 ($-3 <$ log $L <$ +0.5). Both rods and cones can initiate vision. Color perception and resolution are intermediate.

• **Scotopic vision** for luminance less than 0.001 cd/m^2 (log L = -3). Vision is initiated by rods. Scotopic vision has minimal color sensitivity and low resolution.

These levels relate to the differences between photoreceptor types. The **duplicity theory** states that above a certain luminance, the cone mechanism is engaged, providing photopic vision; below this luminance level, the rod mechanism provides scotopic vision. The range where the two mechanisms work together is mesopic vision.

Rods are more suitable for low luminance because they are more sensitive to light than cones over most of the visible spectrum, mainly owing to the rhodopsin capacity[359] and the high convergence ratio. However, due to rod convergence, scotopic visual acuity is poor: It does not resolve fine spatial detail as well as photopic vision (cone-dominated) does. The fine spatial detail resolved by the cones is attributed to their nearly one-to-one convergence ratio and their optimized packing density in the fovea.

---

[359] This sensitivity difference, coupled with the absence of rods in the fovea, explains why we cannot see light sources that are too dim, such as weak starlight, when fixating directly on a star through a telescope. Such a star is too dim to be visible through the all-cone fovea but becomes slightly visible in the periphery—detected by rods.

In addition, cones are more suitable for high levels of steady illumination exactly because they are less sensitive to light. This difference is due to the rhodopsin (rod opsin)/cone opsin distribution, capacity, and saturation properties. Rods saturate easily: Their signal is so strong that additional light does not produce any increase in the already strong signal. On the other hand, cones do not saturate easily, so more light produces a stronger signal.

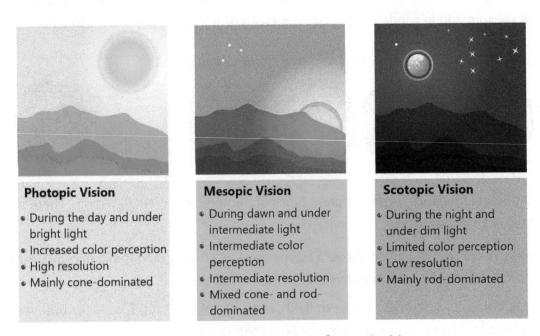

Photopic Vision
- During the day and under bright light
- Increased color perception
- High resolution
- Mainly cone-dominated

Mesopic Vision
- During dawn and under intermediate light
- Intermediate color perception
- Intermediate resolution
- Mixed cone- and rod-dominated

Scotopic Vision
- During the night and under dim light
- Limited color perception
- Low resolution
- Mainly rod-dominated

Figure 4-30: Photopic, mesopic, and scotopic vision.

4.3.3   Light and Dark Adaptation

The ambient light intensity varies by more than 10 orders of magnitude, from 10^{-5} cd/m^2 for a night sky with no stars to 10^6 cd/m^2 for a brightly lit noon sky. This may be approximately 10^{22} photons per m^2 per s. The visual system is challenged to remain sensitive over this enormous luminance range. Fortunately, we typically are not simultaneously exposed to the entire range of illumination levels. Also, the eye has an intricate adaptation response that produces different visual response curves depending on the prevailing level of illumination.

When we walk into a dark room from the outdoors on a sunny day, at first we cannot see much. However, after a little while, our eyes adjust to the darkness. This is **dark adaptation**. If we awaken in a dark room, any light source, such as a cell phone screen, can appear to be too bright. This bright light momentarily dazzles us, and all we see is white light because the eye sensitivity is too high, being tuned to dim light. After some time, the light is not too blinding to check the message on the phone screen. This adaptation from dark to light is **light adaptation**.

Light adaptation	• The change in visual sensitivity that occurs when the prevailing level of illumination is increased, such as when suddenly turning on a lamp in a dark room.
Dark adaptation	• The change in visual sensitivity that occurs when the prevailing level of illumination is decreased, such as when entering a darkened room after being outside on a sunny day.

Light adaptation is initiated by two functions, the first of which is the pupillary reflex response (§ 2.4.2.3). In this response, the pupil constricts to 3–4 mm in diameter under bright light and dilates to (up to) 8 mm under dim light, modulating the amount of light admitted into the eye by a factor of up to 64 ($=2^4$) at the most. This is only a small contribution that covers (at most) a two-order-of-magnitude luminance change. It cannot account for the dramatic, large-scale increase between the very bright and the very dark, which can extend to 10 orders of magnitude.

The most important aspect of adaptation is the change in retinal sensitivity. To adjust its sensitivity, the retina responds to inhibit rod function and favor cone function (light adaptation) or it has the opposite response (dark adaptation).

The retinal sensitivity adjustment relates to rhodopsin/cone opsin concentrations and regeneration. The isomerization of the 11-*cis* retinal chromophore into all-*trans* occurs because light absorption depletes the available rhodopsin concentration, as this combination is no longer photosensitive. The rhodopsin is 'bleached,' a term that reflects the fact that its color changes from red to yellow. Rhodopsin becomes available again via a process of regeneration that occurs at the retinal pigment epithelium and produces vitamin A and opsin.[360] The capacity of this recycling process (Figure 4-31), however, has certain limitations.[361]

Assume that we are in a dark room. Vision is scotopic, and there is a balanced flow between bleached and unbleached rhodopsin. The eye responds adequately to a low-level, incremental increase in luminance, and the sensitivity is high. When luminance suddenly increases, rhodopsin is bleached far more quickly than the regeneration process can replenish it. This reduced rhodopsin availability results in a weaker response to an incremental increase in luminance, thus reducing rod functionality.[362] Vision then switches to photopic, or cone-dominated, and the visual system becomes less sensitive such that it can produce a useful response to a high-level, incremental increase in luminance. This is light adaptation.

---

[360] Wolf G. The visual cycle of the cone photoreceptors of the retina. Nutr Rev. 2004; 62(7 Pt 1):283-6.

[361] Pennisi E. Opsins: not Just for eyes. Science. 2013; 339(6121):754-5.

[362] Boll F. Zur Anatomie und Physiologie der Retina. Monatsber Akad Wissensch. Berlin. 1876; 783-87.

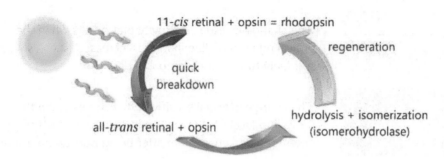

Figure 4-31: The rhodopsin regeneration cycle.[363]

There is an asymmetry in the forward and reverse processes that affects the time course of light adaptation (Figure 4-32). Because they consume far more rhodopsin, rods need more time to match depletion and regeneration rates, and dark adaptation takes up to 30 minutes longer. Cones take approximately 8 to 10 minutes to adapt to an increase in illumination. Figure 4-32 shows the dual nature of dark adaptation in two parts, the red and the blue curve.[364]

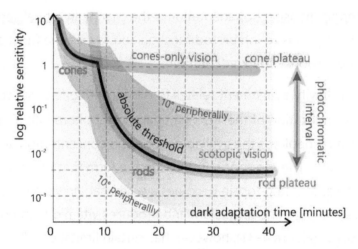

Figure 4-32: Time course of dark adaptation. The solid black curve represents the absolute threshold. The expanded (shaded) area shows the range of peripheral thresholds. [365]

The red curve describes cone vision; when luminance drops below the cone-operating range, rod vision (blue curve) dominates. First, cones become more sensitive until the curve levels off after a few minutes; the cone plateau denotes the minimum photopic threshold. Then the rod system engages in about ten minutes. With a longer recovery time, rods amass enough sensitivity to outperform cones and begin to determine the sensitivity. The inflection point in

[363] Deigner PS, Law WC, Canada FJ, Rando RR. Membranes as the energy source in the endergonic transformation of vitamin A to 11-cis-retinol. Science. 1989; 244:968-71.

[364] Hecht S, Haig C, Chase AM. The influence of light adaptation on subsequent dark adaptation of the eye. J Gen Physiol. 1937; 20(6):831-50.

[365] Gruesser O-J, Gruesser-Cornehls U. Physiology of vision. In Schmidt RF, ed. Fundamentals of Sensory Physiology. New York. Springer-Verlag, 1978.

the absolute threshold curve corresponds to rods becoming more sensitive than cones, signaling the transition from cone function to rod function.

Rod sensitivity continues to improve until it becomes asymptotic (scotopic rod threshold plateau) after about 30 to 40 minutes in the dark. Even within the pure rod (or pure cone) vision, there is some level of adaptation driven by feedback from horizontal cells.[366] The difference in log relative sensitivity between the cone and the rod plateau is the colorless or **photochromatic interval**.[367] The absolute threshold represents the intensity of a chromatic test field from a level sufficiently low to make it just perceptible. This interval is dependent on eccentricity and the spectral (wavelength) and spatial (size) aspects of the stimuli.[368]

Adaptation is also affected by melatonin secretion by a special class of intrinsically photosensitive retinal ganglion cells (ipRGC).[167] These are a subset of ganglion cells (< 5%), situated in the outermost lamina of the inner nuclear layer. Their nonvisual photo-receptive tasks involve signaling light for largely subconscious, non-image-forming visual reflexes, such as pupillary constriction (§ 2.4.1), neuroendocrine regulation, and photoperiodic physiology such as the synchronization of diurnal physiological rhythms that control the circadian cycle.[369]

Mechanisms of light / dark adaptation	• Switchover between rods and cones • Pupillary reflex response • Bleaching—regeneration of rhodopsin • Feedback from horizontal cells that control photoreceptor responsiveness • Intrinsically photosensitive retinal ganglion cells melatonin secretion

A consequence of light/dark adaptation is the appearance of **afterimages**. These are images that appear after the original stimulus ceases. Exposure to a brightly lit screen or an intense flash brings the sense of a (often blueish) spot that moves around in the directions the eyes move, even with eyelids closed. Exposure to bright light causes retinal light adaptation. This light adaptation is local to the region of the retinal image that was stimulated. If, after adapting to a small-sized bright light, we look at a bright uniform field (such as a white wall), the adapted retinal region is less sensitive, and that section of the field appears darker. This is a negative afterimage. On the other hand, if we gaze at a very dark uniform field, there will again be an afterimage that is brighter than the background. This is a positive afterimage.

---

[366] Plainis S, Murray IJ, Charman WN. The role of retinal adaptation in night driving. Optom Vis Sci. 2005; 82(8):682-8.

[367] Lie I. Dark adaptation and the photochromatic interval. Documenta Ophthalmologica. 1963; 17(1):411-510.

[368] Spillmann L, Seneff S. Photochromatic intervals as a function of retinal eccentricity for stimuli of different size. JOSA. 1971; 61(2):267-70.

[369] Touitou Y, Reinberg A, Touitou D. Association between light at night, melatonin secretion, sleep deprivation, and the internal clock: Health impacts and mechanisms of circadian disruption. Life Sci. 2017; 173:94-106.

4.3.4 The Purkinje Shift

The change in opsin sensitivity[370] during light/dark adaptation affects the spectral characteristics of visual perception.[371] Stating that the maximum sensitivity of the eye is 683 lm/W (lumen per watt) around 0.555 μm means that there are 683 lm of luminous flux perceived per 1 W of radiant energy flux if the radiation has a 0.555 μm wavelength. However, this only applies to photopic vision. Under scotopic conditions (rod-dominated vision), the luminous efficiency maximum shifts to shorter wavelengths at the blue-green 0.507 μm (compare Figure 4-29 and Figure 4-33). This peak luminous efficiency reaches 1700 lm/w.

Two effects are associated with the scotopic shift: The eye becomes more sensitive (higher response to less light) to most wavelengths (except for the orange-red) by a factor of more than two, and the maximum sensitivity shifts to 'bluer' wavelengths. This second effect is called the **Purkinje shift**, named after the Czech physiologist Johannes Evangelista Purkinje (Purkyně), who also developed Purkinje images (§ 2.3.1).

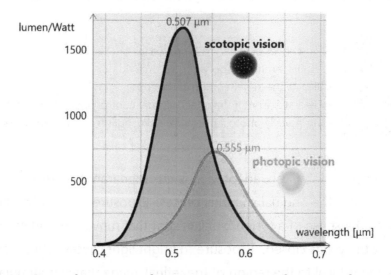

Figure 4-33: Spectral sensitivity: photopic versus scotopic luminosity functions.[372]

This shift has the effect that red, orange, and yellow details appear relatively stronger under bright illumination, whereas blue and green details appear relatively stronger under dim illumination. Red and blue details that appear equally vivid under bright daylight will shift such that the red portions will appear darker than the blue portions in twilight or under dim light.

---

[370] Nathans J, Merbs SL, Sung CH, Weitz CJ, Wang J. Molecular genetics of human visual pigments. Annu Rev Genet. 1992; 26:403-24.

[371] Kalloniatis M, Luu C. Light and Dark Adaptation. In: Kolb H, Fernandez E, Nelson R, eds. Webvision: The Organization of the Retina and Visual System. Salt Lake City (UT): University of Utah Health Sciences Center; 1995-2005.

[372] Baylor DA. Photoreceptor signals and vision. Proctor lecture. Invest Ophthalmol Vis Sci. 1987; 28(1):34-49.

Figure 4-34: Image perception under (left) photopic, (center) mesopic, and (right) scotopic conditions. Gradually, the green area appears brighter in comparison to the red areas, which appear darker.

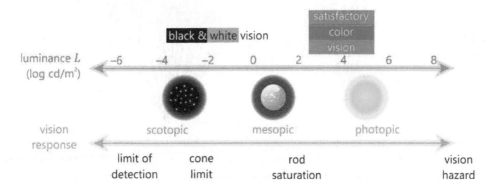

Figure 4-35: The dynamic range of visual color perception.

4.3.5 Receptive Fields

The retinal image is a light-intensity spatial distribution pattern. To detect this image, there needs to be an encoding of the spatially different light intensity values from point to point; for example, at position (x, y) the value is a, and at position (x', y') the value is a'.

In the microcosm of retinal photoreceptors and neural connective tissue, we must reckon the visual stimulus, the action potential, and the spike-firing rate (response) of the ganglion cells. There is also the convergence ratio: The signal communicated to the ganglion cells is the collective input from all of the photoreceptor cells that synapse with it, and this is particularly the case in rods. Deeper in the central nervous system, these factors become even more complex and elaborate.[373] The term **receptive field** describes either (a) the part of the retina that, when stimulated, alters the firing rate of one ganglion cell or (b) the part of the visual field that feeds said part of the retina. When used in context (a), the receptive field is described by a surface area of the retina that covers the photoreceptors converging (indirectly connecting with

---

[373] Famiglietti EV Jr. On and off pathways through amacrine cells in mammalian retina: the synaptic connections of "starburst" amacrine cells. Vision Res. 1983; 23(11):1265-79.

bipolar cells) to the ganglion cell. When used in context (b), it is described by a 3-D, cone-shaped <u>solid angle</u> centered at the ganglion cell. This angle encompasses all of the visual directions in which light may elicit a ganglion cell to increase or decrease its spike-firing rate.

Because of variable degrees of photoreceptor convergence, receptive fields are smallest in the fovea, where they can be on the order of an arcminute, and largest in the peripheral retina, where their angular extent is much larger.[374]

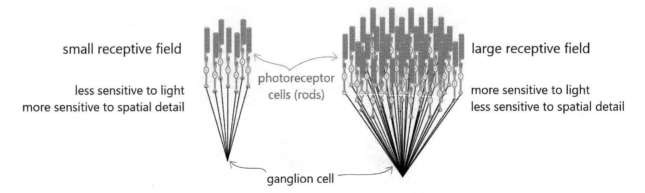

Figure 4-36: *Schematic illustration of the different sizes of receptive fields in (left) the parafoveal region (7° eccentricity) and (right) the peripheral retina (35° eccentricity).*

For this reason, maximum visual acuity is associated with central foveal vision. When staring at an object (such as a traffic sign) at the center of our visual field, its details are perceived with much greater clarity compared to similar-sized objects located peripherally: A traffic sign of the same size cannot be seen clearly if it is not at the center of our visual field. Alternatively, for peripheral objects to be perceived as clearly as the central object, their features must have a larger minimum angular separation.[375]

Figure 4-37: *The peripheral receptive fields are larger than the central, foveal receptive field. In the periphery, objects must be larger or more distinctive to be identified.*

[374] Kalloniatis M, Luu C. Temporal Resolution. In: Kolb H, Fernandez E, Nelson R, eds. Webvision: The Organization of the Retina and Visual System. Salt Lake City (UT): University of Utah Health Sciences Center; 1995-2005.

[375] Shapley R. Retinal physiology: adapting to the changing scene. Curr Biol. 1997; 7(7):R421-3.

The eye communicates with the visual cortex via a signal carried by the optic nerve fibers.

This signal is generated by retinal ganglion cells and is the rate at which these cells produce (fire) spikes.

Each ganglion cell responds to a small region in the visual field—its receptive field.

4.3.6 Ganglion Cell Excitation and Inhibition

There are two types of retinal ganglion cells, differentiated based on their receptive field organization—whether they are predominantly excited by a stimulus <u>within</u> the center, called <u>on-center</u> or by a stimulus <u>in the surround</u> of their receptive field, called <u>off-center.</u> This distinction was first demonstrated in 1953 by Stephen Kuffler in a cat retina[376] and by Horace Barlow in a frog retina,[377] and later in primates by David Hubel and Torsten Wiesel.[378, 379] The exploration of neuron function along the visual pathway and in the primary visual cortex indicated an increasingly complex structure and function of information processing in the visual system. For their work in this area, Hubel and Wiesel were awarded the 1981 Nobel Prize in Physiology or Medicine.

The key finding was that stimulating different parts of the receptive field evokes different ganglion cell responses. In the **on-center** cells, signals fall within the center of the receptive field and excite them, leading to an increase in their firing rate. Signals falling in the concentric periphery inhibit the cells' responses, decreasing their firing rate.[380] This is why we also describe ganglion cells as **on-center**/off surround. Most retinal ganglion cells are of this type: A small bright spot at the center excites a response, while an annulus-shaped light spot inhibits it.

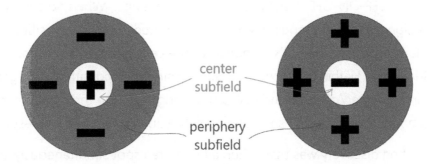

center subfield

periphery subfield

Figure 4-38: Opposing responses of ganglion cells upon receiving a stimulus at the center of their receptive field: (left) on-center / off-surround and (right) off-center / on-surround.

[376] Kuffler SW. Discharge patterns and functional organization of mammalian retina. J Neurophysiol. 1953; 16:37-68.

[377] Barlow HB. Summation and inhibition in the frog's retina. J Physiol. 1953; 119:69-88.

[378] Hubel DH, Wiesel TN. Receptive fields of single neurons in the cat's striate cortex. J Physiol. 1959; 148:574-91.

[379] Hubel DH, Wiesel TN. Receptive fields, binocular interaction and functional architecture in the cat's visual cortex. J Physiol. 1962; 160(1):106-54.

[380] Geffen MN, de Vries SE, Meister M. Retinal ganglion cells can rapidly change polarity from Off to On. PLoS Biol. 2007; 5(3):e65.

An **off-center**/on-surround ganglion cell has the opposite response pattern: It is inhibited by a small bright spot at the center and excited by an annular-shaped stimulation in the surround. In other words, the off-center/on-surround ganglion cells work as detectors of 'darkness.' At the edge between the two receptive subfields, there is an ON-OFF effect that, in essence, serves to facilitate edge detection and contrast (the Mach band effect).

Bipolar cells can also be of either the on-center or the off-center type, distinguished by the opposite sign of their response. The relationship between ganglion cells (their firing rate) and the stimulus is attributed to their synapses with bipolar cells.[381] Some ganglion cells receive excitatory input from both types of bipolar cell and are transiently excited at both the onset and the offset of the stimulus.

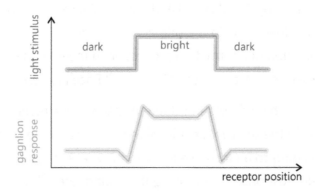

Figure 4-39: Ganglion cell responses for different light stimuli (Mach band effect).

These effects were investigated in the visual systems of felines[382] by shining a small-sized light stimulus (in an OFF-ON-OFF flashing pattern) on the retina. When no stimulus was presented (dark signal), a spontaneous spike firing was noted. For most positions on the retina, a spot of light does not affect the cell's response, as the cell continues to respond at a spontaneous firing rate. Within the receptive field, flashing the spot affects the ganglion cell response. For an on center/off surround cell, a small bright spot in the center increases the cell response and a bright annulus in the surrounding subregion inhibits the cell response.

An interesting discovery was that, when a large-area spot simultaneously stimulates both the center and the surrounding subfields (last example in Figure 4-40), there is only a modest firing rate, almost identical to that of the dark stimulus (first example). This neutral net emission rate is attributed to the opposing responses of the center and the surrounding fields. The large (full-field) spot of light covers both the center and the surrounding subfield and results in the

[381] Miller RF, Dacheux RF. Synaptic organization and ionic basis of on and off channels in mudpuppy retina. III. A model of ganglion cell receptive field organization based on chloride-free experiments. J Gen Physiol. 1976; 67(6):671-90.

[382] Kuffler SW, Fitzhugh R, Barlow HB. Maintained activity in the cat's retina in light and darkness. J Gen Physiol. 1957; 40(5):683-702.

excitation in the center being canceled by the inhibition in the surroundings. This effect is called **lateral inhibition** because it is transmitted laterally across the retina, along the lateral plexus.

On the other hand, if the receptive field of the cell is completely centered on a relatively small stimulus (second example in Figure 4-40), there is a different stimulus at the center and in the surrounding field, so the center and the surrounding signals <u>strengthen</u> one another. Recall that 'signal' is not an increase, but a change in the firing rate; this applies to both the on-center and the off-center cases. The effect is more pronounced in peripheral vision, where lateral inhibition acts over greater distances as a result of the larger receptive field extent.

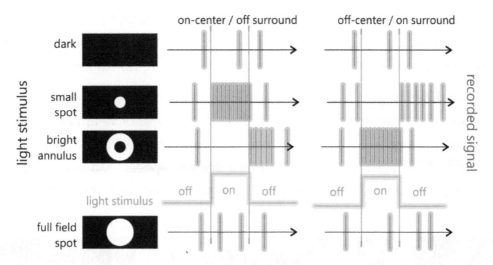

Figure 4-40: Ganglion cell firing-rate responses. (left) Various visual stimuli. (center) Recorded signal for on-center/off-surround and (right) off-center on-surround ganglion cells.

The activity of a given photoreceptor neuron is affected by the activity of nearby neurons.	A single receptor may produce a large response (spike-firing rate) when responding to light stimulus.	The precence of a stimulus to the cell's surroundings causes the cell's response to decrease.	Illumination of receptors inhibits the firing of neighboring receptors.

This contrast (dark/bright) sensation is not at all 'strange' in the human sensory system. The sensation of cold/hot, head turning right/left, the sense of yellow/blue, green/red, follow roughly the same rules. The basic premise is that there are two types of polarization sensing.[383]

---

[383] MacEahren AM. The role of complexity and symbolization method in thematic map effectiveness. Ann Assoc Am Geogr. 1982; 72:495-513.

The illusion of the **Hermann grid**[384] consists of black squares separated by a grid of white horizontal and vertical lines. Gray, ghost-like spots appear at the white right-angled intersections, but there are no dots at these intersections. The appearance dissolves if we look directly at a white intersection (bring that intersection to the center of our view.[385]

The predominant explanation that appears in many textbooks is based on the concentric on-center/off-surround receptive fields.[386] The illusory effect is attributed to differences in the discharge characteristics of retinal ganglion cells when their receptive fields fall along the intersections, as opposed to falling along non-intersecting regions. When a receptive field views a grid intersection of a white horizontal and vertical line, the net result is an inhibition of the on-center. When looking just at a white line, either horizontal or vertical, there is less inhibition. Finally, there is no inhibition when looking at an intersection at the very center of the visual field, and the gray ghost disappears because of the much smaller, cone-dominated receptive fields.

In the **scintillating grid**, a variation of the Hermann grid, there <u>are</u> white circles on the gray intersections separating the black squares. Black dots appear or vanish at the intersections of the gray horizontal and vertical lines. When focusing on a single white dot, some gray dots nearby and some black dots a little farther away also seem to appear. More black dots seem to appear as the eye scans across the image, as opposed to focusing on a single point.

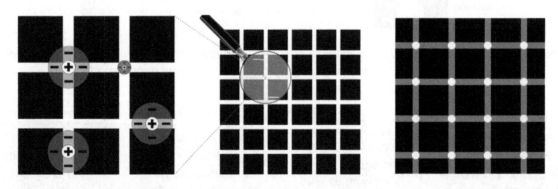

Figure 4-41: (left and center) The Hermann grid illusion and (right) the scintillating grid illusion.

The Hermann grid illusory effect manifests only when the block orientation and grid alignment are perfect,[387] and it is not size-dependent, as it occurs with very small or very large squares and bars.[388] The effect appears with reversed contrast (white squares, black lines) and

---

[384] Hermann L. Eine Erscheinung simultanen Contrastes. Pflügers Archiv für die gesamte. Physiologie. 1870; 3:13-5.

[385] Corney D, Lotto RB. What are lightness illusions and why do we see them? PLoS Comput Biol. 2007; 3(9):1790-800.

[386] Baumgartner G. Indirekte Grössenbestimmung der rezeptiven Felder der Retina beim Menschen mittels der Hermannschen Gittertäuschung. Pflügers Archiv für die gesamte Physiologie. 1960; 272:21-2.

[387] Geier J, Bernáth L, Hudák M, Séra L. Straightness as the main factor of the Hermann grid illusion. Perception. 2008; 37(5):651-65.

[388] Schiller PH, Carvey CE. The Hermann grid illusion revisited. Perception. 2005; 34(11):1375-97.

can be negated with a sinusoidal or waved grid without altering the relationship between the stimulus and the receptive fields. It is possible that this effect arises in the primary visual cortex[389] because of the way S1-type cells (simple cells with just one subfield) respond to the grid.

Figure 4-42: Illusion of simultaneous contrast. The two center gray squares on the left correspond to exactly the same grayscale as seen in the square on the right.

Lateral inhibition affects contrast sensitivity and explains the illusion of **simultaneous contrast**. The two center squares (Figure 4-42) correspond to exactly the same gray value (reflectance). However, they appear different: Lateral inhibition causes a bright surround to an area to appear darker and, conversely, a dark surround to an area to appear lighter.

Figure 4-43: Checkerboards with (left) high contrast and (right) low contrast. In the center of each board is a smaller 4×4 checkerboard patch with a different contrast than that of the surrounding areas. The center patch on the left is exactly the same as the one on the right. However, the contrast of the two patches is not perceived as identical when they are compared to their surroundings.

The checkerboard shadow illusion demonstrates how the human visual system deals with shadows.[390] When attempting to determine the apparent brightness of a surface, our brains know that shadows are misleading as they make surfaces look darker than they normally are. We compensate for this by interpreting shadowy surfaces as brighter.

---

[389] Schiller PH. Central connections of the retinal ON and OFF pathways. Nature. 1982; 297(5867):580-3.
[390] Adelson EH. Perceptual organization and the judgment of brightness. Science. 1993; 262(5142):2042-4.

An aspect of this function is the **contrast adaptation** across space.[391] The surroundings can affect contrast perception. In Figure 4-43, note the left checkerboard with high contrast, as opposed to the right checkerboard with low contrast. Within the center 4×4 patch on the left, the local contrast perception is reduced. On the right side, the reverse happens, even though the shades of gray in the two central 4×4 patches are identical.

Spatial summation[392] is a neural mechanism of eliciting an action potential in a neuron with summed input from multiple presynaptic cells, usually on the dendrites. Spatial summation describes the functional receptive field, applies mainly to rods, and can be conceptualized as the algebraic sum of potentials from different input areas. The area over which summation acts is the critical diameter. Temporal summation describes relay circuits that offer good visual detail but require bright light. The phenomenon occurs when a high frequency of action potentials in the presynaptic neuron elicits the summation of postsynaptic potentials. It applies to cones and enhances the coarse features of a scene at the expense of noisier finer features.

Ricco's law[393] describes spatial summation in the detection of luminance contrast and states that the contrast detection threshold monotonically decreases to a critical area (assumed to have a slope of −1 in log-log coordinates) with stimulus size. According to Ricco's law, within a critical diameter, a threshold is reached when the total luminous energy reaches a constant value k that is less than or equal to the product of the stimulus luminance L, the stimulus area A, and a summation factor n:

Ricco's law:
$$\underbrace{L}_{\text{luminance}} \times \underbrace{A}_{\text{stimulus area}} \times \underbrace{n}_{\text{summation factor}} \geq k \qquad (4.1)$$

The summation factor indicates whether the summation of the receptive field is complete ($n = 1$), partial ($0 < n < 1$), or negligible ($n = 0$). In other words, when the luminance is halved, a doubling in the stimulus area is required to reach the threshold.[394] The critical diameter depends on eccentricity, as the receptive fields increase in size from the fovea because of rod convergence.[375] Ricco's law holds for an area of 0.5° in the parafoveal region (4° to 7° eccentricity) and an area of about 2° at an eccentricity of 35°.[395, 396]

[391] Solomon JA, Sperling G, Chubb C. The lateral inhibition of perceived contrast is indifferent to on-center/off-center segregation, but specific to orientation. Vision Res. 1993; 33(18):2671-83.

[392] Khuu SK, Kalloniatis M. Spatial summation across the central visual field: implications for visual field testing. J Vis. 2015; 15(1):15.1.6.

[393] Riccò A. Relazione fra il minimo angolo visuale e l'intensità luminosa. Ann Ottalm. 1877; 6:373-479.

[394] Graham CH, Brown RH, Mote FA. The relation of size of stimulus and intensity in the human eye: I. Intensity thresholds for white light. J Exp Psychol. 1939; 24(6):555-73.

[395] Davson H. The Eye, Vol. 5: Comparative Physiology. Churchill Livingstone, 1980

[396] Lamming D. Spatial Frequency Channels. Chapter 8. In: Cronly-Dillon J, Vision and Visual Dysfunction, Vol 5. London: Macmillan Press, 1991.

4.4 PHOTORECEPTOR OPTICS

4.4.1 Optical Fiber Guidance

The transit of light inside the photoreceptor cells from the synaptic terminal to the disk area in the cells' outer segments can be described as optical fiber waveguide propagation.[397] An optical fiber is a flexible, thin cylinder of a material that has a refractive index greater than that of the surrounding environment. Light reaches the other end with no losses by successive internal reflections[398] at the core–surrounding interface.

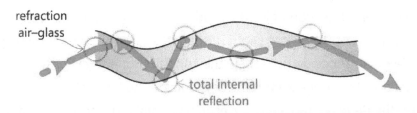

Figure 4-44: Principle of operation of fiber optic light guidance. The governing effect is total internal reflection.

The inner part of a photoreceptor cell has a higher refractive index than its surroundings (1.41 versus 1.36), so light propagates inside the cell in a fashion similar to that of an optical fiber, and even more specifically, a fiber with a graded refractive index.[399]

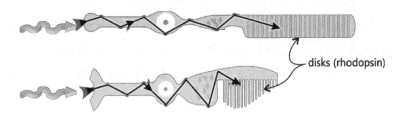

Figure 4-45: The transit of light through cones and rods via multiple total internal reflections.

This function serves several purposes. The first relates to the fact that light must be within a narrowly defined cone of acceptance in order for it to reach the absorption area (disks). Thus, this fiber optic effect favors the detection of directional light from the nodal points,

---

[397] Enoch JM. Active alignment of vertebrate cone and rod photoreceptor waveguides: might this serve as a useful fiber-optics model? In: SPIE Proc. Vol. 7428 Current Developments in Lens Design and Optical Engineering X, Mouroulis PZ, Johnson RB, Mahajan VN, eds.

[398] *Introduction to Optics* § 3.4.4 Waveguides and Optical Fibers.

[399] Barer R, Sidman RL. The absorption spectrum of rhodopsin in solution and in intact rods. J Physiol. 1955; 129(3):60-1.

meaning that it least favors nondesired scattered light (§ 2.5.3), which is unidirectional in nature. It is believed, indeed, that this function is an active, continuously adaptive state;[400] i.e., the orientation of the fiber optic network responds to changes in the visual needs of the eye.[401]

The benefits of this mode include a reduction in the sensation of rays that correspond to scattered light and light that forms large angles with the nodal axis. Additionally, this mode allows for the optimization and normal restriction of the necessary rhodopsin storage volume: Light absorption takes place in a confined area of the cell, so the need for rhodopsin availability is also confined to that area, increasing the readiness of the cell's response.

4.4.2 Stiles–Crawford Effect

To maximize the efficient detection of incident radiation, photoreceptors are oriented toward the posterior nodal point of the eye. As light propagates through the photoreceptors, rays that form a large angle of incidence do not satisfy the condition of entry. For these rays, there is no total internal reflection, but evanescent refraction outside the 'optical fiber' and, eventually, dissipation. Thus, the detected radiation corresponds mainly to a cone of light that reaches the photoreceptors with a relatively small angle with respect to the nodal axis.

Light entering through the pupil center has increased visual sensation compared to light entering peripherally and therefore meets the photoreceptors at a more oblique angle. In other words, rays entering the pupil centrally are more efficient than those entering near the periphery. This is the Stiles–Crawford effect, named after W. H. Stiles and B. H. Crawford.[402, 403]

While a first impression might be that this phenomenon has a negative impact on vision, in fact, it benefits vision, as light forming oblique angles with the photoreceptors mainly corresponds to marginal rays, not chief rays. These rays are more likely to bear high-order aberration content and scatter. In essence, the Stiles–Crawford effect contributes to the

---

[400] Burns SA, Wu S, Delori F, Elsner AE. Direct measurement of human cone photoreceptor alignment. J Opt Soc Amer A. 1995; 12(10):2329-38.

[401] Roorda A, Williams DR. Optical fiber properties of individual human cones. J Vis. 2002; 2(5):404-12.

[402] Stiles WH, Crawford BH. The luminous efficiency of rays entering the eye pupil at different points. Proc R Soc Lond B. 1933; 112:428-50.

[403] This should be called the 'first kind' Stiles–Crawford effect, to differentiate it from the second kind, which relates to the color of the light. Essentially, monochromatic light entering the edge of the pupil is perceived as having different colors than the same light entering the center of the pupil.
Alpern, M. The Stiles–Crawford effect of the second kind (SCII): A review. Perception. 1986; 15(6):785-99.
Pask C, Snyder AW. Theory of the Stiles–Crawford effect of the second kind. In Photoreceptor optics. 1975 (145-58). Springer, Berlin, Heidelberg.

improvement of retinal image quality by reducing the effects of aberrations,[404] with only a small compromise—a slight reduction in perceived image brightness.

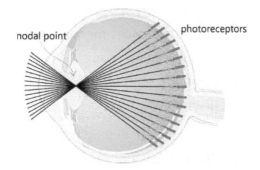

Figure 4-46: Simplified illustration of photoreceptor orientation toward the nodal point.

The Stiles–Crawford effect is simulated in the schematic eye models via apodization.[405] To simulate the effect, pupil transparency is not fixed to 100% but is reduced away from the center. Factors that appear to affect the Stiles–Crawford effect are:

- Wavelength: In the fovea the effect is minimized for the green wavelengths, while it is maximized for the blue and red ends of the visible spectrum. Peripherally (5°), there is a noted minimum for the blue and green wavelengths.
- Eccentricity: Under photopic conditions, the effect appears to reach a maximum slightly outside (approximately 2° to 3°) the fovea, attaining a near doubling of its average value.
- Luminance: The effect occurs even under scotopic conditions but is not as prominent.

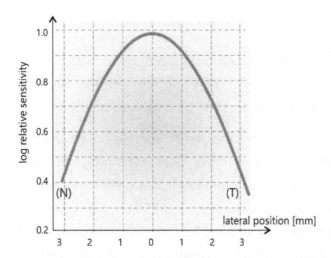

Figure 4-47: Directional lateral sensitivity of the photoreceptor cells.

[404] Bradley A, Xu R, Thibos L, Marin G, Hernandez M. Influence of spherical aberration, stimulus spatial frequency, and pupil apodisation on subjective refractions. Ophthalmic Physiol Opt. 2014; 34(3):309-20.

[405] Atchison DA, Scott DH, Joblin A, Smith G. Influence of Stiles-Crawford effect apodization on spatial visual performance with decentered pupils. J Opt Soc Am A Opt Image Sci Vis. 2001; 18(6):1201-11.

4.5 DIGITAL SIGNAL AND ANALYSIS

A continuous function generally has different values for any incrementally small difference in coordinate space, like the signal on the screen of a common oscilloscope. This is called an analog signal. In contrast, a **digital signal** is represented by specific, discrete values of coordinates that are some specific distance apart.

When we refer to the terms 'analog' and 'digital,' it is useful to think of a clock. In an analog clock, the dials turn in a continuous fashion. In a digital clock, however, the seconds (or even the minutes) are only displayed one at a time. Similarly, a digital optical signal has specific, discrete values of light intensity that change at a specific step along the –x (horizontal) or the –y (vertical) coordinate axis. The minimum step is defined by the spacing of the discrete picture elements along each axis. As the display is composed of picture elements called **pixels**, there are X pixels along the horizontal axis and Y pixels along the vertical axis.

Figure 4-48: Droplet image at pixel resolutions of (left to right) 6×9, 12×18, 24×36, 48×72, and 96×144.

In our digital era, the term resolution is often used in conjunction with the total count, or **pixel density** (which can be reported linearly in pixels/inch). In this commercial use of the term, resolution relates to the pixel count that can be displayed on the screen over a certain area.

For example, in a 32 × 20 cm computer screen, we can have a resolution of 1280 × 800. This may also be reported as 100 pixels/inch (PPI). This display has a total of 1280 × 800 = 1,024,000 pixels = 1 Mpixel, where M = mega = 10^6. Considering the physical size of the screen and a square pixel format, the size of each pixel is 250 μm × 250 μm. Luminance in such a display may only change values by steps of 250 μm along either axis and not by a smaller step, as there is only one, uniform 'light' value corresponding to a single pixel. Obviously, for the same surface size, a larger pixel count means more, and also smaller, pixels. In this case, both the pixel size and their separation are smaller, and the resolution is higher. A higher resolution, indeed, correlates (up to a point) to a better image projection. The higher the resolution the smaller the pixel size and the better (smoother) the image display.

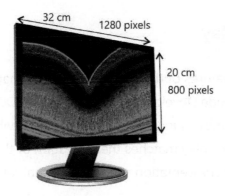

Figure 4-49: The pixels in this standard WXGA high-definition screen have a size of 250 μm × 250 μm.

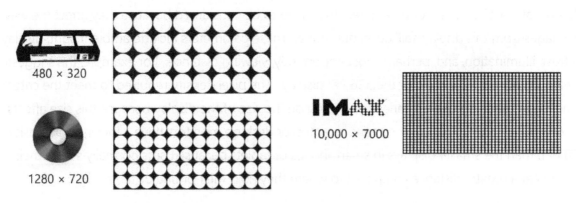

Figure 4-50: Pixels and screen resolutions.

It should be understood, however, that 'more pixels' is only one side of the coin for a better picture. It is true that text, especially smaller fonts, appears sharper and less pixelated in a higher-resolution display. The encoded information to be projected must, however, have at least this embedded pixel density to properly display on the screen.

The projected image must also be perceived by the human visual system. The optical system is tasked with distinguishing details, i.e., perceiving the individual information from each pixel. Optimally, there should be a match between what the digital screen displays and what the human visual system perceives: The display is then coordinated with the capabilities of the human eye. We can only design one of the two components, the display.

Note ☞ : We often read, particularly in trade journals, expressions such as "The camera has 20 megapixel resolution." Technically, this is wrong (and deceptive as well). A camera with 20 megapixel has twenty million sensor pixels to sample the image formed by the optics of that camera. This does not mean that each pixel actually holds useful information about the image content; the number of pixels is related to the resolution but does not define it. It is the optics of the camera that defines resolution and that then must be appropriately sampled by the sensor pixels.

4.5.1 The Retina Display

One of the many fascinating features of the latest-generation smartphones is the Retina display, introduced at the 2010 Worldwide Developers Conference (WWDC) in San Francisco. Eyebrows were raised among retinal scientists and visual optics specialists when Steve Jobs asserted that the pixel density of the Retina display matches the resolution of the human retina. Specifically, this display claimed adequate representation of the perceptual retinal resolution.

The **Retina display** was introduced as a LED-backlit display with a pixel density of 326 pixels per inch (PPI) for a 960×640, 3.5-inch diagonal display (pixel size 78 µm). These are 'hard' numbers. What is not 'hard' is the set of parameters that need to be considered because they affect the way the images from this display 'fall' upon our retina. These parameters include ambient light, display contrast, illumination, and, perhaps most importantly, viewing distance. For example, the suggested viewing distance is 12 inches for the 326 PPI display. The pixel density required to meet the criterion of matching retinal resolution varies depending on the size of the display because this size affects the viewing distance. The larger screens in laptop or desktop monitors have a lower pixel density (220 PPI) than the smaller displays in smartphones or tablets because users normally set up their monitors at a greater distance compared to where they hold their phone or tablet.

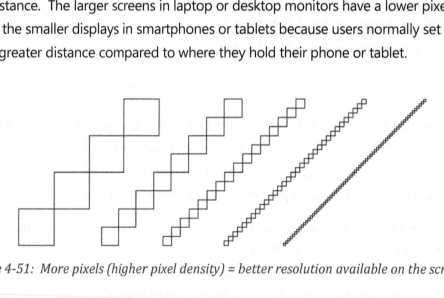

Figure 4-51: More pixels (higher pixel density) = better resolution available on the screen.

Consider the commonly accepted resolution limit for the standard-vision human eye: 1 arcmin (§ 3.2.1). This means that at a distance of 1 ft (= 30.48 cm), we can discern two points if they are 88 µm apart. The pixel density therefore is 1 pixel per 88 µm. Over the area of an inch (25,400 µm), this is about 288 pixels, which we can round up to 300 PPI. Since the Retina display pixel density is higher than that, at 326 PPI, it is fair to accept the claim that this display adequately represents the perceptual resolution of the retina.

Some clarifications are needed. The marketing name Retinal display is based on a standard eye of 20/20 visual acuity. This is not, however, the limit of the human visual acuity: Most young emmetropes have better vision than that. Also, 20/20 visual acuity is meant for distance. The working distances for which these displays are designed are, by no means, distant. It is the intermediate visions, or better yet, the near vision that should be taken into account. Then, we must consider contrast: The optotypes used in visual acuity testing have a black and white contrast, not gray on gray or blue on yellow. Visual acuity therefore typically corresponds to high-contrast, monochromatic details. Often, the pixel details in these displays are of lower contrast, in the sense that the image shown does not carry the full contrast potential of the display.

Even the pixels that appear as white are not a single pixel but three separate subpixels that correspond to red (R), green (G), and blue (B). Are these pixels resolved? No! Each triplet of subpixels is perceived as a single, white pixel.

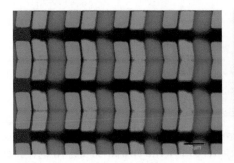

Figure 4-52: (left) Magnified, detailed view of a white section of a Retina display. One pixel is made of three subpixels (the R, G, and B). (right) A magnifying lens or simply a drop of water on the screen will reveal the colors of the subpixels.

4.5.2 Sampling and Digital Sensation

When evaluating the resolution limit, we take into account what is required for two analog signals to be formed as two distinguishable images. We ask: "Are the two formed images separate?" The Rayleigh criterion assumes a continuous, analog, distribution of image light intensity, not a digital distribution. An analog detector simply detects the signal, regardless of how fine or how dim it is. When using digital detectors, however, we also have to ask: "Can the detector 'pick up' the detail formed in the image?"

The retina is a digital sensor, <u>not</u> an analog sensor: While neural signals are continuously variable in terms of their firing rate, their digital aspect relates to the fine, discrete spacing of the cones and rods. To further complicate the explanation, the distribution of the cones and rods is not homogeneous (§ 4.2.1), and their size and inner-retinal circuitry are not uniform (§ 4.2.2). For simplicity, we assume a photosensor array (cone mosaic) that is uniform in density and pixel size. We consider for this purpose the foveal distribution of the hexagonal-shaped cones.

For a target as small as a single light point to be detected, all that is needed is for a single detector element (a cone) to be illuminated: a YES response. Consider now two targets— two small light points. If their images are so close that two adjacent cones are stimulated, the perception is a single target: A YES-YES response is no different from a single YES response! However, to recognize shape, there must be an unstimulated cone between two stimulated ones. This is required to resolve the two targets: We need a YES-NO-YES response by the cones—a form of digital signal like the 1 - 0 - 1 binary response in digital communications. Thus, two individual sources are perceived as two.

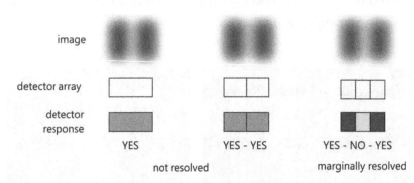

Figure 4-53: (top) Formed image, (middle) detector array, and (bottom) detector response. Only the third array (with three sensors) has adequate cell density to resolve the two lines, i.e., to detect the gap. The first two arrays of one and two cells cannot successfully recognize shape.

This process is called **digital sampling**. The limit to vision is imposed not by diffraction (related to optical resolution), but by the discrete nature of the photoreceptor layer (related to recognition). Even if we assume that an image is perfectly focused on the retina, the next limit on the visual resolution is the spacing of the retinal photoreceptors, which are denser in the foveolar at the central 2°.[258] Experimental data (Table 4–2) suggest that the average linear cone spacing in the foveola is ≈ (2.6±0.1) µm.

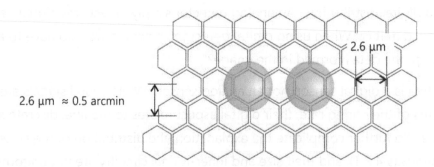

Figure 4-54: Rows of hexagonal retinal cone cells. Their average spacing is ≈ (2.6±0.1) µm, which corresponds to approximately ≈ 0.5 arcmin subtended from the nodal point of the eye.

We convert the linear cone spacing of 2.6 μm into angular spacing (subtended from the nodal point of the eye) using Eq. (6.4), which yields ≈ 0.000156 rad = 0.5 arcmin. In other words, if we draw a line corresponding to 5 arcmin (≈ 26 μm), we cross about 10 cones (Figure 4-55).

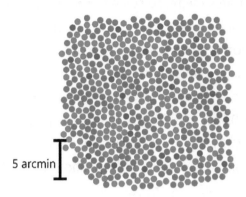

5 arcmin

Figure 4-55: Foveal cone mosaic geometry in the human eye.

Table 4–2: Experimental data for the foveal cone density and spacing.

Source	Linear density (mm⁻¹)	Spacing (μm)
Österberg, 1935[345]	147×10^3	2.43
Yuodelis–Hendrikson, 1986[406]	208×10^3	2.04
Curcio et al., 1990[346]	197×10^3	2.55 ± 0.52
Williams, 1998[407]	129×10^3	2.59 ± 012

This digital **Nyquist limit** to vision derives from the Nyquist sampling theorem, named after Harry Theodor Nyquist. It states that the minimum sampling rate for proper detection of a signal requires sampling at twice the largest frequency of the sampled function.

How is this applied to a spatial signal on the retina? Say we have a sinusoidal signal that varies between max = 1.0 and min = 0 (Figure 4-56). This can be a grating projected onto the retina. To obtain the YES-NO-YES response, we need at least one cone at the maximum, one at the minimum, and another one at the maximum. Thus, two cone spacings are needed for one signal wavelength, i.e., a signal frequency that is half that of the spatial cone (sampling) frequency. Recall that the cone spatial frequency is the reciprocal of the separation between two cones. Half of this is the sampling frequency limit, which is exactly what is illustrated in Figure 4-53: The

---

[406] Yuodelis C, Hendrikson AE. A qualitative analysis of the human fovea during development. Vision Res. 1986; 26(6):847-56.

[407] Williams DR. Topography of the foveal cone mosaic in the living human eye. Vision Res. 1988; 28(3):433-54.

resolution limit derives from the need to properly sample the signal. We can measure only the part of the input signal that falls on the sample positions, which are the cones, by including at least one unilluminated cone (minimum) between two illuminated cones (maximum).

Figure 4-56 (right) illustrates the Nyquist limit: The signal spatial detail (spacing between maximum and minimum) cannot be finer than the cone spacing. Simply put, to find the resolution limit of the human eye in relation to the discrete nature of the photoreceptor mosaic, we consider the average cone spacing of 2.6 μm, which corresponds to ≈ 0.5 arcmin ≈ 60 cycles/degree. At the digital/neural sampling limit, an image of an Airy disk peaking at one cone needs to be angularly sized with a radius ≈ 0.5 arcmin. This is, therefore, the ultimate limit to human vision, as was suggested as early as 1922;[408] population studies have shown that the minimum angle of resolution in healthy emmetropic individuals is, indeed, about 0.6 to 0.7 arcmin.[269]

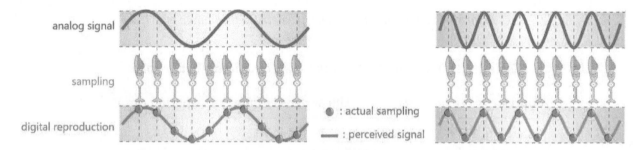

Figure 4-56: Digital sampling (left) at more than the Nyquist limit (oversampling) and (right) at the Nyquist limit. The cone spacing produces a YES-NO-YES response to the projected sinusoidal function.

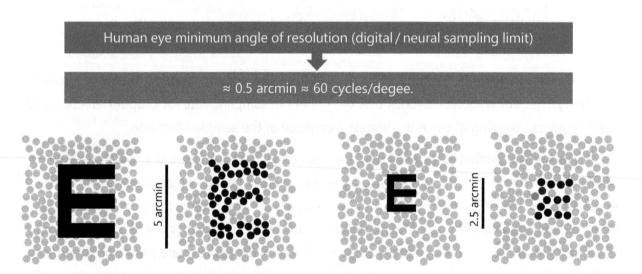

Figure 4-57: Letter E foveal cone sampling. (left) Sampling that corresponds to standard 20/20 visual acuity (1 arcmin MAR) and (right) sampling that corresponds to 20/10 visual acuity (0.5 arcmin MAR).

---

[408] Hartridge H. Visual acuity and the resolving power of the eye. J Physiol. 1922; 57(1-2):52-67.

If we compare this MAR to the limit imposed by diffraction (2 mm pupil), which is ≈ 1 arcmin, the foveal neural sampling allows for about twice as much detail. For example, the letter E for standard visual acuity (20/20 Snellen, logMAR 0.0) is recognized in the human retina as shown in Figure 4-57 (left). The 5 arcmin angle subtended corresponds to a retinal image of size about 25 µm.

Example ☞: What is the image size for an object subtending 5 arcmin at the eye's nodal point?

We first convert 5 arcmin to radians: 5 arcmin = 0.00145 rad. We then use Eq. (6.3) to calculate the retinal image size: $h' = 0.00145 \cdot 17$ mm = 0.0247 mm ≈ 25 µm.

If the retinal image of a standard-vision optotype has a height of 25 µm, then along any line of 25 µm, there are about 10 cone cells that participate in the perception (sampling) of the standard visual acuity optotype E image along either the vertical or the horizontal direction.

We realize, thus, that the standard vision, which can marginally distinguish a letter whose detail is about 1 arcmin, has a lot of room for improvement. The foveolar cone mosaic can resolve shape of about half this size, as we need five cones along the vertical axis (YES-NO-YES-NO) to resolve the limbs of the letter E [Figure 4-57 (right)]. This was demonstrated by Campbell and Green in 1965[409] with sinusoidal interference patterns projected onto the retina.

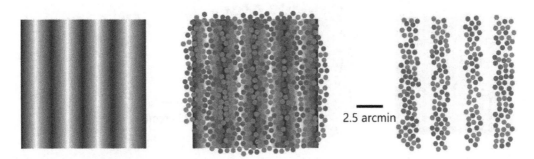

2.5 arcmin

Figure 4-58: Sinusoidal grating resolution at the limit of human visual acuity (veridical limit).

Retinal cone mosaic density:	Sampling by cones sets a limit to vision:	It is about half of the diffraction limit to vision:
• Cone spacing ≈ 2.6 µm	• A pair of illuminated cones separated by a single non-illuminated cone.	• ≈ 0.5 arcmin • ≈ 60 cycles/degree

[409] Campbell FW, Green DG. Optical and retinal factors affecting visual resolution. J Physiol. 1965; 181(3):576-93.

What happens if the letter E becomes even smaller? If a signal has finer detail than this, the spacings (the limbs) of the letter E become too small (too closely packed) to be properly recognized (Figure 4-59).

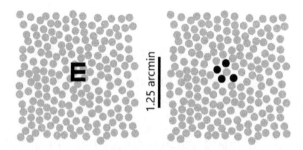

Figure 4-59: Foveoal cone sampling of the letter E beyond the Nyquist limit does not yield recognition.

This lower limit is also determined by the Nyquist theorem. The Nyquist limit provides a theoretical limit to the rate at which we need to sample a signal that contains data at a certain (high) spatial frequency. If the sampling does not comply with the minimum step required by the theorem, not only do we not accurately sample the signal, but the reconstructed data contain artifacts, the aliases.

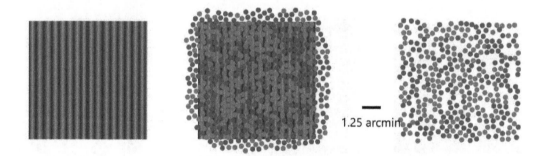

Figure 4-60: Sinusoidal grating resolution beyond the limit of human visual acuity.

In such a case, the sampling is not dense enough to sequentially scan at least a maximum and a minimum. This phenomenon, called **aliasing**, corresponds to a false signal reconstruction. The signal may be represented with a different, smaller frequency, or with no frequency at all. If, for example, the sampling picks one out of two maxima and one out of two minima, then the signal will be reconstructed with half the frequency. If the sampling picks just the midpoints (Figure 4-61), then the reconstructed signal will appear as a flat line.

We stress, once again, that the neural visual acuity limit discussed here refers only to photopic visual acuity, considering cone-dominated vision, adequate luminance, and a small angle with respect to the visual axis. Away from the fovea, and for lower luminance, scotopic/

rod-dominated vision is considered, which corresponds to a coarser 'sampling' spacing—that of the rod receptive fields (§ 4.3.5). Simply put, the 'pixel' is not one cone as in the fovea but is a large number of dependent rods. Thus, it is not the average rod spacing that should be considered, but the average spacing of the groups of rods (and, eventually, ganglion cells) of a single receptive field.

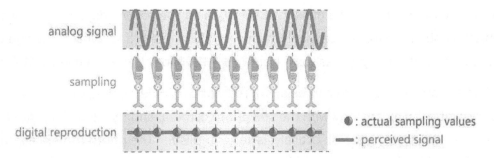

Figure 4-61: Aliasing example: The signal reconstruction fails because sampling is performed by less than half of the minimum required by the Nyquist theorem.

For this reason, the receptor-sampling limit to visual acuity plays a dominant role in the peripheral field. The fovea, however, is usually optically (diffraction) limited.

Another factor that influences the digital limitation of eyes of high (or short) axial length is retinal stretching (§ 6.5.3).[410] In axial myopia (long axial length, § 6.4.1.1), the retina stretches such that there are fewer cone receptors per unit retinal area. Thus, even under the same retinal image size, this reduced cone density leads to fewer receptors being stimulated, so the object appears smaller, and visual acuity drops. On the other hand, in axial hyperopia (short axial length), the cone receptors are pushed closer together; this increased cone density leads to more receptors being stimulated for the same retinal image size. Thus, the object appears larger, and visual acuity improves!

Note: The representations shown in Figure 4-57 and Figure 4-59 may imply that the eye is fixating on the target. However, when the eye is fully stabilized, perception fades. This means that the oculomotor system, which involves constant small eye movements known as saccades, is essential in providing a sharply perceived image. Also, several other simplifications are considered, which include the 1-to-1 convergence ratio of ganglion cells. The information arriving at the visual cortex is far more complex than a simple pixelated image.

[410] Chuia TYP, Yapa MKH, Chana HHL, Thibos LN. Retinal stretching limits peripheral visual acuity in myopia. Vision Res. 2005; 45(5):593-605.

4.5.3 Digital Resolution of the Human Eye? Is it 240 Mpixel?

In the technology world, ever since the Turing machine was first described in 1936, the norm has been digital. The digital revolution began to take photography by storm in the early 2000s. Digital photo cameras have evolved from sub-megapixel to 50 Mpixel. The highest pixel count of a 35 mm sensor today is on the Canon 5DS/R, with a resolution of about 8688 × 5792 (50.6 Mpixel) over a sensor area of 860 mm². The main marketing/selling spec of any digital camera is therefore its megapixel number. Do we realize that human eyes ARE digital? If so, what is the equivalent megapixel count? Is it 240 Mpixel, as some claim? Is it 120 Mpixel, or is it a mere 1 Mpixel?

All of the above questions can be answered positively, depending on the aspect of vision under consideration. The analogy with the still photo camera, and by extension, with a 'resolution' that we can evaluate objectively, is very simplistic. The photo camera captures a full-frame snapshot, while the eye is extremely dynamic during image recording. The eye moves ceaselessly in sub-seconds, and the visual cortex fuses and processes a continuous stream of information—this is what we call vision. The instantaneously formed image can be marginally compared with an image taken by a still camera. It is perhaps more suitable to instead draw parallels between the eye and a digital video camera.

The very high resolution in the eye only corresponds to foveal vision, the central 2°–3° of the visual field (Figure 1-5). Over this relatively small retinal area, the packing density of the cone receptors is high and can be more than 400/mm or 160,000/mm² (Figure 4-23). Therefore, optimal visual acuity (as well as color perception) only relates to this small section of the visual field.

In a more representative estimate, consider a central field of 10° × 10° with an average cone spacing of 0.3 μm, or angularly, 0.5 arcmin, i.e., 2 pixel/arcmin. Recall that there are 60 arcmin per 1°, so the pixel count along a line is 10° × 60 arcmin/° × 2 pixel/arcmin = 1200. This field, thus, corresponds to a resolution of 1200 × 1200 = 1.44 Mpixel.

The constant movement of the eyes, however, allows for the translation of this high-level analysis to multiple adjacent fixation points. Visual processing retains the advantages of this 'localized' high resolution for a much larger section of the visual field, and what we ultimately perceive is an overlaid, processed, high-resolution signal.

In an extended field, say 90° × 90°, the pixel count is 10,800 × 10,800 for an analysis of 116.64 ≈ **120 Mpixel**. In addition, if we consider vision from both eyes, we reach the **240 Mpixel**. The hypothesis here is that visual acuity is optimal over the entire extent of the visual field. This hypothesis does not apply to an instant snapshot; it only applies after the cerebral overlay of a large number of high-resolution images.

4.6 RETINA QUIZ

Retina Optics and Morphology

1) The part of the retina most sensitive to light is the ...
   a) optic nerve head
   b) perimeter
   c) macula
   d) fovea
   e) foveola

2) The lowest concentration of photoreceptors in the retina is found at the ...
   a) optic nerve head
   b) perimeter
   c) macula
   d) fovea
   e) foveola

3) The retina size (diagonally across) is about ...
   a) 2 mm
   b) 12 mm
   c) 22 mm
   d) 32 mm

4) The retina radius of curvature is about ...
   a) 2 mm
   b) 12 mm
   c) 22 mm
   d) 32 mm

5) The fovea extends to about ____ of the visual field.
   a) 0.2° to 1°
   b) 2° to 3°
   c) 5° to 10°
   d) 20° to 30°

6) The blind spot corresponds to (two correct) ...
   a) a central area of damaged photoreceptors
   b) an area of saturated cones
   c) an area of zero photoreceptor concentration
   d) maximum concentration of optic nerve fibers

7) The blind spot is located about ...
   a) 12–15° temporally
   b) 12–15° nasally
   c) 5° inferiorly
   d) 7.5° superiorly

8) The photoreceptors most sensitive to light are the ...
   a) cones
   b) rods
   c) ganglion cells
   d) bipolar cells

9) The highest rod density is encountered ...
   a) 12° nasally to the fovea
   b) 20° nasally and peripherally to the fovea
   c) centrally to the fovea
   d) at the optic nerve head

10) At the fovea, cone cell convergence ratio is about ...
   a) 1:1
   b) 1:10
   c) 1:100
   d) 1:1000

11) The central part of the foveola contains which receptors?
   a) rods only
   b) cones only
   c) cones and rods
   d) horizontal receptors
   e) ganglion receptors

12) Peripherally, rod cell convergence ratio is about ...
   a) 1:1
   b) 1:10
   c) 1:100
   d) 1:1000

13) In the peripheral retina, visual acuity with rod vision is lower than visual acuity with cone vision because ...
   a) more rods converge per ganglion cell
   b) there are fewer rods than cones
   c) there are fewer cones than rods
   d) there is inadequate light to focus properly at light levels at which rods function
   e) having three kinds of cones (but only one kind of rod) decreases visual acuity

14) Cone visual acuity is _____ than rod visual acuity because the cones converge _____ than the rods.

   a) better; more
   b) better; less
   c) worse; less
   d) worse; more

15) The peak response of the eye to light in bright daylight conditions occurs for the ...

   a) red 0.663 µm
   b) orange 0.600 µm
   c) green 0.555 µm
   d) blue 0.450 µm

16) The sensitivity of the eye to different wavelengths of light is called ...

   a) an absolute threshold
   b) a color matching function
   c) a reflectance spectrum
   d) a spectral sensitivity curve
   e) a dark adaptation curve

17) A sign with white letters could be read with the fovea using the least amount of light energy. Which wavelength would you use?

   a) 494 nm
   b) 600 nm
   c) 555 nm
   d) 500 nm
   e) 580 nm

18) Luminance of the starry sky is $L = 10^{-3}$ cd/m^2. This is also referred to as ...

   a) $\log L = -1000$
   b) $\log L = -10$
   c) $\log L = -3$
   d) $\log L = +3$

19) A bright midday sky has luminance up to $\log L = +6$. This luminance is how many orders of magnitude more than a moonlit sky ($\log L = -1$)?

   a) 7
   b) 6
   c) 5
   d) 1

20) When ambient luminance is greater than $\log L = +0.5$, vision is predominantly ...

   a) photopic
   b) mesopic

   c) scotopic

21) The retina is more sensitive to light under ...

   a) photopic conditions
   b) mesopic conditions
   c) scotopic conditions

22) Highest visual acuity is achieved under ...

   a) photopic vision
   b) mesopic vision
   c) scotopic vision

23) The scotopic luminosity function has a peak sensitivity at ...

   a) 455 nm
   b) 507 nm
   c) 545 nm
   d) 555 nm
   e) 567 nm

24) When prevailing illumination suddenly increases, then pupil constriction ...

   a) completely compensates for the increased luminance
   b) compensates for the increased luminance for the most part
   c) only partially contributes by decreasing luminance reaching the retina
   d) contributes to more light reaching the retina

25) The most important adaptation response to increased luminance is ...

   a) pupil constriction
   b) a drop in retinal sensitivity
   c) a shift from cone- to rod-initiated vision
   d) an increase of receptive fields

26) Afterimages are result of ...

   a) Purkinje shift
   b) receptive field increase
   c) cognitive fields persistence
   d) light/dark adaptation

27) The Purkinje shift describes the _____ when conditions change from photopic to scotopic.

   a) shift of the Purkinje image locations
   b) increase in the Purkinje image reflection
   c) increased spectral sensitivity toward shorter wavelengths
   d) shift to cone-initiated vision

28) In old-time submarines, the control room was illuminated with red light for the benefit of the periscope operator. Why is this beneficial?

    a) L cones are most sensitive to red light, allowing them to provide higher acuity when viewing dim scenes through the periscope.

    b) S- and M-cone types do not become light-adapted, allowing the operator to view dim scenes through the periscope.

    c) Periscope operators maintain diets high in a special form of vitamin A initiated by red light, which makes their visual system more sensitive to red light than normal.

    d) Rods are very insensitive to red light, which allows the operator to remain dark-adapted and ready to view dim scenes via the periscope.

29) In a large receptive field, there are more ...

    a) ganglion cells connected to cones
    b) ganglion cells connected to rods
    c) cones connected to ganglion cells
    d) rods connected to ganglion cells

30) A large receptive field ...

    a) enhances sensitivity to light
    b) improves visual acuity
    c) facilitates color vision
    d) helps contrast sensitivity

31) Receptive fields are generally larger ...

    a) peripherally
    b) centrally
    c) temporally
    d) nasally

Retina Neural Function

32) The absence of light stimulus may provoke what reaction at the ganglion cells (two correct)?

    a) initiates their firing
    b) stops their firing
    c) increases their firing rate
    d) decreases their firing rate

33) Whether the firing rate at a ganglion cell will increase or decrease depends on ...

    a) light being turned on or off
    b) spatial location of light stimulus
    c) type of on-center or off-center cell and spatial location of light stimulus
    d) type of on-center or off-center cell and ambient luminance

34) Signal falling within the center of the receptive field in the on-center ganglion cell leads to ...

    a) decrease of the cell's firing rate
    b) increase of the cell's firing rate
    c) decrease of the cell's receptive field
    d) increase of the cell's receptive field

35) On- or off-center cell types include (two correct):

    a) cones
    b) rods
    c) ganglion
    d) bipolar

36) When lateral inhibition occurs, the firing rate of a photoreceptor neuron is ...

    a) reduced if nearby neurons increase firing rate

    b) increased if nearby neurons increase firing rate
    c) matching the firing rate of the nearby neurons
    d) exactly the opposite firing rate of nearby neurons

37) When a large-area spot simultaneously stimulates both the center and the surrounding subfields of a receptive field, the ganglion cell's firing rate ...

    a) increases notably
    b) remains unaffected
    c) decreases notably

38) The highest concentration of rhodopsin is found in what part of the cone/rod cells?

    a) disks
    b) mitochondria
    c) nucleus
    d) synaptic terminals

39) Light energy is absorbed in what part of the cone/rod cells?

    a) disks
    b) mitochondria
    c) nucleus
    d) synaptic terminals

40) What part of the cone/rod cell is closest to the incident light?

    a) disks
    b) mitochondria
    c) nucleus
    d) synaptic terminals

41) To maximize efficient detection of incident light, the cone/rod cells are oriented toward the ...

    a) posterior focal point
    b) posterior nodal point
    c) anterior focal point
    d) optical conjugate of the retina

42) The spatial summation properties of the visual system are, up to a critical value, described by ...

    a) Bloch's law
    b) Ricco's law
    c) the Talbot–Plateau law
    d) the Stiles–Crawford law

43) The cone pathway differs from the rod pathway because ...

    a) the cone pathway is 1:1 and has a low acuity, whereas the rod pathway is many-to-one and has a high acuity
    b) the cone pathway is many-to-one and has a low acuity, whereas the rod pathway is 1:1 with a high acuity
    c) the cone pathway is 1:1 with a high acuity, whereas the rod pathway is many-to-one with a low acuity
    d) the rod pathway has a low absolute light sensitivity
    e) the cone pathway is 1:1 with a high acuity, whereas the rod pathway is many-to-one with a high acuity

Digital Sampling

44) A digital signal ...

    a) changes value gradually over time or space
    b) can only be represented by binary numbers
    c) can only have integer values
    d) attains discrete values over time or space

45) A 100×100 pixel representation has how many more pixels over a 10×10 representation of the same image?

    a) 10,000
    b) 9,900
    c) 100
    d) 10

46) A 1280×800 resolution screen has about how many pixels?

    a) 800
    b) 1280
    c) 2080
    d) 1 million

47) A retina display has what design characteristic?

    a) 120 million pixels
    b) pixel density slightly higher than the density corresponding to the resolving power of the eye for the reading distance of that screen
    c) screen size producing retinal image covering the macula when the screen at the proper reading distance
    d) produces colors to which the retina is most sensitive

48) What should be the screen pixel spacing such that an eye with logMAR = 0.0 visual acuity will barely be able to discern an object when the screen is held at 1 ft (=30.48) cm?

    a) 288 μm
    b) 160 μm
    c) 88 μm
    d) 26 μm

49) Back to Q 48. When this 'threshold' spacing is achieved, the pixel-per-inch (PPI) metric is about ...

    a) 288 PPI
    b) 160 PPI
    c) 88 PPI
    d) 26 PPI

50) At the fovea, the average cone spacing is about ...

    a) 288 μm
    b) 160 μm
    c) 88 μm
    d) 26 μm

51) Back to Q 50. This spacing subtends what angle from the nodal point of the eye?

    a) 1 arcmin
    b) 0.5 arcmin
    c) 0.26 arcmin
    d) 0.1 arcmin

52) A line of about 5 arcmin across the central fovea will stimulate about _____ cones.

a) 20
b) 10
c) 5
d) 1

53) To detect an ON-OFF-ON retinal signal, the following occurs:

a) a cone responding YES
b) two adjacent cones responding YES and NO
c) three adjacent cones responding YES, NO, and YES
d) four adjacent cones responding YES, NO, YES, and NO

54) Aliasing occurs when the spatial density of the presented information is ...

a) more than double that of the sampling rate
b) exactly at the sampling rate
c) half the sampling rate
d) a non-integer multiple of the sampling rate
e) an integer multiple of the sampling rate

55) If the central foveal cone spacing is 0.5 arcmin, the limit of resolution imposed by the cone digital sampling is ...

a) 2 arcmin
b) 1 arcmin
c) 0.5 arcmin
d) 0.25 arcmin

56) Back to Q 55. The visual acuity limit corresponding to the digital sampling is ...

a) logMAR = +0.1
b) logMAR = 0.0
c) logMAR = –0.1
d) logMAR = –0.5

57) Considering the cone digital sampling, a letter E spanning 1.25 arcmin across will be sampled ...

a) satisfactorily
b) marginally
c) poorly
d) not at all

58) A letter E spanning 2.5 arcmin at the fovea is marginally sampled by the cone digital mosaic. This suggests that the cone spacing is about ...

a) 2.5 arcmin
b) 1.0 arcmin
c) 0.5 arcmin
d) 0.25 arcmin

59) If the average cone spacing corresponds to the correct answer given in Q 58, then there are about ....

a) 0.5 pixels/arcmin
b) 1.0 pixels/arcmin
c) 2.0 pixels/arcmin
d) 4.0 pixels/arcmin

60) In a central field of about 10°×10°, if the cone spacing yields 2 pixel/arcmin, then the pixel count provides a resolution of ...

a) 20 pixel
b) 1200 pixel
c) 1.44 Mpixel
d) 120 Mpixel

61) What mechanism represents a finer limit to visual acuity in the human eye?

a) aberrations
b) refractive error
c) diffraction
d) depth of field
e) cone digital sampling

62) An exoplanet ET species has eyes with cone cells of four times the spatial lateral extent compared to human eyes. Everything else being equal, the aspect that is decreased compared to human vision is ...

a) light sensitivity
b) visual acuity
c) color vision
d) peripheral vision

63) Back to Q 62. The pixel density of that ET eye would be about....

a) 0.5 pixels/arcmin
b) 1.0 pixels/arcmin
c) 2.0 pixels/arcmin
d) 4.0 pixels/arcmin

64) Vision ...

a) has peak discrimination ability around the center 2° to 3° of the visual field
b) is consistent acuity over the entire extent of the visual field at any given time
c) has peak light sensitivity around the center 2° to 3° of the visual field
d) is consistent color discrimination across the entire extent of the visual field

4.7 RETINA SUMMARY

The retina is the ocular element tasked with transforming the light energy distribution formed by the retinal image into a neural signal, which is transmitted via the optic nerve and the visual pathway, ultimately, to the visual cortex.

The transformation of light energy into a neural signal entails a complex photochemical process that involves the absorption of light energy by the photoreceptor cells (cones and rods) and initial transformation and processing by bipolar cells, then synapsing to ganglion cells. A network of other retinal cells, which include horizontal cells, amacrine cells, and inner plexiform neurons, also contributes to the first level of processing that takes place in the retina.

Retina Optics

The surface of the retina is curved, with a radius of curvature of approximately 12 mm. This shape helps to compensate for field curvature. The retina is thinnest at its very center, the foveola, which is the central part of the fovea, which, itself, is the central part of the macula.

Anatomically, the retina is a thin multilayer of mainly neuronal cells. The photoreceptor layer is closer to the choroid; thus, light reaching the photoreceptors has to transcend several other layers, including the inner limiting membrane, the nerve fiber layer, the ganglion cell layer, the inner plexiform layer, the inner nuclear layer, the outer plexiform layer, the outer nuclear layer, and the external limiting membrane.

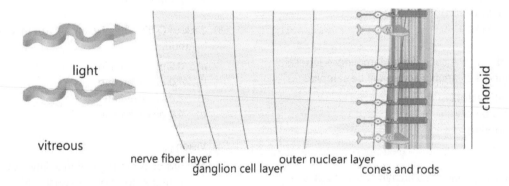

Figure 4-62: Partial detail of the retinal layered structure.

The two types of photoreceptors, cones and rods, differ in their spatial distribution, population, spectral response, and connectivity to upper-level retinal cells.

Cones (about 5 million in the human eye) are active at higher light levels than rods and are responsible for daylight vision. They are mainly concentrated at the fovea and provide high spatial visual acuity. Their peak sensitivity is around the yellow-green, λ = 555 nm.

Rods, which are far more abundant (100 million rods), are responsible for vision at low light levels (scotopic vision). They do not mediate color vision and provide low spatial visual acuity. The photochromatic interval is an expression of the difference between the sensitivities of rod-mediated and cone-mediated vision at any given wavelength.

Depending on the ambient luminance, the ranges of vision can be distinguished as

• Photopic vision applies to luminance above 3 cd/m^2 (log L = +0.5). Initiated by cones, it is highly color-sensitive and of high resolution.

• Mesopic vision applies to luminance between 0.001 and 3 cd/m^2 (–3 < log L < +0.5). Characterized by transitional color perception and resolution, it is initiated by both rods and cones.

• Scotopic vision applies to luminance of less than 0.001 cd/m^2 (log L = –3). Initiated by rods, it has minimal color sensitivity and low resolution.

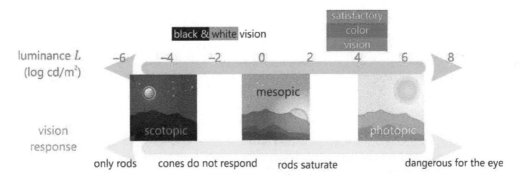

Figure 4-63: Dynamic ranges of vision, depending on luminance.

Digital Sampling and Vision

The retina is a digital sensor due to the fine, discrete spacing of its cones and the rods. Specifically, the spatial arrangement in the central fovea consists of a hexagonal structure, with a spacing of about 2.6 μm, which subtends an angle of 0.5 arcmin from the nodal point of the eye. Per the Nyquist theorem, the minimum sampling rate to properly detect a discrete signal requires sampling at twice the largest frequency of the sampled function.

This leads to a resolution limit of the human eye in relation to the discrete nature of the photoreceptor mosaic; thus, we consider the average cone spacing of 2.6 μm, which corresponds to ≈ 0.5 arcmin ≈ 60 cycles/degree.

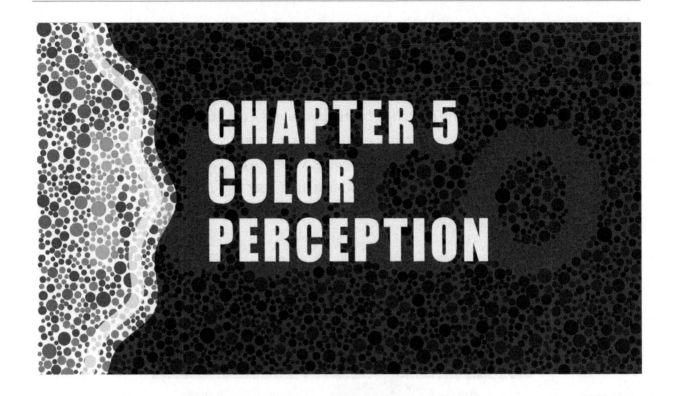

5.1 COLOR IN OPTICS

To understand color vision, we need to understand the physics of light. The question of 'color' is a very interesting one. Color theory encompasses a multitude of definitions and concepts. **Color** is a human physiological perceptual property that we assign to objects or self-illuminating bodies, usually referred to as light sources, on the basis of spectral characteristics. In this sense, color is not only a property of electromagnetic radiation but is also an aspect of the observer's visual perception. In the physical world of photons and electromagnetic waves, however, there are no colors with this familiar meaning. Physics, actually, only regards the different energies of photons that distinguish colors, or, under the wave theory, the different wavelengths or frequencies of the radiation.

A bundle of white light is just a mix of different wavelengths that can be decomposed into the constituent color components if it passes through a prism or water drops, forming a rainbow. Nature is not shy of demonstrating the beauty of colors. Spectra of colors can be observed by thin-film interference: This is essentially the reason we can see the incandescent colors in a soap bubble! The color at each point depends on whether the conditions for constructive interference exist for the specific optical path through the layer of water for that wavelength. Colors that are vivid and engaging appear at sunrise and sunset as a result of the wavelength dependence of the angular features and the scattering intensity of the sunlight.

Physics has a less romantic, but very precise, language to describe color. It is associated with the spectral nature of light, described by its wavelength λ (or, equivalently, its frequency ν). **Visible light** corresponds to a small range of the electromagnetic spectrum, roughly from wavelength 0.38 µm = 380 nm (which we perceive as violet) to 0.70 µm = 700 nm (which we perceive as red). These wavelengths refer to propagation in air (vacuum, to be precise). Recall that 1 µm is one-millionth (10^{-6}) of a meter, and 1 nm is one-billionth (10^{-9}) of a meter.

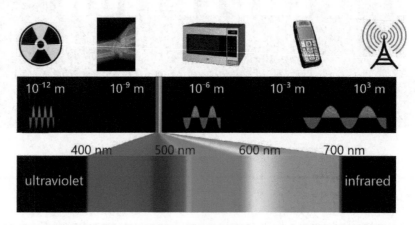

Figure 5-1: The visible part of the electromagnetic spectrum.

White light is visible radiation that consists of several monochromatic components that correspond to different wavelengths. White, in other words, is not a color, but a juxtaposition of colors, perceived as white by the human sense of vision. Black, white, and the shades of gray in between are achromatic 'colors' and have approximately equal distributions across all wavelengths in the visible.

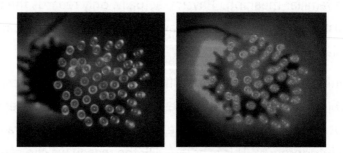

Figure 5-2: The human perception of light emitted by the source is expressed as (left) 'the color is blue' and (right) 'the color is red,' while physics expresses this as 'the wavelength is 480 nm' and 'the wavelength is 680 nm, 'respectively.

To describe the color of a reflecting object, we use **reflectance**, a metric of the fraction of reflected intensity with respect to the incident intensity (§ 2.5.2) which, usually, can be different across the various parts of the visible spectrum. To describe the color of a filter, we use the complementary terms of absorbance and/or transmittance. Absorbance is the relative amount of light absorbed within a filter, and transmittance is the relative amount of light transcending the filter. Typically, these are both reported as either a fraction (values 0 to 1) or as a percentage.

If an object is illuminated with white light, a part of the light is absorbed, and a part is reflected. Each object therefore has color because it reflects, for example, part of the blue, a little yellow, and a bit of red, but in different proportions. Plant leaves are green because their cells contain chloroplasts with chlorophyll pigment, which absorbs deep blue and red. Green is strongly reflected, giving the appearance of a green leaf.

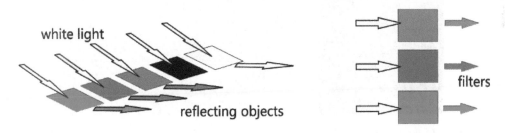

Figure 5-3: The appearance of color in reflecting objects is related to the spectral reflectance characteristics.

Thus, a source that has a narrow bandwidth and emits light at a specific wavelength, say 500 nm, is perceived as blue, while light from a 650 nm source is perceived as red. Such a source is called **monochromatic** because the wavelength of the emitted light is narrowly defined; in other words, the range of possible wavelengths is very limited. Instead, a white light source emits visible radiation that consists of many monochromatic components, with quite different values of their wavelength. The spectral range is extensive, possibly covering a large part of the visible spectrum.

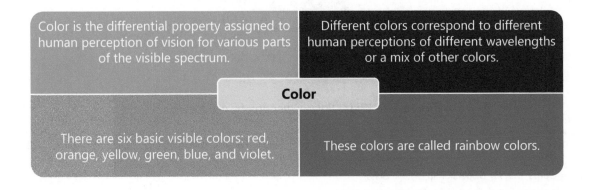

The colors in nature are not an absolute property of objects or light sources, but a result of human perception, which is related to the wavelength of the reflected, transmitted, or emitted radiation. Color, in human visual perception, is the cerebral interpretation of a stimulus that arises from a group of photoreceptor cells responding to this radiation.

As was first discovered by Isaac Newton more than 300 years ago in his second-most-famous experiment, white sunlight is dispersed into its seven distinct colors upon exiting a prism. The fundamental premise underlying this phenomenon, which is called material dispersion,[411] is that there is a different propagation speed for each different wavelength.

 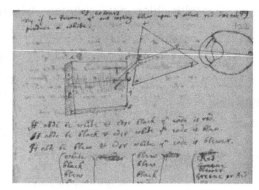

Figure 5-4: (left) Isaac Newton performing his second most famous experiment (no falling apples this time!) and (right) his notes on the results.

Dispersion is expressed by a different refractive index $n(\lambda)$ for different wavelengths λ. Light entering one of the two angled refracting surfaces of a prism[412] emerges (after two successive refractions from the other refracting surface) with an emergent angle that is different for each wavelength.

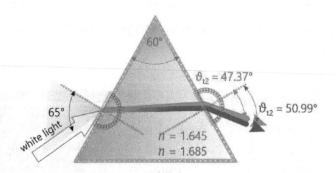

Figure 5-5: White light dispersion by a glass prism.

---

[411] *Wave Optics* § 3.3.2 Dispersion in Optical Glass.
[412] *Introduction to Optics* § 3.3.1 Ray Deviation in a Prism.

However small the difference in the refractive index may be, it results in a different deviation angle. In all relations describing the deviation of a beam by a prism (or by other optical elements), the expression for the refractive index n is not a fixed number but is a material property that is dependent on the wavelength $n(\lambda)$.

Dispersion occurs whenever electromagnetic radiation interacts with matter. Every material presents dispersion, including all ocular media (§ 2.2.2); only in vacuum, where there is no matter to interact with light, is there no dispersion. Usually, the longer the wavelength λ, the lower the value of the refractive index—this is called normal dispersion. The dispersion curve of $n(\lambda)$ versus λ describes the dependence of the refractive index on the wavelength. As shown in Figure 5-6, longer wavelengths tend to have a lower refractive index (normal dispersion). For this glass, the indices range from $n = 1.685$ for indigo-violet ($\lambda = 380$ nm) to $n = 1.645$ for red ($\lambda = 680$ nm).

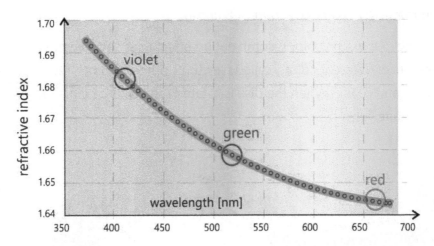

Figure 5-6: Normal dispersion curve in the visible range of the electromagnetic spectrum for a flint-type of silica glass.

The rainbow[121] is nature's most impressive manifestation of dispersion. When a continuous spectrum of sunlight impinges on rain droplets with a proper angle (Figure 5-7), the emerging rays (refraction A, internal reflection B, refraction C) are angularly separated ($\approx 2°$) depending on their wavelength because water displays normal dispersion.

The captivating aura of the rainbow is present in many mythologies. The rainbow has often been conceptualized as a path between the earth and sky, or between humans and gods. In Greek mythology, the messenger Goddess **Iris** followed this path to transfer 'divine water' from the spring called Styx to the Gods, which is why the rainbow colors are called **iris colors**.

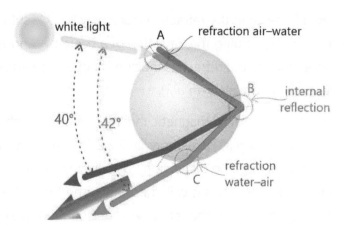

Figure 5-7: The rainbow's principle of operation.

Recombination of the seven iris colors of dispersed white light can lead back to white light. One way to achieve this is to direct the dispersed beam exiting the prism into another prism that is symmetrically reversed. [Figure 5-8 (left)].

Another way to view the color recombination effect uses the Newton disk, a round disk containing segments of different colors, called Newton's primary colors: red, orange, yellow, green, blue, indigo, and violet. When the disk is rotated rapidly, the colors fade to white, giving the perception of white light.

Figure 5-8: (left) White light analysis and re-composition by a two-prism arrangement. (right) Newton's color wheel, which, when rotated at a high speed, produces the perception of white light.

Physically pure or **simple colors** are those associated with a monochromatic spectral wavelength. The iris colors fall in this category: They cannot be further split when they pass through a prism. Conversely, compound colors are composed of various wavelengths: A ray bundle of a compound color can be dispersed into its component simple colors when it passes through a prism.

5.1.1 Primary Colors

A broad range of colors can be produced using just certain simple colors. The famed English physicist Thomas Young[413] demonstrated in 1802 that select parts of the visible spectrum could reproduce white light. The renowned German ophthalmologist Hermann von Helmholtz in the mid-1850s managed to quantify these phenomena and discovered that different amounts of blue, green, and red may lead to the production of a wide range of colors. He also proposed that it is the relative strength of the signals that determines how we interpret color. A wide gamut of colors can be composed that are not physically pure, such as pink, brown, and purple.

Helmholtz used color-matching experiments, where participants would alter the amounts of three different wavelengths of light to match a test color. Participants might not match all colors if they used only two wavelengths but could match any color in the spectrum if they used three. These are the **primary colors**, and the corresponding theory is referred to as the Young–Helmholtz theory of color vision or **trichromacy theory**. The exact primary colors to be used are not critically important, as long as mixing any two of them does not produce the third; in other words, the three primary colors are independent of each other.

This simple technique is applied in the operation of projection screens, such as those used in the cabins of commercial aircraft as recent as 15 years ago and in home theaters. By varying the luminance from each projector, we can achieve a satisfactory gamut of reproduced colors. In most cases, the three selected colors are red (R = 700 nm), green (G = 546 nm), and blue (B = 436 nm). If employed in a subtractive combination, such as used in the mixing of dyes for printing, the set of primary colors may consist of cyan, magenta, and yellow (CMY).

Figure 5-9: (left) Projection of three primary colors onto a movie screen in a 1970s-era long-range jet (Lockheed Tristar L 1011) via cathodic-ray-tube (CRT) projectors. Image by André Malhão, used with permission. (right) The three CRT channels in a home-theater unit of the late 1980s.

---

[413] Young T. Bakerian Lecture: on the theory of light and colours. Philosophical Transactions of the Royal Society A. London. 1802; 92:12-48. doi: 10.1098/rstl.

5.1.2 Color Properties

There are six basic color-appearance parameters related to color perception by an observer. The concept of 'color' can be described by the three perceptual properties of hue, colorfulness, and brightness.

- **Hue**, the degree to which a visual stimulus can be described as being similar to or different from stimuli that we are accustomed seeing to and describe as color. Hue relates pure color in terms of green, red, blue, or yellow. It is the simplest answer to the question, "What color is it?"
- **Colorfulness**, the degree to which the perceived color appears to be more or less 'rich,' i.e., more or less chromatic. Its value is zero when there is no hue (achromatic colors, white, black, or gray) and the largest for a pure color.
- **Brightness**, the degree to which a color appears more or less 'bright'. This changes when a source is radiating (or an object is either reflecting or transmitting) variable amounts of light. Black has zero brightness, while a pure color has maximum brightness.

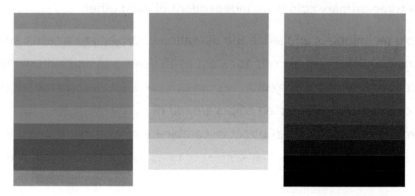

Figure 5-10: Hue (left), colorfulness (center), and brightness (right) variations. Colorfulness and brightness range from 100 % (top) to 0 % (bottom).

There are three more properties that relate to the above parameters.

- **Chroma** is the colorfulness relative to the brightness of a similarly illuminated area that appears to be white or highly transmitting.
- **Lightness** is the relative brightness, derived by comparing an area relative to the brightness of a similarly illuminated area that appears to be white or highly reflecting.
- **Saturation** is another relative property that defines a range from pure color (100%) to gray (0%) at a constant lightness. By definition, saturation is the colorfulness of an area judged in relation to its brightness. Since saturation is defined in terms of two attributes of a single area where it appears, and thus is defined only in terms of those attributes (colorfulness and brightness), it depends on the appearance of light emitted/reflected by that area.

5.1.3 Additive & Subtractive Colors

There are many ways of producing a hue sensation. White can be produced by a continuous source containing all (or most) visible wavelengths, such as the light from the sun, or it may be produced by a mixture of as few as two wavelengths, for example, blue at 475 nm and yellow at 575 nm. When we look at a yellow or a white object, or at any color, we have no way of knowing the spectral composition of the physical stimulus, which can be a physically pure color or can be produced by a composition of two other. There are two basic systems of producing color: the additive color system and the subtractive color system.

The **additive color** system reproduces colors by adding light. The three additive primaries are red, green, and blue (RGB). If no color is present, black results. If all three colors are present at their maximum intensity, white is produced. Mixed in various proportions, the additive color primaries produce a gamut of colors. In the areas where two primary colors overlap, a secondary color appears. Green and blue produce cyan, blue and red produce magenta, and red and green produce yellow. Common additive systems are the cell phone and television displays, and the digital projector screen.

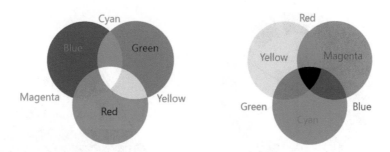

Figure 5-11: (left) Additive and (right) subtractive colors.

The **subtractive color** system reproduces colors by subtracting some wavelengths of light from white. The three subtractive primaries are cyan, magenta, and yellow (CMY). If none of these colors is present, white is being produced because nothing is subtracted from white light. If all of the colors are present at their maximum intensity, black is produced because all of the light is subtracted from the white (often to save on dyes, black is also used in printers).

The subtractive system is associated with pigments that depend on chemicals for their color, such as inks or dyes on paper and dyes on a clear film base (slide films, negative films, inject printers, and motion picture print films). The colors that we see in the subtractive system are a result of the wavelengths that are reflected or transmitted but not absorbed. Cyan absorbs red and reflects or transmits green and blue; magenta absorbs green and reflects or transmits red and blue; and yellow absorbs blue and reflects or transmits red and green.

Figure 5-12: Color subtraction employs yellow, cyan, and magenta.

The complementary colors are the colors that are absorbed by the subtractive primaries. Cyan's complement is red; magenta's complement is green; and yellow's complement is blue. Thus, a combination of a magenta filter and a yellow filter looks red because magenta absorbs the green and yellow absorbs the blue. Only red is left.

On a color wheel, complementary colors are placed opposite to one another. By combining these complementary colors in varying degrees, a gamut of intermediate hues may be created. Since red's complement is cyan, to render an image less red, we add more cyan. To make an image more red, we subtract cyan (or add more red).

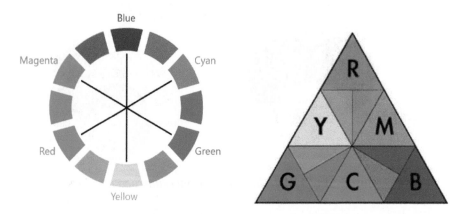

Figure 5-13: (left) The color wheel and (right) the color triangle.

Originally attributed to the German philosopher Johann Wolfgang von Goethe, and presented in his book *'Zur Farbenlehre'* (*Theory of Colors*, 1810), a color triangle is an arrangement of colors within a triangle, based on the additive combination of three primary colors at its apexes and the three subtractive colors at the sides. Any two apex colors additively provide the color on the side between them. Any two side colors subtractively provide the color in the apex between them. An apex color and its opposite side color are complementary.

5.1.4 Color Spaces

According to the trichromacy theory, colors can be produced by a proper mix of the three primary colors. Each color is represented by a weighting function, which is called a **color-matching function**. These functions were established by the international authority on light, illumination, color, and color spaces, the Commission Internationale de l'Eclairage (CIE) [International Commission on Illumination] in the 1931 proceedings and were the first defined quantitative links between the physical pure colors (wavelengths) in the visible spectrum and the perceived colors in human color vision.

The three color-matching functions, $\bar{x}(\lambda)$, $\bar{y}(\lambda)$, and $\bar{z}(\lambda)$, can be conceptualized as the numerical description of the chromatic response of the standard photopic observer (Figure 4-29.) Any color produced by the primary colors blue (B), green (G), and red (R) is a linear product of weighted functions of the color-matching functions, also known as CIE primaries. The factors X, Y, and Z of the relative intensities of the CIE primaries are the tristimulus values.

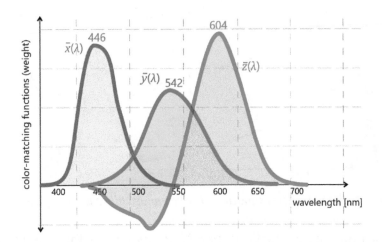

Figure 5-14: The CIE 1931 primaries shown as RGB color-matching functions.

The CIE primaries are not real colors but mathematical constructs. The tristimulus values X, Y, and Z uniquely represent a perceivable hue, and different combinations of light wavelengths that give the same set of tristimulus values will be indistinguishable in chromaticity to the human eye. Thus, a hue **C** may be expressed as

Hue: $$\mathbf{C} = X\mathbf{X} + Y\mathbf{Y} + Z\mathbf{Z} \qquad (5.1)$$

which is interpreted as: there are X parts of primary color **X**, Y parts of primary color **Y**, and Z parts of primary color **Z**. The tristimulus values for a color with a spectral radiance $L_{e,\Omega,\lambda}$ are expressed in terms of the standard observer by

$$\mathbf{X} = \int \bar{x}(\lambda) \cdot E(\lambda) \cdot R(\lambda) d\lambda \quad \mathbf{Y} = \int \bar{y}(\lambda) \cdot E(\lambda) \cdot R(\lambda) d\lambda \quad \mathbf{Z} = \int \bar{z}(\lambda) \cdot E(\lambda) \cdot R(\lambda) d\lambda \tag{5.2}$$

where $E(\lambda)$ is the source spectral power distribution, $R(\lambda)$ is the spectral reflectance of the 'colored' surface, and λ is the wavelength. The integration range covers the visible spectrum (380 to 780 nm). These operations are illustrated schematically in Figure 5-15. For a uniform self-illuminating body, the reflectance is set to unity: The body is reflecting 100% of the incident light. Often, the normalized fractional tristimulus values are used, which are defined as

Fractional tristimulus values: $\quad x = \dfrac{\mathbf{X}}{\mathbf{X+Y+Z}}, \quad y = \dfrac{\mathbf{Y}}{\mathbf{X+Y+Z}}, \quad z = \dfrac{\mathbf{Z}}{\mathbf{X+Y+Z}} \tag{5.3}$

A compound color can be described by a point in a 3-D space x, y, and z. These coordinates provide a percentage value of each primary color used in the compound color.

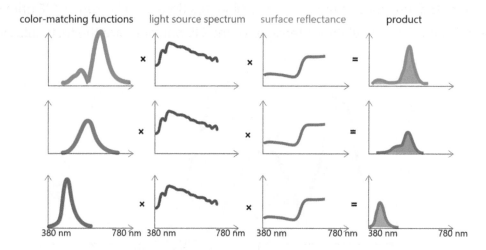

Figure 5-15: Example of schematic determination of tristimulus values used to produced compound colors.

Owing to their normalized fractional nature ($x + y + z = 1.0$), the determination of just two of the coordinates x and y suffices; using the x and y values, the z value is calculated by subtracting the sum of the x and y values from 1.0. Thus, a 3-D quantity may be described in a two-coordinate space. In this (x, y) space, a color is described on a **chromaticity diagram**.[414] The produced colors occupy the CIE X-Y-Z **color space**.

This horseshoe-shaped color diagram of the CIE standard observer (Figure 5-16) represents all of the chromaticities visible to humans: The colored region is the gamut of human vision. It is seen that all visible chromaticities correspond to non-negative values of x, y, and z, and therefore to non-negative tristimulus values. The two subsequent revisions of this

---

[414] Guild J. The colorimetric properties of the spectrum. Philosophical Transactions of the Royal Society of London. Series A, Containing Papers of a Mathematical or Physical Character. 1932; 230:149-87.

diagram (in 1960 and 1976) are plotted on a modified scale, whose coordinates are called u' and v'. While the 1931 version is still mostly used, in the 1976 revision (also known as Uniform Chromaticity Scale, UCS) the distance between any two points on the diagram is approximately proportional to their color difference as perceived by a normal observer.

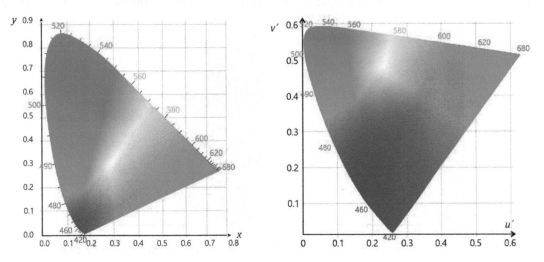

Figure 5-16: (left) The CIE 1931 standard-observer chromaticity diagram. (right) The revised, CIE 1976 Uniform Chromaticity Scale diagram.[415]

The simple spectral (monochromatic) colors are located on the outer curved boundary and range from the 380 nm (bottom left) to 680 nm (bottom right). This is the spectral locus, on which each point represents a pure spectral color. The straight-line segment on the lower part of the gamut connecting the extremes of the visible spectrum is the non-spectral line of purples. However, there is no counterpart in monochromatic light for any of the purples.

Between any two points on the diagram, all colors on the line connecting these points can be formed by mixing these two colors. All colors that can be formed by mixing three judiciously selected colors are confined in the triangle formed by these points. Figure 5-17 (left), clearly shows that the RGB pallet is only a subset of the entire gamut of human color sensation.

The (equal-energy) **white color point** [W in Figure 5-17 (right)] is located at the center of the diagram, with coordinate values $x = y = 0.33 = ⅓$. A random color C can be deduced by the intersection of any straight line passing through a point on the outer boundary, while the ratio of the lengths of the line sections provides the ratio of the two colors. A line segment passing through W and crossing the boundary locus provides the saturation line for this color. The fraction of this line segment from the 'white' to the 'color' point provides the saturation

---

[415] IE: Joint International Standard: Colorimetry – Part 5: CIE 1976 L*u*v* colour space and u', v' uniform chromaticity scale diagram. CIE S 014-5/E:2009/ISO 11664–5 (2009)

value for this color. A point close to the boundary curve is more saturated than a point close to the white center [Figure 5-17 (right) and Figure 5-18]. The two intersections of a line segment passing through the white color point with the spectral locus indicate two **complementary spectral wavelengths**: The example in Figure 5-17 (right) suggests that the 580 nm yellow is complementary to the 480 blue, and that the 600 nm red is complementary to the 490 blue.

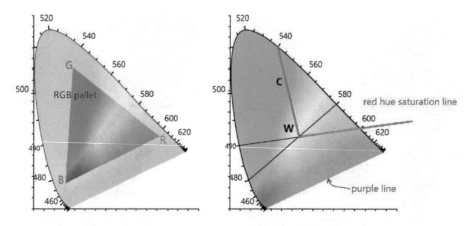

Figure 5-17: (left) RGB pallet and (right) hue saturation lines in the chromaticity diagram.

Figure 5-18: Gradual saturation increase for the red hue saturation line.

To determine the tristimulus values, we need the spectral distribution of the light source illuminating the object. There are three main types of sources, none of which provides uniform distribution over at least a large part of the visible spectrum. One type resembles black-body radiation, an example of which is produced by an incandescent lamp. Another type resembles the sunlight emission spectrum. The first two types have a rather continuous (uninterrupted) spectrum (purple and orange lines in Figure 5-19).

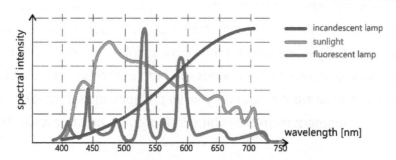

Figure 5-19: Various source spectra across the visible range.

Artificial light sources offer white light sensation by emitting a noncontinuous spectrum that has multiple narrow-band spectra, such as the fluorescent lamp (green line in Figure 5-19). Recently, solid-state sources based on LEDs have started to be used in large-scale general lighting applications and are gradually being established in traditional lighting applications, replacing incandescent and fluorescent lamps[416] owing to their high efficiency (lumens emitted per watt consumed) and very long service life compared with traditional sources.

We can 'feel' a warm body, a body of increased temperature, by its thermal radiation. The warmer it is, the more the energy is radiated, even if we cannot see it, because it may appear black. This is a black body. It is called this because it can absorb radiation that it receives and can also emit it equally well. A **black body** has, according to Gustav Kirchhoff, the capacity to absorb all the electromagnetic radiation directed on it. Any body with a temperature above absolute zero (0 K, −273 °C) emits electromagnetic radiation, and its features are dependent on the temperature of the body. Degrees in Kelvin (K) express the absolute temperature.

Despite its name, a black body does not always appear black, since it also emits radiation. Thus, a black body appears black when it 'deals' only with the absorption part. By default, the body absorbs completely and therefore appears black. However, it may seem bright when it emits: The sun can be described as a black body! Indeed, depending on the temperature, a black body can have a tint.

To explain this effect, we make a simple observation. In the good-old-days, a blacksmith would put a piece of iron to the fire. As the iron is heated, it becomes red, then yellow, and finally, blue. The same might be noticed in an old-fashioned electric heater. The filament, or the glowing iron, is a radiating black body; as it is heated, its electrons begin to collide with the metal lattice, causing oscillations, and these, in turn, cause electromagnetic radiation. We can thus see that a black body can have color!

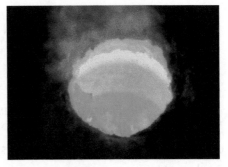

Figure 5-20: Glowing iron has emission properties that can be described by a black body (photos by Manutsawee Buapet www.bmanut.com, used with permission).

[416] Li H, Mao X, Han Y, Luo Y. Wavelength dependence of colorimetric properties of lighting sources based on multicolor LEDs. Opt Express. 2013; 21(3):3775.

The color of glowing iron changes as the temperature increases because most of the emission corresponds to red, then yellow, etc. Every glowing light source can be likened to a black body radiating at the effective temperature to emit the same color. The value of this temperature is the **color temperature** of the source (or the equivalent color temperature for sources with discrete, noncontinuous spectra). The color temperature of the radiation emitted from an ideal black body is defined as its surface temperature in K, or alternatively, in units called mired (micro-reciprocal kelvins). A red-hot body has a specific color temperature, a yellow-hot body has a higher one, and a blue-hot body has an even higher one.

Different light sources produce light with a different tint of white. For example, a candle emits a yellow-reddish light, while the midday sun has a blue tint. Color temperature is the standard by which light sources are compared. A 6500 K source, for example, indicates the spectrum of a source whose maximum emission relates to that of a black body at an effective temperature (defined by the total radiative power per square unit) of 6500 K, whose peak is in the yellow-green. This is known as the typical 'northern light' or CIE illuminant D. During the daytime, ambient light may vary from 6000 K to 15,000 K, or more.

An incandescent lamp emits thermal radiation. At relatively low temperatures, it emits a dull red, and at a higher temperature it emits an almost 'warm' white. To the extent that a radiating body is not an ideal black-body radiator, the color temperature is not the actual temperature of the body. Color temperatures higher than 5000 K are associated with colors such as bluish-white, while lower color temperatures (2200 to 3000 K) are associated with colors perceived as yellowish-white through reddish white. These terms are often used in digital image processing and ratings for LED-type indoor lighting.

Warm .... Cool

Figure 5-21: Color temperature for light bulbs.

Here enters the confusion: Warm colors, as we most likely understand their concept, convey the feeling of a warm tropical climate, while cool colors convey the feeling of a cold, snowy climate—cool, bluish-white is associated with the natural impression of frozen cold. When used in the context of the black-body temperature, the opposite is true; a 'climate-warm' yellowish color is actually of lower color temperature (2200 to 3000 K) than a 'climate-cool' blueish color (>5000 K).

A test of this—not suggested (do not even try it)—is to touch an incandescent source that emits blueish, cool-colored light. It is far warmer than a source that emits a warm-colored light.

The human eye is very efficient at adjusting to different color temperatures, which means that objects appear roughly of the same color whether outside in the sun or indoors under a lightbulb. Digital cameras are not as good at adapting as humans, and, as a result, they record different colors depending on the lighting. This can lead to the rendering of a color cast, an overall blue or orange tint, which may produce unnatural and unpleasing photos.

Figure 5-22: Color cast rendering at (left) 2700 K, (center) 5700 K, and (right) 8500 K.

The **night shift**, a feature recently available in mobile phones, helps to alter the color temperature of the display to the lower-color-temperature, longer-wavelength, reddish end of the visible spectrum. This is related to the fact that increased-color-temperature, shorter-wavelength, bluish light suppresses melatonin secretion and builds up histamine associated with the circadian rhythm, often referred to as the body clock.[417] Because displays in modern phones and tablets have an increased content of blue light compared to the sun,[418] prolonged use of these displays at later hours of the day adversely affects the circadian rhythm, resets the feeling of tiredness, and disrupts the sleep cycle. The night shift enables blue light reduction from the display by moving the color spectrum from a cooler color (blue) toward a warmer color (yellow).

In digital photography, color temperature is sometimes expressed in terms of the **white balance**, a term that describes a setting that allows a remapping of color values to simulate variations in ambient color temperature. Most digital cameras have presets simulating specific conditions (e.g., sunny day, cloudy sky, tungsten indoor lighting, etc.), while more advanced cameras allow explicit entry of white balance values in thousands of K. These settings vary the color temperature values along the blue-yellow, while some software includes additional controls (sometimes labeled tint) that

---

[417] Murray JM, Sletten TL, Magee M, Gordon C, Lovato N, Bartlett DJ, Kennaway DJ, Lack LC, Grunstein RR, Lockley SW, Rajaratnam SM; Delayed Sleep on Melatonin (DelSoM) Study Group. Prevalence of circadian misalignment and its association with depressive symptoms in delayed sleep phase disorder. Sleep. 2017; 40(1). doi: 10.1093/sleep/zsw002.

[418] Sroykham W, Wongsawat Y. Effects of LED-backlit computer screen and emotional selfregulation on human melatonin production. Conf Proc IEEE Eng. Med Biol Soc. 2013; 2013:1704-7.

add the magenta-green. As an individual with optics science background may note, absolute color temperature values are unlikely to be useful to the average photographer.

Table 5–1: White balance settings, color temperature, and light sources.

White Balance	Color Temperature	Light sources
	10,000–15,000 K	Clear blue sky
	6500–8000 K	Cloudy to shady sky
	5500–7000 K	Daylight to noon sunlight
	5000–5500 K	Electronic flash
	4000–5000 K	Fluorescent light
	3000–4000 K	Sunrise - dawn
	2500–3000 K	Indoor lighting
	1000–2000 K	Candlelight

In 1976, CIE proposed two new color spaces, which, unlike the X-Y-Z space, extend the trichromatic theory in 3-D color space with dimensions that correlate to the hue, color sense, and whiteness. The CIELAB (*L**, *a**, *b**) space is defined using the normalization of trichromatic coefficients X, Y, Z of a color with white light Xn, Yn, Zn. It describes all perceivable colors in the three dimensions: *L* for luminosity and *a** and *b** for the color-opponents:

$$L^* = 116\left(\frac{Y}{Y_n}\right)^{1/3} - 16 \qquad a^* = 500\left[\left(\frac{X}{X_n}\right)^{1/3} - \left(\frac{Y}{Y_n}\right)^{1/3}\right] \qquad b^* = 200\left[\left(\frac{Y}{Y_n}\right)^{1/3} - \left(\frac{Z}{Z_n}\right)^{1/3}\right] \qquad (5.4)$$

Coordinate *L** is associated with lightness and ranges from zero for black to 100 for white. Coordinates *a** and *b** reflect the red-green and yellow-blue perception, respectively, and have negative values for the green and the blue. Zero in both cases corresponds to an achromatic stimulus located at the center, near the luminosity axis *L*. Saturated colors are at the edges of the space.

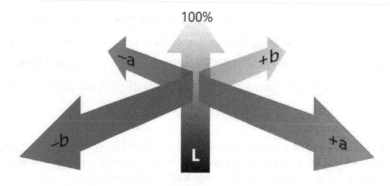

Figure 5-23: Schematic representation of the CIELAB color space.

Using the coordinates $a*$ and $b*$, we can determine color sensation $C*$ and hue h:

$$C^*_{ab} = \sqrt{a^{*2} + b^{*2}} \qquad h = \tan^{-1}\left(\frac{a^*}{b^*}\right) \tag{5.5}$$

The color difference between two colors is defined as

$$\Delta E = \sqrt{\left(L^*_2 - L^*_1\right) + \left(a^*_2 - a^*_1\right) + \left(b^*_2 - b^*_1\right)} \tag{5.6}$$

The color space is designed such that the color differences become uniformly perceived; equally perceived color differences represent equal distances in this space. A value of ΔE close to unity (1) represents two barely distinguishable colors.

Figure 5-24: Example of color analysis into three different systems of color coordinates. Top: Original image. First row: RGB space—red, green, and blue components. Second row: CMY space—cyan, magenta, and yellow components. Bottom row: CIE L*a*b* space—lightness L, a* (R-G), and b* (Y-B) components.

5.2 PERCEPTION OF COLORS IN THE HUMAN EYE

5.2.1 The Three Cone Types

The perception of color is based on the relative signal differences (differential output) between **three** specialized **cone types**. Opsins are heptahelical proteins covalently bound via a Schiff base (SB) to a chromophore (11-*cis* retinal) to form the active photopigment, which is called rhodopsin in rods. The cone photopigments are distinguished by three different types of cone photopigments, referred to as L (long-wavelength), M (middle-wavelength), and S (short-wavelength).[419] These pigments are tuned to preferentially absorb across certain ranges of the visible.

Because of this tuning, cone photopigments have different spectral responsivities across the visible spectrum. The spectral luminous efficiency function $V(\lambda)$ of the CIE photopic observer (Figure 4-29) is a combination of the three individual cone spectral response curves (Figure 5-25). The spectral sensitivities, particularly of the L and M types, broadly overlap, while the peak sensitivity of the S type shifts from the M and L cone peaks by ≈ 0.1 μm (100 nm).

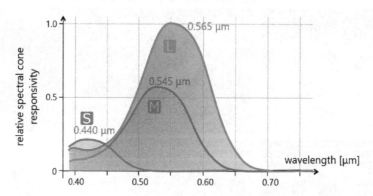

Figure 5-25: Weighted spectral responsivities of the L, M, and S cones in the human eye (based on published data).[420]

These broad spectral responses do not correspond to specific colors. While the L cones are simply referred to as red receptors, their peak sensitivity is in the yellow-green. Similarly, the M and S cones do not strictly correspond to green and blue, respectively. This is significantly different from the clearly separated responsivities used in engineered imaging systems. Thus, the RGB color model, although a convenient system for representing color, shares little similarity with the three-cone system in the human eye.

---

[419] Nathans J, Thomas D, Hogness DS. Molecular genetics of human color vision: the genes encoding blue, green, and red pigments. Science. 1986; 232(4747):193-202.

[420] Stockman A, Sharpe LT. The spectral sensitivities of the middle- and long-wavelength-sensitive cones derived from measurements in observers of known genotype. Vision Res. 2000; 40(13):1711-37.

The difference in spectral responsivity of the three cone types is attributed to the form of **opsin** bound on the **retinal chromophore**. The three opsins are chlorolabe, which is most sensitive to green, erythrolabe, which is most sensitive to red, and cyanolabe, which is most sensitive to blue.

The M and L cones share many histological, physiological, and molecular genetic similarities. However, their spatial distribution is quite different. The S cones are relatively sparsely populated throughout the retina (7% to 10% of the total cone population)[421] and are completely absent in the foveola. The S cones make up about 5.0% to 6.4% of the photoreceptor mosaic at 1° from the foveola.[422] There are far more L and M cones than S cones, and there are about twice as many L cones as M cones. The relative populations of the L:M:S cone types are approximately 12:6:1 (according to other accounts, these are up to 40:20:1),[423] although considerable variability in the L:M ratio occurs even among individuals with normal vision.

The presence of L and M cones perimetrically spans up to about 30°, beyond which the population of L and M cones diminishes notably, leaving the perimeter zone between 30° and beyond 60° with only S cones (and rods); beyond 60° there are no cones, only rods.[424]

The differences in spectral responsivity between the three cone types can be attributed to differences between the opsin amino acids responsible for photon absorption. The S cones further differ in the opsin amino acid sequence, which is autosomal (encoded to a chromosome other than a sex chromosome) and bears little homology to the sequences for the M- and L-cone types, which are X-linked. Anatomical studies use difference to visualize the S cone and its mosaic-like spatial distribution across the retina.[425] The S-cone retinal color channel circuit is projected to the brain via a neuron cluster in the thalamus area that is neurochemically and spatially separated from the more abundant neurons assigned to M- and L-cone signals.[426]

A very small percentage of females may have some aspect of tetrachromatic color vision because of different alleles of the gene for the L opsin on the X chromosome.[427, 428] The

---

[421] Ahnelt PK, Kolb H, Pflug R. Identification of a subtype of cone photoreceptor, likely to be blue sensitive, in the human retina. J Comp Neurol. 1987; 255:18e34

[422] Hofer H, Carroll J, Neitz J, Neitz M, Williams DR. Organization of the human trichromatic cone mosaic. J Neurosci. 2005; 25(42):9669-79.

[423] Calkins DJ. Seeing with S cones. Prog Retin Eye Res. 2001; 20(3):255-87.

[424] Wooten BR, Wald G. Color-vision mechanisms in the peripheral retinas of normal and dichromatic observers. J Gen Physiol. 1973; 61(2):125-45.

[425] Bumsted K, Hendrickson A. Distribution and development of short-wavelength cones differ between Macaca monkey and human fovea. J Comp Neurol. 1999; 403(4):502-16.

[426] Hendry SHC, Reid RC. The koniocellular pathway in primate vision. Annu Rev Neurosci. 2000; 23:127-53.

[427] Okano T, Fukada Y, Yoshizawa T. Molecular basis for tetrachromatic color vision. Comp Biochem Physiol B Biochem Mol Biol. 1995; 112(3):405-14.

[428] Jordan G, Deeb SS, Bosten JM, Mollon JD. The dimensionality of color vision in carriers of anomalous trichromacy. J Vis. 2010; 10(8):12.

probability of tetrachromacy in humans was first suggested back in 1948:[429] A study of women who were heterozygous for color deficiencies[430] identified that, potentially, up to 12% of the female population might have four, not just three, different cone types, and be tetrachromats.

5.2.1.1 Opsins, the Workers of Light

In 1877, the German physiologist and histologist Franz Christian Boll was experimenting with a frog, which he kept in the dark. Boll observed a visual purple in the eye of the frog that faded quickly upon exposure to light. When the frog was placed in the dark again, then, after a while, moved back to the light, this red hue re-appeared, only to fade in the presence of illumination. Boll had observed rhodopsin, the molecule that changes its state by absorbing light.

Figure 5-26: (left) Franz Christian Boll (1849–1879). (right) An opsin heptahelical protein molecule.

Opsins, which are G-protein-coupled receptors, are the 'workers' in the 'factory' called *'Human Light Detection, Inc.'* Photosensitive opsins bond with the 11-*cis* retinal. With the exception of light sensing by cytochrome c oxidase in sponge larvae, animal light sensing is based on either cryptochromes or opsins.[431] Opsins form the basis of visual pigments that react to different wavelengths of light; slightly different cone opsins initiate color vision.[432] Opsins function as sensory molecules, ion channels (pumps) energized by light, and modulators of the circadian cycle. The differentiation in spectral sensitivity between the L- and M-cone opsins is due to variations among the amino acid sites (Ala180Ser, Phe277Tyr, and Ala285Thr).

Opsins of type-I are also found in organisms that do not have specialized eyes (e.g., fungi and green algae). Type-II opsins are unique to animals.[433] The opsin subfamilies

---

[429] de Vries HI. The fundamental response curves of normal and abnormal dichromatic and trichromatic eyes. Physica. 1948; 14(6):367-80.

[430] Jordan G, Mollon JD. A study of women heterozygous for colour deficiencies. Vision Res. 1993; 33(11):1495-508.

[431] Björn LO, Rasmusson AG. Photosensitivity in sponge due to cytochrome c oxidase? Photochem Photobiol Sci. 2009; 8(6):755-7.

[432] Ebrey T, Koutalos Y. Vertebrate photoreceptors. Prog Retin Eye Res. 2001; 20:49-94.

[433] Larusso ND, Ruttenberg BE, Singh AK, Oakley TH. Type II opsins: evolutionary origin by internal domain duplication? J Mol Evol. 2008; 66(5):417-23.

diversified before the deuterostomes (including vertebrates) split from the protostomes (most invertebrates), suggesting that a common animal ancestor had multiple opsin genes.[434]

5.2.2 Process Theories

The response of any individual cone type is unidimensional and cannot by itself provide color determination. When (if) an opsin absorbs a light photon, it does not encode any information regarding the wavelength of that photon, so any spectral information is lost. The photoreceptive cell responds in a binary, 'Yes–No' type of response.

5.2.2.1 Univariance

Univariance states that the spectral information of an absorbed photon is not specific to its wavelength. The value of the wavelength does play a role, meaning that a certain opsin may or may not absorb a photon, depending on what the wavelength is. However, because the spectral response curve of any type of cone is broad, we do not know what the wavelength is, which means we do not know the color of the absorbed photon. For example, an L cone, being more sensitive than an S cone, can absorb a photon whose wavelength ranges from the blue to the red; thus, a photon of 0.565 µm is more likely to be absorbed by an L cone. Likewise, an S cone absorbs a photon whose wavelength ranges from the blue to up to 0.50 µm, so a photon of 0.440 µm is more likely to be absorbed by an S cone (see Figure 5-25). However, after absorption takes place, there is no longer any information regarding the photon's color.

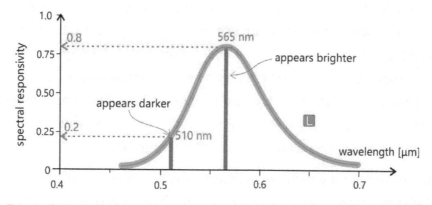

Figure 5-27: Spectral responsivity of L cones for two different wavelengths.

The different spectral absorption curves of the three different cone types result in a perceived difference of luminance. Assume two different spectral illuminations—$\lambda_1 = 0.510$ µm and $\lambda_2 = 0.565$ µm (= 565 nm)—each consisting of 100 photons being reflected off of two white

---

[434] Terakita A. The opsins. Genome Biol. 2005; 6(3):213.

surfaces. Among the photons being detected by L cones, each one corresponds to a different probability of being absorbed by these cones. The spectral probability of absorption for a 0.510 µm (= 510 nm) photon may be as low as 0.20, suggesting that 1 in 5 photons may be absorbed. On the other hand, the spectral probability of absorption for a 0.565 µm photon may be as high as 0.80, suggesting that 4 in 5 photons may be absorbed.

An observer with only L cones who is presented with two objects illuminated with this radiation will sense two different luminosities, a dark one, corresponding to the object reflecting the 510 nm light, and a bright one, corresponding to the object reflecting the 565 nm, which thus appears about four times brighter. Therefore, a single-cone-type response conveys a difference in color (two different wavelengths) as a difference in observed luminance.

5.2.2.2 Trichromatic Theory and Opponent-Process Theory

Today, we accept that color perception results from a multiplexed output of the quantum response firing rates (§ 4.3.6) from the different cone types. Our understanding is founded on two prevailing theories, initially thought to be exclusive. These are the **trichromatic theory**, proposed by Young, Maxwell, and (mainly) Helmholtz, and the **opponent-process theory**, proposed by the German physiologist Karl Ewald Konstantin Hering in 1872.[435]

It is noteworthy that neither theory at the time was supported by a solid explanation of the underlying neural mechanisms. Even today, there is no comprehensive theory providing a satisfactory explanation of color sensation.

The trichromatic theory postulates that the three cone types are preferentially sensitive to red, green, and blue. Red stimulates L cones more than M cones, and barely stimulates S cones; when L cones are predominantly stimulated, we sense red. Blue-green stimulates M cones more than L cones; when M cones are predominantly stimulated, we sense green. Yellowish-green stimulates L and M cones equally, while it stimulates S cones more weakly. Blue stimulates S cones more strongly than red or green, but it stimulates L and M cones more weakly; when S cones are predominantly stimulated, we sense blue.

Sufficient evidence of the trichromatic theory has been presented over the years, including identification of the spectral sensitivities of the two cone pigments by Rushton's retinal densitometry,[436, 437] laboratory identification of the three distinct cone pigments by

[435] Hering H. Zur Lehre vom Lichtsinn (To the doctrine of the sense of light). 1878 Vienna: Gerald and Sohn.
[436] Rushton WA. A cone pigment in protanope. J Physiol. 1963; 168(2):345-59.
[437] Rushton WA. Cone pigment kinetics in the protanope. J Physiol. 1963; 168(2):374-88.

microspectrometry,[438] identification of the genetic codes for L, M, and S cones,[439] development of color-matching functions, isolation of the photoreceptors and measurement of their physiological responses as a function of wavelength,[440] and spectral sensitivity measurements (including the Wald–Marré spectral sensitivity functions[441] and Stiles's π-mechanisms[442]).

In summary, the trichromatic theory postulates that three images are formed by these three sets of receptors that are then transmitted to the brain, where the ratio of the signal strength in each of the images is compared to sort out color appearances and provide color perception. This model, which considers three images being transmitted to the brain, is inefficient and fails to explain several visually observed phenomena.

The opponent-process theory is founded on subjective observations—the appearance of hues, simultaneous contrast, afterimages, and color vision deficiencies. The theory involves three complex and antagonistic processes, called orthogonal channels. Each channel runs along a pair of opposing sensations: black-white, red-green, and yellow-blue; equal stimulation of the two pair members gives rise to a neutral, achromatic (gray) sensation.

Hering noted that certain hues are never perceived together; for example, a color is never described as reddish-green or yellowish-blue, while combinations of red-yellow, red-blue, green-yellow, and green-blue are often perceived. Here is an experiment that demonstrates this phenomenon. Fixate on the small black dot on the left side of Figure 5-28 for about half a minute (30 s). You will probably see some colors around the blue and green circles. After about 30 seconds, shift your gaze to fixate on the black spot to the right.

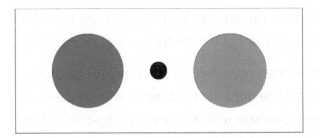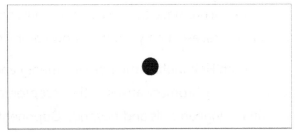

Figure 5-28: Stimulus for the demonstration of opponent afterimages. Note the colors of the elicited afterimages relative to the colors of the original stimuli.

[438] Marks WB, Dobelle WH, MacNichol EF. Visual pigments of single primate cones. Science. 1964; 143(3611):1181-2.

[439] Nathans J, Piantanida TP, Eddy RL, Shows TB, Hogness DS. Molecular genetics of inherited variation in human color vision. Science. 1986; 232(4747):203-10.

[440] Baylor DA, Nunn BJ, Schnapf JL. The photocurrent, noise and spectral sensitivity of rods of the monkey Macaca fascicularis. J Physiol. 1984; 357:575-607.

[441] Yeh T, Smith VC, Pokorny J. The effect of background luminance on cone sensitivity functions. Invest Ophthalmol Vis Sci. 1989; 30(10):2077-86.

[442] Pugh Jr EN, Kirk DB. The π mechanisms of WS Stiles: An historical review. Perception. 1986; 15(6):705-28.

A yellow circle and a desaturated, reddish circle appear in corresponding positions. These perceptions are the result of afterimages, which move around as the eyes move. Similar observations were made of simultaneous contrast, whereby objects placed on a red background appear greener, while those on a green background appear redder, those on a yellow background appear bluer, and those on a blue background appear yellower.

Hering noted the red-green and yellow-blue bipolar antagonism and suggested that color processing begins very early in the visual system process (in the retina) via initial color-opponent mechanisms. The opponent-process theory states that the visual system interprets color in an antagonistic way: red versus green, blue versus yellow, and black versus white. Green-magenta and blue-yellow are scales with mutually exclusive boundaries.

The mathematical formulation of the opponent-process theory was developed much later by Leo M. Hurvich and Dorothea Jameson in 1955.[443] Soon after, using the hue cancellation paradigm, the psychophysical color-opponent channels were isolated.[444] Other evidence in support of the opponent-color theory includes electrical recordings of horizontal cells from a fish retina showing blue-yellow opponent and red-green opponent processes,[445] electrical recordings from the lateral geniculate nucleus showing opponent-color processes,[446] and electrical recordings of ganglion cells from a primate retina showing opponent-color processes.[447]

While initially considered as competing, currently, both theories are accepted as explanations of color vision, each applying to a different stage in the visual physiology. Signals from the three cone types proposed by the trichromatic theory are combined in the three orthogonal channels proposed by Hering. In their own ways, both Helmholtz and Hering were right. The trichromatic theory explains how color vision operates at the receptor level, while the opponent-process theory explains how color vision operates at the postreceptoral, neural level.

Both Helmholtz's trichromatic theory and Hering's opponent-process theory are, thus, correct, but trichromacy arises at the receptor level, while opponent processes arise at the level of retinal ganglion cells and beyond. Opponent mechanisms refer to the opposing-color effect of red-green, blue-yellow, and light-dark. However, in the visual system, it is the activity of the different receptor types that are opposed. Some midget retinal ganglion cells oppose L- and M-cone activity, which loosely corresponds to red-green opponency but runs along a color axis

---

[443] Hurvich LM, Jameson D. Some quantitative aspects of an opponent-colors theory. II. Brightness, saturation, and hue in normal and dichromatic vision. J Opt Soc Am. 1955; 45(8):602-16.

[444] Hurvich LM, Jameson D. An opponent-process theory of color vision. Psychol Rev. 1957; 64, Part 1(6):384-404.

[445] Svaetichin G. Spectral response curves from single cones. Acta Physiol Scand Suppl. 1956; 39(134):17-46.

[446] De Valois RL, Abramov I, Jacobs GH. Analysis of response patterns of LGN cells. J Opt Soc Am. 1966; 56(7):966-77.

[447] Zrenner E, Gouras P. Characteristics of the blue sensitive cone mechanism in primate retinal ganglion cells. Vision Res. 1981; 21(11):1605-9.

from blue-green to magenta. Small bistratified retinal ganglion cells oppose input from the S cones to input from the L and M cones. This is often thought to correspond to blue-yellow opponency but actually runs along a color axis from lime-green to violet.

5.2.2.3 Monochromatic Vision

Monochromatic vision is the most elementary vision. It requires only one type of photoreceptor that responds to light between 400 nm and 700 nm. This is not because colors are in that spectral range, but because the solar emission reaching Earth peaks at this range. Monochromatic vision is common in lower vertebrates and can help to distinguish light from darkness, i.e., luminance gradients. Thus, movement can be perceived as a change of shadow luminance.

Colors cannot be perceived, except if they correlate to a luminance differential. If the luminance is adjusted, what is spectrally the same (i.e., the same color to someone with normal color vision) may simply appear different. No differentiation is possible based on the spectral origin of that luminance. This fact indicates that a luminance differential is the dominant visual information. Such is the human monochromatic vision experience under prevailing scotopic conditions or monochromacy (§ 5.3.1.3).

5.2.2.4 Dichromatic Vision

The dichromatic vision system relies on two types of cone cells; for example, one that is sensitive to yellow-green (Y) and one that is sensitive to blue (B). This allows for the perception of colors in addition to the monochromatic perception of brightness. The most efficient way to accomplish dichromatic vision is to add the responses of cone cells Y and B for determining brightness (luminosity channel) and subtract their responses to identify colors (Figure 5-29).

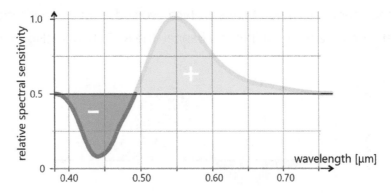

Figure 5-29: Yellow-cyan color opponency.

The signal produced by the sum Y + B creates a response similar to monochromatic vision, while the signal produced by the difference Y − B intensifies the response differential at the ends of the spectrum. Color perception, thus, is possible with just two types of cone receptors. Because of the difference in signal strength, the differential response is called opponency encoding, which is the foundation of color vision.

Dichromatic vision has certain limitations. One is illuminant **metameric failure**: Different spectral distributions can give exactly the same color perception. This phenomenon occurs when two different types of cones are stimulated with the same ratio for some wavelengths. Also, there is no information about the saturation, in other words, color intensity.

5.2.2.5 Trichromatic Vision

In trichromatic vision, three different cone cell types respond to a range of wavelengths with different peak sensitivities. Opponent cells tuned to luminosity are excited by the red, green, and blue signals. The main advantage of trichromatic vision is the unique combination of the cone cells' responses for each spectral wavelength. Metameric failure is now minimized, and the sensation of color saturation is possible.

Thus, most colors are described as a combination of two colors, for example, red and blue (reddish-blue or bluish-red). This is the basis for the CIELab color space. This is also why we cannot see greenish-red or reddish-green. The combination of red-green gives the sensation of yellow: A yellow sensation results from different signal strength from the L and M cones. When those signals are the same, we see yellow with no red or green. An application of this is the Rayleigh match, presented in § 5.4.4.

The identification of the three receptor types responsible for color vision did not occur until many years after the proposal of the trichromatic vision theory. Among mammals, only primates have evolved trichromatic color vision, as they developed an additional pair of opponent photoreceptors, the L and M cones, which evolved from a genetic modulation of the Y cone. Their signals combine to an additional channel, the R-G channel (Figure 5-30).

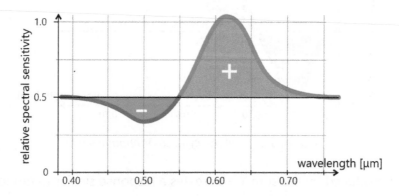

Figure 5-30: Red-green color opponency.

5.2.2.6 Neural Stage Theory

The contemporary theory of color vision (also called **stage theory** or zone theory) accepts three levels of color vision processing. The receptoral stage of trichromatic vision is based on the differential response by the three cone types in response to the same stimulus. The second, the postreceptoral stage, through the mechanism of opponency, involves the encoding of color information into opponent signals. This occurs at the retinal photoreceptive neurons and at their synapses with bipolar cells and then at their synapses with several types of ganglion cells.

The signal comprises <u>three independent</u>, orthogonal channels, B-Y, G-R, and luminance, or the luminosity channel,[448] similar to Hering's theory. The summed (the summation is taken in proportion to the relative populations of the three cone types) output of the three cone types $L + M + S$ provides the luminosity channel. Differencing of the cone signals results in the R-G red-green ($L-M$) and the Y-B yellow-blue ($L + M - S$) opponent channels.[449]

The third stage in the neural stage theory is also neural but physiologically distinct from the second stage. The loci of the unique hues are the lateral geniculate nucleus (LGN)[450, 451] and the visual cortex, in areas V1 (area 17, striate, or primary, cortex), V2 (area 18, parastriate or secondary, cortex), and V3 (area 19, peristriate, or tertiary, cortex).[452] In V1, the simple three-color segregation begins to affect cells that respond differently to some parts of the spectrum, but this color tuning often varies, depending on the adaptation state of the visual system.

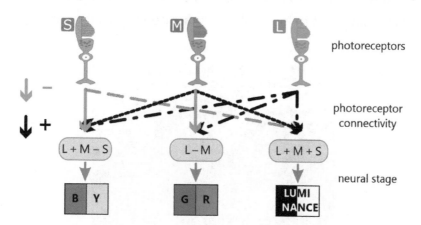

Figure 5-31: Encoding cone signals into opponent signals in the human visual system.

---

[448] Pridmore RW. Cone photoreceptor sensitivities and unique hue chromatic responses: correlation and causation imply the physiological basis of unique hues. PLoS One. 2013; 8(10):e77134.

[449] Ingling CR Jr, Huong-Peng-Tsou B. Orthogonal combination of the three visual channels. Vision Res. 1977; 17(9):1075-82.

[450] Stoughton CM, Conway BR. Neural basis for unique hues. Curr Biol. 2008; 18(16):R698-9.

[451] Boackes J. Where do the unique hues come from? Rev Phil Psych. 2011; 2:601-28.

[452] Fitzpatrick D. The functional organization of local circuits in visual cortex: insights from the study of tree shrew striate cortex. Cereb Cortex. 1996; 6(3):329-41.

Food for Thought ✕: We do not have a yellow receptor. How can we see yellow, then? Actually, we do not see blue (and, for that matter, any color, green and red included) in a direct fashion, either. Blue is the sensation produced by one end of the L + M − S channel, while yellow is the sensation produced by the other end of this channel. Likewise, the sensation of a green hue is not produced because we possess a 'green' type of sensor but is produced by one end of the L − M channel, while the sensation of red is produced by the other end of this channel.

Take-home message ✉: We sense color as a result of the output multiplexing of the three cone types. Luminance corresponds to the sum of all responses; the distinction between green and red is produced (mainly) by the difference between the L- and M-cone types; the distinction between blue and yellow is produced (mainly) by the difference of the combined L-cone and M-cone response to the S-cone response.

A cell with a preferential response to long wavelengths under a bright stimulus might have a different responsivity if the stimulus is dim. Because the color tuning of these cells is not stable, it is stipulated that a different, relatively small, population of neurons in V1 handles color vision. These specialized 'color cells' often have receptive fields that can compute local cone ratios. Such double-opponent cells were initially described in goldfish[453] and primates.[379]

Double-opponent cells are clustered within localized regions of V1 called blobs and come in two variations, red-green and blue-yellow.[454] Red-green cells compare the relative amounts of red and green in one part of a field with the amount of red and green in an adjacent part of the field, responding best to local color contrast (red adjacent to green).[455]

Figure 5-32: Evidence of the opponent channels: Fixate at the center of the image for at least 30 seconds. Then, turn to a white surface. What do you notice?

---

453 Daw NW. Goldfish retina: organization for simultaneous color contrast. Science. 1967; 158(3803):942-4.

454 Livingstone MS, Hubel DH. Anatomy and physiology of a color system in the primate visual cortex. J Neurosci. 1984; 4(1):309-56.

455 Du Y, Tong M, Zhou L, Dong H. Edge detection based on Retinex theory and wavelet multiscale product for mine images. Appl Opt. 2016; 55(34):9625-37.

One may wonder why there is such an uneven spatial and spectral distribution of the different types of cone cells? In other words, why does the eye seem to be more sensitive to yellow-green and not blue? The answer is not easy. One of the possible explanations might be subtle adaptive changes to the spectral peak of the sunlight emission in the yellow-green in the L-cone opsin wavelength absorption during human evolution.

Another possible explanation might be related to chromatic aberration. As discussed in § 2.2.2, the optical elements of the eye refract the blue more strongly than the red, forming a sharp blue image slightly in front of the retina in the case of an emmetropic eye. The human eye may have thus evolved to work primarily on a reduced part of the visible spectrum to minimize the effects of chromatic aberration. This is achieved due to the existence of the vast majority of L- and M-cone cells compared to the S cells, and the proximity of the maxima of the spectral sensitivities of L and M cells.

Another reason might be the increased absorption by the optical elements of the eye at shorter wavelengths (§ 2.5.3), which leads to even less-blue content reaching the retina. In addition, the photoreceptors are oriented to minimize the effect of scattering veiling (the Stiles–Crawford effect, § 4.4.2), which is far stronger in the blue (shorter) wavelengths.

5.2.3 Subjectivity of Color Perception

The correspondence between wavelengths of light in the visual spectrum and human experiences of color is humanly arbitrary. Common variation in color vision exists between both color normal and color deficient subjects.

Although most people are assumed to have the same mapping, English philosopher John Locke recognized that alternatives are possible, and described one such hypothetical case with the 'inverted spectrum' thought experiment. For example, someone might experience green while seeing 'red' (700 nm) and experience red while seeing 'green' (530 nm). Color **synesthesia** (or ideasthesia) is a fairly common condition whereby individuals experience atypical responses (such as color experiences) in association with certain types of stimuli (such as non-colored letters).[456, 457] Color sensation is a subjective psychological phenomenon.

---

[456] Safran AB, Sanda N. Color synesthesia. Insight into perception, emotion, and consciousness. Curr Opin Neurol. 2015; 28(1):36-44.

[457] Mylopoulos MI, Ro T. Synesthesia: a colorful word with a touching sound? Front Psychol. 2013; 4:763.

The ecological valence theory[458] states that an individual's preference for a particular color is determined largely by preferences for all correspondingly colored objects, which are attributed to affective responses to color-associated objects. People generally like colors to the degree that they like the objects associated with those colors. Therefore, individuals should differ in their color preferences to the extent that they have different preferences for the same color-associated objects or to the extent that they experience different objects, or even different political affiliations.[459]

Random note of the day 🌍: There is a notable deviation from the norm in a central non-industrialized society in rural Namibia populated by the Himba tribe, one of the last few semi-nomadic indigenous groups in the world.
Himba adults have been found to sense colors differently from most Caucasians and can easily distinguish close shades of green that are barely discernable by most people.[460] As an adaptation to their specific way of life, the Himba have created a very different color scheme that divides the spectrum into dark shades (*zuzu* in Himba), very light shades (*vapa*), vivid blue and green (*buru*), and dry colors.

The perception of color depends strongly on the context in which the perceived object is presented. For example, a white page under blue, pink, or purple light will reflect mostly blue, pink, or purple light to the eye, respectively; the brain, however, compensates for the effect of lighting (based on the color shift of surrounding objects) and is more likely to interpret the page as white under all three conditions, a phenomenon known as color constancy.

5.2.3.1 The Bezold–Brücke Phenomenon

The Bezold–Brücke (B-B) phenomenon, named after the German meteorologist Johann Friedrich Wilhelm von Bezold and the German physiologist Ernst Wilhelm Ritter von Brücke, pertains to the shift in certain perceived hues when the illuminance of the stimulus is increased or decreased.[461] Because the perceived hue, even if purely monochromatic, is a joint function of wavelength and intensity, certain hues change with increasing intensity, while others that are close to the psychologically primary hues do not. As luminant intensity increases, the perceived spectral colors shift toward the blue (if they are less than 503 nm) or toward the yellow (if they

---

[458] Taylor C, Franklin A. The relationship between color-object associations and color preference: further investigation of ecological valence theory. Psychon Bull Rev. 2012; 19(2):190-7.

[459] Schloss KB, Palmer SE. The politics of color: preferences for Republican red versus Democratic blue. Psychon Bull Rev. 2014; 21(6):1481-8.

[460] Taylor C, Clifford A, Franklin A. Color preferences are not universal. J Exp Psychol Gen. 2013; 142(4):1015-27.

[461] Bimler DL, Paramei GV. Bezold–Brücke effect in normal trichromats and protanopes. J Opt Soc Am A Opt Image Sci Vis. 2005; 22(10):2120-36.

are greater than 503 nm). This effect is a textbook demonstration example of the opponent-process theory.

The hues that do not change (invariant hues) correspond to colors that balance an opponent channel. Hues along the red-green or the blue-yellow channel are invariant to stimuli intensity increases, the latter affecting only the orthogonal, luminosity channel. The invariant points are noted as B (478 nm), G (503 nm), and Y (572 nm),[462] and the hues associated with these wavelengths are called unique hues. Luminance-dependent changes in color appearance pertain to hues that require a combination of more than one channel to be affected. The vector decomposition of these hues into the three components of the three channels is affected if there is a change in one of the channels, the luminosity channel.[463, 464]

5.2.4 Color Vision in Other Species

Light and color perception in the animal kingdom is very diverse, being influenced by habitat and evolutionary factors, feeding, oviposition, safety, mating needs, or whether an animal is diurnal or nocturnal. Thus, animal species have a very diverse color perception, some perceiving light and differentiating colors even outside the range of the spectrum that is visible by human vision.

Ultraviolet light (UV: 300 to 400 nm) to the left of the blue in the 'humanly' visible part of the spectrum is perceived by many species, especially insects. Bees and many other insects,[465] birds such as hummingbirds,[466] turtles, lizards, many fish, and certain rodents, have UV perception. Some avian species have gender-dependent markings on their plumage that are visible only in the ultraviolet. Frogs have a violet-sensitive visual pigment in small, single cone cells and a blue-sensitive visual pigment in green rod cells. Species with UV sensitivity have, in general, limited color perception toward the high-end of the visible, red wavelengths. For example, honeybees' and bumblebees' sensitivity drops at about 590 nm, just before the orange. Birds, however, can see red, although not as far into the spectrum as humans can.[467]

---

[462] Boynton RM, Gordon J. Bezold-Brücke hue shift measured by color-naming technique. J Opt Soc Am. 1965; 55, 78–86.

[463] Purdy DM. The Bezold-Brücke phenomenon and contours for constant hue. Am J Psychol. 1937; 49(2):313-5.

[464] Pridmore RW. Bezold–Brucke hue-shift as functions of luminance level, luminance ratio, interstimulus interval and adapting white for aperture and object colors. Vis Res. 1999; 39(23):3873-91.

[465] Kevan PG, Chittka L, Dyer AG. Limits to the salience of ultraviolet: lessons from colour vision in bees and birds. J Exp Biol. 2001; 204(Pt 14):2571-80.

[466] Telles FJ, Lind O, Henze MJ, Rodríguez-Gironés MA, Goyret J, Kelber A. Out of the blue: the spectral sensitivity of hummingbird hawkmoths. J Comp Physiol A Neuroethol Sens Neural Behav Physiol. 2014; 200(6):537-46.

[467] Tokunaga F, Hisatomi O, Satoh T, Taniguchi Y, Matsuda S, Imanishi Y, Honkawa H, Takahashi Y, Kobayashi Y, Yoshida M, Tsukahara Y. Evolution of visual pigments and related molecules. Novartis Found Symp. 1999; 224:44-52.

Sensitivity to longer wavelengths, such as the red, is important for herbivorous animals, as it helps in the identification of nutritious fruits and newly sprouting leaves in flowering plants. On the other hand, nocturnal species have less-developed color vision since they largely depend on rod vision. Likewise, marine mammals, which have adapted to low-light vision, have only a single cone type and are thus monochromats. Also, the near infrared (NIR: 800 to 1200 nm) to the right of the red is part of color perception in certain species such as reptiles, which can detect prey by sensing their infrared radiation signatures.[468]

In addition to the varying extent of the spectrum that is 'visible' by several species, which pertains to the aspect of light perception, there is a varying degree to how much is visible within that range, in other words, the discrimination among the different parts of the spectrum. This aspect pertains to color perception. Color perception in the animal kingdom is highly variable among species, dependent on the number and type of photosensitive cone types.[469] Just as in humans, rod photoreceptors function in dim-light vision, whereas cone-dominated vision in daylight brings the potential for color perception. Thus, it is the cone types and their plurality that determine color vision.

In the animal kingdom, the majority of 'color' vision is dichromatic.[470] Examples of dichromats are nonprimate mammals, including canines, which see blue and yellow but not green or orange-red (the usual assumption that dogs see in black and white is a misconception). Horses have dichromatic vision that relies on a 'red' and a 'blue' type of cone cell in a fashion similar to vision afforded by humans with red-green color vision deficiencies.[471] Then there are also animals with trichromatic vision. Among placental mammals, some primates, including monkeys, all apes, and some marsupials, have three cone types.[472] Finally, tetrachromatic vision also exists in the animal kingdom: Birds, fish, reptiles, amphibians, and invertebrates have four cone types,[473] which affords superior color vision.[474, 475]

---

[468] Martin M, Le Galliard JF, Meylan S, Loew ER. The importance of ultraviolet and near-infrared sensitivity for visual discrimination in two species of lacertid lizards. J Exp Biol. 2015; 218(Pt 3):458-65.

[469] Kelber A, Vorobyev M, Osorio D. Animal colour vision behavioural tests and physiological concepts. Biol Rev Camb Philos Soc. 2003; 78(1):81-118.

[470] Jacobs GH. The distribution and nature of colour vision among the mammals. Biol Rev Camb Philos Soc. 1993; 68(3):413-71.

[471] Hanggi EB, Ingersoll JF, Waggoner TL. Color vision in horses (Equus caballus): Deficiencies identified using a pseudoisochromatic plate test. J Comp Psychol. 2007; 121(1):65.

[472] Tovee MJ. The molecular genetics and evolution of primate colour vision. Trends Neurosci. 1994; 17(1):30-7.

[473] Koshitaka H, Kinoshita M, Vorobyev M, Arikawa K. Tetrachromacy in a butterfly that has eight varieties of spectral receptors. Proc Biol Sci. 2008; 275(1637):947-54.

[474] Vorobyev M. Ecology and evolution of primate colour vision. Clin Exp Optom. 2004; 87:230-38.

[475] Hunt DM, Peichl L. S cones: Evolution, retinal distribution, development, and spectral sensitivity. Vis Neurosci. 2014; 31(2):115-38.

Interestingly, there is an evolutionary connection in this highly variable manifestation of color vision.[476] It is known that as long as 500 million years ago, the ancestral pattern involved four spectral classes of cone opsins,[477] as evidenced in many fossils,[478] and this pattern remains today in certain avian and other nonmammalian species.[479] However, mammalian evolution went through a prolonged nocturnal phase that led to a reduction in the number of cone types from four to only two, with an additional loss of one more in many species, which subsequently became monochromatic (nocturnal and many marine species). The gene loss is attributed to the fact that a gene cannot be retained unless it is continuously functional, absent a long-term storage mechanism.[480]

Thus, color vision degenerated from tetrachromacy to just dichromacy, only to be partially regained in some primate species by gene duplication, which resulted in the emergence of two distinct type cones, the M- and L-cone types. This evolutionary trichromatic color vision rebound occurred as the ancestors of modern primates switched to diurnal activity. Eutherian mammals other than primates generally have two-cone, hence, dichromatic, color vision.

The most intricate color vision in animals has been found in some stomatopods such as the mantis shrimp (*Haptosquilla trispinosa*), which possesses up to 12 different color receptor types forming multiple dichromatic channels. This type of vision seems to have evolved uniquely, as the photoreceptor outputs do not undergo opponent processing, being sent instead directly to the brain where they can be compared to a template of colors. This type of vision can be advantageous as it requires less processing and is likely to be more rapid.[481]

---

[476] Collin SP, Trezise AE. The origins of colour vision in vertebrates. Clin Exp Optom. 2004; 87(4-5):217-23.

[477] Hunt DM, Carvalho LS, Cowing JA, Davies WL. Evolution and spectral tuning of visual pigments in birds and mammals. Philos Trans R Soc Lond B Biol Sci. 2009; 364(1531):2941-55.

[478] Bowmaker JK. Evolution of vertebrate visual pigments. Vision Res. 2008; 48(20):2022-41.

[479] Wilkie SE, Vissers PM, Das D, Degrip WJ, Bowmaker JK, Hunt DM. The molecular basis for UV vision in birds: spectral characteristics, cDNA sequence and retinal localization of the UV-sensitive visual pigment of the budgerigar (Melopsittacus undulatus). Biochem J. 1998; 330 (Pt 1):541-7.

[480] Parry JW, Peirson SN, Wilkens H, Bowmaker JK. Multiple photopigments from the Mexican blind cavefish, Astyanax fasciatus: a microspectrophotometric study. Vision Res. 2003; 43(1):31-41.

[481] Thoen HH, How MJ, Chiou TH, Marshall J. A different form of color vision in mantis shrimp. Science. 2014; 343(6169):411-3.

5.3 COLOR VISION DEFICIENCY

Color vision deficiency (CVD) is a broad term that encompasses the conditions affecting color perception. The so-called 'normal' human color vision is neither complete nor perfect: A recent study found that the normal human visual system extracts about only 1% of the hues possible from the L, M, and S cones compared to a perfect hue encoder.[482]

Color vision deficiency describes a range of conditions. In most of these conditions, the affected individual's color sensation is not devoid of color sense but is simply different (or less expansive) compared to that of a 'normal' person.[483] With a prevalence of about 5% (affecting mostly the male population), CVD is not considered a rare occurrence.

The first case of CVD was described in 1777 by Joseph Huddart[484] in a shoemaker of Maryport, Cumberland, England. A few years later, the British chemist John Dalton realized that he, himself, and his brother had CVD.[485] Dalton attributed this to an abnormal blue tint of his vitreous, which he thought was selectively absorbing red. After Dalton's death, and according to his wishes, DNA was extracted from his preserved eye tissue, which showed that he was a deuteranope because of mutant M-cone genes.[486] Dalton's work sparked investigative interest in color deficiency, hence, the initially prevailing term Daltonism. In some countries, Daltonism refers to protan defects, as this was the first CVD to be identified. But Dalton had a deutan defect!

Figure 5-33: (left) John Dalton (1766–1844). (right) The desiccated remains of his eyes, preserved at the Science and Industry Museum, Manchester, United Kingdom.

---

[482] Patterson SS, Kuchenbecker JA, Doebley A-L, Neitz M, Neitz J. The normal human visual system extracts about 1% of the hues possible from the L, M and S cones compared to a perfect hue encoder. J Vis. 19(8):81 doi: 10.1167/19.8.81.

[483] Deeb SS. Molecular genetics of colour vision deficiencies. Clin Exp Optom. 2004; 87(4-5):224-9.

[484] Huddart J. An account of persons who could not distinguish colours. Philosophical Transactions of the Royal Society of London. 1977; 67:260-65.

[485] Dalton J. Extraordinary facts relating to the vision of colours: with observations. Memoirs of the Literary and Philosophical Society of Manchester. 1798; 5:28-45.

[486] Hunt DM, Dulai KS, Bowmaker JK, Mollon JD. The chemistry of John Dalton's color blindness. Science. 1995; 267(5200):984-8.

5.3.1 Classification of Color Vision Deficiencies

5.3.1.1 Dichromatic Color Vision Deficiency

Dichromatic CVD presents in three forms: **protanopia**, **deuteranopia**, and tritanopia. Protanopia and deuteranopia both manifest as deficiencies in red and green discrimination; these colors appear as different shades of yellow. The third form, **tritanopia** is a much rarer form of dichromatic CVD that manifests as a deficiency in blue and yellow hue discrimination.

These forms of CVD affect color perception but not visual acuity. The term 'dichromatic' indicates that color vision relies primarily on two, rather than the usual three, cone cell types: two normally functioning cone types and one mutant cone type. Protanopia is associated with a shortage of functional L-cone cells, while deuteranopia is associated with a shortage of functional M-cone cells. Both forms affect males much more often than females. In both defects, the same color channel (R-G) is involved, and the affected individual fails to properly distinguish red from green. Tritanopia is associated with a shortage of S-cone cells.

Anomalous trichromacy is a milder form of dichromatic CVD. It is classified as **protanomaly**, reduced sensitivity to red hues, **deuteranomaly**, reduced sensitivity to green hues (the most common form of CVD), and **tritanomaly**, reduced sensitivity to blue hues. Like tritanopia, tritanomaly is very rare.

Note 🏺 : The nomenclature for dichromatic CVD classification originated from the Greek πρώτο- (first), δεύτερο- (second), and τρίτο- (third) and was introduced by the German physiological psychologist Johannes Adolf von Kries[487] in 1905. It was not based on the physiological nature of the forms but on their relative prevalence, as perceived at that time. In reality, the most prevalent form is deuteranopia.

In the past, tetartanopia (τέταρτο-), a fourth form of dichromatic CVD, was considered, based on a theorized absence/mutation of a 'yellow' cone type that was thought to affect sensitivity in the blue-yellow. Today, the associated symptoms are attributed to some forms of acquired vision deficiency.

The severity of color vision deficiency depends on the degree of degeneration of the spectral responsivity difference between the cone types. In protanopia and protanomaly, there is a lack of functional L cones, although in protanomaly, there are two slightly different M-cone types; in other words, the L-cone responsivity (mutated, shown as a gray line in Figure 5-34 bottom left) is shifted toward the M-cone curve. In deuteranopia and deuteranomaly, there is a

---

[487] Following Helmoltz' theories, von Kries formulated the modern duplicity theory of vision mediated by rod cells at low light levels and three types of cone cells at higher light levels in his work: Kries von J. Die Gesichtsempfindungen. In: Handbuch der Physiologic des Menschen, ed. Nagel, W., 1905 Vol. 3, 109-281, Vieweg, Braunschweig.

lack of functional M-cone cells, although in deuteranomaly, there are two slightly different L-cone types; in other words, the M-cone responsivity (mutated, shown in gray in Figure 5-34 bottom center) is shifted toward the L-cone curve. There is no hard distinction, but instead a continuum, between the '-anopia' and the '-anomaly' types of dichromatic CVD, as these forms can range from almost complete loss of the respective channels to just mild deficiencies.

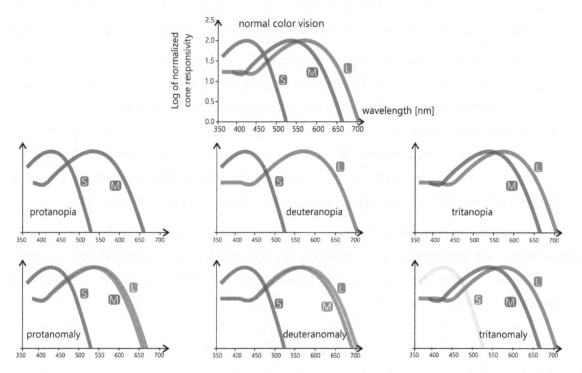

Figure 5-34: Cone responsivity for the major classifications of color vision deficiency. (top row) Normal color vision. (middle row) Dichromatic color vision deficiency. (bottom row) Anomalous trichromacy.

Note 🔍: Color vision deficiency is NOT 'color blindness.' The term 'color blindness' is used today to describe <u>only</u> the <u>most severe form</u> of complete color vision loss and not most cases of CVD. And, no, protanopes and deuteranopes do not see red-green simply as shades of gray; this is a misconception. Individuals with red-green deficiencies confuse a host of reds, greens, browns, and oranges as various shades ranging from yellow to gray.

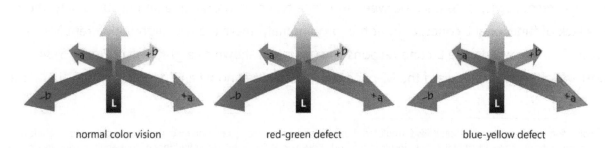

Figure 5-35: Normal color vision versus red-green and blue-yellow defects in the CIELAB color space.

Figure 5-36: Example of color vision perception. (top row) Normal color vision. (middle row) Dichromatic color vision deficiency (left to right, protanopia, deuteranopia, and tritanopia). (bottom row) Anomalous trichromacy (left to right: protanomaly, deuteranomaly, tritanomaly).

Finally, normal color perception is spatially restricted. Due to the variable perimetric distribution of L, M, and S cones, 'true' trichromatic vision pertains to a retina expanse only between the central foveola (which, as we know, is deficient of S cones, so technically is blue-blind) to about 30°. Beyond the perimetry of 30°, vision is dichromatic, as the population of L and M cones diminishes significantly, making the S cones the dominant ones; beyond 60° there are no cones, only rods. Therefore, color vision deficiency may be present in various zones perimetrically, even in a normal retina.[424]

5.3.1.2 Confusion Lines

The term 'color discrimination' refers to color that is observed differently and can be objectively measured. Color discrimination failure can be significant if the observer confuses one primary color for another, or it can be mild if the observer mistakes slightly different hues. Normal color vision observers are capable of distinguishing a large number of chromaticities and perceive small color differences over a broad part of the color space diagram. At the same time, the average normal-color-vision human observer may perceive a range of differing chromaticities as the same. This range of chromaticities was first described by the American physicist and color scientist David Lewis MacAdam and is often represented in a **MacAdam ellipse**, a plot that illustrates regional boundaries on the chromaticity diagram that enclose color coordinates that are indistinguishable to the normal observer from the color at the center of the elliptic boundary.[488]

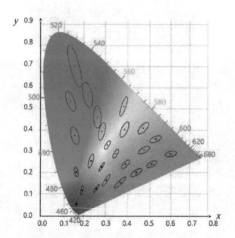

Figure 5-37: A series of boundaries (MacAdam ellipses) around several color targets on the 1931 CIE chromaticity diagram, illustrating the extent to which a normal-color-vision observer can deviate before perceiving a difference from the target color (center dot in each ellipse).

A common misconception is that the red-green dichromatic color deficiencies pose a challenge for the proper color discrimination of reds and greens. Likewise, the yellow-blue dichromatic deficiencies are assumed to fail to distinguish blue from yellow. In reality, color vision disorder does not relate to just two chromaticity pairs but affects the entire color gamut— many other colors are being confused.

The confused colors in L-, M-, and S-cone-mediated discrimination can be visualized on a CIE chromaticity diagram; two equal-luminosity chromaticities (normal metamers) can be distinguished by a normal observer as long as their separation is greater than a given amount on that space.[489] However, a dichromat ordinarily fails to distinguish some chromaticity pairs, even if their spacing on the diagram is appreciably greater.

The loci of these confused chromaticities form a family of **chromatic confusion lines** for the given type of color vision deficiency.[490] These loci form directional straight lines, and the set of confusion loci for each deficiency passes through a single point (common origin), called the copunctal point or the center of confusion.[491] The copunctal point represents the position of the

---

[488] MacAdam DL. Visual sensitivities to color differences in daylight. J Opt Soc Am. 1942; 32(5):247-74.

[489] Lakowski R. Theory and practice of colour vision testing. A review. Part I. Br J Ind Med. 1969; 26: 173-89 and Part II; 26:265-88.

[490] König A, Dieterici C. Die Grundempfindungen in normalen und anomalien Farbensystemen und ihre Intensitätsverteilung im Spectrum. (The basic sensations in normal and anomalous color systems and their intensity distribution in the spectrum) Z Psychol. 1893; 4:241-347.

[491] Judd DB. Standard response functions for protanopic and deuteranopic vision. J Res Nat Bur Standards. 1944; 33:407.

missing fundamental color.[492] The protan point has *x-y* coordinates *x* = 0.747 and *y* = 0.253; the deutan point is at *x* = 1.080 and *y* = –0.800 (falling outside the normal plotting range), and the tritan point is at *x* = 0.171 and *y* = 0.000. Any color along a given confusion line appears the same to the affected individual. Thicker lines that degenerate into bands indicate more severe forms, while thinner and shorter lines signify milder forms of the deficiency.

We note that protanopes confuse the 500 nm blue-green with red, deuteranopes confuse the 500 nm blue-green with purple (see the intersection of the confusion line with the purple line), and tritanopes confuse the 500 nm blue-green with blue.

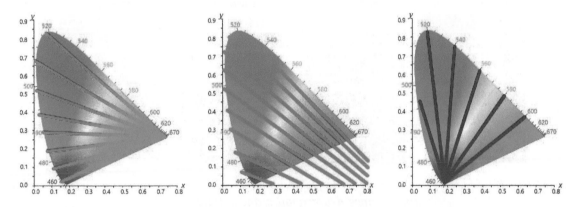

Figure 5-38: The protan (left), deutan (center), and tritan (right) chromatic confusion lines overlaid on the CIE chromaticity diagram.

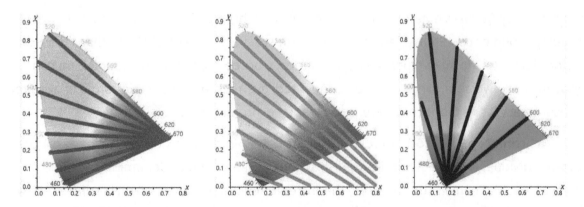

Figure 5-39: The protan (left), deutan (center), and tritan (right) chromatic confusion lines overlaid on the CIE chromaticity diagram as seen by a protanope, deuteranope, and a tritanope individual, respectively.

While several of the confusion lines for the protan and deutan defects have unique paths, there are some that are close together, particularly near the upper-right part of the color space. If the protan and deutan confusion lines run close, then both defect types share similar

---

[492] Wright WD. The characteristics of tritanopia. J Opt Soc Amer. 1952; 4:509-521.

pairs of confused colors: red, orange, yellow, green, and brown. This occurs mainly between the protan and deutan lines between the 520 nm green and the 670 nm red. In different parts of the color space, such as the blue-purple area, there is a clear distinction between protan and deutan lines; i.e., the colors of confusion in the color spectrum are quite different.

In the examples of confused pairs shown in Figure 5-40, the two colors were picked along a confusion line of a dichromatic deficiency. Pairs in rows (1, top) and (3) can be confused by either a protanope or a deuteranope, while the pair in row 2 (second from top) can be confused by a protanope only and the pair in row 4 (bottom) by a tritanope only.

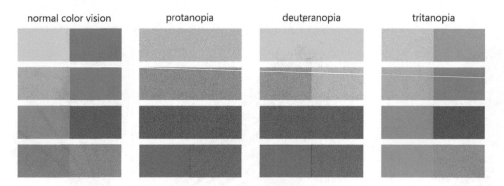

Figure 5-40: Examples of color pairs as seen by a normal (left column) and dichromat CVD individuals (protanopes, deuteranopes, and tritanopes).

5.3.1.3 Monochromacy

Monochromacy (μόνο- single, -χρῶμα- color, - ὄψις, sight) represents a very rare color-vision-deficiency group of conditions pertaining to the most severe form of CVD—perhaps the closest to color blindness. Its main types are achromatopsia, or rod monochromacy, and blue cone monochromacy, which is considered to be inherited; even more rare are two forms of acquired monochromacy: cone monochromacy, and cerebral achromatopsia.

Achromatopsia or **rod monochromacy** is considered complete color blindness: The affected individual is only able to distinguish shades of gray, even under ample photopic conditions. As the name suggests (rod), there are no functional cones; vision is supported by rod perception. Rod monochromacy is very rare in the general population (1:20,000 to 1:50,000). Even at this infrequency, rod monochromacy is still the most common type of 'complete' color blindness. The condition is highly symptomatic; affected individuals have additional vision problems, such as increased sensitivity to light (photophobia), involuntary back-and-forth eye movements (nystagmus), and poor visual acuity. Visual acuity loss is associated with impairment of the midget cell pathway and its related function.[493]

---

[493] Kolb H. Anatomical pathways for color vision in the human retina. Vis Neurosci. 1991; 7(1-2):61-74.

Figure 5-41: Example of color vision perception with (left) rod monochromacy and (right) blue cone monochromacy during twilight. The normal-color-vision image is shown in the top row of Figure 5-36.

Blue cone monochromacy (BCM),[494] or atypical monochromacy, is an even less common form of inherited monochromacy. In BCM, there are only rods and S-type cones.[495] Reds are seen as rather dark, and blues are more bright.[496] Under low ambiance, where both the rods and S cones are working, color perception can be compared with dichromatic vision. BCM affects about 1 in 100,000, mostly males. BCM is associated with vision problems such as eccentric fixation and low visual acuity.[497] Because the symptomatology between blue cone monochromacy and rod monochromacy is similar, differential diagnosis can be provided by spectral sensitivity measurements under light-adapted conditions: BCM-affected individuals have a peak sensitivity at about 440 to 450 nm, similar to the spectral characteristics of normal S cones, while rod-monochromacy-affected individuals have a peak sensitivity at about 505 nm.[494]

Cone monochromacy is also termed complete achromatopsia and is also a very rare form of CVD, considered to be acquired. Cone monochromats have either L cones (L- or red-cone monochromacy) or M cones (M- or green-cone monochromacy) but not both; the S cones are assumed to be totally absent or inactive.[498] Compared to blue-cone or rod monochromacy, cone monochromacy is not associated with reduced visual acuity or any special light sensitivity; therefore, it is sometimes referred to as complete achromatopsia with normal visual acuity.[499]

Cerebral achromatopsia is an acquired form of CVD that is associated with damage to the extrastriate cortex rather than with retina or optic nerve pathology:[500] The cone color receptors still function properly, but their output is not properly processed or does not reach the

[494] Blackwell HR, Blackwell OM. Blue mono-cone monochromacy: a new color vision defect. J Opt Soc Am. 1957; 47:338-41.

[495] Nathans J, Davenport CM, Maumenee IH, Lewis RA, Hejtmancik JF, Litt M, Lovrien E, Weleber R, Bachynski B, Zwas F. Molecular genetics of human blue cone monochromacy. Science. 1989; 245(4920):831-8.

[496] Alpern M, Lee GB, Maaseidvaag F, Miller SS. Colour vision in blue-cone 'monochromacy'. J Physiol. 1971; 212(1):211-33.

[497] Zrenner E, Magnussen S, Lorenz B. Blue cone monochromasia: diagnosis, genetic counseling and optical aids. Klin Monbl Augenheilkd. 1988; 193(5):510-7.

[498] Alpern M. What is it that confines in a world without color? Invest Ophthalmol. 1974; 13(9):648-74.

[499] Weale RA. Cone-monochromatism. J Physiol. 1953; 121(3):548-69.

[500] Bartolomeo P, Bachoud-Lévi AC, de Schotten MT. The anatomy of cerebral achromatopsia: A reappraisal and comparison of two case reports. Cortex. 2014; 56:138-44.

occipital-temporal region of the human visual cortex.[501] The earliest known cases of probable cerebral achromatopsia were described by the English oculist, Dawbeney Turbervile in 1684.[502] Color vision loss may be complete or partial, depending on the areas of damage, and may occur separately or in conjunction with other cognitive and perceptual losses. It is often manifested as a sudden onset of color vision loss due to a severe head injury or damage to the ventromedial occipital and temporal lobes by a stroke or similar ischemic event.[503]

Table 5–2: Dichromatic and anomalous trichromatic CVD prevalence by type and gender. Monochromacy is not listed, as it is very rare in the general population.[504, 505, 506]

Color Vision Deficiency Type	Male	Female
Dichromacy Overall	2 % to 2.4 %	0.06 %
Protanopia	1 % to 1.3 %	0.02 %
Deuteranopia	1 % to 1.2 %	0.01 %
Tritanopia	0.005 %	0.003 %
Anomalous Trichromacy Overall	6.3 %	0.4 %
Protanomaly	1.3 %	0.02 %
Deuteranomaly	5.0 %	0.35 %
Tritanomaly	0.0001 %	0.0001 %

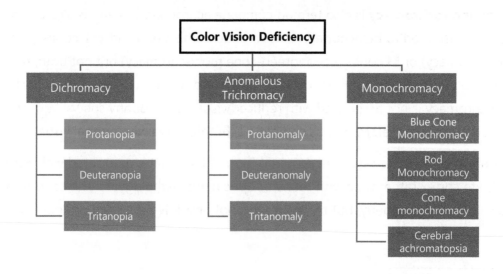

[501] Zeki S, McKeefry DJ, Bartels A, Frackowiak RS. Has a new color area been discovered?. Nat Neurosci. 1998; 1(5):335-6.

[502] Turbervile D. Two letters from the great, and experienced Oculist, Dr. Turbervile of Salisbury, to Mr. William Musgrave S.P.S. of Oxon, containing several remarkable cases in Physick, relating chiefly to the eyes. Philos Trans R Soc. 1684; 14:736e8

[503] Cowey A, Heywood CA. Cerebral achromatopsia: colour blindness despite wavelength processing. Trends Cogn Sci. 1997; 1(4):133-9.

[504] Birch J. Worldwide prevalence of red-green color deficiency. J Opt Soc Am A Opt Image Sci Vis. 2012; 29(3):313-20.

[505] Sato S. Statistical observations on congenital abnormalities in colour vision in Japan. Acta Soc Ophthalmol Jpn. 1935; 38:2227-30.

[506] Iinuma I, Handa Y. A consideration of the racial incidence of congenital dyschromats in males and females. Mod Probl Ophthalmol. 1976; 17:151-7.

5.3.2 Inheritance of Color Vision Deficiency

Color vision impairment may be evoked by genetic deficiencies (heredity) or can be acquired.

Hereditary or **congenital** color vision deficiencies are attributed to a mutated gene in the development of one or more of the three cone types. Hereditary CVD equally affects both eyes in the entire field of vision and is present from birth. It remains unchanged through life in type and severity, and its effects on vision are stable and predictable, since there are well-defined confusion lines, although chromatic sensitivity may decrease gradually with age.[507] There is no ocular morbidity (the condition is not vision-threatening), although daily activities are undeniably affected.

Hereditary red-green CVD is the most frequent type and has X-chromosome-linked recessive inheritance.[508] The reason is that the **opsin pigment genes** associated with color vision (OPN1LW and OPN1MW) are coded on the X chromosome; CVD results from a mutated opsin pigment gene. Rarely, red-green color vision deficiencies can be caused by inactivating point mutations, such as the Cys203Arg in the red and/or green opsin genes.

Notes from the gene book 👆 : The genes responsible for cone photopigments are the OPN1LW, the OPN1MW, and the OPN1SW.[509]

The OPN1LW gene is associated with the red-sensitive opsin in the L cones and the OPN1MW gene with the yellow/green-sensitive opsin in the M cones. These genes are coded in a head-to-tail tandem array on the long arm of the X chromosome.[510] The first gene to be coded is a copy of the -LW gene, followed by one or more copies of the -MW gene. The OPN1SW gene, associated with the blue-sensitive opsin present in the S cones, is coded on chromosome 7. The rhodopsin gene is coded on chromosome 3.

Opsin pigment gene activity is regulated at the locus control region (LCR).[370] The genes nearest the LCR, generally the -LW and the first copy of the -MW (the first two genes in the array) actively contribute to color vision.[511] The -LW gene is highly polymorphic, with many variants identified.[512] Variations in the -MW gene are rare, and the observed variants have significantly less effect on spectral sensitivity.

---

[507] Knoblauch K, Vital-Durand F, Barbur JL. Variation of chromatic sensitivity across the life span. Vision Res. 2001; 41(1):23-36.

[508] Earle P. On the inability to distinguish colors. American Journal of Medical Science. 1845; 9:346-54.

[509] Nathans J, Sung CH, Weitz CJ, Davenport CM, Merbs SL, Wang Y. Visual pigments and inherited variation in human vision. Soc Gen Physiol Ser. 1992; 47:109-31.

[510] Knau H, Kremers J, Schmidt HJ, Wolf S, Wissinger B, Sharpe LT. M-cone opsin gene number does not correlate with variation in L/M-cone sensitivity. Vis Res. 2002; 42(15):1888-96.

[511] Deeb SS, Motulsky AG. Genetics of Color Vision Defects in: Reference Module in Biomedical Sciences, 2014. Retrieved from www.sciencedirect.com/topics/neuroscience/opn1lw.

[512] Verrelli BC, Tishkoff SA. Signatures of selection and gene conversion associated with human color vision variation. Am J Hum Genet. 2004; 75(3):363-75.

Several forms of congenital CVD have been implicated in retinal dystrophy phenotypes. Congenital CVD arises if genes are lost (due to intergenic non-homologous recombination), if genes become nonfunctional (due to missense or nonsense mutations, or coding sequence deletions), or if genes are altered (due to intragenic recombination between genes of different types or possibly point mutations). Mutations can arise in gene coding for the cone photopigments,[513, 495] in gene coding proteins involved in the phototransduction cascade,[514] or in gene coding for the A- or B subunits of the cones' cyclic-guanosine-monophosphate-gated cation channels.[515]

In X-linked inheritance, a father cannot pass traits to his sons, who acquire the defective gene from their mother. The X-linked recessive nature also explains why females are affected much less frequently than males: In a male (one X and one Y chromosome), a mutated gene in the single X chromosome is sufficient for the disorder to manifest because there is no normal gene to oppose the deficiency expression. Recessive means that, in a female (two X chromosomes), the defective gene must be present <u>on both X chromosomes</u> for the disorder to manifest (homozygosity). A defective gene on only one X chromosome makes a female a carrier who, however, is not affected[516] because the absence of the mutation on the other X chromosome masks the trait.

Note 🌐 : Color vision deficiency is an Old World disease! The OPN1LW and OPN1MW opsin genes arose via gene duplication about 40 million years ago in the Old World, after its separation from the New World.[517] The two genes are about 96% identical in sequence, which resulted in a relatively frequent unequal crossing over and gene conversion. This explains why the common occurrence of the red-green color vision deficiency, which is ≈ 6% in males and ≈ 0.4% in females, is present in individuals of European descent or Brahmins of Indian origin.[518] About 15–16% of the female population of European origin is a heterozygote for arrays associated with red-green color vision defects, but most have normal color vision.

In an interesting twist to history, CVD is associated with the first study of gene mapping of the rules governing its inheritance by the pioneering American cell biologist Edmund Beecher Wilson in 1911.

---

[513] Weitz CJ, Went LN, Nathans J. Human tritanopia associated with a third amino acid substitution in the blue-sensitive visual pigment. Am J Hum Genet. 1992; 51(2):444-6.

[514] Aligianis IA, Forshew T, Johnson S, Michaelides M, Johnson CA, Trembath RC, Hunt DM, Moore AT, Maher ER. Mapping of a novel locus for achromatopsia (ACHM4) to 1p and identification of a germline mutation in the α subunit of cone transducin (GNAT2). J Med Genet. 2002; 39(9):656-60.

[515] Kohl S, Marx T, Giddings I, Jägle H, Jacobson SG, Apfelstedt-Sylla E, Zrenner E, Sharpe LT, Wissinger B. Total colourblindness is caused by mutations in the gene encoding the α-subunit of the cone photoreceptor cGMP-gated cation channel. Nat Genet. 1998; 19(3):257.

[516] Neitz J, Neitz M. The genetics of normal and defective color vision. Vision Res. 2011; 51(7):633-51.

[517] Garth TR. The incidence of color blindness among races. Science. 1933; 77(1996):333-4.

[518] Drummond-Borg M, Deeb SS, Motulsky AG. Molecular patterns of X chromosome-linked color vision genes among 134 men of European ancestry. Proc Natl Acad Sci USA. 1989; 86(3):983-7.

Wilson's study of the genes responsible for red-green congenital CVD being attributed to the X chromosome is considered the beginning of the mapping of the human genome.[519]

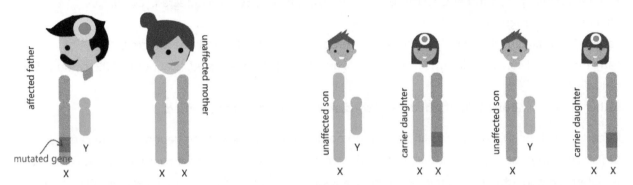

Figure 5-42: CVD heredity when the male parent carries a mutated gene (is affected) and the female parent is unaffected (no mutated genes). No son is affected; all daughters are carriers (one mutated gene).

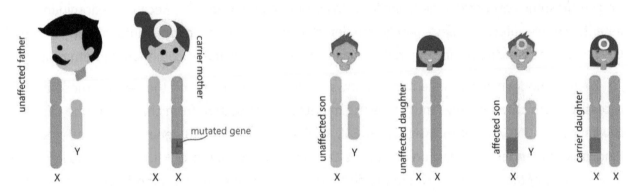

Figure 5-43: CVD heredity when the male parent is unaffected while the female parent carries one mutated gene (CVD carrier). Sons are 50% affected; daughters are 50% carriers (one mutated gene).

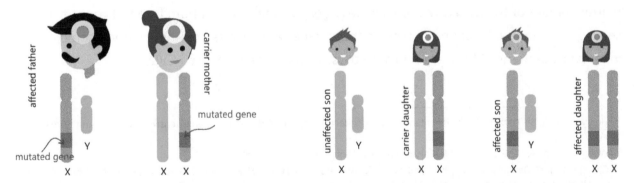

Figure 5-44: CVD heredity when the male parent is affected and the female parent carries a mutated gene (CVD carrier).

[519] Baxter AL. Edmund B. Wilson as a preformationist: some reasons for his acceptance of the chromosome theory. J Hist Biol. 1976; 9(1):29–57.

Practice with CVD inheritance rules 🖐 :

Father CVD affected / Mother normal ⸱⸱⸳ No sons affected, all daughters carriers.

Father CVD affected / Mother CVD carrier ⸱⸱⸳ Sons 50% affected, 50% not affected. Daughters 50% affected, 50% carriers.

Father CVD affected / Mother CVD affected ⸱⸱⸳ All sons affected. All daughters affected.

Father normal / Mother CVD carrier ⸱⸱⸳ Sons 50% affected, 50% not affected. Daughters 50% carriers, 50% not affected.

Father normal / Mother CVD affected ⸱⸱⸳ All sons affected. All daughters carriers.

If the grandfather is CVD affected and the grandmother is normal, all of their daughter(s) are carriers. When a daughter becomes a mother, even with a normal husband, 50% of her sons will be CVD affected: A maternal grandfather passes the trait to his grandson! This is the most common case of CVD inheritance.

Blue-yellow CVD (tritan) inheritance follows an autosomal dominant pattern (trait carried on chromosomes other than the X and Y), with complete penetrance.[520] Because in dominant inheritance the defect manifests if only one defective gene is inherited, one mutated copy of the OPN1SW gene is sufficient for the trait to manifest, although mutated copies are in both cells.[521]

Rod monochromacy inheritance follows a rare autosomal (not on the sex chromosomes), recessive (both chromosomes must have the mutated gene) pattern from changes in one of several genes: CNGA3, CNGB3, GNAT2, PDE6C, or PDE6H.[522] A CNGB3 gene mutation affects Pingelapese islanders, who live on one of the Eastern Caroline Islands of Micronesia, also known as *The Island of the Colorblind*, where the disorder occurs at an extremely high frequency: 4% to 10% of this island population has the disorder, and approximately 30% carry the gene.[523, 524]

Blue cone monochromacy inheritance is associated with genetic changes—either loss or rearrangement of the OPN1LW and OPN1MW genes—that prevent both L and M cones from serving their normal function.[525] Because these genes are encoded on the X chromosome, inheritance patterns of BCM are similar to those of red-green inherited CVD.

---

[520] Henry GH, Cole BL, Nathans J. The inheritance of congenital tritanopia with the report of an extensive pedigree. Ann Hum Genet. 1964; 27:219-31.

[521] Went LN, Pronk N. The genetics of tritan disturbances. Hum Genet. 1985; 69:255-62.

[522] Chang B, Grau T, Dangel S, Hurd R, Jurklies B, Sener EC, Andreasson S, Dollfus H, Baumann B, Bolz S, Artemyev N. A homologous genetic basis of the murine cpfl1 mutant and human achromatopsia linked to mutations in the PDE6C gene. Proc Natl Acad Sci USA. 2009; 106(46):19581-6.

[523] Winick JD, Blundell ML, Galke BL, Salam AA, Leal SM, Karayiorgou M. Homozygosity mapping of the achromatopsia locus in the Pingelapese. Am J Hum Genet. 1999; 64(6):1679-85.

[524] Sundin OH, Yang JM, Li Y, Zhu D, Hurd JN, Mitchell TN, Silva ED, Maumenee IH. Genetic basis of total colourblindness among the Pingelapese islanders. Nat Genet. 2000; 25(3):289.

[525] Gardner JC, Michaelides M, Holder GE, Kanuga N, Webb TR, Mollon JD, Moore AT, Hardcastle AJ. Blue cone monochromacy: causative mutations and associated phenotypes. Mol Vis. 2009; 15:876.

An interesting aspect of inheritance is that, even among primates, color vision differs between New World (platyrrhine) and Old World (catarrhine) monkeys and great apes. New World monkeys may or may not have trichromatic color vision.[526] In most species, males are dichromats and about 60% of females are trichromats, but owl monkeys are cone monochromats, and both genders of howler monkeys are trichromats.[527] Differences between males and females within a species are attributed to the opsin pigment genes associated with color vision (OPN1LW and OPN1MW) being coded on the X chromosome.

5.3.3 Acquired Color Vision Deficiencies

Acquired color vision deficiencies are secondary to certain ocular, visual pathway, neurologic, or systemic diseases, medications, trauma and/or neurotoxic environmental or chemical exposure.[528] In contrast to hereditary CVD, assuming that at some stage the individual had a normally functioning color vision, the effects relating to color vision change over time, usually deteriorating. On the other hand, if the underlying condition is reversible, there may be a regression (improvement) of the effects associated with that type of CVD.

Acquired CVD may affect one eye or both eyes to varying, asymmetric degrees and may affect the visual field in a non-uniform way. Traditionally, acquired CVD is considered a separate entity from hereditary/congenital CVD,[529] although emerging clinical and molecular genetic data suggest a degree of overlap. The reason is that although acquired CVD can be secondary to a causative ocular or neural disease, that disease may itself be hereditary. These cases are sometimes referred to as **developmental CVD**.

Summary 📷 : In a simple classification, acquired CVD can be caused by:

- Chronic conditions: Alzheimer's, diabetes mellitus, glaucoma,[530] leukemia, liver disease, chronic alcoholism, macular degeneration,[531] multiple sclerosis, Parkinson's, sickle cell anemia, and retinitis pigmentosa.
- Ocular accidents or cerebral strokes that affect the retina or areas of the visual pathway.

---

[526] Jacobs GH. Evolution of colour vision in mammals. Philos Trans R Soc Lond B Biol Sci. 2009; 364(1531):2957-67.

[527] Kawamura S. Color vision diversity and significance in primates inferred from genetic and field studies. Genes Genomics. 2016; 38:779-91.

[528] Simunovic MP. Acquired color vision deficiency. Surv Ophthalmol. 201; 61(2):132-55.

[529] Hart WM Jr. Acquired dyschromatopsias. Surv Ophthalmol. 1987; 32:10e31.

[530] Drance SM, Lakowski R, Schulzer M, Douglas GR. Acquired color vision changes in glaucoma: use of 100-hue test and Pickford anomaloscope as predictors of glaucomatous field change. Arch Ophthalmol. 1981; 99(5):829-31.

[531] Krill AE, Deutman AF. Dominant macular degenerations. The cone dystrophies. Am J Ophthalmol. 1972; 73(3):352-69.

- Medications such as antibiotics, barbiturates, anti-tuberculosis drugs, high-blood-pressure medications, and medications for nervous disorders, such as chloroquine, used to treat Plasmodium vivax malaria.[532]
- Exposure to neurotoxic chemicals such as carbon monoxide, carbon disulfide, and lead.[533]

It is challenging to accurately determine the prevalence of acquired CVD. Publications based on occupational or case studies suggest that acquired CVD is present in about 15% of the general population regardless of gender.[534] Perhaps more importantly, the assessment of acquired color vision defects and their prevalence may be complicated by shifting priorities and the confounding variables associated with a concurring ocular pathology, (often) low visual acuity, presence of an undiagnosed congenital color defect, or other concomitant problems.

Acquired CVD most often affects the S cones, thus manifesting as a blue-yellow deficiency, particularly among the elder population,[535] considering the increasing prevalence of vision degenerations with advancing age.[536] The fact that S cones are mostly affected may be explained by the fact that, if a fixed proportion of all cone types is affected, the loss will be greatest for the S cones because of their relative paucity compared with L or M cones.[537] However, there is a 'red-green' type of acquired CVD, and even an achromatopsia type as well.

The existing classifications of acquired CVD are neither universal nor complete. From a pathology perspective,[538] blue-yellow acquired CVD may be caused by glaucoma, vascular retinopathies, retinitis pigmentosa, and macular degenerations (generally classified as lesions affecting the outer layers of the retina).[539] Conversely, Stargardt's disease and optic nerve pathology (affecting inner retinal or optic nerve layers) most commonly result in a red-green defect,[540, 541] a notable exception being optic atrophy,[542] which may lead to a blue-yellow

---

[532] Vu BL, Easterbrook M, Hovis JK. Detection of color vision defects in chloroquine retinopathy. Ophthalmology. 1999; 106(9):1799-804.

[533] Gobba F, Cavalleri A. Color vision impairment in workers exposed to neurotoxic chemicals. Neurotoxicology. 2003; 24(4-5):693-702.

[534] Delpero WT, O'Neill H, Casson E, Hovis J. Aviation-relevent epidemiology of color vision deficiency. Aviat Space Environ Med. 2005; 76(2):127-33.

[535] Schneck ME, Haegerstrom-Portnoy G, Lott LA, Brabyn JA. Comparison of panel D-15 tests in a large older population. Optom Vis Sci. 2014; 91(3):284.

[536] Jafarzadehpur E, Hashemi H, Emamian MH, Khabazkhoob M, Mehravaran S, Shariati M, Fotouhi A. Color vision deficiency in a middle-aged population: the Shahroud Eye Study. Int Ophthalmol. 2014; 34(5):1067-74.

[537] Williams DR, MacLeod DI, Hayhoe MM. Foveal tritanopia. Vision Res. 1981; 21(9):1341-56.

[538] Köllner H. Die Störungen des Farbensinnes ihre klinische Bedeutung und ihre Diagnose. The American Journal of the Medical Sciences. 1912; 144(5).

[539] Verriest G. Further studies on acquired deficiency of color discrimination. JOSA. 1963; 53(1):185-95.

[540] Simunovic MP, Moore AT. The cone dystrophies. Eye. 1998; 12(3b):553.

[541] Mäntyjärvi M, Tuppurainen K. Color vision in Stargardt's disease. Int Ophthalmol. 1992; 16(6):423-8.

[542] Krill AE, Smith VC, Pokorny J. Similarities between congenital tritan defects and dominant optic-nerve atrophy: coincidence or identity? J Opt Soc Am. 1970; 60(8):1132-9.

defect.[543] Other classifications of acquired CVD are based on the affected visual field, i.e., the part of the retina that is affected.[544]

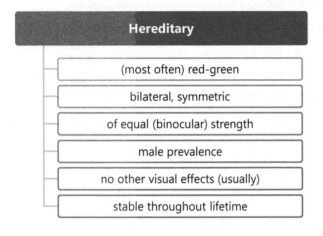

Hereditary
(most often) red-green
bilateral, symmetric
of equal (binocular) strength
male prevalence
no other visual effects (usually)
stable throughout lifetime

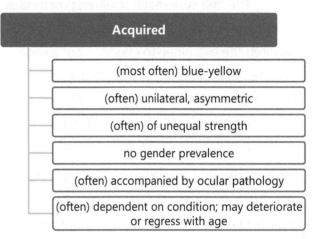

Acquired
(most often) blue-yellow
(often) unilateral, asymmetric
(often) of unequal strength
no gender prevalence
(often) accompanied by ocular pathology
(often) dependent on condition; may deteriorate or regress with age

5.4 TESTING COLOR VISION DEFICIENCY

Testing for CVD seeks to identify the existence, type, and severity of the color vision deficiency, providing thus a basis for the evaluation of the condition's impact on the affected individual's daily life activities and professional performance. Some tests may screen for the presence of a CVD, such as the inherited red-green deficiencies, while other tests provide additional information regarding the severity of CVD. Some tests may signify possible CVD with respect to its impact on a particular vocation.[545] The performance and outcome of CVD tests vary as well.

Several CVD tests have been developed over time. Depending on their complexity and precision, there are screening tests that help identify affected individuals and diagnostic tests that enable the determination of the type and severity of the deficiency. One of the earliest screening tests compared the individual's color naming of everyday objects with that of a normal person. This was the way that Huddart discovered that Harris could not distinguish certain colors, and Dalton wondered about his own vision; Dalton was once derided when he inquired about the

[543] Simunovic MP, Votruba M, Regan BC, Mollon JD. Colour discrimination ellipses in patients with dominant optic atrophy. Vision Res. 1998; 38(21):3413-9.

[544] Marré M, Pinckers A. Basic phenomena of acquired color vision defects. Bull Soc Belge Ophtalmol. 1985; 215:17-25.

[545] Makunyane P. An update on diagnostic tests for colour vision defects in individuals working in the aviation industry: Back to basics. Occupational Health Southern. 2016; 22(3):12-16.

color differences of the khaki uniforms of the military contingent in comparison to the light green grass. An early test of this kind was Holmgren's colored wool test.

The first systematic screening method is attributed to the German physicist Ludwig Friedrich Wilhelm August Seebeck, who, in 1837, constructed a (time-consuming) test that required the examinee to choose from a wide range of more than 300 colored-paper samples that matched or most closely resembled a selected test sample.[546] With this test, Seebeck discovered two different classes of red-green color deficiencies with differences in severity from weak to strong in both classes. Ever since then, more sophisticated testing methods have evolved.

Because our understanding of color vision mechanisms has also evolved, we know that the fundamental characteristics of color vision exploit perceived discrimination ability around or near the loci of the confusion lines. Based on the method of administration, a gross classification of CVD tests forms four major groups: vocational tests (such as lantern tests), presentation test plates using pseudoisochromatic (PIC) plates, arrangement tests, and matching tests either on hue chips or via instruments such as anomaloscopes.[547]

The majority of CVD tests are subjective as they depend on a response provided by the examinee based on his/her perception of a stimulus. There are some objective tests that are based on electrophysiological methods, which include the measurement of chromatic visual evoked potentials[548] and chromatic electroretinographic techniques. These stimulus technique tests evaluate cone function separately from parvocellular visual pathway integrity and have been used to study the contribution of signals originating in the different photoreceptor types.[549]

Clinical note 👁 : CVD testing should be performed monocularly. The majority of CVD is indeed congenital; hence, its presentation is bilateral and symmetrical, which begs the question, why should we test monocularly, thus doubling the exam time?

The answer is that acquired CVD is unilateral and asymmetric. A test that is administered monocularly may reveal the (rare, indeed) possibility of acquired CVD when the results are different between the two eyes; otherwise, if the test is administered binocularly, the (possibly) affected individual could be guided by the less-affected and better-performing eye to falsely pass the color vision screening test, thereby misidentifying normal color vision.[547]

---

[546] Seebeck A. Über die Verarbeitung bei manchen Menschen, die Zwecklosigkeit. Pogg Ann Phys Chem. 1837; 42:177-233.

[547] Melamud A, Hagstrom S, Traboulsi E. Color vision testing. Ophthalmic Genet. 2004; 25(3):159-87.

[548] Pompe MT, Kranjc BS, Brecelj J. Chromatic visual evoked potential responses in preschool children. J Opt Soc Am A Opt Image Sci Vis. 2012; 29(2):A69-73.

[549] Kremers J. The assessment of L-and M-cone specific electroretinographical signals in the normal and abnormal human retina. Prog Retin Eye Res. 2003; 22(5):579-605.

5.4.1 Lantern Tests

A major task in a vocational test is to establish whether the examinee has adequate skills for a particular color task or to satisfy some safety and operational criteria. There are occupations in which defective color vision is either undesirable or downright unacceptable because the entailed work requires recognition or classification of colored signals or objects. Typical examples of such occupations are in the electronics and telecommunications industries, as well as the transportation industry.

Lantern tests were designed as a practical means for determining the ability of seamen, railway personnel, and (later) airline pilots to identify and discriminate between navigational aids and signals. Accordingly, these vocational tests emphasize correct color recognition as an important testing variable. The advantage of these tests is that the task can be made to closely simulate a real-life situation: A lantern test consists of a series of colored lights or combinations of pairs of colored lights. The examinee must identify the colors by name; incorrect naming of some colors indicates color deficiency.

The lantern test was introduced in 1903 by C. H. Williams,[550] who was then the Chief Medical Director of the Burlington Railroad company in Massachusetts. The test was meant to assess the suitability of an individual for employment in the railroad service, in which auditory and visual sensory abilities were so important. Williams' lantern had on its face a single disc with 18 colored glass plates and, within the lantern, two lights and a shutter arranged such that either one or two of the colored glasses could be illuminated at the same time. Lantern tests simply need a system that presents colored lights that are facsimiles of traffic or navigational lights.

The lantern test is still used today for transport workers. Several lantern models are (or were) available: the Giles–Archer, Edridge-Green, Martin, Sloan Color Threshold Tester, Farnsworth Lantern (FaLant), and Holmes–Wright Lantern.

5.4.2 Pseudoisochromatic Tests

Testing with pseudoisochromatic plates is perhaps the most frequently used form of CVD screening. Printed plates (and, recently, computerized screens) are presented at a normal reading distance, and the examinee is asked to identify a pattern or to match colors. Advantages include ease of testing with rapid administration, availability, and affordability. Finally, these tests require simple instruction and can be used on illiterate subjects and children.

---

[550] Williams CH. An improved lantern for testing color perception. Trans Am Ophthalmol Soc. 1903; 10:187-9.

Considerations of the illumination and pattern angular subtense are important because color vision can be different under photopic or mesopic conditions or a narrow (2°) or wide angular subtense. Viewing conditions were established by the 1931 CIE proceedings, in which the surface of a test plate is illuminated at an angle of 45° by a source of a color temperature of 6500 K (the standard CIE illuminant D, whose peak is in the yellow-green), while viewing must be perpendicular to the surface with luminance levels above 10 cd/m^2 (nit), ensuring photopic sensation by reaching 100 to 300 trolands of retinal illumination.[489]

The **pseudoisochromatic** (PIC) plates were introduced in 1879 by the German ophthalmologist Jakob Stilling, who published the first PIC test.[551] Pseudoisochromatic (ψευδο- for false, -ίσο- for equal, -χρωματικό, for color) stands for false appearance. A normal (color vision) observer can distinguish between individual colors in the plate and identify the intended pattern; therefore, the PIC plates appear to be isochromatic only to affected individuals.

The **Stilling principle** breaks the stimulus into a mosaic of circular spots of varying luminance and varying size (2 to 10 mm)—called spatial noise. The obfuscated-pattern target (numeral, geometrical shape, or a pattern) is formed by grouped spots of color(s) that differ from the background color(s). Because of luminance and spatial noise, the color difference, which is chosen to be aligned with, or close to, the confusion lines (§ 5.3.1.2) of the deficiency being screened, is the only differentiator of the concealed pattern from the background.[552] The pattern target is correctly distinguished from the background by individuals not having the defect under test. Those having the color vision deficiency under test perceive these dots—falsely—as either the same as the background (so they do not see the pattern), or as a different pattern.

Figure 5-45: Stilling principle: (left) spatial noise contours, (center) concealed pattern, and (right) background.

[551] Stilling J. Über den Stand der Farbfrage. (About the state of the color question). Archiv für Augenheltkunde. 1879 and Über Entstehung und Wesen der Anomalien des Farbensinnes. (About the origin and nature of the anomalies of color sense). Zsch. F. Sinnesphysiol. 1910; 44:371-427

[552] Regan BC, Reffin JP, Mollon JD. Luminance noise and the rapid determination of discrimination ellipses in color deficiency. Vision Res. 1994; 34(10):1279-99.

The pseudoisochromatic test plates comprise the following designs:

- Demonstration design uses a pattern that is defined by a significant luminous reflectance difference from the background such that color vision is not needed for correct identification. Hence, the delineated object should be correctly identified by all individuals, whether they have normal color vision or are or color vision deficient. These designs are presented at the start of the exam.

- Vanishing or disappearing design comprises the simplest and most frequently used plates found in every PIC test, some of which are entirely composed of this type. The pattern differs chromatically from the background whose colors are aligned with or are close to the dichromatic confusion line that is to be identified. Thus, the pattern is not visible to individuals with that deficiency but is visible to individuals with normal color vision.

- Transformation or alteration design has a pattern that is either not seen at all or is mistakenly recognized as another pattern. The pattern uses some colors that might be confused with the background and some that cannot be confused; thus, there is always some response for the color vision deficient person. The affected individual will see a pattern, but not the pattern seen by a person with normal color vision. Transformation designs are meant to provide positive evidence of color vision deficiency, whereas vanishing designs provide negative evidence.

- Combination plates have a vanishing pattern and a demonstration pattern on the same plate. An affected individual will see one pattern (the demonstration), while an individual with normal color vision will see two patterns. The variation is the hidden-digit design, in which the pattern is only seen by individuals with color deficiency. The pattern colors lie around a confusion line, and all of the background colors lie on a different confusion line.

- Classification/diagnostic design has a pattern that is seen differently by individuals with a protan or a deutan deficiency. These designs, known as disappearing plates, comprise two figures, one to be confused by protans and one by deutans. The colors are chosen from the loci of greatest difference between the protan and deutan confusion lines.

In all of these designs, colors in the concealed and background patterns may be such that they are confused (failed) by both protans and deutans. This is possible if the pattern colors are chosen to straddle the selected adjacent protan and deutan confusion lines. See, for example, Figure 5-46; on the left side of the diagram, the confusion lines are very similar for both protan and deutan types. Hence, regardless of having a protan- or deutan-type of defect, the affected individual will see no pattern at all. This way, these plates can rapidly screen for either form of red-green CVD, but at the same time, they cannot differentiate between the type of CVD.

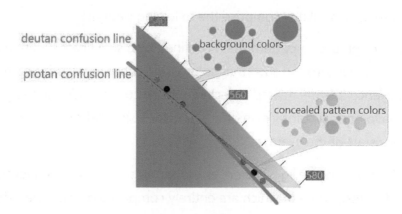

Figure 5-46: In pseudoisochromatic testing, background and concealed pattern chromaticity coordinates are chosen near the locus positions so that the concealed pattern spots serve for both protan and deutan defects since their isochromatic confusion lines (fully presented in Figure 5-38) can be very similar.

The **Ishihara test**, originally published in 1906 by the Japanese ophthalmologist Shinobu Ishihara, was the first commercially available pseudoisochromatic test and helped to popularize the technique.[553] Even today, many available pseudoisochromatic tests refer to an 'Ishihara compatibility' and claim to be evolutions of this test. The Ishihara test is considered the benchmark for the rapid screening of red-green color deficiencies.

The test consists of several plates (depending on the version, the test may contain 38 plates, 24 plates or 14 plates), each of which has a circle filled with dots of random color and size. The concealed pattern is a numeral (single or double-digit) or a path-shape, forming vanishing and transformation designs for red-green defects. The examinee is asked to name/identify the number shown or follow the concealed pattern using a fingertip.

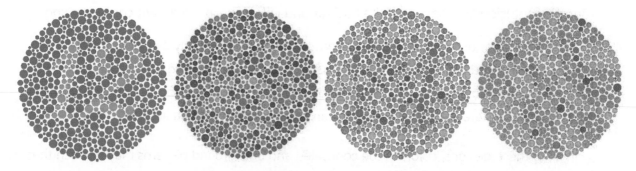

Figure 5-47: Ishihara test plates. (left) Demonstration plate: The numeral shown is viewable by all, including the red-green deficient. The second plate is vanishing design (reading the numeral 6; if you read the numeral 5, you may have red-green deficiency). The third plate is transformation design (reading 74 here and not 21). (right) The fourth design is a blue line to most observers. (The colors in these images as seen on this page/screen might not be reproduced accurately due to differences in the reflectance from the printed surface and the viewing illuminance compared to those intended for the exam.)

[553] Birch J. Efficiency of the Ishihara test for identifying red-green colour vision deficiency. Ophthalmic Physiol Opt. 1997; 17:403-8.

The Ishihara plates may miss weak deutans[554] and do not identify tritanopia. Due to the lack of accurate classification scoring criteria, the number of errors provides little information regarding the extent of the defect; thus, it does not indicate the severity of the CVD.[555]

The **H-R-R pseudoisochromatic test**, named after its developers, LeGrand Haven Hardy, Marie Gertrude Rand Ferree, and M. Catherine Rittler, was published by American Optical Co. (Southbridge, Massachusetts) in 1954.[556, 557] It consisted of 24 plates, each concealing either one or two shapes, such as a cross, a circle, or a triangle, located in a quadrant. The background is formed of similarly random-sized circular dots of gray variations. The colors in the concealed shape have chromaticity coordinates on or close to the dichromatic confusion loci and pass through the chromaticity coordinates of the gray background.

The examinee is asked to identify the shape of each symbol and to show its location on the plate. The test includes ten grading plates for the protan/deutan defects; examinees who make one or more errors in the two plates with the most-saturated colors are graded as severe, and those who make an error in the next three most-saturated plates are graded as medium. Those who make errors only with the five least-saturated plates are graded as mild.

Figure 5-48: (left to right) Shinobu Ishihara, LeGrand Hardy, Gertrude Rand, and M. Catherine Rittler.

The most updated H-R-R test was presented in 2002 by Richmond Products (Albuquerque, New Mexico; now Good-Lite Co., Elgin, Illinois) and re-engineered by Drs. Jay Neitz and James E. Bailey.[558] The updated test employs colors nearer to the protan and deutan confusion lines based on a better understanding of color vision defects gained since the original version. The background pattern is formed of variations of gray dots.

[554] Dain SJ, Grey S, Tran L. Colorimetric analysis and performance assessment of the Hahn New Pseudoisochromatic Colour Vision Test. Color Res Appl. 1998; 23:69-77.

[555] Crone RA. Quantitative diagnosis of defective color vision. A comparative evaluation of the Ishihara test, the Farnsworth dichotomous test and the Hardy-Rand-Rittler polychromatic plates. Am J Ophthalmol. 1961; 51:298-305.

[556] Hardy LH, Rand G, Rittler MC. HRR polychromatic plates. J Opt Soc Am. 1954; 44:509-23.

[557] Hardy LH, Rand G, Rittler MC. A screening test for defective red-green vision. J Opt Soc Am. 1946; 36:610-4.

[558] Bailey JE, Neitz M, Tait DM, Neitz J. Evaluation of an updated HRR color vision test. Visual Neurosci. 2004; 21(3):431-6.

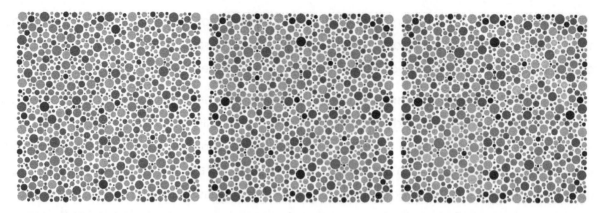

Figure 5-49: H-R-R test plates from the 2002 fourth edition. (left) Demonstration plate with no apparent visible pattern, (center) plate #23, and (right) plate #24. Images courtesy of Good-lite Company.

The test plates form a series of classification/diagnostic plates with increasing color difference and thus help differentiate protans from deutans while providing a determination of severity.[559, 560] There are also test plates for the diagnosis of tritan defects, such as plate #24.

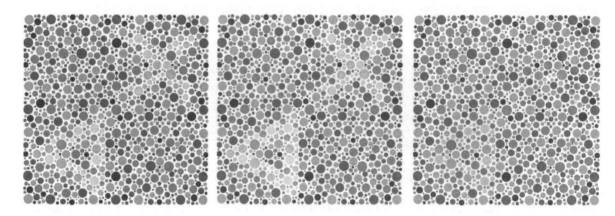

Figure 5-50: Simulation of the H-R-R test plate #24 from the 2002 fourth edition as seen by an individual with (left) protanopia, (center) deuteranopia, and (right) tritanopia, in which only one of the two concealed patterns, the triangle shape, is visible.

Color Vision Testing Made Easy (CVTME) and the Waggoner PIP24 published by Waggoner Diagnostics (Roger, Arkansas) are pseudoisochromatic tests developed by Dr. Terrace L. Waggoner. The CVTME test, validated by Dr. Susan Cotter,[561] is a pediatric color vision test with simple symbols (circle, star, square) and objects (dog, house, boat)—children do not need

---

[559] Dain SJ. Colorimetric analysis of four editions of the Hardy-Rand-Rittler pseudoisochromatic test. Visual Neurosci. 2004; 21(3):437-43.

[560] Cole BL, Lian KY, Lakkis C. The new Richmond HRR pseudoisochromatic test for colour vision is better than the Ishihara test. Clin Exp Optom. 2006; 89(2):73-80.

[561] Cotter SA, Lee DY, French AL. Evaluation of a new color vision test: "color vision testing made easy." Optom Vis Sci. 1999; 76(9):631-6.

to know their numbers. It is also suitable for individuals with intellectual disabilities.[562] Both tests screen for protan/deutan/tritan color vision deficiencies. The Waggoner PIP24 edition has 16 adult and 7 pediatric protan/deutan/tritan test plates plus an additional test plate to quantify the deficiency as mild or severe. Several of the Waggoner PIP 24 test plates are offered in a computerized version as well (see § 5.4.5).

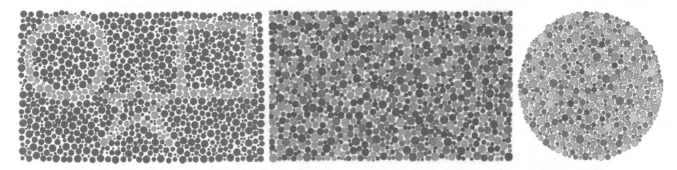

Figure 5-51: (left) Color Vision Testing Made Easy (CVTME) PIC test plate serving as a demonstration plate with three simple symbols: circle, star, and square. (center) CVTME PIC test plate with a child-friendly pet design. (right) A test plate from the Waggoner PIP24. Images courtesy of Dr. T. J. Waggoner per information contained in www.ColorVisionTesting.com and www.WaggonerDiagnostics.com.

Other PIC tests include the Analphabetic Ishihara plates (Handaya, Tokyo, Japan), the Standard Pseudoisochromatic Plates (SPP)[563] by Kawakami, Igaku-Shoin (Tokyo, Japan), the City University Tritan test, the Dvorine test, and the Neitz Test of Color Vision.

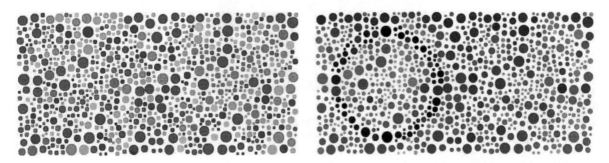

Figure 5-52: The City University Test (2nd edition) has five pseudoisochromatic plates for detection and evaluation of congenital tritan defects and acquired type 3 (tritan) defects.[564]

[562] Barnhardt C, Block SS, Deemer B, Calder AJ, DeLand P. Color vision screening for individuals with intellectual disabilities: A comparison between the Neitz Test of Color Vision and Color Vision Testing Made Easy™. Optometry. 2006; 77(5):211-6.

[563] Hovis JK, Cawker CL, Cranton D. Comparison of the standard pseudoisochromatic plates -parts 1 and 2- as screening tests for congenital red-green deficiency. J Am Optom Assn. 1996; 67:320-6.

[564] Landers A, Murdoch IE, Birch J, Cousens SN, Babalola OE, Lawal B, Abiose A, Jones BR. Blue-yellow colour vision in an onchocercal area of northern Nigeria. Br J Ophthalmol. 1998; 82(5):510-6.

The Analphabetic Ishihara test involves child-friendly patterns modified on Ishihara round designs for pediatric screening.[565] The SPP test has two volumes, the first for congenital red-green deficiencies, and the second for screening for acquired color vision deficiencies.[566]

The Dvorine test was developed by Israel Dvorine, the first American optometrist to develop a test for color vision deficiency.[567] It is similar in structure (slightly different font, believed to be easier to read) and administration to the Ishihara test. It consists of one demonstration, 12 screening, and two classification plates, all with numerals.

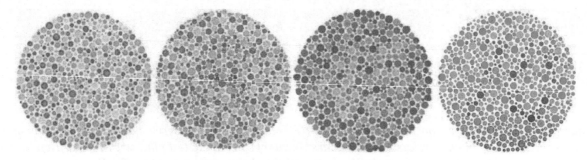

Figure 5-53: Dvorine pseudoisochromatic plates. (left and two center plates) vanishing design and (right) protan/deutan classification plate.

Figure 5-54: Dr. Israel Dvorine (right) with Mrs. Dvorine (center) accepts the 1983 National Optometrist of the Year Award from American Optometric Association President Wendel D. Waldie (left). Image used with permission from the Collections and Exhibits, The Jewish Museum of Maryland.

The Neitz Test of Color Vision is a psychophysical test, designed at the Neitz Laboratories (University of Washington, Seattle, Washington).[568] The test consists of a sheet of paper with nine fields where Stilling patterns conceal a pattern of a circle, square, diamond, or triangle. The

---

[565] Pompe MT, Kranjc BS. Which psychophysical colour vision test to use for screening in 3–9 year olds?. Slovenian Medical Journal. 2012; 82.

[566] Pinckers A, Nabbe B, Vossen H. Standard pseudoisochromatic plates part 2. Ophthalmologica. 1985; 190(2):118-24.

[567] Powell LG. Israel Dvorine: pioneer in color vision testing. Defective color vision is a risk factor as the number of occupations relying on color grows. Occup Health Saf. 2011; 80(6):19.

[568] www.neitzvision.com/neitz-test/ Accessed 07/15/2019.

child examinee must identify the colored pattern within the gray dot background. Below each pattern are five response options: a circle, a triangle, a square, a diamond, and nothing, one of which is the correct response that needs to be marked.[569]

In a broader sense of plate tests, there is the City University Color Vision Test (Keeler, Malvern, Pennsylvania),[570] in which the examinee is asked to identify which of four colors is the most similar to a standard color, and the Sloan Achromatopsia test,[571] designed to detect achromatopsia, in which the examinee is asked to identify which circle matches a gray rectangle.

5.4.3 Arrangement Tests

The **arrangement test** is a class of CVD test that requires the examinee to arrange color samples (colored caps) by similarity in a sequential color series laid over a panel (hence, the 'panel test' moniker). Initially developed by W. O. D. Pierce in 1934,[572] this test was the first to be used in the National Institute of Industrial Psychology in London, United Kingdom.

The examinee grades and then matches a series of samples that vary in saturation and hue; thus, the arrangement test has two steps, grading and matching. In the grading part of the test, several caps (or disks) of one hue with varying saturation are presented in a random order, and the examinee is asked to arrange the caps by order of saturation. In the matching part of the test, prearranged series of caps of one color are presented, and the examinee is asked to select a match from a duplicate group of caps.

A current-day variant of the arrangement test involving hue discrimination is the Farnsworth dichotomous test, or the **Farnsworth D-15 test**, developed by Dean Farnsworth in 1943.[573, 574, 575] The name dichotomous derives from the test's intended purpose of identifying subjects as belonging to one of two groups: group 1, strong/medium CVD, or group 2, mild CVD/ normal color vision. Some shortcomings of the D-15 test include false-positive results and low sensitivity to mild color deficiency.

---

[569] Block SS, Lee D, Hoeppner J, Birr A. Comparison of the Neitz test of color vision to the Ishihara color vision tests and the anomaloscopic classification. Invest Ophthalmol Vis Sci. 2004; 45(13):1384.

[570] Birch J. Clinical use of the City University test. Ophthalmic Physiol Opt. 1997; 17(6):466-72.

[571] O'Connor PS, Tredici TJ, Ivan DJ, Mumma JV, Shacklett DE. Achromatopsia. Clinical diagnosis and treatment. J Clin Neuroophthalmol. 1982; 2(4):219-26.

[572] Pierce WOD. The Selection of the Colour Workers. London: Sir Isaac Pitman and Sons. (1934)

[573] Farnsworth D. The Farnsworth-Munsell 100-hue and dichotomous tests for color vision. J Opt Soc Am. 1943; 33(10):568-78.

[574] Shrestha RK, Shrestha GS. Assessment of color vision among school children: a comparative study between the Ishihara test and the Farnsworth D-15 Test. J Nepal Med Assoc. 2015; 53(200):266-9.

[575] Hovis JK, Ramaswamy S, Anderson M. Repeatability indices for the Farnsworth D-15 test. Vis Neurosci. 2004; 21(3):449-53.

Derivatives of this test include the **Roth 28** hue test with 28 caps, the **Lanthony desaturated D-15** test (this involves more elaborate administration but can detect subtle color vision deficiencies),[576] and the **H16 test** with more saturated colors to avoid false positives.

reference 1   2   3   4   5   6   7   8   9   10 11 12 13 14 15

Figure 5-55: The D-15 Farnsworth disks (caps), originally defined by Farnsworth.[577, 578] Their color coordinates are situated close to the common intersection of the protan, deutan, and tritan confusion lines.

In these tests, the examinee is asked to arrange the caps in the correct color by picking the most similar color, starting from the reference pilot patch; then, the examiner maps the results by plotting connecting lines of the number field corresponding to the ordered caps on a prescribed arc-like arrangement.[579] As shown in Figure 5-56 (left), the connecting line describing the (correct) selected order of the plates has a perfect, uninterrupted numerical succession (e.g., from 1 to 2, 2 to 3, and so on); this is the case presented by a normal color vision examinee, whose results, when plotted, appear as a circle-like connection.

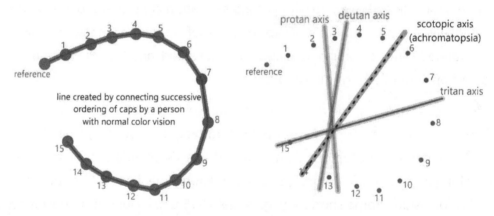

Figure 5-56: (left) Plotted D-15 Farnsworth test results for normal color vision. (right) The prevailing axes in the major CVD types as evaluated by the Farnsworth test.

Individuals with CVD arrange the caps in such a way that the numerical order of the selected test plates shifts (in comb-like crossings) between numbers (e.g., from 14 to 1, then to 2, then to 13, etc. (Figure 5-57).

---

[576] Named after French Ophthalmologist Philippe Lanthony, first reported in: Lanthony P. The new color test. Doc Ophthalmol. 1978; 46(1):191-9.

[577] Farnsworth D. The Farnsworth Dichotomous Test for Color Blindness Panel D-15 Manual. New York, The Psychological Corp., 1947, pp. 1-8.

[578] Wyszecki G, Stiles WS. Color Science: Concepts and Methods, Quantitative Data and Formulae. New York, Wiley and Sons, 1982.

[579] Bassi CJ, Galanis JC, Hoffman J. Comparison of the Farnsworth-Munsell 100-Hue, the Farnsworth D-15, and the L'Anthony D-15 desaturated color tests. Arch Ophthalmol. 1993; 111(5):639-41.

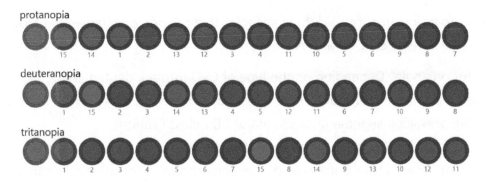

Figure 5-57: Arrangement of D-15 caps in the three forms of dichromatic CVD.

Some distinct features are revealed when these results are plotted. In the top row of Figure 5-58, which shows examples of protanopia, deuteranopia, and tritanopia, the key observation is that these shifts produce lines that are aligned along a common axis that is distinct for different types of dichromatic CVD, such as the axes shown in Figure 5-56 (right).

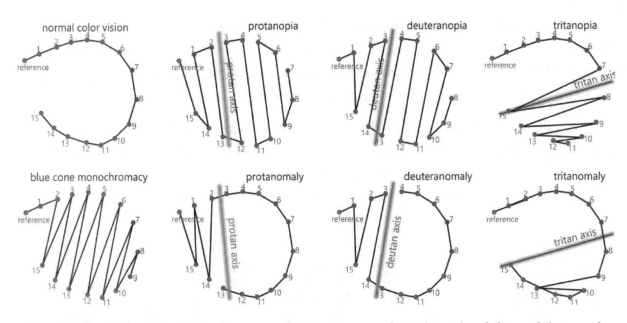

Figure 5-58: Color vision deficiencies screened by the Farnsworth D-15 test. (top, left to right): normal color vision, protanopia, deuteranopia, and tritanopia. (bottom, left to right): blue cone monochromacy (blocks arranged by brightness), protanomaly, deuteranomaly, and tritanomaly.

Anomalous trichromacy is differentiated from dichromatic CVD in the plotted results by notably fewer crossings. The alignment with the axis is the same between the mild and the severe forms of CVD; the axis in the –anomaly case is the same as in the –anopia case, but the crossings on the plot are fewer. In other words, the result appears as the normal color vision continuous line, supplemented by a few comb-like crossings. Even in normal subjects, the test results are often not ideal: Confusion among adjacent color discs (e.g., 2 confused with 3, or 10 confused with 11) are frequent but usually indicate placement error rather a form of CVD.

Such cap arrangements yield three variables that provide qualitative (the type of) and quantitative (the severity of) CVD analysis:[580]

- The confusion angle. Depending on the type of CVD (protan, deutan, tritan, or achromatopsia), the line produced by the test has a prevailing alignment. Figure 5-56 (right) defines the prevailing alignment for the major CDV classifications.

- The confusion index (C-index), which quantifies the severity relative to a perfect cap arrangement. The C-index is the ratio of the major radius of the affected arrangement to the major radius of a normal-vision arrangement. A ratio below 1.2 indicates normal color vision or slight deficiency. Values above 4 indicate severe color deficiency.

- The selectivity index (S-index), which quantifies the amount of polarity or lack of randomness in a cap arrangement. For example, more crossings increase the polarity index. A low ratio (< 2.0) indicates no color deficiency (or random ordering of the caps). A large ratio (> 6.0) suggests high parallelism, indicating a severe form of the deficiency.

A more elaborate, time-consuming, but more precise, test is the **Farnsworth–Munsell 100 hue test**.[573] As the name suggests, this test has 100 color caps (or 85 in some variations Figure 5-59). It uses four rows of similar hues, each with 25 distinct variations of the hue. The examinee must arrange the caps in the tray to create a continuum of gradually changing hues.

The score page resembles a polar coordinates graph, on which the error in the placement of caps in the series is logged. The pattern obtained in dichromatic CVD—produced by the clustering of maximum error displacements in two opposing regions—has a distinct polarity. Thus, the type of deficiency is indicated by the orientation of the pattern (Figure 5-59).

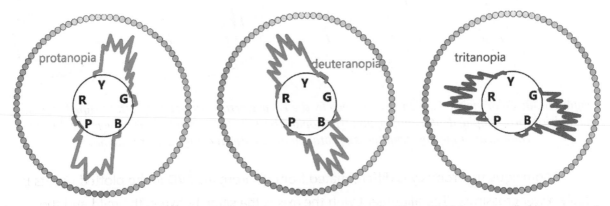

Figure 5-59: Color vision defect scoring charts with the Farnsworth–Munsell 85 hue test: (left) protanopia, (center) deuteranopia, and (right) tritanopia.

---

[580] Vingrys AJ, King-Smith PE. A quantitative scoring technique for panel tests of color vision. Invest Ophthalmol Vis Sci. 1988; 29(1):50-63.

Similar to the scoring for the D-15 test, the severity of the deficiency is proportional to the magnitude and range of the peaks (the average of the distance by which the caps are misplaced).[581] An affected individual with acquired CVD will err throughout the range in a non-coordinated form, so the scoring pattern will not produce a well-defined axis.

Arrangement tests can be administered to people who have monochromacy and can simply arrange the disks by perceived brightness.

The **Mollon–Reffin test**, whose computer-based version is known as the Cambridge color test,[582] has a set of gray achromatic chips of varying lightness that serve as the background chips, a set of colored probe chips, and an orange demonstration chip.[583]

The chromaticities of the probe chips lie along the dichromatic confusion lines that cross the chromaticity of the gray chips. The examinee is simply required to identify, by touching it with a pointer, a colored probe chip placed among five achromatic distractor chips of varying brightness. The examiner next draws a probe chip from the middle of the protan series. If the examinee correctly identifies this probe chip, the examiner then moves inwards along the confusion line and presents the least saturated chip. If the response to the first protan probe is incorrect, then the examiner moves outwards to the most saturated chip.

On subsequent trials, a simple staircase procedure is used to establish the maximal chroma at which the examinee errs. The same process is then repeated for the other two confusion lines. For a normal individual, the test can be completed in about one minute; an individual with a color deficiency requires only a little longer. The test is ideal for monitoring acquired color vision deficiencies, is rapid, and presents the easiest possible task to the subject. The test may be administered in children as young as three years of age.[584]

An alternative screening test is called preferential looking, whereby the child looks at, or points to, a target that is chosen as a preference to a comparison stimulus. This technique forms the basis of the proposed PACT test.[585] Objective testing with the use of a color-sweep visual evoked potential (VEP) technique has also been tried[586] and is still in the early development stages.

---

[581] Mantyjarvi M. Normal test scores in the Farnsworth-Munsell 100 hue test. Doc Ophthalmol. 2001; 102(1):73-80.

[582] Mollon JD, Reffin JP. A computer-controlled color-vision test that combines the principles of Chibret and of Stilling. J Physiol (Lond). 1989; 414: 5P.

[583] Mollon JD, Astrell S, Reffin JP. A minimalist test of colour vision. In: B. Drum, JD. Moreland & A. Serra, eds. Colour Vision Deficiencies X, pp. 59-67. 1991 Kluwer Academic Publishers. Dordrecht, the Netherlands.

[584] Shute RH, Westall CA. Use of the Mollon-Reffin minimalist color vision test with young children. J AAPOS. 2000; 4(6):366-72.

[585] Pease PL, Allen J. A new test for screening color vision: concurrent validity and utility. Am J Optom Physiol Opt. 1988; 65(9):729-38.

[586] Ver Hoeve JN, France TD, Bousch GA. A sweep VEP test for color vision deficits in infants and young children. J Pediatr Ophthalmol Strabismus. 1996; 33(6):298-302.

5.4.4 The Anomaloscope

Certain spectral colors, when mixed appropriately, can create the sensation of another color. For example, when the 545 nm green and 670 nm red are mixed, normal trichromats sense a full range of hues from yellow-green to yellow to orange to yellow-red, depending on the proportion of red to green in the mix. That is not the case for individuals with CVD. In 1881, this observation was first made by Lord Rayleigh, who noted that color matches by certain observers are very different from matches by individuals with normal color vision. Anomalous trichromats accept color matches that a normal observer does not due to proper color sensitivity in the latter. In the extreme case, monochromats can match any color by simply adjusting the brightness of a single primary.

Rayleigh then proposed the use of this matching in the diagnosis of congenital red-green color vision deficiency. The technique is relatively quick and easy to perform compared to full-spectrum color matching. The match that compares a spectral yellow 589 nm to a mixture of green 545 nm and red 670 nm is known as the Rayleigh match or **Rayleigh equation**.[587]

Rayleigh Equation: green (545 nm) + red (670 nm) = yellow (589 nm) (5.7)

These three wavelengths were selected mainly for their source availability and reproduction consistency. For example, the 589 nm yellow is none other than the sodium yellow line, and the 545 nm is the mercury green line. Rayleigh used thallium green and lithium red at the time. These colors are well-suited for testing red-green deficiencies since they are at the wavelengths to which the S cones are extremely insensitive.

A **metameric match** occurs when two physically dissimilar colors give rise to identical color sensations. The sensation produced by viewing a colored object is unrelated to the possibility that the color may be pure spectral yellow or a combination of green and red.

Some other metameric matches include the Pickford–Lakowski, the Engelking–Trendelenburg, and the Moreland match. In the Pickford–Lakowski match, white light from a tungsten source is compared to a mix of blue 470 nm and yellow-orange 585 nm.[588] The Engelking–Trendelenburg match[589] involves a comparison of cyan-blue 490 nm to a mix of blue 470 nm and green-cyan 517 nm. These matches were designed for the evaluation of blue-yellow

---

[587] Rayleigh L. Experiments on colour. Nature.1881; 25:64-6.

[588] Pickford RW, Lakowski R. The Pickford-Nicolson anomaloscope for testing and measuring colour sensitivity and colour blindness, and other tests and experiments. Brit J Physiol Optics. 1960; 17:131-50.

[589] Trendelenburg W. Ein Anomaloskop zur Untersuchung von Tritoformen der Farbenfehlsichtigkeit mit spektraler Blaugleichung. An anomaloscope for investigating tritoforms of color vision defects with spectral bleaching. Klin MBL Augenheilk. 1941; 106:537-46.

color defects. A tritanope can match all spectral colors to a mixture of two primaries located on either side of 565 nm and will have a wide matching range in the Engelking–Trendelenburg and Pickford–Lakowski equations.[590] The Moreland match involves the comparison of an indigo and green mix (originally 430 nm and 500 nm, respectively, but subsequently revised to 436 and 490 nm and then to 440 and 488 nm) to a cyan (a mix of 480 nm and 580 nm).[591]

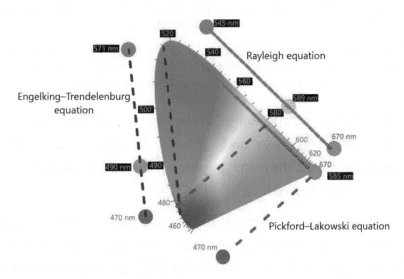

Figure 5-60: Loci of the Rayleigh, Engelking–Trendelenburg, and Pickford–Lakowski equations.

The **anomaloscope** ($\alpha\nu\acute{\omega}\mu\alpha\lambda o$- irregular, $-\sigma\kappa o\pi\acute{\omega}$, seeing), introduced by German ophthalmologist Willibald A. Nagel,[592] is an optical instrument that tests CVD using metameric matching. The original Nagel anomaloscope implements the Rayleigh equation.

Through a viewfinder, the examinee is presented a circular Trendelenburg bipartite field formed by two horizontally divided semicircular half-fields (Figure 5-61). This screen forms an approximately 3°15´ angular subtense and consists of two isolated halves. The upper half-field is a mix of two narrow spectral bands [centered at green (545 nm) and red (670 nm)] in varying proportions and controlled by turning a scaled mixture dial. This half-field appears as green, yellow-green, yellow, orange, or red, depending on the ratio of green to red. The lower half-field, the comparison half-field, consists of pure yellow (589 nm), whose brightness can be modified by turning a scaled brightness dial. The objective is to determine the range of red or green ratios that can be matched in color to the yellow. The narrower the range the higher the color sensitivity; thus, the individual is identified as 'not affected.'

---

[590] Engelking E. Die Tritanomalie, ein bisher unbekannter Typus anomaler Trichromasie (Tritanomaly, a previously unknown type of abnormal trichromatosis). V Graefes Arch Ophthalmol. 1925; 116:196-243.

[591] Moreland JD. Moreland match revisited. Vis Neurosci. 2004; 21(3):471-6.

[592] Nagel WA. Zwei Apparate für die Augenärzliche Funktionsprüfung. Adaptometer und kleines Spektralphotometer (Anomaloskop). Zeitschrift für Augenheilkunde 1907; 17:201-22.

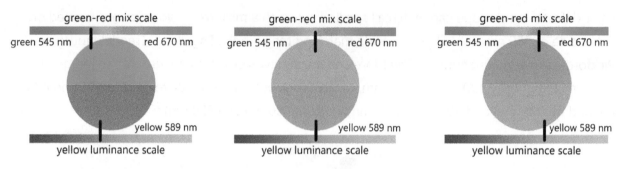

Figure 5-61: Half-fields with a varying red-green mixtures (top half-field) and yellow luminance (bottom half-field). (left) Not matched, green shifted. (center) Match achieved over a narrow range of settings in the two scales. (right) Not matched, red-shifted.

The examinee matches the appearance of the two halves in both color and brightness by adjusting the red/green ratio and the yellow brightness. An individual with normal color vision (or a tritanope!) can reliably make the match to yellow [Figure 5-61 (center)] by a very narrow range of proportions of green and red.

The matching range includes all ratios of green-red that an observer can match to the yellow. Higher sensitivity in differentiating between colors indicates a narrow matching range. Individuals with normal vision have a very narrow matching range over which the two half-fields evoke the same sensation. Just a small change in the green-red mix ratio upsets the color match, and the matching range is termed narrow. In normal trichromats, the distribution of match midpoints describes a bell-shaped or normal curve that includes only a rather narrow group of settings. The midpoint of the matching range lies in the center, between the 30 and 40 marks on the green-red scale, which is where the protanope and the deuteranope matching lines intersect; any variations to this midpoint depend on the M:L cone ratio.[593]

The test is so sensitive that it can identify the deviant/normal observer—a normal trichromat whose Rayleigh equation lies within the normal range but with the midpoint displaced by more than ±2 standard deviations from the mean of average observers. Conversely, individuals with red-green color vision deficiency accept a wide variety of green-red mix scale values as a match for the yellow half-field. The slope of the curve determines the type of defect. The slope in protanopia is notably more negative than the slope in deuteranopia. The breadth (extent) of the curve determines the severity of the condition. In protanomaly, the matching range is about half of that of protanopia, with a redder mix, and in deuteranomaly, the matching range is about half of that of deuteranopia, with a greener mix.[594] The anomaloscope

[593] Thomas PB, Mollon JD. Modelling the Rayleigh match. Vis Neurosci. 2004; 21(3):477-82.
[594] Barbur JL, Rodriguez-Carmona M, Harlow JA, Mancuso K, Neitz J, Neitz M. A study of unusual Rayleigh matches in deutan deficiency. Vis Neurosci. 2008; 25(3):507-16.

is generally accepted as the gold standard in clinical practice for quantifying and discriminating between deutan and protan deficiency.[595]

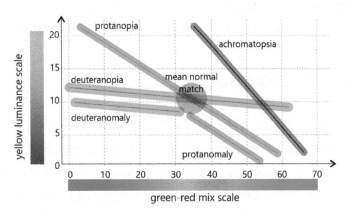

Figure 5-62: Color matches obtained with a Nagel anomaloscope.

The Nagel model I (Schmidt + Haensch, Berlin, Germany) is a constant-deviation spectroscope with three entrance slits. In the Nagel model II, the Engelking–Trendelenburg equation is included as well. Other known anomaloscopes are the Pickford–Nicolson (Rayner and Keiller, London), the Neitz (Neitz Instrument, Tokyo, Japan), and the Oculus/Heidelberg Multi-Color (HMC) anomaloscope (Oculus Optikgeräte GmbH, Wetzlar, Germany).

The Pickford–Nicolson anomaloscope is a filter anomaloscope that uses broadband filters to provide the primary comparison and test wavelengths along the Pickford–Lakowski equation. The Neitz anomaloscope uses interference filters to provide the primary comparison and test wavelengths. The HMC anomaloscope uses light-emitting diode sources coupled with interference filters and has an additional blue-green mixing test and a lower comparison field with cyan and desaturation with yellow, which is adjusted in brightness. This blue-green test can detect acquired color vision deficiencies and offers early detection of progressive diseases such as intoxication of the retina and the optic nerve.

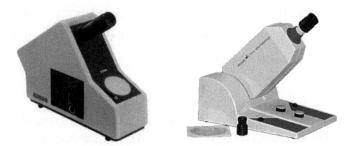

Figure 5-63: (left) the Neitz and (right) the Oculus/Heidelberg Multi-Color (HMC) anomaloscopes.

---

[595] Birch J. Diagnosis of defective color vision using the Nagel anomaloscope. Docum Ophthal Proc Series 1982; 33:231-5.

The anomaloscope's relatively high acquisition cost and complexity are detrimental to its appeal to the average clinical practitioner, so its use is limited to the research community. However, for the skilled examiner, its advantages as a diagnostic instrument far outweigh any inconveniences, as it is especially accurate in the diagnosis of color defects.[596]

5.4.5 Computerized CVD tests

Color vision screening must be comprehensive yet quick and accurate to both enhance the lives of affected individuals and satisfy the requirements laid out by industry and professional standards. With the growing popularity of digital equipment, there is a natural progression to digital color vision screening tests, which have the advantage of speed, cost, portability, consistency, and facility of automated scoring. Perhaps the future of color vision testing lies in computer-based tests, as computerized counterparts have been developed for several of the 'table' version tests, such as the Munsell computerized test.

Some of these computerized color vision tests have been validated for the market. These include the Waggoner Computerized Color Vision Test (WCCVT),[597] the Rabin Cone Contrast Test (Inova Systems, Burr Ridge, Illinois),[598] the Colour Assessment & Diagnosis (CAD) test, and the accompanying new Colour Grading System,[599] developed by researchers at City University of London, United Kingdom,[600] and the Cambridge Test, developed at the Department of Experimental Psychology, University of Cambridge, United Kingdom.[601]

The WCCVT was developed by Dr. Terrace L. Waggoner and his son, T. J. Waggoner. The test employs technology that stimulates specific cones using selected confusion colors and gray-scaled contrast sensitivity. The WCCVT has a suite of tests, including pediatric (CVTME), D-15, and advanced in-depth diagnostic tests that not only detect congenital and acquired CVDs (protan, deutan, or tritan) but specify the type of deficiency and the degree (mild, moderate, or severe). The test is adaptive, self-administered, and self-scoring; its plates are randomized, and it has progression analysis charting to monitor changes in acquired CVDs caused by diabetes mellitus, glaucoma, macular degeneration, multiple sclerosis, etc., or ocular accidents, medications, and exposure to neurotoxic chemicals.

---

[596] Williams CH. Nagel's anomaloscope for testing color vision. Trans Am Ophthalmol Soc. 1915; 14(Pt 1):161-5.

[597] Ng JS, Self E, Vanston JE, Nguyen AL, Crognale MA. Evaluation of the Waggoner computerized color vision test. Optom Vis Sci. 2015; 92(4):480-6.

[598] Rabin J, Gooch J, Ivan D. Rapid quantification of color vision: the cone contrast test. Invest Ophthalmol Vis Sci. 2011; 52(2):816-20.

[599] www.color-blindness.com/2007/05/21/city-university-online-color-vision-test/ Accessed 07/12/2019.

[600] Barbur JL, Harlow J, Plant GT. Insights into the different exploits of colour in the visual cortex. Proc Biol Sci. 1994; 58(1353):327-34.

[601] Paramei GV, Oakley B. Variation of color discrimination across the life span. JOSA A. 2014; 31(4):A375-84.

The **Rabin Cone Contrast Test**, introduced by Professor Jeff C. Rabin, derives from principles underlying grayscale contrast sensitivity. It is a computer-assisted administered test that stimulates a more select population of cells than contrast sensitivity. Using a combination of color and contrast, the Rabin Cone Contrast Test is a quantifiable measure of color vision, allowing the detection of both hereditary and acquired color vision loss.

Figure 5-64: Screen for administering the Rabin Cone Contrast Test.

A small amount of retinal and/or neural damage may be detected; damage may or may not be specific to red, green, or blue, but the lack of redundancy in neural coding provides more sensitivity to early effects of the disease. In this test, colored letters isolate cone functions by cone type. Low-contrast letters detect threshold, while 'cone scores' indicate inherited and acquired CVD. Progression analysis identifies degeneration and improvement in acquired CVD.

In addition to the above tests, various apps are abundant for cell phones and tablets. There are still, however, concerns about the consistency and accuracy of these digital color app' tests because of variations in screen resolution and luminance. A display may have a different color gamut, resolution, and color temperature. This affects test administration; therefore, only calibrated computer screens should be used to perform computer-based color vision tests.

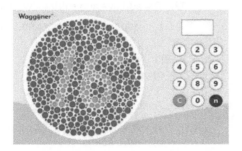

Figure 5-65: (left) The Waggoner CVD computerized test screen. (right) The Munsell test screen.

5.5 COLOR PERCEPTION QUIZ

Color Theory

1) Color is a (an) _____ property (select two)

   a) objective
   b) physical
   c) subjective
   d) physiological

2) Light is associated with color via ...

   a) wavelength
   b) intensity
   c) amplitude
   d) phase

3) The spectrum of visible light contains _____ colors.

   a) primary
   b) all possible
   c) pure (simple)
   d) additive

4) On a color wheel, complementary colors are placed ...

   a) next to each other
   b) opposite each other
   c) in the same semi-circle
   d) in the same quarter-circle

5) White light can be produced by ...

   a) passing sun light via a prism
   b) any mix of two colors
   c) any mix of three colors
   d) spinning Newton's wheel

6) Dispersion describes ...

   a) light bending when passing through a prism
   b) light mixing in overlapping projections
   c) color produced in subtractive combinations
   d) the dependence of refractive index on wavelength

7) When two primary colors are mixed, a _____ color is produced.

   a) neutral
   b) tint
   c) secondary color
   d) shade

8) Under normal dispersion, what wavelength has the greatest value of refractive index?

   a) violet
   b) green
   c) yellow
   d) red

9) A distinct property of primary colors is that ...

   a) they come in triplets of red, green, and blue
   b) they are additive colors
   c) they are subtractive colors
   d) any third color cannot be produced by mixing the other two

10) The color property describing whether the appearance is gray (minimum) or pure color (maximum) is ...

    a) hue
    b) colorfulness
    c) brightness
    d) chroma
    e) lightness

11) Distinct colors are distinguished by ...

    a) hue
    b) colorfulness
    c) brightness
    d) chroma
    e) lightness

12) The additive and subtractive color system utilizes ...

    a) additive and subtractive colors
    b) primary colors
    c) secondary colors
    d) tertiary colors

13) The CIE chromaticity diagram is a depiction of ...

    a) spectral colors
    b) pure colors
    c) primary colors
    d) secondary colors
    e) additive and subtractive colors
    f) possible colors perceived by humans

14) The spectral locus on a CIE chromaticity plot is on the ...

   a) purple line
   b) boundary of the diagram
   c) triangle specified by three primary colors
   d) white saturation line

15) The area defined by three primary colors occupies _____ on the CIE chromaticity diagram.

   a) the entire color space
   b) part of the color space
   c) the purple line
   d) the boundary of the color space

16) When using normalized fractional tristimulus, coordinate y is 0.5 and coordinate z is 0.3. What is the value of the (not shown) coordinate x?

   a) 0.5
   b) 0.3
   c) 0.2
   d) 0.1

17) The white 'color' point on a chromaticity diagram has coordinate values of ...

   a) $x = 0.1; y = 0.1$
   b) $x = 0.5; y = 0.5$
   c) $x = 0.33; y = 0.33$
   d) $x = 0.9; y = 0.1$

18) A line segment from the white color point crossing the boundary locus at 520 nm provides the ....

   a) saturation line for 520 nm
   b) complementary colors for 520 nm
   c) colors that when mixed produce 520 nm
   d) brightness line for 520 nm

19) Which of the following pairs of colors differ only in their saturation?

   a) yellow and orange
   b) pink and red
   c) blue and green
   d) red and green
   e) blue and yellow

20) Based on the information provided by a CIE 1931 chromaticity diagram, white light can be produced by mixing about equal amounts of 420 nm spectral light and _____ spectral light.

   a) 510 nm
   b) 540 nm

   c) 570 nm
   d) 620 nm

21) Which of the following bodies can have the behavior of a black body?

   a) the sun
   b) a highly reflecting surface
   c) a non-transparent surface
   d) a red filter

22) A chromatically warm light bulb has _____ color temperature than a chromatically cool light bulb.

   a) a lower
   b) the same
   c) a warmer
   d) a higher

23) On a CIE 1931 chromaticity diagram, a color has coordinates of $x = 0.7$ and $y = 0.3$. This color is ...

   a) green 540 nm
   b) red 620 nm
   c) purple
   d) white

24) Back to Q 23. What is the third (z, not shown) chromaticity coordinate for that color?

   a) 0.0
   b) 0.2
   c) 0.3
   d) 1.0

25) Using the CIE 1931 chromaticity diagram, what is the complementary spectral color of green 540 nm?

   a) red 630 nm
   b) orange 580 nm
   c) blue 490 nm
   d) none of the above

26) Using the CIE 1931 chromaticity diagram, what is the complementary spectral color of blue 480 nm?

   a) red 630 nm
   b) orange 580 nm
   c) blue 490 nm
   d) none of the above

27) What words pair can describe color temperature?

   a) light and dark
   b) hot and cold
   c) black and white
   d) warm and cool

28) Under what color temperature can a radiating source appear more bluish?

   a) 2700 K
   b) 3500 K
   c) 5500 K
   d) 8500 K

29) A fluorescent lamp operates at 5000 K color temperature, while an incandescent lamp operates at 2400 K color temperature. This means that ...

   a) the fluorescent lamp is physically hotter than the incandescent lamp by about 2600 K
   b) the fluorescent lamp is emitting about 2× the lumen output as the incandescent lamp
   c) only the fluorescent lamp output is considered white light
   d) the spectral output of the fluorescent lamp (compared to the incandescent) corresponds to a radiation output of a black body operating at about 2× the temperature.

Color Perception

30) If the human eye had only one type of cone photoreceptors, it would ...

   a) have a flat sensitivity to light wavelength
   b) be more sensitive to green
   c) be more sensitive to red
   d) be more sensitive to blue

31) In the human eye, the distinction between green and red is produced (mainly) by the ....

   a) difference between the L- and M-cone response
   b) difference between the combined L- and M-cone response to the S-cone response
   c) combined response of the L- and M-cone types
   d) response of the S-cone types

32) In the human eye, the distinction between blue and yellow is produced (mainly) by the ...

   a) difference between the L- and M-cone type response
   b) difference of the combined L- and M-response to the S-cone response
   c) combined response of the L- and M-cone types
   d) response of the S-cone types

33) Which of the following statements about L, M and S cones is not true?

   a) S-type cones are morphologically distinguishable from L- and M-type cones.
   b) L- and M-type cones make up >90% of all cone types at all eccentricities.
   c) L- and M-type cones are morphologically distinguishable from each other.
   d) S-type cones are essentially absent in the central foveola.

   e) L-, M- and S-type cones are the basis of the trichromatic theory of color vision.

34) The foveola has what types of cone cells?

   a) S
   b) L
   c) M
   d) L and M
   e) S and L
   f) S and M

35) A 455 nm photon may be absorbed by ...

   a) S-type cones, most likely
   b) either S-type or M-type cone, but not L-type
   c) either S-type or L-type cone, but not M-type
   d) S-type, or M-type, or L-type, with equal probability

36) A 545 nm photon may be absorbed by ...

   a) M-type cones, most likely
   b) L-type cones, most likely
   c) either L-type or M-type cone, with equal probability
   d) either S-type or M-type cone, but not L-type
   e) either S- type or L-type cone, but not M-type

37) A stream of photons is absorbed by L-type cones with 20% probability. Their wavelength is ... (select two)

   a) 400 nm
   b) 510 nm
   c) 565 nm
   d) 640 nm

38) A single cone type response to different wavelengths is perceived as a difference in observed ...

a) hue
b) luminance
c) color
d) saturation

39) The minimum number of cone types necessary for color perception is ...

a) one
b) two
c) three
d) four

40) The Bezold–Brücke phenomenon refers to:

a) change in hue perception with varying light intensity
b) brightness shift from photopic to scotopic light levels
c) change in hue perception with varying duration of a stimulus
d) change in hue perception with varying area of a stimulus

41) Humans do not possess a yellow cone receptor. Yet yellow sensation is produced by ...

a) multiplexing cone output as L+M – S
b) combining afterimage of red and green
c) differentiating L-cone from M-cone output (L–M)

d) adding Long- and Medium-cone output (L+M)

42) Humans have very few S-type cone receptors. Yet we see blue abundantly in the form of ...

a) multiplexing cone output as L+M–S
b) producing afterimage of red and green
c) subtracting (differentiating) long from medium cone output (L–M)
d) adding long and medium cone output (L+M)

43) Human vision at very low light levels has diminished color perception because ...

a) the photoreceptors that function in dim light are sensitive to only one wavelength of light
b) only one type of photoreceptor operates at low light levels
c) there is not enough light to photoisomerize rhodopsin molecules
d) all types of photoreceptors have the same spectral sensitivity at night

44) We sense the color red by utilizing the ...

a) L-cone output alone
b) M-cone output alone
c) combined L+M cone output
d) differential L–M cone output

Color Vision Deficiency (CVD)

45) An alternative proper name for color vision deficiency is ...

a) color blindness
b) Daltonism
c) tritanomaly
d) achromatopsia
e) none of the above

46) Which of the following forms of CVD share deficiencies along the same color channel?

a) protanopia and deuteranopia
b) tritanomaly and protanopia
c) deuteranomaly and tritanomaly
d) protanomaly and blue cone monochromacy

47) What forms of CVD fail to property discriminate red-green (two correct)?

a) protanopia
b) deuteranopia
c) tritanopia

d) achromatopsia
e) normal color vision

48) The MacAdam ellipses on a CIE chromaticity diagram pertain to a person with ...

a) protanopia
b) deuteranopia
c) tritanopia
d) achromatopsia
e) normal color vision

49) Which color pairs are most likely to be confused in deuteranopia?

a) red-green as gray
b) red-blue as purples
c) yellow-blue as sky blue
d) red-green as yellow

50) A confusion line drawn on a CIE diagram links the pure 560 nm green with the pure 440 nm blue. This means that the affected individual confuses ...

    a) all pure (spectral) colors with wavelengths between 560 and 440 nm

    b) only the two pure colors 560 and 440 nm as either green or either blue

    c) colors that can be produced by mixing the 560 and 440 nm pure spectral colors

    d) the two pure colors 560 and 440 nm with gray

51) If a CVD affected individual confuses the spectral blue 480 nm with the spectral red 670 color, his/her condition is most likely (consult confusion lines) ...

    a) protanomaly

    b) deuteranomaly

    c) tritanomaly

    d) blue cone monochromacy

52) If two colors fall along the same confusion line in a given CVD, then these two colors appear ...

    a) gray, regardless of CVD type

    b) red, if protanopia

    c) blue, if tritanopia

    d) similar, depending on the CVD type

53) The colors in the national flag of Portugal are confusing to a ... (select two)

    a) Spaniard

    b) protanope

    c) deuteranope

    d) tritanope

54) What photoreceptor cell types are not affected in rod monochromacy?

    a) rods

    b) L-type cones

    c) M-type cones

    d) S-type cones

55) What photoreceptor cell types are not affected in blue cone monochromacy (select two)?

    a) rods

    b) L-type cones

    c) M-type cones

    d) S-type cones

56) Complete achromatopsia with normal visual acuity is what type of the following CVD?

    a) achromatopsia

    b) rod monochromacy

    c) blue cone monochromacy

    d) cone monochromacy

57) The most prevalent form of CVD is ...

    a) protanopia

    b) protanomaly

    c) deuteranopia

    d) deuteranomaly

    e) tritanopia

    f) tritanomaly

58) Inherited CVDs manifest (select two) ...

    a) bilaterally

    b) symmetrically

    c) unilaterally

    d) asymmetrically

59) What type of CVD is autosomal inherited?

    a) red-green

    b) protanopia and protanomaly

    c) deuteranopia and deuteranomaly

    d) tritanopia and tritanomaly

60) What happens under 'X-linked recessive inheritance'?

    a) I have no idea, let me search the web...

    b) In females, gene mutation on both X chromosomes must be present to cause phenotype expression.

    c) In females, gene mutation on just one X chromosome suffices to cause phenotype expression.

    d) In males, gene mutation on the X and on the Y chromosomes must be present to cause phenotype expression.

61) In inherited CVD, the term 'carrier' is applicable to ...

    a) males; mutated gene on the X chromosome

    b) males; mutated gene on the Y chromosome

    c) females; mutated gene on one X chromosome

    d) females; mutated gene on both X chromosomes

62) Father has red-green CVD, mother is unaffected / but not carrier. They have two daughters; which one inherits CVD and in what form?

    a) Both daughters are carriers.

    b) Both daughters are affected.

c) One daughter is affected; the other is a carrier.

d) One daughter is not affected; the other is carrier

e) One daughter is not affected; the other is affected.

63) Father has normal color vision, mother is a red-green CVD carrier. They have two children, a boy and a girl. What are the chances that they inherit CVD and in what form (select two)?

a) Boy will be 50% carrier.
b) Boy will be 50% affected.
c) Girl will be 50% carrier.
d) Girl will be 50% affected.

64) Mark has CVD even though neither of his parents expressed CVD. What are the two likely causes of his inheritance?

a) His mother was a carrier; his maternal grandfather was affected.
b) His mother was a carrier; his maternal grandmother was a carrier.
c) His mother was unaffected; his maternal grandfather was affected.
d) His father was a carrier; his paternal grandfather was affected.
His father was unaffected; his paternal grandmother was affected.

65) Mother has CVD, father does not. They have two daughters and two sons. What is the inheritance (select two)?

a) both daughters carriers
b) both daughters affected
c) no daughters affected
d) one daughter carrier, one daughter affected
e) no sons affected
f) both sons affected
g) one son not affected, one son affected

66) Which of the following cannot be a differentiator between tritanopia and acquired CVD ...

a) the severity of the deficiency
b) monocular examination revealing unilateral expression
c) sudden onset of the deficiency
d) concurrent loss of visual acuity

67) Pseudoisochromatic plates implement ...

a) colors along confusion lines of the CVD to be screened

b) complementary colors of those confused by the CVD
c) primary colors confused by the CVD
d) secondary colors confused by the CVD

68) To screen for both protan and deutan deficiencies, a pseudoisochromatic plate uses ...

a) colors from two disparate confusion lines, for the protan and the deutan deficiency
b) colors from two adjacent confusion lines, for the protan and the deutan deficiency
c) different spatial noise for the protan than for the deutan deficiency
d) a combination of a vanishing and a hidden digit pattern

69) A red-green dichromatic CVD examinee is presented a transformation design test plate in an Ishihara plate. He is expected to ...

a) see a different pattern than a normal color vision individual will see in that plate
b) not see any pattern at all
c) see one but not the two patterns seen by a normal color vision individual
d) see a pattern that a normal color vision individual cannot see at all

70) The Farnsworth D-15 test identifies the type of CVD by the ...

a) count of discontinuities between successive numbered dot-patches
b) prevailing alignment of the lines connecting the dot-patches
c) completeness of the of the lines connecting the dot-patches
d) the confusion index—the radio between the major radius and the major radius of a normal-vision arrangement

71) The differential diagnosis between deuteranopia and deuteranomaly in the D-15 test is facilitated by ...

a) more time to complete the test
b) incomplete placement of the caps
c) different orientation of the deutan axis (steeper confusion angle)
d) larger value of selectivity index (polarity)

72) What types of cones are missing in an anomalous trichromat?

a) L type, if protanomaly
b) M type, if tritanomaly

c) S type, if deuteranomaly

d) None are missing, but one type is not functioning properly

73) Two metameric fields A and B are presented to a color normal observer side-by-side in a bipartite matched field. Which statement is true regarding fields A and B?

a) they have the same chromaticity coordinates

b) they have the same spectral distribution

c) they produce the same number of isomerizations

d) they have the same number of light quanta

74) A normal color vision individual has different metameric matching from an anomalous trichromat in that ...

a) the normal individual achieves a mean normal match at a different green-red mix scale

b) the anomalous trichromat accepts a much narrower range of the green-red mix scale

c) the normal color vision individual accepts a much narrower range of green-red mix scale

d) the normal color vision individual finishes the test in a much shorter time

75) For which type of CVD does there exists a metameric match that is also accepted by normal color vision?

a) protanomaly

b) deuteranomaly

c) tritanomaly

d) all of the above

76) The reason that a tritan can make an equally precise metameric match along the Rayleigh equation as an individual with normal color vision is that the Rayleigh equation (select two) ...

a) runs across adjacent confusion lines for red-green deficiency

b) contains no yellow

c) contains no blue

d) runs nearly perpendicular to the tritan confusion lines

77) Narrow metameric match range occurs when ...

a) Specific mix ratios of red-green match a specific yellow luminance.

b) Broad mix ratios of red-green match a narrow range of yellow luminance.

c) Only one mix ratio of red-green matches several ranges of yellow luminance. Broad mix ratios of red-green match a broad range of yellow luminance.

78) Which condition has the broadest range of Rayleigh equation metameric match?

a) normal color vision

b) protanomaly

c) protanopia

d) tritanomaly

e) tritanopia

79) The differential diagnosis between protanopia and deuteranopia in the Nagel anomaloscope is achieved by observing ...

a) the slope in the protanopia curve (more negative)

b) that the protanopia curve is half of the deuteranopia curve

c) that the protanopia curve is twice the deuteranopia curve

d) that the protanopia curve does not intersect the normal color vision match point

80) Gertrude has typical rod monochromacy. She views two lights side by side. Light source A consists of wavelength A and has a 0.10 probability of being absorbed by the rod photopigment; source B consists of wavelength B and has a 0.20 probability of being absorbed. Gertrude will not be able to distinguish source A from source B ...

a) if the photon count of A equals that of B

b) under any conditions because these people are completely color blind

c) if the photon count of A is twice that of B

d) if the photon count of A is half that of B

e) if the photon count of A is a quarter that of B

5.6 COLOR PERCEPTION SUMMARY

Color

Color is a perceptual property of human vision. The human eye is sensitive to electromagnetic radiation whose wavelength is between 0.38 nm (380 nm), perceived as violet, and about 0.7 nm (700 μm), perceived as red. This part of the EM radiation is called visible light.

Usually, light consists of a mix of several wavelengths that contribute to the sensation of its color. A prism can disperse light into purely monochromatic components: These are the **physically pure**, or simple colors, uniquely associated with a specific **spectral wavelength**; e.g., pure yellow-green corresponds to 555 nm.

The sun emits light across many wavelengths in the electromagnetic spectrum. Objects appear colored because physical objects reflect some spectral components and absorb some other spectral components differently. A plant leaf is an example of a reflecting object that appears as green because it absorbs most wavelengths in the visible but reflects strongly around 550 nm. A red filter appears as red because it absorbs relatively little between 680 and 590 nm, the part of the visible spectrum we perceive as red; this part is subsequently transmitted through the filter, giving the appearance of red. Light sources appear to have different colors due to a combination (mixture) of emission wavelengths.

The appearance properties by which we characterize color are hue (what color is it?), colorfulness (the degree to which color appears rich, from no color to pure color), and brightness (the degree to which a color appears more or less bright, from black to maximum brightness). Other, relative properties are chroma, lightness, and saturation.

A broad range of colors can be produced using three **primary colors**, named as such because mixing any two of them does not produce the third. The three primary colors often used in additive combinations (such as in overlapping projection lights or electronic screens) are red, green, and blue (RGB). For a subtractive combination of colors, such as used in the mixing of dyes for printing, the set of primary colors may consist of cyan, magenta, and yellow (CMY). Secondary colors are produced by mixing two primary colors in a given color space. Tertiary colors are produced by mixing a primary and a secondary color.

The CIE chromaticity diagram depicts tristimulus values that help define quantitative links between wavelengths and physiologically perceived colors by the human color vision and serves as a standard reference against which many other color spaces are defined.

The CIE chromaticity diagram shows the mathematical limit of human vision as far as color is concerned; its boundaries are occupied by physically pure colors. The usefulness of the CIE diagram is that it provides a model for the relative amounts of the primaries required to match any color. Thus, it helps to numerically specify a given color. The 2-D graph is produced by converting the tristimulus values to relative units (x and y chromaticity coordinates); coordinate z is calculated by subtracting the sum of x and y from 1.

Color Perception

The human eye responds differently to different wavelengths as described by the photopic luminosity function $V(\lambda)$, named as such (for daylight conditions) based on the 1924-CIE established standard photopic observer. The peak sensitivity occurs at 0.555 µm (yellow-green). This, however, is different from color discrimination, which, in humans, is attributed (mainly) to three types of cone photoreceptors called L, M, and S. The difference in the spectral responsivities of the three cone types is attributed to the form of opsin bound on the retinal chromophore. These cone types have different spectral sensitivities across the visible spectrum; their weighted average produces the luminosity function $V(\lambda)$.

The two prevailing theories that explain color perception in the human eye are the trichromatic theory, proposed by Young, Maxwell, and explored further by Helmholtz, and the opponent process theory, proposed by Hering. The trichromatic theory is primarily based on color mixing experiment and suggests that a combination of three channels explains color discrimination functions. The theory postulates that the three cone types are preferentially sensitive to red (mostly L cones), green (mostly M cones), and blue (mostly S cones). However, the trichromatic theory fails to account for the four unique colors—red, green, yellow, and blue—and also fails to explain why dichromats can perceive white and yellow. It also fails to fully explain color discrimination functions and opponent color perception.

The opponent process theory is founded on subjective observations—the appearance of hues, simultaneous contrast, afterimages, and color vision deficiencies. The theory involves three complex and antagonistic processes, called orthogonal channels. Each of these processes takes place along a channel consisting of a pair of opposing sensations, with each sensation responding in an antagonist way. These sensations are black-white, red-green, and yellow-blue; an equal stimulation of the two pair members gives rise to a neutral, achromatic (gray) sensation. This theory, however, does not reject the initial stages of processing expressed by the trichromatic theory.

While neither theory is complete, we understand that the human color sensation results from multiplexing of the three-cone-type output. Luminance corresponds to the sum of all responses; the distinction between green and red is produced (mainly) by the difference between the L- and M-cone types; the distinction between blue and yellow is produced (mainly) by the difference of the combined L and M response to the S response.

Color Vision Deficiency

Color vision deficiency (CVD) is a broad term that encompasses the conditions affecting color perception. The so-called 'normal' human color vision is neither complete nor perfect. The color vision of the affected individual is simply different (or less complete) compared to that of a 'normal' vision person. With a prevalence of about 5%, various forms of CVD affect primarily the male population.

The most common form of CVD is anomalous trichromacy, which is a milder form of dichromatic CVD (protanomaly, deuteranomaly, and tritanomaly). 'Regular' dichromatic CVD includes protanopia, deuteranopia, and the much less common, tritanopia. Both protan and deutan types are classified as red-green CVD.

Monochromacy represents a very rare CVD group of conditions in its most severe form, the closest to color blindness. Its main types are achromatopsia, or rod monochromacy, and blue cone monochromacy; even more rare are two forms of acquired monochromacy, cone monochromacy and cerebral achromatopsia.

Hereditary or congenital color vision deficiencies are attributed to a mutated gene in the development of one or more of the three cone types. Hereditary red-green CVD is the most common type and has X-chromosome-linked recessive inheritance. This means that:

- In females, gene mutation on both X chromosomes must be present to cause phenotype expression; gene mutation on just one X chromosome makes the person a carrier.
- In males, gene mutation on the X chromosome suffices to cause phenotype expression.

Acquired color vision deficiencies are secondary to certain ocular, visual pathway, neurologic, or systemic diseases; or medications, trauma and/or neurotoxic environmental or chemical exposure.

Testing Color Vision Deficiency

Most tests screen for the presence of a CVD, such as inherited red-green deficiencies; more advanced tests also provide information regarding the severity of the CVD. The most frequently used form of CVD screening involves the use of pseudoisochromatic plates. These tests use the

Stilling principle, which breaks the stimulus into a mosaic of circular spots of varying luminance and varying size (2 to 10 mm), forming spatial noise. The obfuscated pattern target (numeral, geometrical shape, or a pattern) is formed by grouped spots of color(s) that differ from the background color.

The anomaloscope is based on the inability of the visual perception system to determine which wavelengths of light comprise the observed color. This ability is called metameric matching: The sensation of a pure spectral 590 nm color is yellow, and the same sensation can be obtained with a mix of red 680 nm and green 540 nm. An individual with 'normal' color vision can see the mix of red and green as the exact yellow only over a very narrow mix of ratios between this green and this red and the yellow's brightness. An individual with a color vision deficiency may report a similar perception between the red-green mix and yellow over a very wide range of mix ratios.

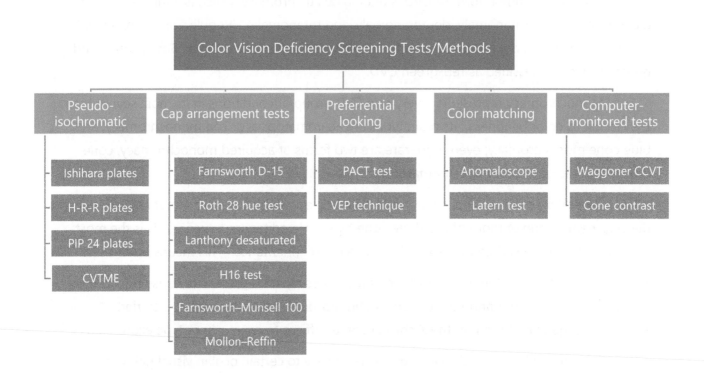

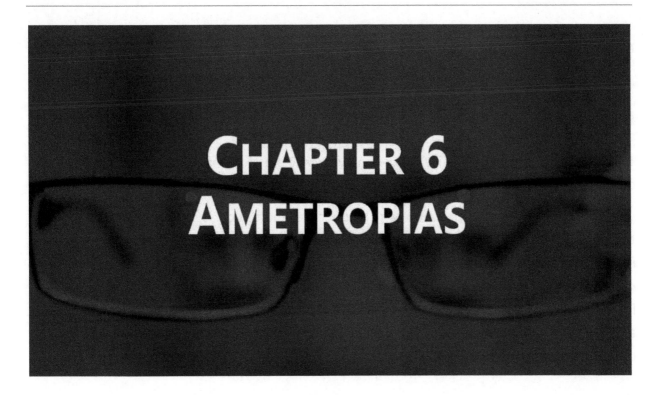

CHAPTER 6
AMETROPIAS

The notion that all rays from an object point meet at a single common image space 'point' belongs to the realm of geometrical approximation. Geometrical optics, indeed, employs terms such as the focal or image 'point.' A point is, simply, a mathematical construct, not a physical entity. A point has no dimension, volume, surface area, or length. In reality, and specifically, as it applies to optics, the concept of the point is used to denote a very small surface area.

Although the focal point is a conceptual construct, physically it corresponds to a constricted, physical distribution of light, called the **blur circle**. Even in geometrical optics (in other words, ignoring diffraction), there is always some blur. We may call it an image 'point,' if all rays from an object converge to what may be considered a very small surface area and cross-section.

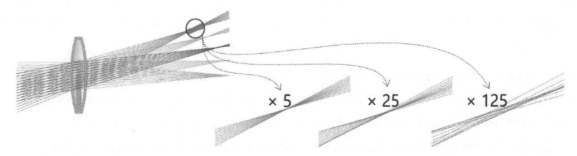

Figure 6-1: Under increasing magnification, the 'point' of convergence reveals that the 'focus' point is not a point, but has a small, specific surface area. The 'point' is not a point!

6.1 FOCUSING IN THE EYE

6.1.1 Vergence and Effective Power

The concepts of optical (refractive) power and vergence are of ultimate importance in the description, understanding, and management of ametropias.

The refractive, or **optical power** of an optical element such as a spectacle lens is, essentially, its capacity to transform an optical beam/ray bundle. When a collimated beam is incident on a positive (plus) lens, it converges; hence, the lens is said to have positive (plus) optical power. If the beam diverges (the case with a minus lens), the optical element is said to have a negative (minus) optical power. If the beam remains collimated (even if its cross-section area increases or decreases, something that occurs in beam expanders), the element has zero optical power (plano).

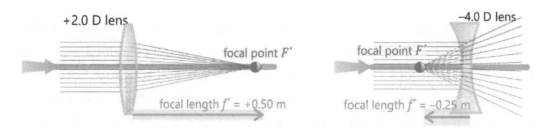

Figure 6-2: (left) Positive and (right) negative optical power.

The unit of measurement of optical power is the **diopter** (D, or dpt $= m^{-1}$). The closer to the optical element the collimated beam comes to focus the greater the optical power; therefore, the optical power is the reciprocal of the distance (the numerator being the refractive index of the medium of propagation) the collimated beam travels to focus. A lens with optical power 1.00 D brings a collimated beam to focus in 1 m (when traveling in the air). When light propagates in a medium of $n = 1.336$, the necessary distance to focus is 1.336 m. This is exactly what is implemented in relationships (1.1) and (1.3).

The beam may be propagating parallel to itself and maintain its collimation, but it can also converge or diverge. The physical quantity that describes this property is **vergence** L, defined as the reciprocal of the distance l needed for the beam to travel to its point of convergence. A collimated beam has zero vergence, a converging beam has a positive vergence, and a diverging beam has a negative vergence. The unit is, again, the diopter (D). If we invoke the notion of wavefront instead of rays, vergence is the curvature of the wavefront.

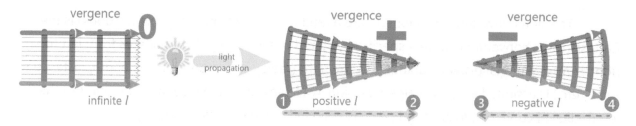

Figure 6-3: (left) Collimated beam with zero vergence. (center) Converging beam with positive vergence. (right) Diverging beam with negative vergence.

In the example shown in Figure 6-3 left, the beam does not converge; therefore, the distance to convergence is ∞, and its reciprocal is zero. In the case of the converging beam (center), assuming a distance to convergence of +0.5 m, vergence is +2.0 D. In the case of the diverging beam (right), vergence is –2.0 D because the distance from the 'source' is –0.5 m, the negative sign indicating that the point where the rays meet is to the left of the point of reference (diverging beam). In all cases here, the medium is air ($n = 1.0$).

If the medium is not air but has a refractive index ≠1.0, then the 'reciprocal' distances are multiplied by n. Thus, instead of +2.00, vergence is +2.762 D if n = 1.336 (in the aqueous, for example). When light travels in a medium of refractive index n, vergence is, specifically,

$$\text{Vergence } L \text{ [D]} = \frac{\text{refractive index } n}{\text{distance to convergence } l \text{ [m]}} \qquad (6.1)$$

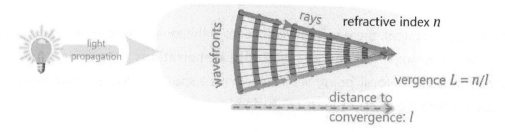

Figure 6-4: Vergence when light is propagating in a medium of refractive index n.

Vergence (L)

- The wavefront curvature, expressed in diopters (D), the reciprocal of the distance l required to converge.
- ☞ in air, $L = 1/l$.
- ☞ in a medium with refractive index n, $L = n/l$.
- For a collimated ray bundle, vergence is zero.
- If the beam converges, vergence is positive; if the beam diverges, vergence is negative.

The sign convention mentioned herein (and followed throughout this textbook) is the Cartesian sign convention. Unless specifically stated otherwise, light propagates from left to right. Any directional distance pointing to the right (radius of curvature, focal length, distance to focus, etc.) is assigned a positive algebraic sign, while any directional distance pointing to the left (radius of curvature, focal length, etc.) is assigned a negative algebraic sign.

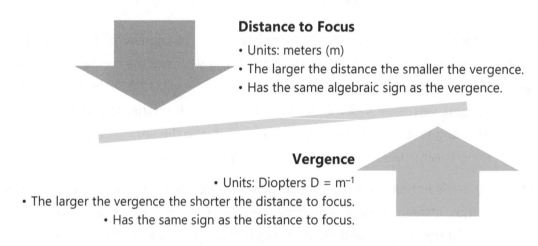

Distance to Focus
• Units: meters (m)
• The larger the distance the smaller the vergence.
• Has the same algebraic sign as the vergence.

Vergence
• Units: Diopters D = m^{-1}
• The larger the vergence the shorter the distance to focus.
• Has the same sign as the distance to focus.

Figure 6-5: Distance to focus and vergence.

6.1.2 The Circle of Least Confusion

In every real optical system, there exist deviations from the ideal that result in a not 'perfect' blurred image. These imperfections are called **optical aberrations**. Where we would ideally expect the formation of a focal 'point,' we instead have a spot or defocused blur disk, whose smallest size is called the **circle of least confusion**.

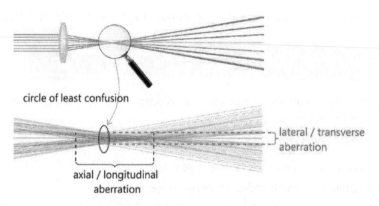

circle of least confusion

lateral / transverse aberration

axial / longitudinal aberration

Figure 6-6: The circle of least confusion. Its lateral and its axial extent are associated with lateral and axial aberrations.

For practical purposes, it is important to know where the circle of least confusion is—it is where the image is most likely to be formed. The size (extent) of the circle of least confusion relates to how clear the image is—the smaller the better. If an object point can form a very small circle of least confusion, then an extended object will form a reasonably sharp image.

When we attempt to optimize an optical system, for example, by minimizing (or compensating for) aberrations, we evaluate how the size of the circle of least confusion is affected. Conversely, if we can estimate the size of the circle of least confusion, we can evaluate the effect of aberrations or refractive errors in the optical system, such as the eye.

Circle of Least Confusion

- Its extent relates to the severity of aberrations in an optical system.
- It corresponds to the smallest transverse cross-section at the image plane.
- According to geometrical optics, this should be an ideal point, but even in the total absence of aberrations, the wave nature of light sets a limit to how small this 'point' can be.
- The diffraction-limited case is an Airy disk.

6.1.3 The Near and Far Points

Object location is a parameter that determines image location for a given lens/optical system, such as the eye. Consider an eye with optical power 64.0 D, which means that the focal length inside the eye is $P'F' = 20.875$ mm. For an object at infinity $(=\infty)$, we apply the lens imaging formula, as developed in the Geometrical Optics part of this series:[602]

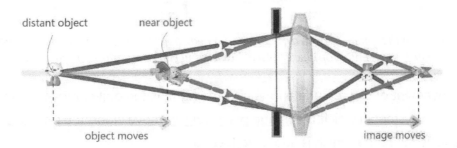

Figure 6-7: Imaging of a distant and a near object by a lens of fixed optical power.

$$\underbrace{L}_{\text{object vergence}} + \underbrace{F_{\text{eye}}}_{\text{eye optical power}} = \underbrace{L'}_{\text{image vergence (in the eye)}}$$

$$\underbrace{\frac{1}{\infty \to \text{object location}}}_{\text{object vergence}} + \underbrace{64\,\text{D}}_{\text{eye optical power}} = \underbrace{\frac{1.336}{x' \to \text{image location}}}_{\text{image vergence in the eye}}$$

---

[602] *Geometrical Optics* § 4.1 Lens Imaging Relationship.

Here, object space n = 1.0, and image space n' = 1.336. The result is that the image is formed at x' = +20.875 mm, which, luckily, is exactly on the retina.

We now bring the object closer to the eye, for example, a newspaper at 25 cm. Now, its location is not ∞ but x = −0.25 m (the algebraic sign − denotes that the object is to the left of the eye). We apply again the lens imaging relationship:

$$\underbrace{\underbrace{\frac{1}{-0.25 \text{ m} \rightarrow \text{object location}}}_{\text{object vergence}} + \underbrace{64 \text{ D}}_{\substack{\text{eye optical power}}} = \underbrace{\underbrace{\frac{1.336}{x' \rightarrow \text{ image location}}}_{\text{image vergence in the eye}}}$$

which leads to a different image location, x' = +22.266 mm. This means that the image is formed 1.39 mm past the retina. For this near object, the retina and the location where the optically conjugate image is (to be) formed do not coincide.

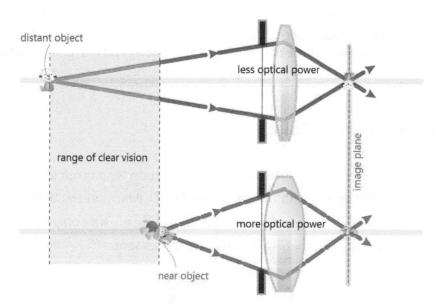

Figure 6-8: To form the image of both a distant and a near object in the same plane, the required lens power is different. (top) Less optical power and (bottom) more optical power.

The movement of the conjugate image to the right as the object moves closer to the eye is not desired in a system in which the image plane cannot move along the optical axis; the eye's sensitive 'plane' is the retina, which is at a fixed location.

So, how can we capture a sharp image at the same image location for both distant and near objects? An option (the only one, perhaps) is to change (increase) the optical power of the lens. We increase the optical power to F = +68 D. For the near object, x = −0.25 m, L = −4 D, and $L' = L + F$ = −4 D + 68 D = 64 D. Now the image is formed at $x' \approx$ +20.875 mm. This is also the image location in the eye for the far object when the optical power is F = +64 D.

The above examples are a good approximation of what happens in the human eye. The mechanism by which the eye increases optical power is called accommodation (§ 7.1). In its natural state, the eye is relaxed, which means there is no accommodation.

The **far point** (punctum remotum) is the farthest point at which an object must be placed such that a sharp image can be formed on the retina. When fixating on the far point, the eye is 'relaxed,' or 'not accommodating,' i.e., there is no increase in the optical power of the crystalline lens.

The **near point** (punctum proximum) is the closest point at which an object can be placed such that a sharp image can still be formed on the retina. To achieve this, the eye accommodates at its largest capacity (§ 7.1.2); i.e., the crystalline lens achieves its maximum optical power.

These two limiting positions define the **range of clear** (or sharp) **vision**.

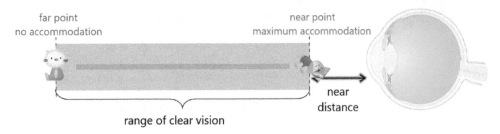

Figure 6-9: Far and near points in the human eye.

The locations of the far and the near points depend on the refractive state of the eye (emmetropia or ametropia). The near point is also dependent on the accommodative ability of the eye (presbyopia, § 7.7). In an emmetropic eye, the far point is situated at infinity. In an emmetropic eye of a young individual, the near point may be closer than 25 cm, while for an aging eye with limited accommodative ability, it may be farther away.

6.1.4 Depth of Field and Depth of Focus

The depth of field of the human eye is the range, along the optical axis, between the proximal and the distal limiting points (positions) for objects that can be simultaneously seen with the same perceived clarity, without a change in accommodation.[603] Therefore, these points should not be confused with the near and far points, as the near point involves a maximum and the far point zero accommodation, so these states cannot be achieved at the same time. The depth of field is therefore a small subset of the range of clear vision (more details in § 6.1.5).

---

[603] Campbell FW. The depth of field of the human eye. Opt Acta (Lond). 1957; 4(4):157-64.

The depth of field is the axial range in object space within which objects may form reasonably sharp images. Therefore, the extent of the depth of field is determined by how the images at its two limiting points are projected onto the retina. Each object, at either the proximal or distal point, projects a defocused retinal image. These defocused images have a blur size of at least a perceived blur circle, which exceeds the circle of least confusion by a limited amount; the blur produced at the two depth of field limiting positions can only be a bit greater than the circle of least confusion before it gets 'noticed.'

Thus, the size of the circle of least confusion provides a benchmark criterion of the blur circle size that can be perceived as acceptably sharp. The parameter 'perceived' denotes the subjective nature of perception, which depends on the individual eye.

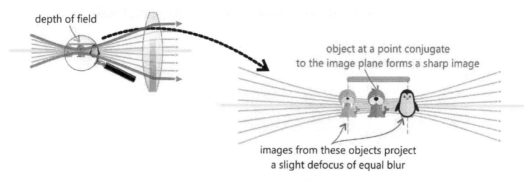

Figure 6-10: Depth of field: The range along the optical axis, between the proximal and the distal limiting positions, for objects that can form reasonably sharp images.

Figure 6-11: (left) Large depth of field and (right) shallow depth of field. In the shallow depth of field, only a small area of the objects can form sharp images.

The **linear depth of field**, reported in units of length, is the interval of distances between the endpoints, the distal and the proximal limiting points. Between these two positions, there is a point that is optically conjugate to the image-forming plane. The **dioptric depth of field**, reported in diopters, is the dioptric range between the limiting positions. It is considered to be positive; i.e., it is the farthest point vergence minus the nearest point vergence. Owing to the nature of the imaging relationship, the dioptric depth is symmetrical about the conjugate object point.

Example ☞: If the distal point has –1.0 D vergence difference from the conjugate object point, the proximal point has +1.0 D vergence difference from the conjugate object point. Then the dioptric depth of field is reported as 2.0 D or ±1.0 D. Note that the linear depth of field is not symmetrical with respect to the conjugate point since distances are reciprocal and not proportional to vergence.

Example ☞: Rigoletto is holding a lens in the air. The distal limiting position has –2.0 D vergence, and the proximal limiting position has –8.0 D vergence. Estimate the dioptric and the linear depth of field.

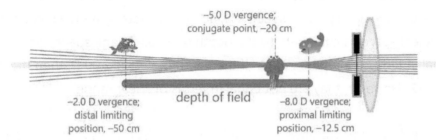

Figure 6-12: Example of linear depth of field calculation when the dioptric depth of field is 6.0 D.

The dioptric DoF is [(–2.0 D) – (–8.0 D)] = 6.0 D or ±3.0 D. The conjugate point is at –5.0 D vergence (the dioptric midpoint between the distal and proximal limiting points, spaced by ±3.0 D); therefore, its location is (1/–5.0 D) = –20 cm in front of (before) the lens.

The distal point, with –2.0 D vergence, is at (1/–2.0 D) = –50 cm in front of the lens, and the proximal point, with –8.0 D vergence, at (1/–8.0 D) = –12.5 cm in front of the lens. The linear depth of field of Rigoletto's lens is the interval between the two limiting points (50 cm – 12.5 cm) = 37.5 cm.

The corresponding expanse in image space (inside the eye) is the **depth of focus.** In photography, the depth of focus is the range in which the sensor (or the film) can be moved back and forth with respect to the lens with no manifest change in image sharpness. In the eye, the depth of focus is the range of perceptual tolerance to out-of-focus images; within the depth of focus, small differences in image sharpness are not noticeable.

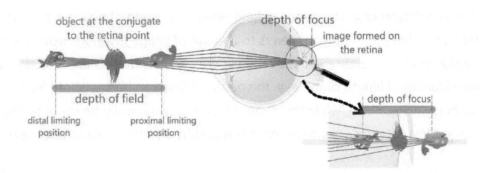

Figure 6-13: The depth of focus is the perceptual tolerance of the retinal defocus. Any possible sharpness difference for images formed within the depth of focus is not noticeable. See also Figure 3-37.

Although, theoretically, a perfectly sharp retinal image is formed only from an object placed at the optical conjugate point with the macula, which means a narrowly defined location, slightly defocused images formed within the depth of focus are also interpreted as equally sharp.[604]   Therefore, the larger the depth of focus the greater the tolerance of the visual system for objects being at different distances in front of the eye. Hence, the clinical relevance of the depth of focus—it determines the precision of a refractive correction.

The depth of focus and the depth of field refer to an interval of distances, or a dioptric range in the object and image space, respectively, and both relate to a similar concept. The depth of field (object space) is conjugate to the depth of focus (image space); as a consequence, the two are equal in terms of dioptric range. If the depth of field is 2.00 D, then the depth of focus is also 2.00 D. However, they are not equal in terms of linear range.

Example ☞: Estimate the dioptric and linear depth of focus of Rigoletto's lens (recall that depth of field = 6.0 D). Rigoletto's lens has power of +35.0 D.

The conjugate image point to the distal object position is produced at −2.0 + 35.0 D = +33.0 D, which suggests an image formed at 1/33.0 = 0.03 m = 3.0 cm.

The conjugate image point to the proximal object position is produced at −8.0 + 35.0 D = +27.0 D, which suggests an image formed at 1/27.0 = 0.037 m = 3.7 cm.

Thus, the dioptric depth of focus is [(+33.0 D) − (27.0 D)] = 6.0 D or ±3.0 D, which <u>equals the dioptric depth of field</u> (this is always the case!). The linear depth of focus is the interval between the two image points (3.7 cm − 3.0 cm) = 0.7 cm, which does not equal the linear depth of field (37.5 cm).

Because of the similarities in name and nature, the depth of field and the depth of focus are often confused. Some similarities include the following: Any object within the depth of field forms its image within the depth of focus; the extent of both 'depths' depends on the pupil diameter (they increase with a smaller pupil).

Now, some differences: The <u>depth of field</u> refers to a range of <u>object locations</u> from the optical system, while the <u>depth of focus</u> refers to a range of <u>image locations</u> from a sensor (e.g., the digital sensor or film in cameras, or the retina in the eye). As objects are typically far from the (relatively small) focal length of the eye, the depth of field can be anywhere from a fraction of a meter to many meters long, while the depth of focus may typically be some fractions of a millimeter long. Most often, the depth of focus is reported only dioptrically, not linearly.

---

[604] Legge GE, Mullen KT, Woo GC, Campbell FW. Tolerance to visual defocus. J Opt Soc Am A. 1987; 4(5):851-63.

Depth of field	Depth of focus
• An interval in object space (in front of the eye).	• An interval in image space (in the eye).
• Separation of object locations that can be seen equally clearly with no change in accommodation.	• Separation of image locations that can be seen equally clearly with no change in accommodation.
• Depends on the pupil diameter (the larger the diameter the smaller the depth of field).	• Depends on the pupil diameter, optical parameters of the eye, and retinal, neural, and psychophysical factors.
• Centered dioptrically on the fixation point.	• Centered dioptrically on the retina.

Similar to the dependencies of the effect of depth of field, depth of focus depends chiefly on pupil diameter.[605] In a diffraction-limited eye, depth of focus increases inversely proportionally to the square of pupil diameter.[606] Thus, this ideal, diffraction-limited eye may have a very shallow depth of focus for a large pupil diameter; the dioptric depth of focus can be even less than 0.50 D for a pupil size greater than 3 mm in diameter [Figure 6-14 (top)]. To the contrary, a constricted eye with a smaller pupil diameter [Figure 6-14 (bottom)] leads to an increased depth of field and an increased depth of focus.

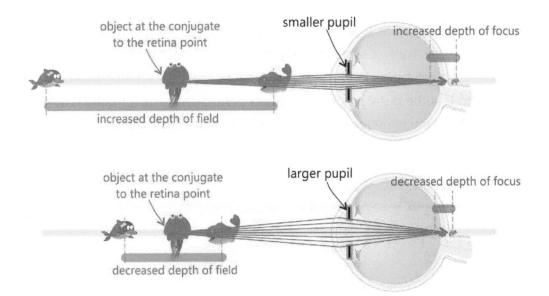

Figure 6-14: Depth of field and depth of focus for a larger (top) and smaller (bottom) pupil diameter.

[605] Charman WN, Jennings JAM. The optical quality of the monochromatic retinal image as a function of focus. Br J Physiol Opt. 1976; 31(3):119-34.

[606] Charman WN, Whitefoot H. Pupil diameter and the depth-of-field of the human eye as measured by laser speckle. Opt Acta (Lond). 1977; 24(12):1211-6.

6.1.5   Depth of Field and Range of Clear Vision

The depth of field extends the range of acceptable vision around a fixation point without any change of accommodation. This fixation point can be anywhere within the range of clear vision and is conjugate to the retina, producing a clear retinal image. Thus, for a given fixation point, the eye views, with nearly the same clarity, objects within the depth of field surrounding that fixation point (Figure 6-15), from the proximal to the distal limiting points, all without changing accommodation. The depth of field has a much shorter span than the range of clear vision, particularly when it is shallow (0.5 D to 2.0 D; see § 6.5.4). Thus, at a conjugate point between the far and the near points, the depth of field is a subset of the range of clear vision.

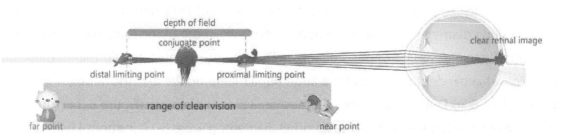

Figure 6-15: Relationship between depth of field and range of clear vision for an object placed randomly in the range of clear vision.

When the eye fixates at either the near point or the far point (maximum or zero accommodation, respectively), then, effectively, the range of clear vision is extended by the half of the depth of field that corresponds to the proximal or the distal limiting points (Figure 6-16). If the background is at the distal point of the depth of field, then the far point is in the middle of the depth of field and the hyperfocal point coincides with the distal point.

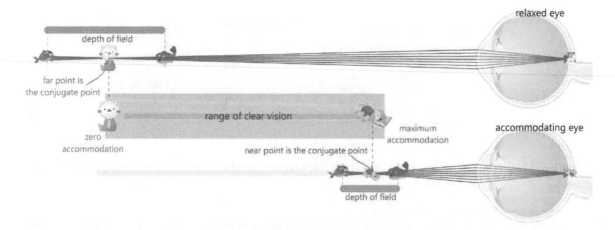

Figure 6-16: Relationship between depth of field and range of clear vision at the far point (top) and the near point (bottom).

6.2 EMMETROPIA

In visual optics, **emmetropia** (*εντός-* for within & *-μέτρο* for the rule) is the ideal refracting configuration of the eye whereby the image of a distant object is focused (formed sharply) on the retina. Translated literally, the term emmetropia indicates an eye that has, in itself (i.e., without corrective spectacles), the capacity to obtain an accurate measurement of an object's physical appearance (the rule). In imaging terms, the retina is the optical conjugate of optical infinity. The far point of an emmetropic eye is at infinity.

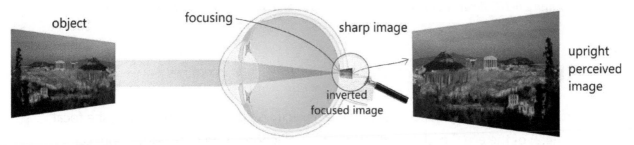

Figure 6-17: In a relaxed emmetropic eye, the image of a distant object is sharply formed on the retina. This image is inverted but is perceived as erect after cerebral processing.

The image formed (focused) on the retina is small, real, and inverted. The fact that it is inverted means that the world is 'upside-down,' or laterally reversed, in this image. Cerebral processing renders the worldview upright, as we perceive it.

6.2.1 Axial Length and Focal Length

The 'length' of the eye, the distance between its anterior and the posterior poles, is the **axial length**. A typical eye may have an axial length between 22 and 25 mm. The Listing reduced model (presented in § 1.5.2.1) uses a value of 22.2 mm for the axial length, and the Gullstrand model (§ 1.5.2.2) uses 24.4 mm.

The **focal length** in the image space (within the eye) is the separation between the posterior principal point P' and the posterior focal point F'. Extensive studies of the optics of the human eye have determined that the principal point P' is situated inside the eye, approximately 1.6 mm from the anterior cornea. The value of 1.6 mm is a mean value that applies to an average emmetropic, young adult eye. The axial length is, approximately, longer than the focal length (distance) by 1.6 mm (Figure 6-18).

$$\text{Focal length } f' = \text{Axial length} - 1.6 \text{ mm} \qquad\qquad (6.2)$$

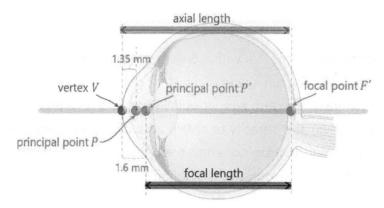

Figure 6-18: Relationship between axial length and focal length in an emmetropic eye.

Note 🔍 : The exact locations of the principal points and the focal points in a specific eye may be different since they depend on several parameters, such as corneal curvature, lens location, and lens power.

In an emmetropic eye, the focal point lies exactly on the retina. Therefore, the focal length (§ 1.4.2) of the eye f' and, by extension, its axial length, is 'in sync' with its optical power.[607] It is important to stress that this is by no means trivial or the general rule. The optical power of the eye is determined by the properties of the cornea and the crystalline lens, such as their curvatures, their separation, and their refractive indices. The focal length f' is calculated by the refractive index of the aqueous/vitreous ($n' = 1.336$) divided by the optical power.

Examples ☞:
Giuseppe's eye has optical power 64.0 D. The focal length in the eye f' is 1.336/64.0 D = 0.020875 m = 20.875 mm. Giuseppe's eye is emmetropic if its axial length is (20.875 + 1.6) = 22.475 mm.

La Duchesse Hélène's eye has power 70.0 D. The focal length in the eye f' is 1.336/70.0 D = 19.086 mm. Hélène's eye is emmetropic if its axial length is (19.086 + 1.6) = 20.686 mm.

In emmetropia, the relaxed eye can bring into focus an object at infinity without any change in optical power, in other words, with no accommodation. The far point, thus, is at infinity, or practically, at any distance greater than 6 m. The circle of least confusion has its smallest possible size and often is only limited by diffraction. Unaided visual acuity is typically 20/20 or better, except for ocular pathology (for example, retinal degeneration). In that case, it is not the image formation but the impaired perception of that image that is limiting vision.

---

[607] Larsen JS. Axial length of the emmetropic eye and its relation to the head size. Acta Ophthalmol. 1979; 57(1):76-83.

6.2.2 Retinal Image Size in the Emmetropic Eye

The optical system of the eye forms the image of a distant object at its secondary focal point, which coincides with the macula, whose central part is the fovea. The image is called the **retinal image**. It is real, inverted, and—significantly—smaller (minified) than the object. It is real because the rays that form it converge. In a very simple approach, Figure 6-19 describes the formation of an image by a positive lens surrounded by air on both sides.

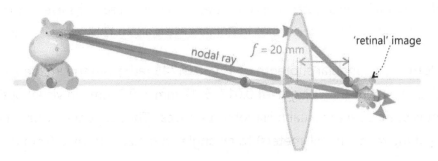

Figure 6-19: The retinal image is real, inverted, and (much) smaller than the object. The nodal ray is used to compute the retinal image size.

Figure 6-20 presents a very simplified approach to calculate the retinal image height h' formed by a distant object of height h. A ray is launched from the object through the anterior nodal point N (§ 1.4.1). This ray translates over the optical axis to the posterior nodal point N' and then emerges undeviated (equal angle ϑ with respect to the optical axis) to form the image on the retina. This ray is the visual axis (nodal ray); in practice, it is approximated by the line of sight (§ 2.4.3), which is known as the chief ray in geometrical optics. The angle ϑ is the angle subtended by the object extended from the anterior nodal point N of the eye. The closer to the eye the object (up to the near point) the larger the angle and thus the larger the retinal image.

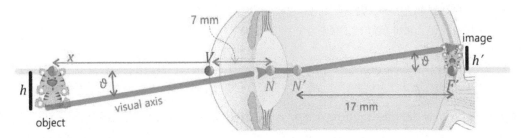

Figure 6-20: Retinal image geometry and size determination for a far object (distance x not drawn to scale). Compare cardinal points with those in Figure 1-19 (the 7 mm and 17 mm distances are rounded).

We then express the image size (height) h' as the product of the angle ϑ [rad]·distance $N'F'$ that separates the posterior nodal point N' from the posterior focal point F', which in an emmetropic eye lies on the retina. If the angle is expressed in radians and the nodal-focal point distance is $N'F' \approx 17$ mm, the expression is summarized as:

Retinal Image Size ($N'F'$ = 17 mm in emmetropia) $h' = \vartheta \cdot (N'F') = \vartheta [\text{rad}] \cdot 17 \, [\text{mm}]$ (6.3)

Examples ☞:

A tree 5 m tall at a distance of 50 m from the eye forms an angle ϑ = 5/50 = 0.1 rad, so the retinal image is 0.1·17 mm = 1.7 mm tall.

The Marquis of Calatrava is 2 m tall, standing 20 m away from Donna Leonora's eye. His image forms an angle ϑ = 2/20 = 0.1 rad, so the image formed in Donna's eye is also 0.1·17 mm = 1.7 mm tall.

A ray forming an angular subtense of 1° (=0.01745 rad) from the image space nodal point N' reaches the retina at a 'height' of 0.01745·17 mm = 0.3 mm. In visual optics, the angular extent is preferable to actual millimeter distances. Thus, a general rule for converting the linear size of the retina (in millimeters) to an angle (in radians) formed from the nodal point N' is

Retinal Image Size and Angle: 1 mm ⤳ 0.06 rad = 3.345° ≈ 200 arcmin   (6.4)

Example ☞: What is the image size for an object subtending 2° at the eye's nodal point?
We first convert 2° to 0.0349 rad. The retinal image size is 0.0349 · 17 mm = 0.59 mm ≈ 0.6 mm.

Note 🧠 : A rigorous derivation of relationship (6.3) for an object with height h at a distance x from the cornea vertex V determines that the retinal image height is $h' = \vartheta \cdot (|x| + VN)$ (6.5)

where VN is the distance separating the vertex V from the nodal point N (≈ 7 mm). The angle ϑ is the angle formed by the chief ray directed to the nodal point N and equals the angle formed by this ray with the optical axis leaving the nodal point N'. It is the same angle in expressions (6.3) & (6.5) owing to the defining property of the nodal points; therefore,

$$\frac{h'\,[\text{mm}]}{N'F'} = \frac{-h\,[\text{mm}]}{|x| + VN} \Rightarrow h'\,[\text{mm}] = -h\,[\text{mm}] \cdot \frac{N'F'}{|x\,[\text{mm}]| + VN} \approx -h\,[\text{mm}] \cdot \frac{17}{|x\,[\text{mm}]| + 7}$$

where the (–) sign simply denotes that the image is inverted. Here x is also negative since the object is located to the left of the lens; hence, we use its absolute value. If the object is adequately far (in the optics of the eye, any distance of more than 6 m), then $x + 7 \approx x$, and the retinal image size is expressed as

$$h'\,[\text{mm}] \approx -h\,[\text{mm}] \frac{17}{|x\,[\text{mm}]|} \approx 17 \frac{h\,[\text{mm}]}{x\,[\text{mm}]} \approx 17 \frac{\text{object height}}{\text{object distance from the eye}} = 17 \cdot \vartheta\,[\text{rad}]$$

6.3 Ametropia ≠ Emmetropia

Emmetropia is the exception rather than the rule. Often, the optical power of the human eye is not harmonized with its axial length; in this case, the focused image is <u>not</u> formed on the retina, but either before it or after it. What is projected onto the retina is a blurred image. This is called **ametropia** (α- for not & -μέτρο for the rule). In imaging terms, the retina is no longer the optical conjugate of infinity. Ametropia is classified primarily as myopia, hyperopia, and astigmatism.

6.3.1 Chromatic Aberration and Vision

Before we explore ametropia, let us re-visit the concept and classification of aberrations. Light is a wave; its wavelength determines its color. Ocular refractive elements such as the cornea and the crystalline lens have different values of optical power/focal length for different colors (as seen in § 2.2.2). Typically, shorter wavelengths correspond to larger refractive indices (Figure 2-29), which, according to the lens-maker's formula,[608] lead to shorter focal lengths. If the object is composed of white light, the blue or green part focuses first, followed by the red part.

Therefore, aberrations also depend on the value of the wavelength. This aspect is termed **chromatic aberration**.[30] To a certain extent, vision compensates for this aberration through cone trichromatic differential sensitivity and cerebral processing. The aspect that describes the different focal points for different chromatic components along the optical axis is longitudinal chromatic aberration. The aspect that describes the different tinted blur surrounding the images is lateral chromatic aberration; for example, the blurred blue image creates part of the tinted blur surrounding the red focused image.

The bichrome or **duochrome test** (red-green) is an important part of the optometric examination, which utilizes longitudinal chromatic aberration, or the separation of foci along the axis. Due to longitudinal chromatic aberration, light from the green and blue ends of the spectrum (blue has a shorter wavelength, close to 400 nm) focuses before the light from the red end of the spectrum (longer wavelength, up to 700 nm). This dioptric difference can be on the order of 2.0 D and can produce significantly different contrast perception among the different spectral components of the retinal image.[609, 610, 611]

---

[608] *Geometrical Optics* § 2.4 Lens Optical Power.

[609] Bedford RE, Wyszecki G. Axial chromatic aberration of the human eye. J Opt Soc Am. 1957; 47:564-5.

[610] Marcos S, Burns SA, Moreno-Barriusop E, Navarro R. A new approach to the study of ocular chromatic aberrations. Vision Res. 1999; 39:4309-23.

[611] Howarth PA, Bradley A. The longitudinal chromatic aberration of the human eye, and its correction. Vision Res. 1986; 26:361-6.

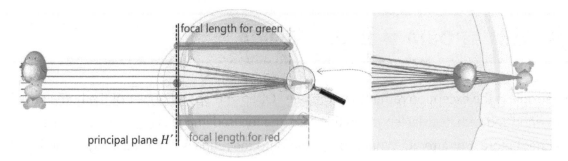

Figure 6-21: Axial (longitudinal) chromatic aberration in the human eye. In comparison to the red, the refractive power for the green is larger, so the focal length is shorter. The case illustrated here corresponds to an emmetropic, or a corrected, eye.

Figure 6-22: Simulated vision with strong transverse (shown as separation of images perpendicular to the axis) chromatic aberration. Note the color fringe along the edges of the newspaper and along the letters.

A duochrome test is commonly used to refine the final sphere in refraction when a corrected eye becomes, from the optical perspective, emmetropic. The test uses a split screen with a green and red background and either black letters [Figure 6-23 (right)] or Verhoeff's circles serving as recognition targets. The examinee is asked to compare the clarity of the letters on the green part and the red part. The part that is focused nearest to the retina is perceived as the clearest. Because of chromatic aberration, the shorter-wavelength components (green) always focus in front of the longer-wavelength components (red) [Figure 6-23 (left)].

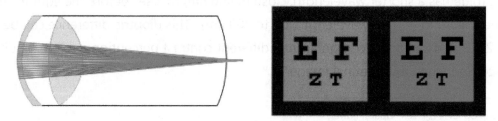

Figure 6-23: Duochrome test endpoint in an eye that has been properly corrected, or in which no correction is needed—an emmetropic eye. (left) Focusing of the red and green components. (right) The two chromatic targets appear to be nearly equal in sharpness.

If the eye is emmetropic, or the proper correction is worn, then the green part focuses just in front of the retina, the red part focuses just behind the retina, and both parts appear to be equally sharp [Figure 6-23 (right)]. The images of either color part appear to be equally acceptable, or almost clear. This endpoint is called 'neutrality' or 'balance.'

When the red part appears sharper than the green part [Figure 6-24 (left)], the eye has more power than is needed (myopic). Both parts focus in front of the retina, the green focusing farther away. Then a minus lens (in –0.25 D steps) is added to bring the two parts to neutrality.

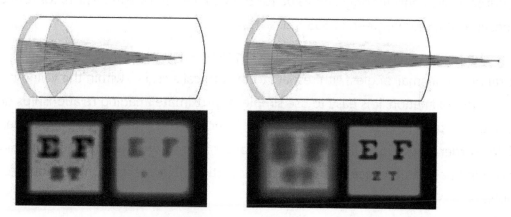

Figure 6-24: Duochrome test in an eye with excess optical power (myopic, left) and an eye with deficient optical power (hyperopic, right).

When the green part appears sharper than the red part [Figure 6-24 (right)], the eye has less power than is needed (hyperopic). Both halves focus behind the retina , the red focusing farther away. Then a plus lens (in +0.25 D steps) is added to bring the two parts to neutrality.

Clinical note 📷 : RAM and GAP: What do they stand for?

RAM stands for Red Add Minus. When the eye sees a clearer red image [Figure 6-24 (left)], it is myopic, so a minus corrective lens should be used.

GAP stands for Green Add Plus. When the eye sees a clearer green image [Figure 6-24 (right)], it is hyperopic, so a plus corrective lens should be used.

Because this test is based on chromatic aberration and not on the ability to see color, it is used even for people with color vision deficiency (discussed in § 5.3). The defocus effects do not depend on the individual's ability to also recognize the surrounding color. The examiner then may ask 'left/right?' instead of 'red/green?'.

Note 🎨 : One may wonder, why green and not blue for the shorter wavelength? Indeed, blue would produce greater chromatic separation from the red (compared to the green). However, the eye is much less sensitive to blue than to green, so changes in green are more reliably detected.

6.3.2 Monochromatic Aberrations

Aberrations, of course, occur even when we use monochromatic light, i.e., when we use only a small fraction of the optical spectrum at any one time. These are **monochromatic aberrations**. In each case of monochromatic aberration (e.g., myopia), there is the additional component of the chromatic aberration, even in emmetropia. In the rest of this chapter, we will investigate only monochromatic aberrations and will assume that the chromatic aberration is absent. For this purpose, we consider only one value for the wavelength of light, which, for reference purposes, is the yellow-green at 555 nm.

There are two main classes of monochromatic aberrations: low-order and high-order aberrations. For small angles with respect to the optical axis, i.e., within the validity of the paraxial approximation, it is easy to use simple, approximate imaging relationships derived from geometrical optics to describe the aberration. Hence, in this paraxial region, we deal mostly with low-order aberrations. In contrast, high-order aberrations become most prominent in larger pupils, a fact that necessitates the consideration of increased contributions from peripheral rays instead of paraxial rays.

Low-order monochromatic aberrations are, both quantitatively and qualitatively, the dominant aberrations in the human eye. These low-order aberrations, which are the simplest refractive errors, are also called **spherocylindrical** because they can be corrected with spherical or cylindrical spectacles (discussed in § 6.6). With the proper correction, such an eye may reach a corrected-distance visual acuity as good as an emmetropic eye, i.e., 20/20 vision.

The spherical part of the spherocylindrical error is the **defocus**, or spherical refractive error, whose clinical manifestation is myopia and hyperopia.[612] In defocus, the image projected onto the retina is blurred because it is out of focus. In this case, the real, conjugate image is not formed on the retina but at another point on the optical axis, before (myopia) or after (hyperopia) the retina. This results in an increase in the size of the circle of least confusion on the retina, adversely affecting resolution and visual acuity.

By another account, defocus is not a true aberration, as the optical system does, indeed form a very sharp image—it is the image plane that is not at the right place. Defocus is a mismatch between axial length and optical power.

The '**cylinder**' part of a spherocylindrical aberration, on the other hand, can be considered a true aberration. No 'point' is formed; instead, two focal lines that run parallel and at right angles to the cylinder axis are formed (see § 9.5).

---

[612] Norton TT, Manny R, O'Leary DJ. Myopia - global problem, global research. Optom Vis Sci. 2005; 82(4):223-5.

6.4 MYOPIA AND HYPEROPIA

6.4.1 Myopia

If the optical power of the eye is stronger than what is needed for its size, the image is formed at a finite distance in front of the retina. The eye simply has too much converging power. This is **myopia** ($\mu\acute{\upsilon}\omega$-, close & - $\acute{o}\psi\iota\varsigma$, sight) or near-sightedness. For example, an eye with optical power 68 D (and therefore an equivalent focal length $P'F' = 1.336/68 = 0.0196$ m = 19.6 mm) and an axial length of 22.5 mm is myopic because the focal length is shorter than what corresponds to its axial length. This eye would be emmetropic if it had an axial length of $19.6 + 1.6 = 21.2$ mm. There is a mismatch of about 1.3 mm between the actual axial length and the axial length required for emmetropia.

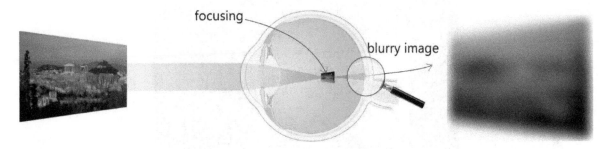

Figure 6-25: In a myopic eye, the retinal image from a distant object focuses before the retina. Hence, a defocused image is projected onto the retina.

This eye cannot bring distant objects into focus; the image from an object at optical infinity (vergence = 0.0 D) cannot be formed on the retina. What reaches the retina is a blurred version of the image formed in front of the retina. However, this myopic eye can bring into focus an object situated at a given range of distances in front of the eye (i.e., not at infinity).

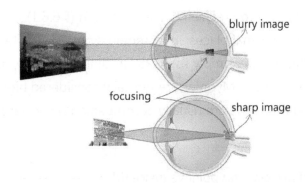

Figure 6-26: A myopic eye focusing (top) on an object at infinity and (bottom) on a nearby object.

Consider the 68.0 D myopic eye; an object at infinity forms an image 1.3 mm before the retina. However, an object such as a newspaper held 23.56 cm in front of the eye (which is 1.35 mm + 23.56 cm = 23.70 cm from the anterior principal point P) forms an image exactly on the retina. The <u>far point</u> for this eye is 23.56 cm in front of the eye.

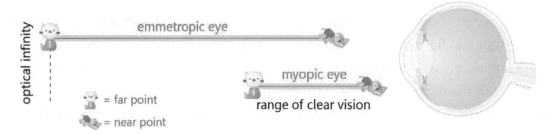

Figure 6-27: *Far and near points for an emmetropic eye and a myopic eye.*

Figure 6-28: *Simulated vision of a myopic eye. Nearby objects can be clearly seen (as long as they are within the range of clear vision), but distant objects cannot form sharp retinal images. The newspaper might be at the far point of this myopic eye.*

The closer the far point the larger the myopia. Specifically, vergence at the far point is the magnitude, or **degree of myopia**, expressed in diopters (D). In our example, the vergence at the –23.56 cm far point [negative sign because the object is before (to the left of) the principal plane H] is $1/(-0.2356 \text{ m}) = -4.25$ D. This eye has –4.25 D of refractive error, which, as we will see, also represents the required refractive correction (§ 6.6.1). The refractive correction is usually reported with two decimal places, in increments of 0.25 D, often without the diopter (D) units; i.e., we report this myopia simply as –4.25. In clinical practice, myopia is considered low if it is between 0.00 and –4.00. Myopias are typically considered high if they are > –6.00. Myopias beyond –12.00 are rare and are usually accompanied by ocular pathology. The degree of myopia is given by

$$\text{degree of myopia = far-point vergence [D]} = \frac{1}{\text{far-point distance [m]}} \qquad (6.6)$$

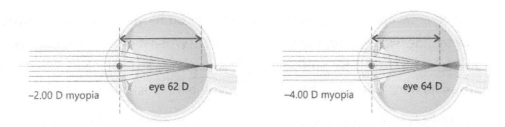

Figure 6-29: The larger the myopia the farther the focus is from the retina. Therefore, on the retina, the projected image is progressively blurred. Here the object is at optical infinity.

6.4.1.1 Classification of Myopia

Myopia can be caused by a large axial length, in which case it is **axial myopia**; the eye is too long. The eye may be of normal length but simply have excess power (a steep cornea)—this is **refractive myopia**. Usually, low myopia has both axial and refractive components; moderate to high myopias are mostly axial. The corneal radius of curvature is ≈ 7.7 mm (§ 2.1.3); a steeper cornea has a smaller radius of curvature. A ratio of axial length (average value of 24 mm) to the radius of curvature (average value of 7.7 mm) that is > 3.00 is an indication of myopia.[613]

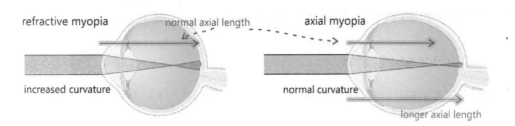

Figure 6-30: In refractive myopia (left). the axial length is normal, while the corneal curvature is increased (steeper). In axial myopia (right), the axial length is larger, while the corneal curvature is normal.

High myopia is associated with ocular pathology that increases the risk of severe, irreversible vision loss. High axial myopia suggests a long eye, where the retina stretches deep into the socket. This can lead to posterior staphyloma, an abnormal protrusion of the uveal tissue and the sclera toward the orbit.[614] This protrusion represents increased risk for retinal detachment[615] and subretinal neovascularization.[616] High refractive myopia indicates corneal ectatic conditions such as keratoconus,[617] where the curvature becomes highly abnormal, with a radius of curvature as short as 5 mm, and the axial length is within the normal range.

---

[613] Grosvenor T. High axial length/corneal radius ratio as a risk factor in the development of myopia. Am J Optom Physiol Opt. 1988; 65(9):689-96.

[614] Ohno-Matsui K, Akiba M, Modegi T, Tomita M, Ishibashi T, Tokoro T, Moriyama M. Association between shape of sclera and myopic retinochoroidal lesions in patients with pathologic myopia. Invest Ophthalmol Vis Sci. 2012; 53(10):6046-61.

[615] Polkinghorne PJ, Craig JP. Northern New Zealand Rhegmatogenous Retinal Detachment Study: epidemiology and risk factors. Clin Experiment Ophthalmol. 2004; 32(2):159-63.

[616] Montero JA, Ruiz-Moreno JM. Treatment of choroidal neovascularization in high myopia. Curr Drug Targets. 2010; 11(5):630-44.

[617] Asimellis G, Kaufman EJ. Keratoconus. StatPearls [Internet]. Treasure Island (FL): StatPearls Publishing; 2018. PMID: 29262160.

The degree of myopia is often almost the same for both eyes. Usually, the myopic difference between the two eyes does not exceed 1.00 D. When it differs by more than the clinically significant 1.00 D, we have **anisometropic myopia**, or anisomyopia. Simple myopic anisometropia exists when one eye is emmetropic and the other is myopic.

Anisometropia is the case where the defocus (either type) difference between the two eyes is greater than 1.00 D. Anisometropia becomes <u>clinically significant</u> when it is more than 2.00 D because of the different retinal image size perception between the two eyes, a condition called **aniseikonia** (*a-*, not, *-ίση-*, equal & *-εικόνα*, image). Anisometropia is the optical cause, while aniseikonia is the clinical effect as perceived by an individual with anisometropia.

A difference in retinal image size of more than 3–5% can contribute to significant vision problems. A notable difference in the (corrected) retinal image size of the same object between the two eyes can induce fusional disparity and binocular vision disorders, with a reduction of stereopsis perception. Because corrective lenses result in approximately a 1.5% angular magnification difference per 1.00 of corrective lens (§ 9.3), an anisometropia of ≈ 2.00 D to 3.25 D can be considered the threshold for aniseikonia symptoms, although variations are common among individual perceptions and types of ametropia.

6.4.1.2 Prevalence of Myopia

The prevalence of myopia varies significantly, depending on the age group, ethnic background, and geographical location.

Age appears to influence myopia due to an increase in axial length;[618] there is a gradual shift toward increasing myopia in the young, which often continues into adulthood. Myopia is common in teenagers (20–25%) and in young adults (25–35%).[619] This trend toward increased myopia halts by the age of 45 years: At this age, myopia affects about 20% of the general population then declines to 14% by the age of 70. A family history of myopia appears to be a factor (hereditary myopia).[620] Studies have shown a 33–60% prevalence of myopia in children whose parents are both myopic; this drops to 23–40% if only one parent has myopia, and to 6–15% if neither parent does.[621]

[618] Zadnik K, Sinnott LT, Cotter SA, Jones-Jordan LA, Kleinstein RN, Manny RE, Twelker JD, Mutti DO, the Collaborative Longitudinal Evaluation of Ethnicity and Refractive Error (CLEERE) Study Group. Prediction of juvenile-onset myopia. JAMA Ophthalmol. 2015; 133(6):683-9.

[619] Sperduto RD, Seigel D, Roberts J, Rowland M. Prevalence of myopia in the United States. Arch Ophthalmol. 1983; 101(3):405-7.

[620] Goss DA, Jackson TW. Clinical findings before the onset of myopia in youth: Parental history of myopia. Optom Vis Sci. 1996; 73(4):279-82.

[621] Lam DS, Fan DS, Lam RF, Rao SK, Chong KS, Lau JT, Lai RY, Cheung EY. The effect of parental history of myopia on children's eye size and growth: results of a longitudinal study. Invest Ophthalmol Vis Sci. 2008; 49(3):873-6.

There is significant evidence that myopia is increasing globally,[622] both in prevalence and in average magnitude.[623] Significantly high myopia is strong in urban, industrialized East Asia / Pacific Rim.[624, 625, 626] This has been termed the 'myopia epidemic.'[627] The substantial increase in occupational close work on a regular basis, such as reading text on mobile phones or computer screens, is a contributing factor for acquired myopia. Studies associate myopia with more years of education, type of occupation, greater academic disposition, and more time spent on near vision (less time spent outdoors).[628, 629] It's possible that excessive time spent watching television or playing computer games instead of being outside is contributing to the increase in juvenile myopia.[630]

Several factors influence the prevalence and progression of myopia. These include genetic predisposition, environmental exposures, and habitual activities.[631] It has been suggested that, because close work requires continuous accommodative effort, an intense amount of close work can cause chronic spasms of the ciliary muscle (§ 7.1.2). If the ciliary muscle cannot relax, distance vision becomes 'myopic,' even in an emmetropic eye, and 'more myopic' in a myopic eye. This may lead to myopia development.[632, 633] Other studies, however, report a weak association or no association between prolonged near-distance work and myopia progression.[634, 635, 636]

---

[622] Holden BA, Fricke TR, Wilson DA, Jong M, Naidoo KS, Sankaridurg P, Wong TY, Naduvilath TJ, Resnikoff S. Global prevalence of myopia and high myopia and temporal trends from 2000 through 2050. Ophthalmology. 2016; 123(5):1036-42.

[623] Vitale S, Sperduto RD, Ferris FL 3rd. Increased prevalence of myopia in the United States between 1971-1972 and 1999-2004. Arch Ophthalmol. 2009; 127(12):1632-9.

[624] Foster JP, Jiang Y. Epidemiology of myopia. Eye (Lond). 2014; 28(2):202-8.

[625] Sun J, Zhou J, Zhao P, Lian J, Zhu H, Zhou Y, Sun Y, Wang Y, Zhao L, Wei Y, Wang L, Cun B, Ge S, Fan X. High prevalence of myopia and high myopia in 5060 Chinese university students in Shanghai. Invest Ophthalmol Vis Sci. 2012; 53(12):7504-9.

[626] Lin LL-K, Chen C-J, Hung P-T, Ko L-S. Nationwide survey of myopia among schoolchildren in Taiwan, 1986. Acta Ophthalmol. 1988; 66(suppl 185):29-33.

[627] Park DJ, Congdon NG. Evidence for an 'epidemic' of myopia. Ann Acad Med Singapore. 2004; 33(1):21-6.

[628] Rosner M, Belkin M. Intelligence, education, and myopia in males. Arch Ophthalmol. 1987; 105(11):1508-11.

[629] Morgan IG, French AN, Ashby RS, Guo X, Ding X, He M, Rose KA. The epidemics of myopia: Aetiology and prevention. Prog Retin Eye Res. 2018; 62:134-49.

[630] Yu L, Li Z-K, Gao J-R, Liu J-R, Xu C-T. Epidemiology, genetics and treatments for myopia. Int J Ophthalmol. 2011; 4(6):658-69.

[631] Morgan I, Rose K. How genetic is school myopia? Prog Retin Eye Res. 2005; 24(1):1-38.

[632] Baldwin WR. A review of statistical studies of relations between myopia and ethnic, behavioral, and physiological characteristics. Am J Optom Physiol Opt. 1981; 58(7):516-27.

[633] Saw SM, Zhang MZ, Hong RZ, Fu ZF, Pang MH, Tan DT. Near-work activity, night-lights, and myopia in the Singapore-China study. Arch Ophthalmol. 2002; 120(5):620-7.

[634] Mutti DO, Mitchell GL, Moeschberger ML, Jones LA, Zadnik K. Parental myopia, near work, school achievement, and children's refractive error. Invest Ophthalmol Vis Sci. 2002; 43(12):3633-40.

[635] Saw SM, Chua WH, Hong CY, Wu HM, Chan WY, Chia KS, Stone RA, Tan D. Nearwork in early-onset myopia. Invest Ophthalmol Vis Sci. 2002; 43(2):332-9.

[636] Low W, Dirani M, Gazzard G, Chan YH, Zhou HJ, Selvaraj P, Au Eong KG, Young TL, Mitchell P, Wong TY, Saw SM. Family history, near work, outdoor activity, and myopia in Singapore Chinese preschool children. Br J Ophthalmol. 2010; 94(8):1012-6.

6.4.2 Hyperopia

Hyperopia (hypermetropia, far-sightedness) (*υπερ-* in excess/far & - *ὄψις* sight) occurs when the optical power of the eye is so weak that the image is 'focused' somewhere behind the sentient layer of the retina. The eye simply lacks adequate converging power. The image never actually comes into focus; it forms a blurry shape on the retina.

The relaxed hyperopic eye cannot focus zero vergence, i.e., on an object at optical infinity. It can only bring to focus positive vergence, i.e., a virtual object located ... behind it (which is impossible for real objects; this is the virtual extension of the range of clear vision). Thus, a relaxed hyperopic eye cannot clearly see near or far objects. Very close objects, such as a newspaper, are even harder to read, as they appear even more blurry. This is, in a sense, the opposite of myopia, in which the closer the object is to the eye the less blurry it appears.

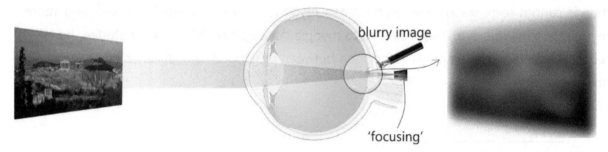

Figure 6-31: In the case of hyperopia, the retinal image is formed (would be formed) behind the retina. Hence, a defocused image is projected onto the retina.

This impossibility becomes a possibility by accommodation (see § 7.1). Depending on the degree of hyperopia and the age, and therefore the amplitude of accommodation, the eye can adapt to bring the image of a distant object to the retina. A hyperopic eye can see clearly at infinity because it habitually offsets the ocular power deficiency by drawing 'resource' from the crystalline lens. The hyperope needs to continuously accommodate for far observation and more so for close observation; here 'more so' indicates more accommodation than what an emmetrope needs. This is particularly the case in young hyperopes.

Using the language of the far point, because the relaxed hyperopic eye cannot focus a collimated beam (zero vergence, object at optical infinity) but can only focus positive vergence (a beam that is converging to a point beyond the eye), it has a far point located to the right of the retina—or beyond infinity, as some say. Obviously, this is a case of a 'virtual' range of sharp vision. However, there is still a large range of clear vision in front of a hyperopic eye, provided that accommodation is engaged.

Figure 6-32: Simulated vision of a hyperopic eye (without accommodation). Neither near nor distant objects can be clearly seen; the near objects are more 'fuzzy' than the distant objects.

For example, an eye with optical power 60.0 D, and therefore equivalent focal length (internal to the eye) $P'F' = 1.336/60.0 = 0.0222$ m $= 22.22$ mm, is hyperopic if its axial length is 22.00 mm. (This eye would be emmetropic for an axial length of 22.22 +1.6 = 23.82 mm—a big mismatch). This focal length is thus too large for its axial length, as it exceeds the length of the eye! This eye can only bring an object from infinity into focus 1.82 mm after the retina.

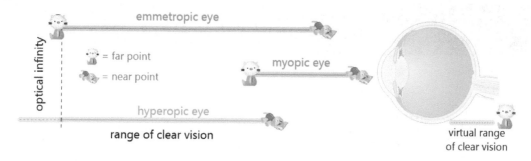

Figure 6-33: Comparison of far and near points for emmetropia, myopia, and hyperopia. In hyperopia, the far point is <u>not</u> in front of the eye, but behind it.

Note: The far point is the farthest point the eye can see clearly without using any accommodation. The near point is the closest point the eye can see clearly when using all available accommodation. The range of clear vision runs between these two points.

A <u>virtual</u> object corresponding to a location 18.85 cm <u>to the right of the vertex of this eye</u> (18.72 cm to the right of the principal point P) would form a sharp image exactly on the retina. The far point for this hyperopic eye is therefore 18.85 cm to the right of the principal point P. The vergence at +18.85 cm (the positive sign means that the object is after—to the right of—the principal plane)[637] is $1/(+0.1885\,\text{m}) = +5.30$ D.

---

[637] *Geometrical Optics* § 4.7 Virtual Object Imaging.

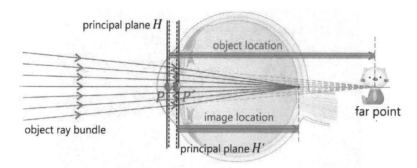

Figure 6-34: The far point in a hyperopic eye is a point behind the eye, from which the (virtual) object ray bundle would have originated if it were to form a sharp image on the retina.

Just as in myopia, the closer the far point is to the eye the larger the hyperopia. Specifically, the far-point vergence is the magnitude, or **degree of hyperopia**, in diopters (D).

$$\text{degree of hyperopia} = \text{far-point vergence [D]} = \frac{1}{\text{far-point distance [m]}} \qquad (6.7)$$

Degree of myopia	• far-point vergence • negative because the far point is in front (to the left) of the eye
Degree of hyperopia	• far-point vergence • positive because the far point is behind (to the right) of the eye

Figure 6-35: In hyperopia, a sharp image would be formed after the retina. Therefore, on the retina, the projected image is progressively blurred with increasing hyperopia.

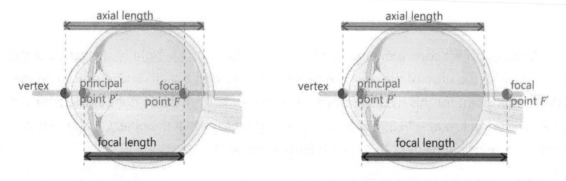

Figure 6-36: Axial and focal lengths in myopia (left) and hyperopia (right). Compare with Figure 6-18.

In the clinical practice, hyperopia is considered low if it is between 0.00 and +2.00 and moderate if it is between +2.25 and +5.00. Hyperopia is typically considered high if > +5.25; even a young person may fail to comfortably draw the required amplitude of accommodation (see Figure 7-32) to compensate for this large amount of hyperopia.

High hyperopia is associated with binocular vision problems and/or developmental disabilities and syndromes. Infants with moderate to high hyperopia (> +3.50 D) are up to 13× more likely to develop strabismus by 4 years of age if their eyes are left uncorrected and are 6× more likely to have reduced visual acuity compared to infants with low hyperopia or emmetropia.[638]

The association of high hyperopia with a greatly increased risk of amblyopia and strabismus is a major justification for the universal vision screening of young children.[639] High hyperopia is also associated with microphthalmos and nanophthalmos,[640] a developmental disorder in which one (unilateral) or both (bilateral) eyes are abnormally small and have anatomic deformations. Although rare, it is possible for an individual to have one myopic eye and one hyperopic eye in a condition called **antimetropia**, a specific case of anisometropia.

6.4.2.1 Classification of Hyperopia

Just as in myopia, there is **axial** hyperopia due to a short axial length but a 'normal' optical power, and **refractive** hyperopia due to a small power (the cornea is flatter, so the corneal power is less) but a reasonably 'normal' axial length. Regardless of the type, axial or refractive, in hyperopia, the eye's optical power is a bit too weak for its axial length. Hyperopes are refractive power underachievers, while myopes are refractive power overachievers.

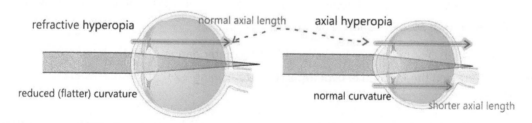

Figure 6-37: (left) In refractive hyperopia, the axial length is normal, while the corneal curvature is reduced. (right) In axial hyperopia, the axial length is shorter, while the corneal curvature is normal. The focus point in the right figure coincides with the location of the retina in the left figure.

---

[638] Atkinson J, Braddick O, Nardini M, Anker S. Infant hyperopia: detection, distribution, changes and correlates-outcomes from the Cambridge infant screening programs. Optom Vis Sci. 2007; 84(2):84-96.

[639] Aurell E, Norrsell K. A longitudinal study of children with family history of strabismus: factors determining the incidence of strabismus. Br J Ophthalmol. 1990; 74(10):589-94.

[640] Relhan N, Jalali S, Pehre N, Rao HL, Manusani U, Bodduluri L. High-hyperopia database, part I: clinical characterisation including morphometric (biometric) differentiation of posterior microphthalmos from nanophthalmos. Eye (Lond). 2016; 30(1):120-6.

Classification of hyperopia can be based on the role of accommodation (§ 7.1). The first distinction is between manifest and latent. **Manifest** hyperopia, as the name suggests, is measured by typical manifest refraction. Hyperopia can also be latent, i.e., not manifest. **Latent** hyperopia (LH) is normally masked by the accommodative response. Due to the much larger amplitude of accommodation in young individuals, LH is encountered more in youth (in about 35% of individuals up to 30 years of age), with an average magnitude ranging between 0.4 to 0.7 D.[641] LH is notably less prevalent in individuals of more than 45 years of age; naturally, as the eye ages, manifest hyperopia becomes more prominent.

The distinction between the two forms of hyperopia can be revealed by a cycloplegic refraction examination. Manifest hyperopia is the hyperopia measured without cycloplegia, by using the strongest positive lens with which maximum visual acuity is achieved. When cycloplegia is used, the total magnitude of hyperopia is the sum of the latent and manifest hyperopia. Thus, latent hyperopia is the difference between the refraction measured with and without cycloplegia; the latter should be performed first to avoid post-cycloplegic effects.

Manifest hyperopia can be either facultative or absolute. **Facultative** hyperopia can be compensated for (neutralized) by the effort of accommodation, while **absolute** hyperopia cannot.[642] Naturally, as the eye ages, a majority of the cases of manifest hyperopia becomes absolute hyperopia. Absolute hyperopia can be measured by the weakest positive lens with which the maximum visual acuity is achieved. Because manifest hyperopia is measured by the strongest positive lens in the same setting, facultative hyperopia is indirectly measured as the difference between manifest and absolute hyperopia.

Example ☞: Il Padre Guardiano has manifest hyperopia +4.50 D and 2.00 D of accommodative ability. What are his amounts of absolute and facultative hyperopia?

Because there is +4.50 D of hyperopia but only 2.00 of accommodation, the absolute hyperopia is their difference, +2.50 D, and the facultative hyperopia is the remaining +2.00 D.

Example ☞: Fra Melitone's cycloplegic examination shows +3.50 D hyperopia; subjective noncycloplegic refraction measures +2.50 D hyperopia. Melitone's manifest hyperopia is +2.50 D, as in the noncycloplegic examination. The additional +1.00 D, measured with cycloplegia, represents the latent hyperopia.

Example ☞: Preziosilla, a 35-year-old ragazza, has 20/20 uncorrected distance visual acuity. We may think he is an emmetrope. Most likely, however, Preziosilla is a latent hyperope of +0.50 D of hyperopia.

---

[641] Jackson E. Manifest and Latent Hyperopia. Journal of the American Medical Association. 1892; 19(9):251-3.
[642] Morgan MW. The nature of ametropia. Am J Optom. 1947; 24:253-61.

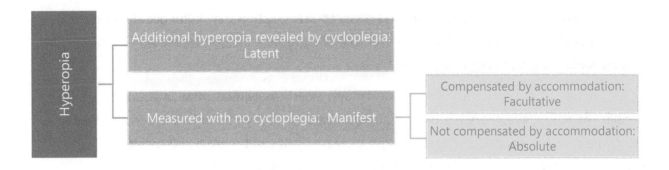

6.4.2.2 Prevalence of Hyperopia

Myopia and hyperopia are collectively called **spherical** or **defocus error**. The distribution of defocus as myopia (negative diopters) or hyperopia (positive diopters) in a large sample population is illustrated in Figure 6-38.

Hyperopia is less prevalent than myopia. It is less likely to encounter an individual with +4.00 hyperopia than with −4.00 myopia. The topic is well studied, evidenced by the number of prevalence studies in the peer-reviewed literature; a PubMed literature search using the keywords 'myopia or hyperopia' and 'prevalence or epidemic' reveals several thousand published manuscripts. However, any attempt to quantify the proportion of subjects affected by refractive error is challenging and may produce different results. Different results exist among various studies; in some cases, the reported prevalence is significant. It is likely, however, that these differences are due to the use of different criteria. Some studies may consider an eye to be hyperopic if it is +0.50 D or more, while others use a standard of +2.00 D or more.

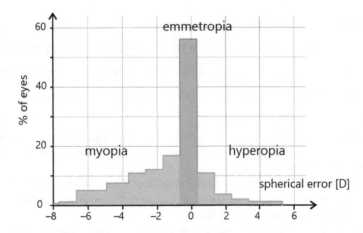

Figure 6-38: Typical distribution of spherical error (defocus). Myopia corresponds to negative spherical error, while hyperopia corresponds to positive spherical error.[643]

---

[643] Flitcroft DI. Emmetropisation and the aetiology of refractive errors. Eye (Lond). 2014; 28(2):169-79.

There is evidence that ethnicity and geographical location may influence the prevalence of hyperopia.[644] Groups with a higher prevalence of hyperopia include Native Americans, African Americans, and Pacific Islanders.[645]

Hyperopia is more common in children and elderly individuals than in young or adult people. At school age, there is a gradual trend toward more myopia or less hyperopia (both in incidence and degree) due to an axial length increase.[646] It can be predicted that a child who is hyperopic in kindergarten will likely still be hyperopic in high school.[647]

- One is hyperopic, if hyperopia is greater than +1.50 D.
- One is emmetropic, if hyperopia is between +0.50 D and +1.25 D.
- One is myopic, if hyperopia is less than +0.50 D.

Advanced age appears to correlate with a 'hyperopic shift,' a trend toward decreasing myopia and increasing hyperopia, that is especially notable between the ages of 45 and 60.[648, 649] Particularly when a hyperopic person reaches the fourth decade of life, there is some bad news. The decreased accommodation ability (Figure 7-32) may functionally highlight an otherwise 'manageable' hyperopia. Close work may suddenly become a problem, even in low hyperopia.

6.4.3   Defocus, Axial Length, and Corneal Curvature

The magnitude of spherical/defocus error (either myopia or hyperopia) is dependent on (a) the optical power of the eye and/or (b) the axial length. The first parameter, optical power, is an expression of the refractive part of the defocus. As shown in Figure 6-39, there is an average change of 1.00 D of refractive error per 1.00 D of excess ocular power.

This is, essentially, the foundation of the refractive correction of ametropia: The principle is that to correct 1.00 D of excess defocus, there has to be a modification of the optical power of the eye by 1.00 D. Hence, the excess power with which a myopic eye is corrected is a minus power modification of equal magnitude but opposite sign. Modification of the power of the eye

[644] Wen G, Tarczy-Hornoch K, McKean-Cowdin R, Cotter SA, Borchert M, Lin J, Kim J, Varma R, Multi-Ethnic Pediatric Eye Disease Study Group. Prevalence of myopia, hyperopia and astigmatism in non-Hispanic white and Asian children: multi-ethnic pediatric eye disease study. Ophthalmology. 2013; 120(10):2109-16.

[645] Crawford HE, Haamar GE. Racial analysis of ocular deformities in schools of Hawaii. Hawaii Med J. 1949; 9:90-3.

[646] Hirsch MJ, Weymouth FW. Prevalence of refractive anomalies. In: Grosvenor T, Flom M, eds. Refractive anomalies. Research and clinical applications. Boston: Butterworth-Heinemann, 1991:15-38.

[647] Grosvenor T. Primary Care Optometry, 5th ed. Part I, Chapter 4. Boston: Butterworth-Heinemann, 2007.

[648] Hirsch MJ. Changes in refractive state after the age of forty-five. Am J Optom. 1958; 35(5):229-37.

[649] Vitale S, Ellwein L, Cotch MF, Ferris FL 3rd, Sperduto R. Prevalence of refractive error in the United States, 1999-2004. Arch Ophthalmol. 2008; 126(8):1111-9. doi: 10.1001/archopht.126.8.1111.

is implemented by a multitude of options, which include refractive laser surgery, in which the corneal curvature (§ 2.1.3) is modified by either excimer laser ablation or corneal tissue removal. The curvature of the modified cornea results in a modified optical power of the eye.

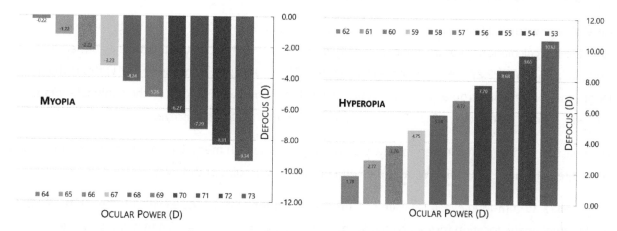

Figure 6-39: Dependence of defocus error on ocular power. (left) Myopic eyes with 22.5 mm axial length become more myopic as ocular power increases from 64 D to 73 D. (right) Hyperopic eyes with 22.5 mm axial length become more hyperopic as ocular power decreases from 62 D to 53 D.

A second parameter is the dependence of the axial-length mismatch on defocus error. Axial-length mismatch is the difference between the axial length of an emmetropic eye of the same optical power as that of the specific eye (how longer or shorter the eye is). As shown in Figure 6-40, for low myopia/hyperopia, there is an average change of 3.00 D defocus per 1 mm of axial- length mismatch when calculations use a refractive index of the eye of $n' = 1.336$.

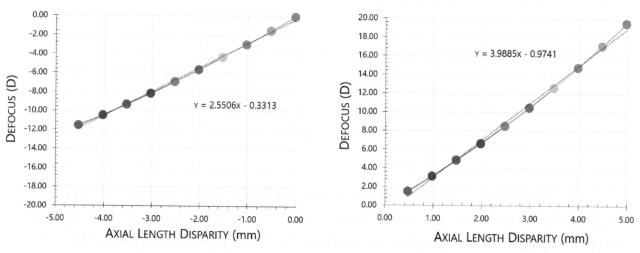

Figure 6-40: Effect of axial-length mismatch on refractive error. (left) Myopic eyes with 64.0 D power become more myopic as the axial length increases from 22.5 mm to 27.0 mm (a mismatch range of –0.07 mm to –4.57 mm). (right) Hyperopic eyes with 64.0 D power become more hyperopic as the axial length decreases from 22.0 mm to 17.5 mm (a mismatch range of +0.43 mm to +4.93 mm). Data were calculated implementing a step change (increase/decrease) of 0.5 mm of axial length.

Examples ☞:

Riccardo's eye with 60.0 D and 24 mm axial length is (almost) emmetropic: The focal length f' is 1.336/60.0 D = 22.27 mm, and the axial length to achieve emmetropia is 1.6+22.27 = 23.87 mm. (If calculated in detailed precision, Riccardo's eye is slightly myopic, –0.36 D).

Amelia's eye with 60.0 D and 25 mm axial length is myopic, about –3.00 D (–2.92 D, to be precise). Here are the calculations: For an object at infinity ($x = \infty$, $L = 0$ D), the conjugate image is formed at ($L' = +60.0$ D, $x' = n'/L'$) 22.27 mm from the principal point P', or 23.87 mm from the vertex V; this is the axial length to achieve emmetropia. However, Amelia's eye has 25 mm axial length, so the conjugate image is formed 1.13 mm before the retina. This is the axial-length mismatch for this eye.

The question is, how many degrees of myopia does this axial-length mismatch correspond to? The answer lies in the definition of myopia: What is the vergence of the far point of this eye?

For Amelia's 25-mm-long eye, it is desired that the far point forms its image exactly on the retina. Thus, the 'desired' image location formed by the far point is $x'_{\text{far point}} = 25 - 1.6 = 23.4$ mm; image vergence should then be $L'_{\text{far point}} = n'/x'_{\text{far point}} = 57.09$ D. Using the vergence imaging relationship, the far-point object vergence to enter the eye is $L_{\text{far point}} = L'_{\text{far point}} - F = 57.09$ D $- 60.0$ D $= -2.92$ D. This is therefore the degree of myopia corresponding an axial mismatch of 1.13 mm.

There are some subtle differences between myopia and hyperopia in this regard. The 3.00 D per 1 mm is an average over a large span of axial-length mismatches. For high myopia, the slope is 2.3 D of defocus per 1 mm of axial length, and for low myopia, the slope is 2.8 D of defocus per 1 mm of axial length. For low hyperopia, the slope is 3.4 D of defocus per 1 mm of axial length, and for high hyperopia, the slope is 4.6 D of defocus per 1 mm of axial length.

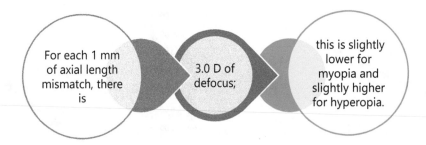

For each 1 mm of axial length mismatch, there is 3.0 D of defocus; this is slightly lower for myopia and slightly higher for hyperopia.

This dependence is of paramount importance in the clinical planning and design of cataract lens extraction surgery. When an intraocular lens (IOL) is to be used, we need to select its optical power to the best possible accuracy (0.25 D). Ocular biometry is employed to accurately measure corneal topography[67] and the axial length of the eye[330] with submillimeter precision.[650] These data are used in detailed formulas for the calculation of the IOL power.

---

[650] *Ocular Imaging* § 2.2 Optical Low-Coherence Interferometry.

6.5 EFFECTS OF AMETROPIA

6.5.1 Cardinal Points in Ametropia

As the optical properties in an ametropic eye are different from those in an emmetropic (Figure 1-19), relaxed (not-accommodating) eye, so are the locations of the cardinal points.

In refractive ametropia, there is a shift in the locations of the cardinal points. In refractive myopia, the focal point F and the nodal point N approach (come closer to) the principal plane H /principal point P. In refractive hyperopia, the focal point F and the nodal point N move away from the principal plane H/principal point P. Similarly, inside the eye, the corresponding cardinal points such as the focal point F' shift locations. In myopia, F' is closer to the principal point P', while in hyperopia, it is farther away. Thus, in myopia, the focal length inside the eye = $F'P'$ is shorter, while in hyperopia it is longer.

On the other hand, in axial ametropias, there is <u>no shift of the cardinal points</u>. The optics of the eye are essentially the same—the eye is simply either longer (myopia) or shorter (hyperopia). In axial myopia, the position where the image is formed (the focal point F') is thus before the retina, while in axial hyperopia, the focal point F' is beyond the retina.

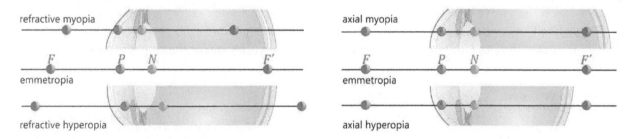

Figure 6-41: Comparison of the cardinal points with respect to an emmetropic eye: (left) in refractive myopia and refractive hyperopia, and (right) in axial myopia and axial hyperopia.

6.5.2 Retinal Image Size and Blur in Uncorrected Ametropia

The retinal image size in uncorrected ametropia depends on whether the ametropia is axial or refractive and whether it is myopia or hyperopia. Recall the emmetropic case discussed in § 6.2.2: The retinal image size is proportional to the angle that the nodal/chief ray forms with the optical axis and the axial length of the eye. To locate the image, we trace a nodal ray (flowing along the visual axis) from the object through the anterior nodal point N. This ray 'teleports' over the optical axis to the posterior nodal point N' and then emerges with the same angle with respect to the optical axis to form the retinal image at the posterior focal point F'.

In axial ametropias, there is no change in the locations of the cardinal points. The fovea simply moves away from the posterior focal point F'. It is thus easier to handle retinal image size in axial ametropias than in refractive ametropias. As illustrated in Figure 6-42, as the eye's axial length increases, the size of the retinal image also increases proportionally. In axial hyperopia (shorter axial length), the retinal image is smaller than in emmetropia. Conversely, in axial myopia (longer axial length), the uncorrected retinal image is larger than in emmetropia.

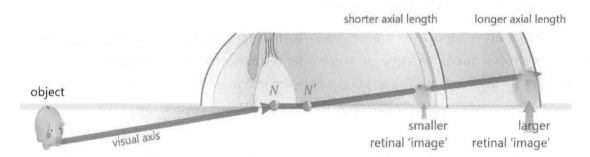

Figure 6-42: Retinal image size changes in axial ametropia: Eye elongation increases the image size. Compare with Figure 6-20, which illustrates the retinal image for the emmetropic eye.

In refractive ametropias, the axial length of the eye does not change. The cardinal points, on the other hand, shift in relation to the emmetropic eye. In refractive myopia, the object space nodal point N is closer to the anterior principal point P (to the left, as in Figure 6-43 top). In refractive hyperopia, the nodal point N shifts away from the anterior pole of the eye (to the right, as in Figure 6-43 bottom). Thus, the angle of the chief ray / visual axis is only moderately affected by the different corneal refraction, leading to a relatively small change in the retinal image size. In myopia, the image slightly increases, while in hyperopia, it slightly decreases.

Note 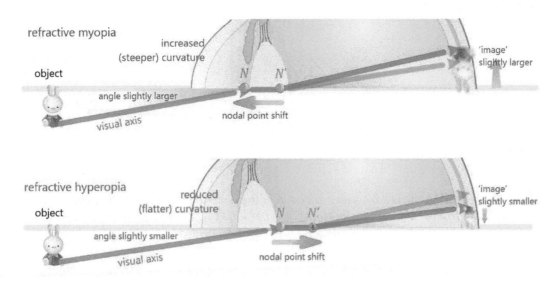: The nodal points are particularly poorly defined in astigmatism (§ 8.1.2) since there is a different spherical value along the meridians, ranging from the minimum for the flatter meridian to the maximum for the steeper meridian. Hence, the locations of the nodal points are not uniquely defined, complicating matters such as the definition of 'the' visual axis.

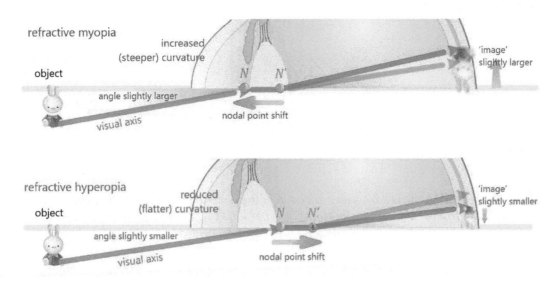

Figure 6-43: Retinal image size changes in refractive ametropia: (top) refractive myopia and (bottom) refractive hyperopia.

Useful note : In axial ametropia, the retinal image size is about 2% different per 1 D of refractive error. In refractive ametropia, the retinal image size differs by much less, about 0.5% per 1 D of refractive error.

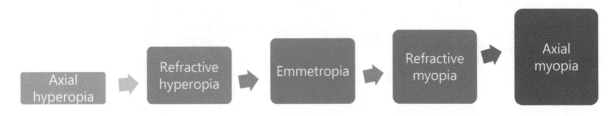

Figure 6-44: Variation in uncorrected retinal image size by type of ametropia.

The retinal image in ametropia is not in focus. This means that the uncorrected retinal image is <u>blurred</u>. What is projected onto the retina is a blurred version of the actual sharp image focused in front of the retina in myopia (Figure 6-45 top) or behind the retina in hyperopia (Figure 6-45 bottom). The geometrical blur on the projected image can be modeled by the **defocus blur disk**, which is the size of a point of the focused image projected on the retina wall. The size and the shape of the defocus blur disk depend on parameters that include the refractive error, severity and type of aberrations, and pupil size and shape.[605]

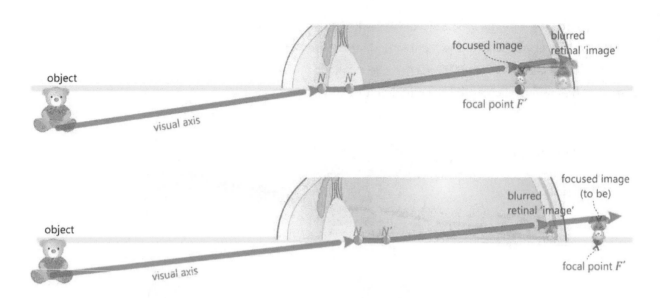

Figure 6-45: The retinal image is a blurred projection of the focused image. (top) In myopia, the focused image is situated in front of the retina. (bottom) In hyperopia, the focused image is (would be) formed behind the retina.

To model this, we invoke the geometrical blur, a notion explored in pupil effects in geometrical optics.[651] This blur describes the expanse of a focused beam away from its finest point, the focus. We use the chief ray, which intersects the center of the entrance pupil and the center of the blur circle, as the focused beam.

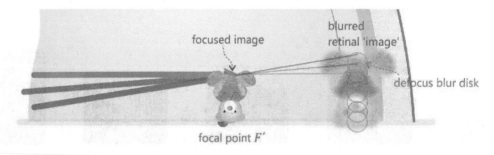

Figure 6-46: Size comparison between the focused image in a myopic eye and the blurred image projected onto the retina. The defocus blur disk may be circular under certain conditions, which include a circular pupil and a negligible astigmatic error.

The two dependencies that are the easiest to model are the pupil diameter and the distance to focus. With a large pupil diameter, the defocus blur disk has a larger size for the same distance from the focus compared to a system with a small pupil. Likewise, for the same pupil diameter, a larger distance from focus results in a proportionally larger defocus blur.

---

[651] *Geometrical Optics* § 7.6 Geometrical Image Blur.

6.5.3 Effect of Ametropias on Visual Acuity

Because refractive errors project a blurry image onto the retina, they affect visual acuity. The primary clinical sign of myopia is reduced unaided distance visual acuity: A −1.00 D myope may have uncorrected distance visual acuity of about 0.5 logMAR (20/63), a −2.00 D myope may have about 0.8 logMAR (20/125), and a −3.00 D myope may have about 1.0 logMAR (20/200), the latter meaning that even the top line in the visual acuity test chart is not read.[652]

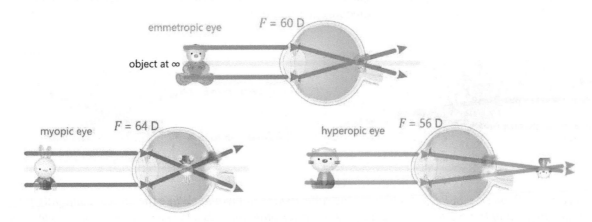

Figure 6-47: Emmetropic, myopic, and hyperopic eye for an object at optical infinity. We assume no accommodation (a relaxed eye).

These effects are, to a large degree, similar in hyperopia, although this case is further complicated by accommodation (use or lack thereof), which compensates for some hyperopia. For example, a +3.50 D hyperope who uses 2.50 D of accommodation is effectively a +1.00 D hyperope, and the defocus effects are analogous to +1.00 D.

Another fine difference between myopia and hyperopia relates to the differences in axial length. As myopic eyes tend to be longer than the average eye, they exhibit what is known as **retinal stretching**.[653] In large axial myopias, the shape of the retina is not a smooth curve (Figure 6-48) but is recessed. This leads to coarse neural sampling due to an increased average cone cell spacing, adversely affecting the digital cone sampling (as discussed in § 4.5.2).

An additional aspect to be considered is the dependence of visual acuity loss on <u>pupil size</u>. The geometrical blur size indeed depends on how far the 'image plane' is displaced from the foveal sharp focus (the larger this distance the larger the ametropia). However, variations in pupil diameter (§ 2.4.2.3) also affect the extent of the blur size for the same ametropia.

---

[652] Peters HB. The relationship between refractive error and visual acuity at three age levels. Am J Optom. 1961; 38:194-8.

[653] Coletta NJ, Watson T. Effect of myopia on visual acuity measured with laser interference fringes. Vision Res. 2006; 46(5):636-51.

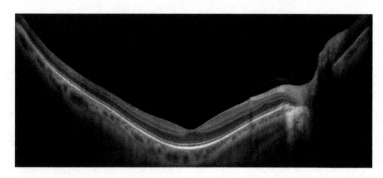

Figure 6-48: OCT image of the retina in a –18.0 D myopic eye. Notice the very caved retinal shape. Compare with Figure 4-7.

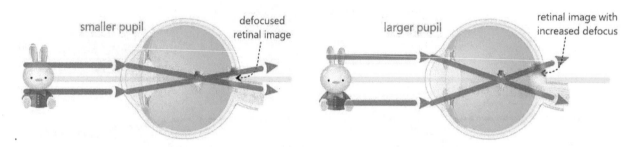

Figure 6-49: Pupil size and defocus blur for the same degree of myopia. While the optical conjugate image formed in front of the retina is identical in size, a larger pupil induces a larger geometric blur away from the conjugate point; the increased blur circle effects increased defocus of the retinal image.

This is by no means to say that the pupil size affects the degree of ametropia. A –2.00 myope is a –2.00 myope, regardless of the pupil diameter. With a dilated pupil, the amount of visual acuity drop per defocus diopter is greater. A constricted pupil, by contrast, limits the perceived blur circle, so the drop in visual acuity is less. This is why ambient lighting that affects the pupil size should be considered during the visual acuity testing (§ 3.2.3.3).

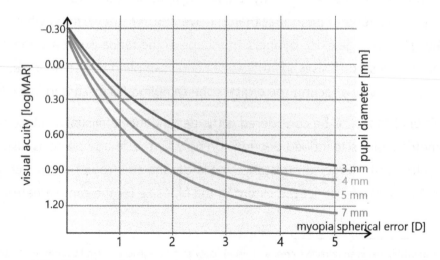

Figure 6-50: Visual acuity versus increasing refractive error for different pupil sizes.

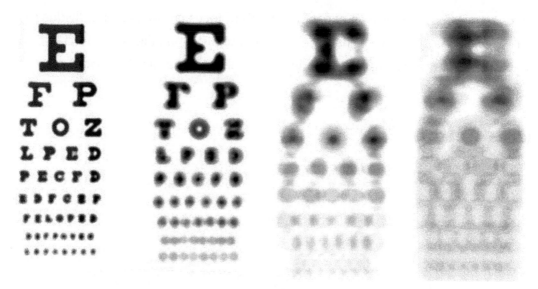

Figure 6-51: Effect of myopic defocus on visual acuity, as demonstrated on a Snellen eye chart. Myopia increasing from left to right: –0.50, –1.00, –2.00, and –3.00 D.

Thus, for the same magnitude of spherical defocus error, the loss of visual acuity is dependent on pupil size. The larger the pupil, the more rapid the loss of visual acuity per degree of spherical defocus error. Conversely, for a small pupil, the loss of visual acuity per degree of error is less. During an eye exam, it is important to understand that examinees may naturally tend to decrease their pupil size by squinting to improve visual acuity.

6.5.4   Effect of Ametropias on Depth of Focus

As presented in § 6.1.4, several mathematical models predict that the depth of focus in a diffraction-limited emmetropic eye increases inversely proportionally to the square of the pupil diameter.[606] This means that, in such a theoretical condition, if an eye has a depth of focus of 1.00 D when the pupil diameter is 2 mm, the depth of focus will be just 0.25 D when the pupil expands to 4 mm in diameter. In reality, however, it is rather rare for the depth of focus to be less than 0.50 D, even in an emmetropic eye.

Among the reasons for this is that several other contributing factors exist, such as high-order aberrations, either chromatic[603] or monochromatic,[654] that do not permit a much finer depth of focus. An eye whose ultimate resolution is limited by optical (or even neural) parameters is inherently more tolerant to defocus than an eye capable of high visual acuity. Hence, individuals with low visual acuity may be more tolerant of defocus than people with

---

[654] Rocha KM, Vabre L, Chateau N, Krueger RR. Expanding depth of focus by modifying higher-order aberrations induced by an adaptive optics visual simulator. J Cataract Refract Surg. 2009; 35(11):1885-92.

normal vision and may perceive an expanded depth of focus compared to individuals with high visual acuity, who may perceive a shallower depth of focus. The Stiles–Crawford effect (§ 4.4.2) is an example of an optical mechanism that limits how shallow the depth of focus can be.

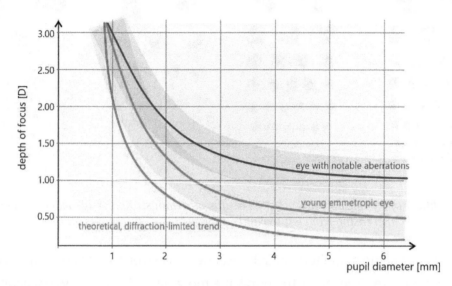

Figure 6-52: Depth of focus versus pupil diameter for different eye refractive states. Aberrations contribute to an increased the depth of focus even at larger pupil diameters when compared to an ideal, diffraction-limited eye.

In addition to its expanse, there is one more optical consideration associated with the depth of focus,[283] which is the size of the circle of least confusion over the sharpest point. Typically, in a shallow depth of focus, the circle of least confusion over the vicinity of minimal focus is small. To the contrary, in an expanded depth of focus, the circle of least confusion over the vicinity of minimal focus is enlarged.

Being a perceptual, hence, a subjective, metric, the extent of the depth of focus depends on neural and psychophysical factors, in addition to optical factors.[286] An unlikely variable that influences depth of focus is illumination. At low illumination, it is expected that the mesopic or photopic, rod-dominated, prevailing vision has reduced spatial discrimination. This reduced perceptional ability, being less sensitive to sharp focus, can tolerate a greater range of defocus; hence, a greater depth of focus can be registered under low illumination.[655, 656, 657]

[655] Van Nes FL, Bowman MA. Spatial modulation transfer in the human eye. 1962; J Opt Soc Am. 1967; 57:401-6.

[656] Green DG, Campbell FW. Effects of focus on the visual response to a sinusoidally modulated spatial stimulus. J Opt Soc Am. 1965; 55(9):1154-7.

[657] Stockman A, MacLeod DIA, DePriest DD. The temporal properties of the human short-wave photoreceptors and their associated pathways. Vis Res. 1991; 31:189-208.

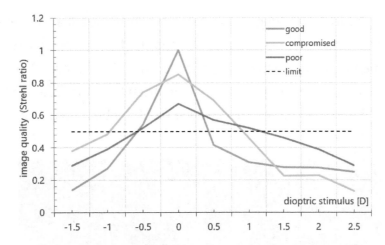

Figure 6-53: Dependence of depth of focus on image quality. An eye with compromised image quality may be more tolerant to defocus and hence register a greater depth of focus. In this example, the eye with good image quality has a depth of focus equal to 1.00 D, while the eye with compromised image quality has depth of focus equal to 2.00 D.

Determination of the depth of focus is dependent on the methodology and criteria employed, for example, whether absolute minimum value or relative value of visual acuity is used. Some consider the depth of focus to be the dioptric range over which visual acuity drops a fixed percentage of its optimum value.[658, 659] For practical purposes, the depth of focus can be determined by a simple letter-legibility criterion.[660] Most studies suggest that the depth of focus of the human eye is between 0.5 D and 1.5 D.

Because the depth of focus is a perceptual property, a fitting measurement technique should be subjective, i.e., dependent on the examinee's responses to dioptrically modified stimulus.[661] The challenge is, however, the confounding contribution of accommodation (§ 7.1); recall that the proximal point corresponding to the depth of focus should be measured without eliciting accommodation.[662]

Objective techniques can also be used for measuring the depth of focus. In these techniques, the depth of focus is the dioptric range for which an objective image quality metric does not change appreciably, based on objective measured criteria, such as the Strehl ratio (which is a measure of PSF degradation) or the cut-off frequency [which is a measure of

---

[658] Yi F, Iskander DR, Collins M. Depth of focus and visual acuity with primary and secondary spherical aberration. Vision Res. 2011; 51(14):1648-58.

[659] Tucker J, Charman WN. The depth-of-focus of the human eye for Snellen letters. Am J Optom Physiol Opt. 1975; 52(1):3-21.

[660] Lopez-Gil N, Martin J, Liu T, Bradley A, Diaz-Munoz D, Thibos LN. Retinal image quality during accommodation. Ophthalmic Physiol Opt. 2013; 33:497-507.

[661] Atchison DA, Charman WN, Woods RL. Subjective depth-of-focus of the human eye. Optom Vis Sci. 1997; 74(7):511-20.

[662] Yao P, Lin H, Huang J, Chu R, Jiang BC. Objective depth-of-focus is different from subjective depth-of-focus and correlated with accommodative microfluctuations. Vis Res. 2010; 50(13):1266-73.

modulation transfer function (MTF) degradation].[291] One technique that can be employed for this is double-pass aberrometry,[663] in which the PSF and the MTF of the observer's eye are recorded and evaluated to provide a metric for the blur away from focus.[664] As defocus shortens and broadens the PSF profile, a metric for depth of field can be set to describe the dioptric increase required for the PSF height to drop below 50% of the best-focus PSF height.

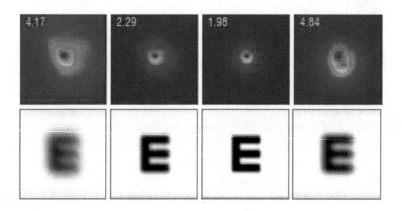

Figure 6-54: Example of narrow depth of focus (0.50 D) in an emmetropic eye. (top) PSF views and (bottom) simulation of the 20/20 letter E. Each group is spaced by a 0.50 D dioptric interval. The two letter images pertaining to the central images are clearly more legible than the two images on the ends.

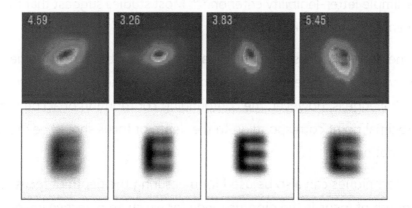

Figure 6-55: Example of depth of focus (1.00 D) in an emmetropic eye. (top) PSF views and (bottom) simulation of the 20/20 letter E. Each group is spaced by a 0.50 D dioptric interval. The two letter images pertaining to the central images are almost as legible as the two images on the ends.

[663] *Ocular Imaging* § 5.3.4 Modulation Transfer Function and § 6.2.6 Double-Pass Aberrometry.

[664] Marcos S, Moreno E, Navarro R. The depth-of-field of the human eye from objective and subjective measurements. Vis Res. 1999; 39(12):2039-49.

6.6 SPECTACLE CORRECTION OF MYOPIA AND HYPEROPIA

6.6.1 Correction of Myopia: Optical Principles

Let us see what it takes to correct myopia. Regardless of the type (refractive/axial), the image of a distant object (collimated beam, vergence 0.0 D) is formed before (in front of) the retina. The purpose of the correction is to bring (shift) the focal point of the system 'Eye + Correction' exactly to the retina. Using the terminology of the far and near points, in a myopic eye, the far point is at a finite distance in front of the eye. Equivalently, thus, we want to shift the far point of the system 'Eye + Correction' to infinity. Consider a far point at 2 m (noted as –2 m because it is to the left of the eye, against light propagation). By definition, this eye has –0.50 D of myopia, as the far-point vergence is

$$\text{far-point vergence} = \frac{1}{-2 \text{ m}} = -0.5 \text{ D} \tag{6.8}$$

How can we correct this eye? This eye can clearly see (without accommodation) only those objects that are located just 2 m in front of it, not distant objects at optical infinity. The solution is simple: <u>Bring the image</u> of a distant object to where the eye can see it—to <u>its far point</u>.

This can be achieved with a corrective lens whose optical power F_{corr} is such that, when presented with an object at infinity (vergence = $1/\infty$ = 0 D), it forms an image 2 m to its left. Such a lens is a minus lens of focal length $f' = -2$ m, or of optical power $F_{corr} = -0.5$ D. The secondary focal point of this corrective lens is placed at the far point of the myopic eye.

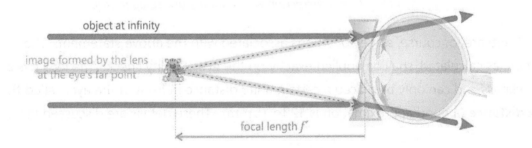

Figure 6-56: A minus lens with a focal length equal to the far distance of a myopic eye brings an image from optical infinity to the far point.

The image formed by the minus lens is now the object observed by the eye, located at the far point of the myopic eye. The image of this object is formed sharply on the retina. Now, the system 'Eye + Correction' performs optically like an emmetropic eye.

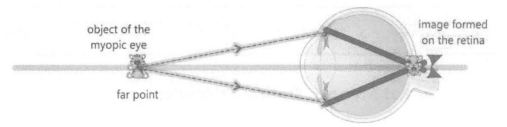

Figure 6-57: The image formed by the minus lens is now the object, located at the far point of the myopic eye. The resultant image is formed sharply on the retina.

The above are confirmed by applying the imaging relationship:[602]

$$\underbrace{L = 0.00\ \text{D}}_{\text{object vergence}} + \underbrace{F_{\text{corr}} = -5.00\ \text{D}}_{\text{lens power}} = \underbrace{L' = -5.00\ \text{D}}_{\text{vergence of the observed image at the far point}} \tag{6.9}$$

We realize therefore that, to correct a –5.00 myopia, we need a –5.00 D lens. This is a general conclusion. To manage myopia, we need to apply a reduction of the optical power of the eye by exactly the same amount, which is called **sphere power** (negative, for myopia). For a –2.50 myopia, we need a –2.50 D sphere power.

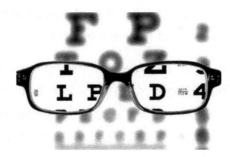

Figure 6-58: Myopia correction with a minus, diverging lenses.

There are, of course, some conditions associated with the above statement. The correction, as calculated, shall be applied exactly on the eye. Reality check: The lens has a non-zero thickness and can only be placed a certain finite distance in front of the eye, called the **vertex distance** (a good approximation is 12 to 15 mm). These details are discussed in § 9.2.4.

6.6.2 Correction of Hyperopia: Principles

In hyperopia, the collimated beam from an object at infinity focuses behind (to the right of) the retina, so the far point is behind the eye. Just as in myopia, the purpose of the correction is to bring (shift) the focal point of the system 'Eye + Correction' exactly to the retina. Equivalently, thus, we want to shift the far point of the system 'Eye + Correction' from behind the hyperopic eye to infinity.

Just as in myopia, in hyperopia, the optical power of the corrective lens F_{corr} should equal the vergence of the far point of the relaxed hyperopic eye, i.e., the degree of hyperopia. The only difference is that now the lens is converging (a plus lens). Therefore, this lens forms a real image at its secondary focal point, which coincides with the far point of the hyperopic eye.

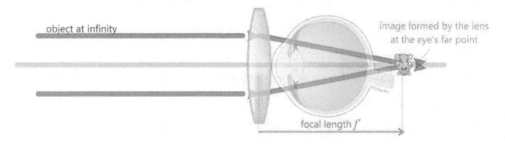

Figure 6-59: A plus lens with a focal length equal to the far distance of a hyperopic eye forms an image from optical infinity to the far point of the hyperopic eye.

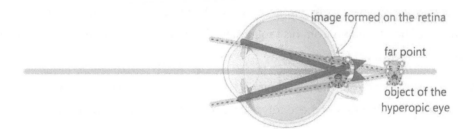

Figure 6-60: The image formed by the plus lens is now the object, located at the far point of the hyperopic eye. The resultant image is formed sharply on the retina.

In simple words, to correct hyperopia, we need to increase the optical power of the eye by the amount that corresponds to the degree of hyperopia. For example, to correct a +2.00 hyperopia, we need a converging lens of +2.00 D.

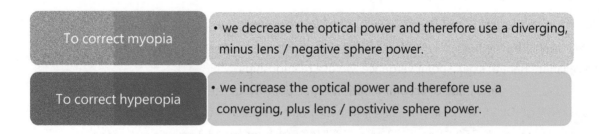

To correct myopia	• we decrease the optical power and therefore use a diverging, minus lens / negative sphere power.
To correct hyperopia	• we increase the optical power and therefore use a converging, plus lens / postivive sphere power.

6.6.3   The Challenge of Hyperopia Correction

A clinical distinction between correcting myopia and correcting hyperopia is that accommodation plays an important role in determining the hyperopia prescription (see § 7.1 and § 7.2 for the definitions and examples of calculating accommodative demand). The reason is that, in hyperopia, accommodation can mask the refractive error. The amount of available accommodation can be clinically measured, so we can determine whether all or part of the hyperopia should be corrected; for example, manifest refraction may indicate +4.00 D, but the prescription (noted as Rx) may be +2.00 D.

Often, individuals with latent hyperopia do not tolerate the full hyperopic correction indicated under cycloplegia. Young children, generally, need only a short period of adaptation to tolerate their hyperopic correction. When there is intolerance to full or partial correction, as in the case of latent hyperopia, the prescription may be used only for near vision.[665] Individuals with absolute hyperopia are more likely to accept the full correction because accommodation does not mask the refractive error, so the correction brings improvement in visual acuity.

Example ☞: Gustavo, a 25-year-old hyperope, has total hyperopia of +3.00 D. He complains of headaches during his daily routine of reading from his tablet, held 25 cm away. He has an accommodative amplitude of 9.00 D. Does he need spectacle correction?

The accommodative demand for distance/infinity is (+3.00 D) – (0.00 D) = +3.00 D, which is well within the available amplitude. Thus, there is no need for distance correction; 3.00 D can be easily drawn out of 9.00 D.

The accommodative demand for near vision (for example, fixation point at 25 cm) is (+3.00 D) – (–4.00 D) = +7.00 D. Therefore, reading at 25 cm requires 7.00 D of accommodation. This nearly 80% demand (7/9) may not be sustainable; Gustavo needs a spectacle prescription to alleviate this accommodative response.

Example ☞: Renato, a 30-year-old hyperope, has an accommodative amplitude of 9.00 D. Retinoscopy reveals that Renato's correction should be +3.50 D. However, he is fitted with an Rx = +2.00 D. What is his far point and what is his near point using this Rx?

Renato is an effective (+3.50 D) – (2.00 D) = +1.50 D hyperope, so his far point has a vergence of +1.50 D, meaning that the far point is located 1/1.50 D = +0.66 m = +66.6 cm to the right of (behind) the eye. To calculate Renato's near-point vergence, we use relationship (7.2):

Amplitude of accommodation = (far-point vergence) – (near-point vergence).

9.00 D = (1.50 D) – (near-point vergence), so near-point vergence = (1.50 D) – (9.00 D) = –7.50 D. The near point is 1/(–7.50 D) = –0.133 m = –13.3 cm, which means 13.3 cm in front of the eye.

---

[665] Silbert JA, Alexander A. Cyclotherapy in the treatment of symptomatic latent hyperopia. J Am Optom Assoc. 1987; 58(1):40-6.

What if the individual were a myope?

Example ☞: Silvano, a 30-year-old myope, has an accommodative amplitude of 9.00 D. His myopia is –3.50 D, but he is fitted with an Rx = –2.00 D. What is his far point and what is his near point using this Rx?

Effectively, Silvano is a (–3.50 D) – (–2.00 D) = –1.50 D myope. The far point has –1.50 D vergence using this Rx. Therefore, the far point is located 1/(–1.50 D) = –0.667 m = –66.7 cm to the left (in front) of the eye.

To calculate Silvano's near-point vergence, we use relationship (7.2):

Amplitude of accommodation = (far point vergence) – (near point vergence).

9.00 D = (–1.50 D) – (near point vergence), so near-point vergence = (–1.50 D) – (9.00 D) = –10.50 D. The near point is 1/(–10.50 D) = –0.095 m = –9.5 cm, which means 9.5 cm in front of the eye.

6.6.4 The Correction of Aphakia

Aphakia (α- none, -phakia, $\varphi\alpha\kappa\acute{o}\varsigma$, the lens) is a condition in which the crystalline lens is absent. This absence can be due to surgical removal, a perforating wound or ulcer, or congenital anomaly. Even as late as the 1970s, cataract surgery often involved only lens extraction and was not customarily followed by an IOL implantation. Individuals with no crystalline (or substitute) lens in their eye are aphakic.

Aphakia significantly alters the optical properties (refraction) of the eye, mainly due to optical power deficiency, which now depends solely on the corneal power. An individual who becomes aphakic will most likely be an extreme hyperope. Several optical changes are associated with the absence of the crystalline lens, including a significant shift in the cardinal points, whose locations now collapse to one point for the principal point (at the corneal vertex) and one point for the nodal point (at the corneal center of curvature). The reduced optical power also means a longer focal length; the anterior focal point is now about 24 mm in front of the eye.

Correction of the aphakic eye requires a very strong plus corrective lens, often more than +10.00 D, depending on the placement of the lens with respect to the corneal plane and the refraction of the eye before extraction of the crystalline lens. The correction obtained with such spectacles is far from ideal.[666] The large dioptric correction also leads to significant retinal image magnification (by about 25%) and a reduced visual field through the lens. Lastly, the absence of the crystalline lens reduces the capacity of the eye to absorb harmful ultraviolet radiation.

---

[666] Kaufman HE. The correction of aphakia: XXXVI Edward Jackson memorial lecture. Am J Ophthalmol. 1980; 89(1):1-10.

Refractive power	• Reduced by about 20 D.
Focal points	• Posterior focal point is farther behind the retina (by about 10 mm). Anterior focal point is farther out from the cornea (about 24 mm instead of 16.6 mm).
Principal points	• Collapse to a single point at the vertex of the cornea.
Nodal points	• Collapse to a single point close to the center of curvature of the cornea (about 7.7 mm to the right of the vertex).

6.6.5 Knapp's Rule

Consider a spectacle lens placed 16 to 17 mm in front of the eye, i.e., near the primary (anterior) focal length of the eye. With the lens at this location, the total optical power (hence, the focal length) of the system 'Eye + Corrective lens' does not change. To prove this, we use Gullstrand's relationship (§ 1.4.2) for the system 'Eye + Corrective lens,' where in place of d we insert f_{eye}:

$$F_{corrected\ eye} = F_{lens} + F_{uncor\ eye} - \frac{f_{uncor\ eye}}{1} F_{lens} \cdot F_{uncor\ eye} = F_{lens} + F_{uncor\ eye} - F_{lens} = F_{uncor\ eye} \quad (6.10)$$

This relationship proves that the optical power of the system remains the same. The argument can also be understood by using ray tracing: The ray directed at the front focal point of the eye (Figure 6-61) simultaneously passes through the center of the corrective lens, which is exactly at that location. Thus, the ray proceeds undeviated to the eye.

Since the ray crosses the focal point of the eye, it is refracted by the eye at the principal plane and proceeds parallel to the optical axis. Thus, it does not follow a different path because of the corrective lens. As the optical power remains unchanged, the magnification is unaffected, too. The only difference is <u>a shift in the image position</u> to its proper place, which is on the retina.

This shift in image position means that, when a different correction for each eye is required, differing image transverse magnifications are mitigated. The placement of the corrective lens at the primary focal point for the correction of axial ametropia is known as **Knapp's rule**, named after the German-American ophthalmologist and otolaryngologist, Jacob Hermann Knapp, who first introduced it in 1869.[667]

---

[667] Knapp H. The influence of spectacles on the optical constants and visual acuteness of the eye. Archives of Ophthalmology and Otology. 1869; 1:377-410.

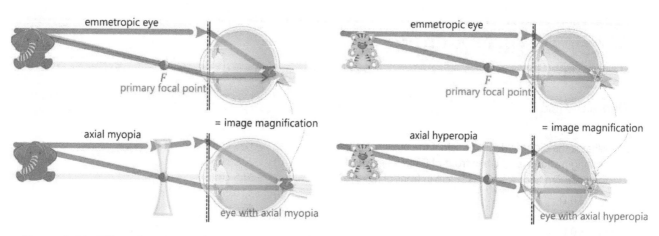

Figure 6-61: When the correction is implemented at the position of the front focal point of the eye, there is no change in retinal image size. (left) Axial myopia and (right) axial hyperopia.

The practical problems with Knapp's rule are that ametropia is rarely purely axial and the distance of 15–17 mm is not practical for the placement of corrective lenses.

There are also neurophysiological issues due to **retinal stretching** (§ 4.5.2).[410] Even if the retinal images are of equal size, retinal cone sampling may lead to a different perception. In axial myopia, the reduced cone density due to a stretched retina means that fewer cone receptors are being stimulated for the same corrected retinal image size; thence, the object appears smaller. In axial hyperopia, the compressed retina due to the smaller globe has more stimulated cone receptors for the same corrected retinal image size; thence, the object appears larger.

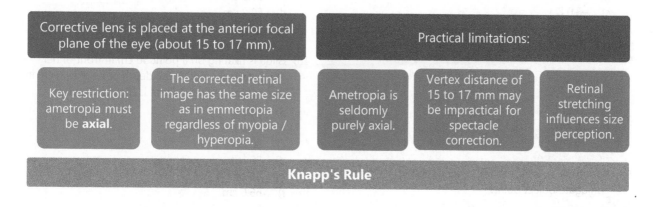

Knapp's rule is applicable in **anisometropia**. To reduce aniseikonia, if there is axial anisometropia (either myopia or hyperopia), the correction should be applied with spectacle lenses close to 15 mm. In the case of refractive ametropia, proper correction is applied close to the principal plane (correction with contact lenses is the closest we can do), so that the power of the system is as close as possible to that of an emmetropic eye.

6.7 AMETROPIA QUIZ

Depth of Field

1) What is the dioptric depth of field if the proximal limiting position is 20 cm in front of Daniéli's eye and the distal limiting position is 50 cm in front of her eye?

   a) 2.0 D
   b) 2.5 D
   c) 3.0 D
   d) 5.0 D
   e) 8.0 D

2) The conjugate object point (two correct) ...

   a) focuses exactly on the retina
   b) provides the same retinal quality as optical infinity
   c) produces a real image with half the resolution of the proximal point
   d) produces a virtual image with the same resolution as the distal point
   e) is dioptrically located halfway between the proximal point and the distal point

3) Back to Q 1. What is the vergence of the conjugate object point?

   a) −2.0 D
   b) −2.5 D
   c) −3.0 D
   d) −3.5 D

4) Back to Q 1. What is the linear depth of field?

   a) 20 cm
   b) 28 cm
   c) 30 cm
   d) 50 cm
   e) 70 cm

5) Back to Q 1. Where is the location of the conjugate object point?

   a) −20 cm
   b) −28 cm
   c) −30 cm
   d) −50 cm
   e) −70 cm

6) If the dioptric depth of field of Giorgio's eye is ±3.0 D and the conjugate point vergence is −5.0 D, where is the distal point?

   a) −12.5 cm
   b) −20.0 cm
   c) −37.5 cm
   d) −50.0 cm
   e) −62.5 cm

7) Back to Q 6. Where is the proximal point?

   a) −12.5 cm
   b) −20.0 cm
   c) −37.5 cm
   d) −50.0 cm
   e) −62.5 cm

8) Back to Q 6. Where is the conjugate point?

   a) −12.5 cm
   b) −20.0 cm
   c) −37.5 cm
   d) −50.0 cm
   e) −62.5 cm

9) Back to Q 6. What is the linear depth of field?

   a) 12.5 cm
   b) 20.0 cm
   c) 37.5 cm
   d) 50.0 cm
   e) 62.5 cm

10) Gilda is fixating on a point 50 cm in front of her. The proximal point of the depth of field is 40 cm in front of the object. Where is the distal point?

   a) 10 cm
   b) 26.6 cm
   c) 30 cm
   d) 50 cm
   e) 60 cm
   f) 66.6 cm

11) Back to Q 10. What is the linear depth of field?

   a) 10 cm
   b) 26.6 cm
   c) 30 cm
   d) 50 cm
   e) 50 cm
   f) 66.6 cm

12) Back to Q 10. What is the dioptric depth of field?

a) ±0.5 D
b) ±1.0 D
c) ±1.5 D
d) ±2.0 D

13) Back to Q 10. As Gilda is fixating on a point 50 cm away, her pupil constricts. The following changes will occur (two correct answers):

a) the conjugate point moves closer to the eye
b) the distal point moves closer to the eye
c) the proximal point moves closer to the eye

d) the conjugate point moves away from the eye
e) the distal point moves away from the eye
f) the proximal point moves away from the eye

14) Back to Q 13. The most likely dioptric depth of field would be ...

a) ±0.15 D
b) ±0.25 D
c) ±0.5 D
d) ±1.0 D

Emmetropia

In the following questions, V is vertex, P' is principal point, N' is nodal point, F' is focal point, f' is focal length, and $'$ indicates image space. The refractive index of the eye is $n'=1.336$.

15) In an emmetropic eye, the axial length _____ the focal length.

a) equals
b) is slightly longer (by the amount VP') than
c) is slightly shorter (by the amount VP') than
d) is slightly longer, by the amount VN') than

16) In an emmetropic eye, the axial length and the focal length share the same ...

a) endpoint F'
b) origin V
c) endpoint N'
d) origin P'

17) In an emmetropic eye with optical power 62.0 D, the focal length f' is ...

a) 16.13 mm
b) 17.00 mm
c) 21.55 mm
d) 23.15 mm

18) In an emmetropic eye with optical power 62.0 D, the axial length is ...

a) 16.13 mm
b) 17.00 mm
c) 21.55 mm
d) 23.15 mm

19) Which of the following illustrations properly identifies the axial length and the focal length in an emmetropic eye?

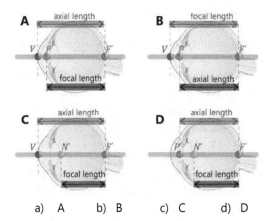

a) A   b) B   c) C   d) D

20) Which of the following illustrations properly shows the inverted image perception in an emmetropic eye?

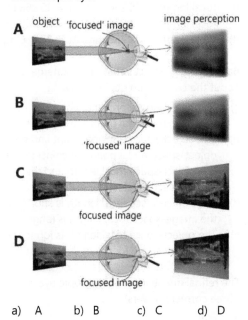

a) A   b) B   c) C   d) D

21) In a relaxed emmetropic eye, the optically conjugate point of the retina is (two answers) ...

   a) the far point of the eye
   b) the near point of the eye
   c) the front (primary) focal point of the eye
   d) infinity
   e) the posterior (secondary) focal point of the eye

22) In a relaxed emmetropic eye, the optically conjugate point of infinity is the (two answers) ...

   a) retina
   b) near point of the eye
   c) front (primary) focal point of the eye
   d) posterior (secondary) focal point of the eye
   e) principal point of the eye
   f) far point of the eye

23) The average optical power of the eye is about 60.0 D. The refractive index of the aqueous is 1.336, while the refractive index of air is 1.0. This means that the focal length (two answers) ...

   a) inside the eye is the reciprocal of 60.0 D
   b) inside the eye is the reciprocal of 60.0 D multiplied by the aqueous refractive index
   c) outside the eye is the reciprocal of 60.0 D
   d) outside the eye is the reciprocal of 60.0 D multiplied by the aqueous refractive index

24) Back to Q 23. What are the approximate focal length and axial length (AL) of this eye, if it is emmetropic?

   a) focal length = 16.66 mm, AL = 18.266 mm
   b) focal length = 18.266 mm, AL = 19.866 mm
   c) focal length = 23.866 mm, AL = 22.266 mm
   d) focal length = 22.266 mm, AL = 23.866 mm

25) Back to Q 23. Select two correct statements about the cardinal points in the eye ...

   a) The object-space principal point and the object-space nodal point are separate.
   b) The object-space principal point and the object-space nodal point are coincidental.
   c) The object-space focal length and the image-space focal length are equal.
   d) The object-space focal length is shorter, and the image-space focal length is longer.
   e) The object-space focal length is longer, and the image-space focal length is shorter.

26) The retinal image in an emmetropic eye is ... (three correct answers)

   a) real

   b) virtual
   c) inverted
   d) magnified
   e) minified
   f) erect

27) The retinal image size in emmetropia is proportional to ...

   a) the angle ϑ subtended by the object from the nodal point
   b) the nodal point separation from the vertex
   c) the power of the eye
   d) the focal length of the eye

28) An object subtends an angle $\vartheta = 0.05$ rad from the nodal point of the eye. Its retinal image size in an emmetropic eye is ...

   a) 0.05 mm
   b) 0.85 mm
   c) 1.7 mm
   d) 3.4 mm

29) Which of these objects forms the largest retinal image?

   a) the full moon, which subtends 30 arcmin
   b) two fingers at arm's length, which subtend 2°
   c) a 2-cm-long thimble held 0.40 m from the eye
   d) a 2-m-tall man, standing 100 m away

30) In exoplanet X, the emmetropic eye of our ET friend is such that the image-space nodal point N' is 8.5 mm from the posterior pole. Compared to Earthlings, the retinal image in the ET eye for the same object at the same distance is ...

   a) half as long
   b) identical in length
   c) twice as long
   d) eight and a half times as long

31) An object forms a 0.3-mm-long retinal image in Giovanna's emmetropic eye. This means that the object subtends an angle from the eye of about ...

   a) 1 rad
   b) 0.1 rad
   c) 0.01 rad
   d) 1°
   e) 0.1°
   f) 0.01°

32) The size of the retinal image formed by a logMAR 0.00 optotype (subtending a 5 arcmin angle) in an emmetropic eye is ...

   a) 5 μm

b) 25 μm
c) 0.25 mm
d) 0.5 mm

33) In a duochrome test endpoint on an emmetropic eye, _____ exactly on the retina.

a) only the red focuses
b) only the green focuses
c) both the green and the red focus

Myopia - Hyperopia

35) The far point in hyperopia is situated ...

a) at infinity
b) some distance in front of the eye
c) some distance behind the eye
d) There is no far point in hyperopia.

36) The farthest a relaxed eye can read a newspaper is 50 cm in front of the eye. This is an eye with ...

a) −5.00 myopia
b) −2.00 myopia
c) +5.00 hyperopia
d) +2.00 hyperopia

37) The greatest distance at which a relaxed eye can read text on a tablet is 20 cm. This is an eye with ...

a) −5.00 myopia
b) −2.00 myopia
c) +5.00 hyperopia
d) +2.00 hyperopia

38) The far point of an eye is 100 cm in front of the eye. This indicates ...

a) myopia (−10.00)
b) myopia (−1.00)
c) myopia (−0.10)
d) emmetropia
e) hyperopia (+1.00)

39) The far point of an eye is 25 cm in front of the eye. This indicates ...

a) myopia (−4.00)
b) myopia (−2.50)
c) myopia (−0.50)
d) emmetropia
e) hyperopia (+4.00)

40) Il Conte Ceprano, a −2.00 myope, has a 2-mm pupil diameter. Marullo, also with −2.00 myopia, has a 6-

d) neither the green nor the red focuses

34) When performing the duochrome test on an emmetropic eye, usually the (select two) ...

a) red focuses slightly behind the retina
b) red focuses slightly before the retina
c) green focuses slightly behind the retina
d) green focuses slightly before the retina

mm pupil diameter. If neither wears correction, which is true regarding an eye chart examination?

a) Ceprano has a better chance of reading more lines.
b) Marullo has a better chance of reading more lines.
c) Each has an equal chance of reading the same number of lines.
d) Neither is able to read any line.

41) Stiffelio, a −6.00 myope, has a 2-mm pupil diameter. Lina, also with −6.00 myopia, has a 6 mm pupil diameter. If neither wears correction, what is true regarding an eye chart examination?

a) Stiffelio has a better chance of reading more lines.
b) Lina has a better chance of reading more lines.
c) Each has an equal chance of reading the same number of lines.
d) Neither is able to read any line.

42) Henri, a young Siciliano, has uncorrected distance visual acuity of 20/80. With a subsequent pinhole exam of the same eye, his visual acuity should ...

a) remain the same
b) improve
c) worsen
d) Io non parlo italiano

43) Ninette, a young cameriera, was measured with uncorrected distance visual acuity logMAR = −0.15. We then proceed with a pinhole examination of the same eye. Ninette's visual acuity is expected to ...

a) definitely increase
b) most likely increase
c) most likely not increase
d) definitely not increase

44) In an uncorrected myopic eye, visual acuity improves using a pinhole occluder because the pinhole ...

a) increases diffraction effects, thereby reducing resolution

b) increases depth of field, thereby improving the range of perceptual tolerance
c) decreases aberrations, thereby improving retinal image geometrical blur
d) eliminates refractive errors

45) In a diffraction-limited emmetropic eye with a pinhole occluder, visual acuity does not improve (and perhaps decreases) because the pinhole ...
   a) increases diffraction effects, thereby reducing resolution
   b) increases depth of field, thereby improving the range of perceptual tolerance
   c) decreases aberrations, thereby improving blur detection
   d) eliminates refractive errors

46) When performing the duochrome test in a myopic eye, it is expected that (worse = farther than) ...
   a) red focuses before the retina, worse than green
   b) green focuses before the retina, worse than red
   c) green and red straddle the retina equally
   d) red focuses after the retina, worse than green
   e) green focuses after the retina, worse than red

47) When performing the duochrome test in a −0.25 D myopic eye, which part focuses sharply on the retina?
   a) red
   b) green
   c) neither, both focus in front
   d) neither, both focus behind

48) When performing the duochrome test in a hyperopic eye, it is expected that (two correct) ...
   a) red focuses before the retina
   b) green focuses before the retina
   c) red focuses after the retina
   d) green focuses after the retina

49) When performing the duochrome test in a hyperopic eye, usually the ...
   a) red focuses closer to the retina than the green
   b) green focuses closer to the retina than the red
   c) green focuses behind the retina; red in front
   d) red focuses behind the retina; green in front

50) Which of the following cases is expected to have (on average) the greatest corneal power?
   a) refractive myopia
   b) axial myopia
   c) emmetropia
   d) refractive hyperopia

e) axial hyperopia

51) Which of the following cases is expected to have (on average) the longest axial length?
   a) refractive myopia
   b) axial myopia
   c) emmetropia
   d) refractive hyperopia
   e) axial hyperopia

52) Dottore Grenvil's cycloplegic examination measures +2.25 D hyperopia, while subjective noncycloplegic refraction measures +1.50 D. What is the amount of latent hyperopia?
   a) 3.75 D
   b) 2.25 D
   c) 1.50 D
   d) 0.75 D

53) Matteo Borsa's myopic eye has power 66.0 D. The focal length f' is ...
   a) 15.15 mm
   b) 18.64 mm
   c) 20.24 mm
   d) 21.84 mm

54) Back to Q 53. Borsa's eye axial length is ...
   a) less than 15.15 mm
   b) equal to 18.64 mm
   c) equal to 20.24 mm
   d) more than 21.84 mm

55) Raffaele's hyperopic eye has power 58.0 D. The focal length f' is ...
   a) 24.63 mm
   b) 23.03 mm
   c) 21.43 mm
   d) 17.24 mm

56) Back to Q 55. Raffaele's eye axial length is ...
   a) less than 24.63 mm
   b) equal to 23.03 mm
   c) equal to 21.43 mm
   d) slightly more than 17.24 mm

57) For the cardinal points in a 60.0 D eye with axial myopia, compared to a 60.0 D emmetropic eye, ...
   a) all locations remain identical
   b) principal point P' shifts to the right
   c) focal point F' shifts to the left
   d) nodal point N' shifts to the right

58) In a 60.0 D eye with axial hyperopia, the following occurs regarding the image-space focal point F' compared to an emmetropic eye of 60.0 D:
   a) It shifts to the right.
   b) It has no change in location.
   c) It shifts to the left.
   d) It remains on the retina.

59) In a 58.0 D eye with refractive hyperopia, the following occurs regarding the image-space focal point F' compared to an emmetropic eye of 60.0 D:
   a) It shifts behind the eye, to the right.
   b) It has no change in location.
   c) It shifts in front of the retina.
   d) It remains on the retina.

60) For the cardinal points in a 64.0 D eye with refractive myopia compared to a 60.0 D emmetropic eye, ...
   a) all locations remain identical
   b) principal point P' shifts to the right
   c) focal point F' shifts to the left
   d) nodal point N' shifts to the right

61) Which eye most likely has axial myopia?
   a) power 56.0 D, axial length 24 mm
   b) power 56.0 D, axial length 26 mm
   c) power 60.0 D, axial length 24 mm
   d) power 60.0 D, axial length 26 mm
   e) power 64.0 D, axial length 24 mm

62) Which eye most likely has refractive hyperopia?
   a) power 56.0 D, axial length 24 mm
   b) power 56.0 D, axial length 26 mm
   c) power 60.0 D, axial length 24 mm
   d) power 60.0 D, axial length 26 mm
   e) power 64.0 D, axial length 24 mm

63) If an eye with a 24 mm axial length and 60.0 D power is emmetropic, an eye with the 'same' 60.0 D power but with 26 mm axial length is most likely ...
   a) +2.00 hyperopic
   b) −2.00 myopic
   c) −3.00 myopic
   d) −6.00 myopic

64) If an eye with 24 mm axial length and 60.0 D power is emmetropic, an eye with the 'same' 24 mm axial length but with 58.0 D power is most likely ...
   a) +4.00 hyperopic
   b) +2.00 hyperopic
   c) −2.00 myopic
   d) −4.00 myopic

65) In which spherical error is the largest retinal image encountered, compared to emmetropia?
   a) axial myopia
   b) refractive myopia
   c) axial hyperopia
   d) refractive hyperopia

66) The size of the retinal image in myopia compared to the conjugate image formed in front of the retina, is ...
   a) similar in size
   b) slightly larger due to geometric blur
   c) slightly smaller due to diffraction
   d) slightly larger due to depth of field

67) In correcting ametropia with a spectacle (or contact) lens, the working principle is that the lens' ...
   a) primary focal point F coincides with the far point of the eye
   b) secondary focal point F' coincides with the far point of the eye
   c) primary focal length equals the axial length of the eye
   d) secondary focal length equals the axial length of the eye

68) The following are conjugate pairs in a corrected eye with spectacle lens (two correct answers):
   a) infinity and secondary focal point of the lens
   b) far point of the eye and retina
   c) infinity and primary focal point of the lens
   d) secondary focal point of the eye and retina

69) In a myopic eye wearing a minus spectacle lens, the object of the myopic eye is a (two correct) ...
   a) virtual image created by the lens
   b) real image created by the lens
   c) real object for the eye
   d) virtual object for the eye

70) In a hyperopic eye wearing a plus lens, the object of the hyperopic eye is a (two correct) ...
   a) virtual image created by the lens
   b) real image created by the lens
   c) real object for the eye
   d) virtual object for the eye

71) In a −1.00 myopic eye, we fit a +1.00 D trial frame lens. This 'eye + lens' system is ...
   a) myopic −1.00
   b) myopic −2.00
   c) emmetropic

d) hyperopic +1.00
e) hyperopic +2.00

72) A –2.00 D lens is placed in front of Donna Leonora's emmetropic eye. This 'eye + lens' system becomes …

a) myopic –1.00
b) myopic –2.00
c) emmetropic
d) hyperopic +1.00
e) hyperopic +2.00

73) Which of the following eyes has the largest myopia?

a) far point –1.00 m
b) far point –10 cm
c) far point +10 cm
d) far point +100 m

74) We place a –5.00 D lens 15 mm in front of Don Alvaro's +66.66 D myopic eye. What is the power of the system (eye + lens)? (Use Gullstrand's formula.)

a) –5.00 D
b) +61.66 D
c) +66.66 D
d) +71.66 D

75) Violetta Valéry's –3.00 D myopic eye is fitted with a –1.00 Rx lens. What is her far point wearing this lens?

a) –0.25 m
b) –0.33 m
c) –0.50 m
d) –1.00 m

76) If a diffraction-limited eye has a depth of focus of 1.00 D with a pupil diameter of 2.00 mm, what is the ideal depth of focus when the pupil dilates to 4.00 mm?

a) 2.00 D
b) 1.00 D
c) 0.25 D
d) 0.125 D

77) Gastone de Letorières has –4.00 D of myopia. What is the finest line he can read on an ETDRS eye chart under normal examination conditions?

a) no line at all
b) the 1.0 logMAR line
c) the 0.4 logMAR line
d) the –0.4 logMAR line

78) Back to Q 77. What can we do to improve Gastone's chances of reading the top line?

a) fit him with a +4.00 lens
b) dilate his pupil
c) place a red color filter in front of his eye
d) use a pinhole occluder

79) Giorgio has +0.50 hyperopia. He has never worn glasses, nor has he ever complained of vision problems. This is because he is (two correct) …

a) a physicist who thinks he knows best
b) a latent hyperope
c) compensating using the toricity of his cornea
d) too busy to go for a proper eye exam

80) Giorgio's daughter, upon enrolling at Pentucket Regional Elementary, is found to be +1.00 hyperopic. Upon reaching high school, his daughter is expected to be …

a) magna cum laude valedictorian
b) a hyperope of about +2.00 D
c) an emmetrope
d) a myope of about –2.00 D

81) Usually, the degree of ametropia between the two eyes is about the same. The Duke of Mantua's right eye (OD) is +1.00 D, while his left eye (OS) is –2.00 D. What is his optical condition?

a) hypermyopia
b) anisometropia
c) anisomyopia
d) right-left anisocoria
e) anisohyperopia

82) What is the clinical effect associated with the Duke of Mantua's condition described in Q 81?

a) Knapp's rule
b) anisometropia
c) aniseikonia
d) facultative myopia

83) What is the difference between the two corrected retinal images in the Duke of Mantua's eyes?

a) size (retinal magnification)
b) orientation (one inverted, the other erect)
c) type (one real, the other virtual)
d) no difference at all

84) An aphakic eye is expected to be …

a) highly myopic
b) highly hyperopic
c) highly astigmatic
d) moderately myopic
e) moderately hyperopic

6.8 AMETROPIA SUMMARY

Vergence

Vergence L is an expression of the wavefront curvature. Its measure [D] is the reciprocal of the distance l required to converge.

o   in air: $L = 1/l$

o   in a medium with refractive index n: $L = n/l$ (reduced vergence)

For a collimated ray bundle, vergence is zero. If the beam converges, vergence is positive; if the beam diverges, vergence is negative.

Near and Far Points – Depth of Field

The far point is the farthest point at which an object must be placed in order for a sharp image to be formed on the retina. When fixating on the far point, the eye is 'relaxed,' or not accommodating; i.e. there is no increase in the optical power of the crystalline lens.

The near point is the closest point at which an object can be placed and still form a sharp image on the retina. To achieve this, the eye is accommodating at its largest capacity; i.e., the crystalline lens achieves its maximum optical power. These two limiting positions define the range of clear (or sharp) vision.

The depth of field (DoF) is the range along the optical axis between the proximal and the distal limiting positions for objects that can be simultaneously seen with the same perceived clarity, without a change in accommodation. The DoF is a subset of the range of clear vision. The dioptric DoF, reported in diopters, is the dioptric range between the limiting positions. The corresponding expanse in image space (inside the eye) is the depth of focus.

Emmetropia, Myopia, and Hyperopia

Emmetropia is the ideal refracting configuration of the eye whereby the image of a distant object is focused (formed sharply) on the retina. In emmetropia:

- The axial length of the eye has the 'perfect' measure for its refractive power. It is about equal to the focal length $(P'F')$ + 1.6 mm (vertex to principal point P').
- The retinal image size h' is about $= \vartheta \cdot (N'F') = \vartheta[\text{rad}] \cdot 17 \, [\text{mm}]$, where ϑ is the angle subtended by the extended object from the eye.
- The far point is at infinity.

Myopia is the refractive configuration of the eye whereby the image of a distant object is focused before the retina. In myopia:

- The axial length of the eye is too long for its refractive power; equivalently, the eye has too much optical power for its axial length.
- The (uncorrected) retinal image size h' is larger than that of an emmetropic eye (notably larger in axial myopia).
- The far point is in front of the eye (negative far-point distance).
- The degree of myopia is the far-point vergence, i.e., 1/far-point distance.

Hyperopia is the refractive configuration of the eye whereby the image of a distant object is (to be) focused after the retina. In hyperopia:

- The axial length of the eye is too short for its refractive power; equivalently, the eye has insufficient optical power for its axial length.
- The (uncorrected) retinal image size h' is smaller than that of an emmetropic eye (notably larger in axial hyperopia).
- The far point is after (behind) the eye (positive far-point distance).
- The degree of hyperopia is the far-point vergence, i.e., 1/far-point distance.

$$\text{degree of spherical error (myopia/hyperopia)} = \text{far-point vergence [D]} = \frac{1}{\text{far-point distance [m]}}$$

Myopia and hyperopia are collectively referred to as spherical error. Myopia and hyperopia can be either axial (longer/shorter axial length) or refractive (excess/insufficient refractive power). Approximately, 1 mm of mismatch between the ideal axial length (emmetropic) and the actual axial length leads to about 3.0 D of spherical error (a shorter axial length indicates hyperopia; a longer axial length indicates myopia).

Spectacle Correction

Spectacle correction of spherical error is achieved with a lens whose secondary focal point is placed at the far point of the eye; thus, the sphere power of the corrective lens is the far-point vergence of the eye.

A special type of correction, applicable to axial ametropia, places the corrective lens at the anterior (primary) focal point of the eye. Then, the corrected retinal image has the same size as in emmetropia, regardless of the degree of myopia or hyperopia (Knapp's rule).

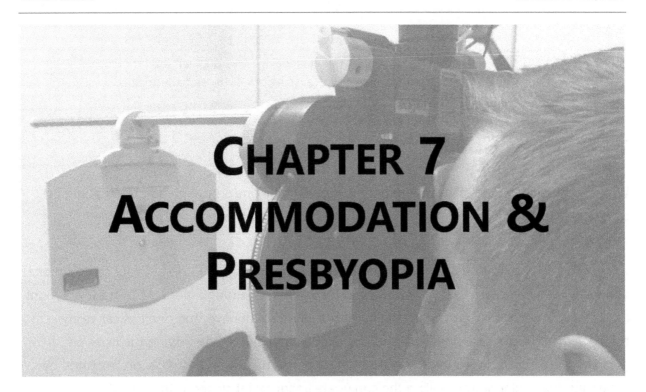

CHAPTER 7
ACCOMMODATION &
PRESBYOPIA

7.1 THE NATURE OF ACCOMMODATION

7.1.1 The Need to Adapt to Shorter Distances

Naturally, the eye is set to observe objects at far distances; the emmetropic eye has the optical power to form a sharp retinal image from an object situated at a far distance, which, in the optics of the eye, refers to any location 6 m or more away. On the other hand, when we are reading, writing, or texting, the objects are not at a far distance but instead are close, at a short distance, usually at arm's length. The closest distance to which an object can be brought and still be optically conjugate to the retina is the **near point** (§ 6.1.3). A typical value for the near point is 25 cm, although it varies significantly with age, status of eye ametropia, and other factors.

To bring close objects into focus, the eye needs **accommodation**, defined as the ability of the eye to make the retina optically conjugate to a range of target distances.[668] When the object is located at the near point, accommodation is maximum. When the object is located at the **far point** (§ 6.1.3), accommodation is zero, and the state of the eye is called **relaxed**, unaccommodated, or disaccommodated.

---

[668] Duke-Elder S, Abrams D. System of Ophthalmology. in: Ophthalmic Optics and Refraction, S. Duke-Elder, ed. Henry Kimpton, London, 1970. Vol. V:156-7.

The eye obeys the laws of optics:	• It cannot simultaneously focus on near and far objects. • It needs to increase its power to see near objects.

7.1.2 Accommodation Theories

Whatever the mechanism of accommodation, it must fulfill one critical parameter, that it must be reversible; the adjustment should be easily and effectively reverted such that targets at varying distances are clearly, easily, and rapidly seen.

Perhaps no other visual optics issue has received such a multitude of proposed solutions nor has given rise to such vastly contradicting theories as accommodation. All of these solutions involve two aspects: one structural, relating to the length of the eye, and one optical, relating to the power of the eye. Structurally, a solution can be implemented by varying the axial length (pushing the retina outward toward the conjugate point). Optically, it can be implemented by increasing the ocular power (pulling the conjugate image point closer to the retina).

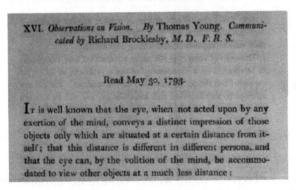

Figure 7-1: The introductory paragraph from Thomas Young's lecture at the Royal Society in 1793 mentioning accommodation.

The variation in the axial length can be either static, for example, in a retina that is tilted like a ramp, or dynamic, for example, in an eye that moves like an accordion. In the ramp retina, the upper portion may correspond to a longer axial length and the lower portion to a shorter axial length; then, a slight eye rotation can move the image to a retinal point that corresponds to a longer or shorter axial length. Ramp retina is seen in some fish, such as the stingray.[669] The dynamic accordion eye is found in the eel. A muscle that pulls back against the anterior sclera shortens the eye, thus moving the retina inward; when relaxed, this muscle allows the eye to elongate, thus moving the retina outward.

---

[669] Sivak JG. The accommodative significance of the "ramp" retina of the eye of the stingray. Vision Res. 1976; 16(9):945-50.

Optically, accommodation involves an increase in the ocular power to accomplish the task of bringing the image of the near point to the retina. In the example of Figure 7-2 (upper right), 64.0 D is not sufficient power to bring the near object into retinal focus. This eye needs more power, in the amount of optical vergence of the near object = 1/0.25 m = 4.0 D. Thus, an optical power of 64.0 + 4.0 = 68.0 D (lower right) can form the sharp image on the retina.

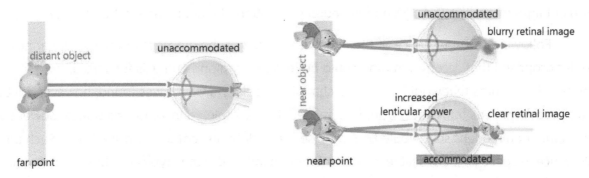

Figure 7-2: The eye accommodates by bringing the conjugate image to the retina (the case shown corresponds to an emmetropic eye).

Considering that the eye is a complex optical system, ocular power can be increased by increasing corneal power (by steepening the cornea curvature or increasing the refractive index of the cornea); increasing lenticular power (by steepening the lens curvature or increasing the refractive index of the lens); and reducing the separation (spacing d) between the cornea and the lens. If the lens is closer to the cornea, the ocular power increases (examples of how this spacing affects ocular power are presented in § 2.3.2 using the Gullstrand relationship).

Bringing the image of the near object onto the retina does not necessarily require an increase in optical power (see pseudoaccommodation § 7.3.3). An increase in the depth of field, such as when the pupil contracts, does the task. As the Swiss anatomist Albrecht von Haller and Christoph Scheiner[1] observed, pupil size (diameter) decreases when an object is brought closer; the smaller pupil increases both the depth of field (§ 6.1.4) and its image-space counterpart, the depth of focus, which now reaches the retina. Geometrically, the smaller pupil reduces the blur away from the conjugate image point; now the less blurry retinal image can be acceptably perceived, allowing acceptable vision over a larger range of object locations.

With so many ways to achieve accommodation, <u>which one has been adopted</u>? Over time, all of the described mechanisms have been used in attempts to explain how accommodation works, some rising to prevalence during their respective periods. Some are not at all practical; for example, we cannot modulate (increase) the refractive index of the cornea or the lens in a controlled and reversible manner that can be implemented sufficiently fast when the gaze shifts from far to near, and vice versa. Some historical hindsight can help to explain why and how these theories emerged.

The very term 'accommodation' was introduced in 1738 by William Porterfield[670] and was re-iterated by Albertus Burow in 1841.[671] Porterfield, an authority on vision, devised the first optometer and examined accommodation after cataract surgery operations.[672] According to Porterfield, *'our eyes change their conformation, and accommodate themselves to the various distances of objects'*. The word 'adaptation' was previously used to describe accommodation; currently, this word is used to describe changes in retinal sensitivity in response to varying ambient light intensities (§ 4.3.3), and in neural perception, the neural adaptation to blur.

Following the emergence of the initial description of the dioptrics of the eye, Johannes Kepler proposed that accommodation could be realized by along-the-axis forward and backward lens shifts that would result in a change in ocular power. It was found, however, that a much-too-large lens translation would be needed; for example, to increase the optical power by 4.0 D, the required lens shift would be 6 mm (see, e.g., data presented in Figure 2-36). Such an allowance in space is not available, as the anterior chamber depth is typically about 3 to 4 mm.

Some accommodation theories that appeared to emerge as plausible around the turn of the 19th century include accommodation by an 'expandable' eye (the expansion being initiated by extraocular muscle contraction), as proposed by Jacques Sturm,[673] and accommodation by increased corneal power through a corneal bulging, as proposed by Everald Home.[674]

7.1.3 Variable Lenticular Power

The prevailing theory states that it is the increase in lenticular power that brings about the required power for accommodation. This theory was presented by Thomas Young[675] in his landmark dissertation entitled *Observations on Vision*, which earned him Fellowship of the Royal Society of London.[676] In his dissertation, presented in 1791, Thomas Young demonstrated and explained that it is the lens that provides the necessary increase in ocular power by changing to a more curved shape.[677] Thomas Young was not the first to propose this theory; others had either speculated or proposed similar theories. These include René Descartes in his *'Traité de*

[670] Porterfield W. An essay concerning the motions of our eyes: Part 2. Of their internal motions. Edinburgh Medical Essays and Observations. 1738; 4:124-294.

[671] Burow A. Beiträge zur Physiologie und Physik des menschlichen Auges. Berlin. 1841 pp. 38

[672] Wade NJ. The Vision of William Porterfield. In: Whitaker H. Smith CUM, Finger S., eds. Brain, Mind and Medicine: Essays in Eighteenth-Century Neuroscience. 2007. Springer, Boston, MA doi: 10.1007/978-0-387-70967-3_12.

[673] Sturm JC. Dissertatio de Presbyopia et Myopia. Altdorfii. 1697.

[674] Home E. The Croonian lecture on muscular motion. Phil Trans R Soc Lond. 1795; 85:1-23. doi: 10.1098/rstl.1795.0002.

[675] Young T. The Bakerian Lecture. On the mechanism of the eye. Phil Trans R Soc Lond. 1801; 91:23-88. doi: 10.1098/rstl.1801.0004.

[676] Young T. Observations on Vision. Phil Trans R Soc Lond. 1793; 83:169-81. doi: 10.1098/rstl.1793.0017.

[677] Atchison DA, Charman WN. Thomas Young's contribution to visual optics: the Bakerian Lecture "on the mechanism of the eye." J Vis. 2010; 10(12):16,1-16.

l'Homme' in 1677 and anatomist John Hunter, who formed a similar theory of the changing power of the lens. According to Hunter, '...there is a power in the eye by which it can adapt itself to different distances far too extensive for the simple mechanism of the parts to effect.'

7.1.3.1 Optical Considerations

The lenticular optical power can be increased by an increase in the curvature (decrease in the radii of curvature) of its interfaces with the aqueous. Here is an example: Consider a biconvex lens of n_{lens} = 1.416 submerged in a medium with n_{ext} = 4/3 = 1.333. The anterior radius of curvature is r_1 = +10 mm, and the posterior radius of curvature is r_2 = –6 mm. The optical power of this lens is approximately the sum of the powers of the anterior and posterior interfaces:

$F_1 = (n_{lens} - n_{ext})/r_1 = (1.416 - 1.33)/(+0.010 \text{ m}) = +8.267 \text{ D}$ and

$F_2 = (n_{ext} - n_{lens})/r_2 = (1.33 - 1.416)/(-0.006 \text{ m}) = +13.77 \text{ D} \Rightarrow F = F_1 + F_2 = +22.04 \text{ D}.$

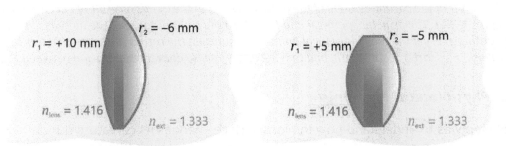

Figure 7-3: A biconvex lens simulating (left) relaxed and (right) accommodated lens curvatures.

The new radii of curvature are r_1 = +5 mm and r_2 = –5 mm. Now, the optical power is

$F_1 = (n_{lens} - n_{ext})/r_1 = (1.416 - 1.33)/(+0.005 \text{ m}) = +16.53 \text{ D}$ and

$F_2 = (n_{ext} - n_{lens})/r_2 = (1.33 - 1.416)/(-0.005 \text{ m}) = +16.53 \text{ D} \Rightarrow F = F_1 + F_2 = +33.066 \text{ D}.$

We realize that this specific lens can increase its power by about 11 D (from 8.33+13.8 = 22.10 D to 16.6+16.6 = 33.2 D) with a simple change of its shape.

In the human eye, accommodation is brought about by the combination of (a) an increase in the anterior lens surface curvature and (b) a shift of the anterior lens surface closer to the cornea. (The effects at the posterior lens surface are less change in curvature and a smaller shift toward and away from the cornea.) These effects reduce the separation between the focal points and the principal points of the eye, which leads to an increase in the optical power of the eye.

This mechanism is supported by ample clinical evidence; for example, Purkinje reflex images (§ 2.3.1) show that the lens anterior surface changes shape (curvature) during accommodation.[678, 679] Specifically, image P₃, formed by the anterior lens surface, becomes markedly smaller, and image P₄, formed by the posterior lens surface, becomes somewhat smaller. Images P₁ and P₂, formed by the anterior and the posterior cornea, respectively, do not change during accommodation, indicating no participation of corneal curvature in accommodation. Additionally, Scheimpflug imaging provides ample evidence of physiological lenticular changes during accommodation via an increase in lenticular curvature and thickness.[680]

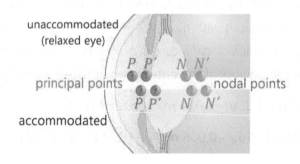

Figure 7-4: Shift of the cardinal points of the optical system of the eye as a result of accommodation. (See also Figure 1-27.) The principal points P and P' shift to the right because of the increased power in the accommodating eye, yet the secondary focal point F' remains on the retina (not shown in this figure). Thus, P'F' takes on a shorter focal length, and to a lesser degree, so does the separation between P' and N'.

7.1.3.2 Physiological Mechanism

The next step was to understand how the lens surface changes its curvature during accommodation. The first proposal came from Christoph Scheiner, who in 1619 stated that the ciliary processes are endowed with a certain movement capacity, through which the entire eye either extends or shortens such that the fluids themselves move the crystalline lens and the vitreous body forward and backward to slightly flatten the shape of the crystalline lens or make it more spherical. Scheiner observed not only a displacement of the lens but also an alteration in the shape of the lens for accommodation.[1] More than 200 years later, in the year 1855, the renowned German ophthalmologist Hermann Ludwig Ferdinand von Helmholtz[681, 682, 683] noted that, in the accommodated state, the curvature and the thickness of the lens both increase.

---

[678] Allen MJ. The stimulus to accommodation. Am J OptomArch Am Acad Optom. 1955; 32(8):422-31.

[679] Patnaik B. A photographic study of accommodative mechanisms: changes in the lens nucleus during accommodation. Invest Ophthalmol. 1967; 6(6):601-11.

[680] Rosales P, Dubbelman M, Marcos S, van der Heijde R. Crystalline lens radii of curvature from Purkinje and Scheimpflug imaging. J Vis. 2006; 6(10):1057-67.

[681] Helmholtz von HH. Ueber die Accommodation des Auges. Archiv für Ophthalmologie. 1855; 1(2):1-74.

[682] Helmholtz von HH. Mechanism of accommodation. In: Southall JPC, ed. Helmholtz's treatise on physiological optics. New York: Dover; 1909; 143-73.

[683] Glasser A. The Helmholtz mechanism of accommodation. In: Current Research in Eye Surgery Technology (CREST). K. Tsubota, BS. Boxer Wachler, DT. Azar, D. Koch, eds. Marcel Dekker, Inc., New York 2003; 27-47.

This proposed mechanism was refined by the English optical scientist[684] Edgard Frank Fincham,[685] who noted that during accommodation the lens thickens to a greater degree than the decrease in anterior chamber depth (ACD, § 2.3.2). This suggests that the anterior lens surface moves outward (closer to the cornea) and the posterior lens surface moves (by a smaller amount) in the opposite direction (away from the cornea). Further, the choroid moves forward and the *ora serrata* also moves forward (about 0.05 mm/D).

Helmholtz proposed that these changes are all commanded by contractions of the ciliary muscle, a ring-like muscle located in the vascular layer, whose tone is controlled cerebrally.

Before we state the repercussions of this muscle contracting or relaxing to bring about the physiological accommodation changes, let us recall that the lens is suspended by ligament fibers, the zonules of Zinn, which are attached to its circumferential equatorial edge (§ 2.2). This is not a simple 'suspension' in place, however. The lens is encapsulated (surrounded) by a highly elastic membrane, the capsule (capsular bag); the capsule (not the lens itself) is attached to and held under an outwardly oriented equatorial tension by the zonules. Thus, the lens passively fills the capsular bag like a viscous gel; any changes in the capsule bring about lens shape changes.

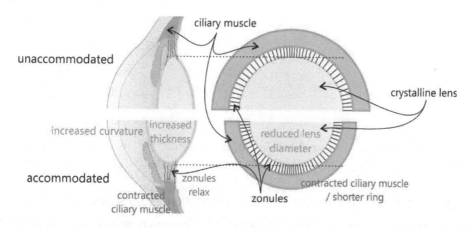

Figure 7-5: Change of curvature of the crystalline lens during accommodation.[686]

In the accommodated state, the ciliary muscle contracts, so the ciliary ring contracts and the lens equator moves inward. This reduces the outwardly oriented equatorial zonular tension. This causes an increase in the lens thickness and an increase in the curvature of the lenticular surface (mostly anterior). The lens becomes rounder, i.e., steeper, which means that its optical power increases.

---

[684] Dartnall HJ. Edgar Frank Fincham (1893-1963). Vision Res. 1964; 4(3):273-4.

[685] Fincham EF. The mechanism of accommodation. Br J Ophthalmol. 1937; VIII:7 80.

[686] Koretz JF, Handelman GH. How the human eye focuses. Sci Am. 1988; 259:92-9.

In the unaccommodated state, the ciliary muscle relaxes. This increases the zonular tension. Now the zonules pull the capsular bag like a spring, which causes the lens to become flatter,[687] resulting in a reduced curvature and a less optically powerful lens.

In an average eye, for an accommodative change of 8.00 D, the central lens thickness increases by about 0.5 mm (for example, from 3.5 to 4.0 mm), the lens diameter decreases by about 0.5 mm (from about 10.0 mm to 9.5 mm), and the lens shifts anteriorly by about 1.0 mm via a combination of thickening and ciliary muscle contraction. The most significant change, however, is the decrease in the radius of curvature (increase of curvature) of the anterior surface from 11 mm to 5.5 mm and, to a lesser degree, the decrease in the radius of curvature of the posterior surface from 6 mm to 5 mm.

Lenticular changes during accommodation	The lens thickens axially.
	The equatorial lens diameter decreases.
	The anterior radius of curvature decreases (curvature increases).
	The posterior radius of curvature decreases (curvature increases).
	The anterior lens surface shifts anteriorly.

Figure 7-6: Cross-section of a (left) relaxed and (right) accommodative eye. Note the changes in the lens in the accommodating eye per thickness, surface location, and surface curvature.

An alternative theory that explains how the lens increases its power during accommodation was proposed by Ronald Schachar.[688] The main difference lies in the effects of tension on the capsular bag. The elastic capsule has an elliptic shape with an aspect ratio (minor axis/major axis) of about 0.6 that affects its acquired shape during accommodation. Specifically, it steepens at the center but (here comes the difference from Helmholtz) flattens at the periphery. This means that during accommodation the equatorial diameter of the lens increases.[689] Schachar then introduced a new mode of presbyopia management based on scleral expansion bands that increase the distance between the lens equator and the ciliary

---

[687] Glasser A. Accommodation: mechanism and measurement. Ophthalmol Clin N Am. 2006; 19(1):1-12.

[688] Schachar RA. Zonular function: a new hypothesis with clinical implications. Ann Ophthalmol. 1994; 26(2):36-8.

[689] Schachar RA, Tello C, Cudmore DP, Liebmann JM, Black TD, Ritch R. In vivo increase of the human lens equatorial diameter during accommodation. Am J Physiol. 1996; 271(3 Pt 2):R670-6.

muscle.[690] However, this has not proven to work consistently and predictably, so the validity of this theory has been put into question.[691]

Another alternative theory is the catenary (hydraulic suspension) theory,[692] which assumes that the lens, the zonules, and the anterior vitreous form a diaphragm between the anterior and posterior chambers. Contraction of the ciliary muscle initiates a pressure gradient between these chambers that results in central lens steepening and peripheral lens flattening.

7.2 MAGNITUDE AND AMPLITUDE OF ACCOMMODATION

7.2.1 Magnitude of Accommodation

Consider an emmetropic eye fixating at optical infinity; in this perfect world there is no need for accommodation because the retina and the object situated at the point of optical infinity are optical conjugates. When the object is brought closer and the eye is still fixated for distance, the image as projected onto the retina is blurred; this is a dioptric stimulus for accommodation. The retinal blur is one of the major sensory cues that elicits an increase in lenticular power, which is needed to focus on the near object.

Optically, this increase in power compensates for the most divergent wavefront that originates from the fixation point, if it is not the far point. Thus, the **magnitude of accommodation** is the dioptric difference between the far-point vergence and the point-of-fixation vergence.

The magnitude of accommodation is always a positive dioptric quantity because we subtract (often from zero) a more-negative value: the vergence at the 'closer' fixation point. Recall that an object in front of the eye corresponds to a negative location, as the origin of the Cartesian system is 'the eye'[693] and the object is to the left of it. In addition, vergence, expressed in diopters [D], is calculated by the reciprocal of the object location, the latter being expressed in meters [m].

[690] Schachar RA. Cause and treatment of presbyopia with a method for increasing the amplitude of accommodation. Ann Ophthalmol. 1992; 24(12):445-7, 452.

[691] Malecaze FJ, Gazagne CS, Tarroux MC, Gorrand JM. Scleral expansion bands for presbyopia. Ophthalmology. 2001; 108(12):2165-71.

[692] Coleman DJ. Unified model for accommodative mechanism. Am J Ophthalmol. 1970; 69(6):1063-79.

[693] To calm the protesting Geometrical Optics Professor, we state that, in object space, locations are measured from the object-space principal plane H of the eye. Thus, object location x is measured from about 1.35 mm inside the eye. In image space, locations such as image location x' and focal length f' are measured from the image-space principal plane H', about 1.35 mm inside the eye.

Note 📝 : The magnitude of accommodation is often expressed either as accommodative demand or as accommodative response. **Accommodative demand** is the magnitude of accommodation <u>needed</u>. **Accommodative response** is the actual magnitude of accommodation that <u>the person exerts</u> for the same configuration. While both the demand and the response are expressions of the magnitude of accommodation and ideally the response would exactly match the demand, this is not always the case.

The 'response' is the physiological response to 'demand.' Because the accommodation is neurologically controlled, and is both dynamic and flexible, the response may lag (be less than) or even exceed (be greater than) the demand. The dioptric difference between accommodative demand and accommodative response is termed **lag of accommodation**. A normal lag is usually positive (lesser response), about 0.50 to 0.75 D.[694]

The lag can often simply be transient (temporal, lasting about half a second); then the temporal lag is an expression of the time lapse between application of the stimulus and the resulting reaction. On average, far-to-near temporal lag is 0.64 s, while near-to-far temporal lag is 0.56 s.[695]

In an emmetropic eye (far point at infinity $\Rightarrow L_{FP} = 0$),
Magnitude of Accommodation A equals and is of opposite sign to the fixation-point vergence (L_x).

In any eye, regardless of emmetropia or ametropia,

Magnitude of Accommodation = (far-point vergence) – (fixation-point vergence)

$$A = L_{FP} - L_x \qquad\qquad (7.1)$$

Magnitude of Accommodation A:
the difference between the far-point vergence (L_{FP}) and the fixation-point vergence (L_x).

Far point:	Within the range of clear vision:	Near point:
zero accommodation	some accommodation	maximum accommodation

Example ☞: What is the vergence L_x for an object placed 66.6 cm <u>in front</u> of the eye?

[694] Labhishetty V, Cholewiak SA, Roorda A, Banks MS. Lags and leads of accommodation in humans: Fact or fiction?. J Vis. 2021; 21(3):21.

[695] Harb E, Thorn F, Troilo D. Characteristics of accommodative behavior during sustained reading in emmetropes and myopes. Vis Res. 2006; 46(16):2581-92.

We convert this distance to meters. Also, we use the minus sign to indicate that the object is to the left. Therefore, object location is $x = -0.66$ m. Then, vergence is $L_x = 1/(-0.66$ m$) = -1.50$ D.

Example ☞: Odysseus, an emmetrope (∴ far point at infinity), is reading a scroll at arm's length (66.6 cm). What is the magnitude of accommodation A?

At that fixation point, vergence is $1/(-0.66$ m$) = -1.50$ D. Odysseus has a far point at infinity, so the far-point vergence = 0.0 D. The magnitude of accommodation is the difference between the far-point vergence (0 D) and the fixation-point vergence (-1.50 D): (0.0 D) $-$ (-1.50 D) $= +1.50$ D.

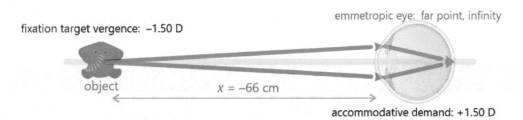

Figure 7-7: Emmetropic eye and an object 66 cm in front of it = accommodative demand +1.50 D.

7.2.2 Amplitude of Accommodation

The closest an object can be brought to the eye and still be clearly viewed is the near point. At this near point, an individual exerts the maximum accommodative response, whose magnitude is the **amplitude of accommodation** (*AoA*).

$$\text{Amplitude of accommodation} = \text{(far-point vergence)} - \text{(near-point vergence)} \qquad (7.2)$$

Example ☞: Odysseus' emmetropic eye (∴ far point at infinity, $L_{FP} = 0.0$ D) has a near point at 25 cm in front of it ($L_{NP} = -4.00$ D). The amplitude of accommodation is $AoA = +4.00$ D:

$$AoA = L_{FP} - L_{FP} = \underbrace{\frac{1}{\infty}}_{\text{far-point vergence}} - \underbrace{\left(\frac{1}{-0.25 \text{ m}}\right)}_{\text{near-point vergence}} = 0.00 \text{ D} - \left(-4.00 \text{ D}\right) = +4.00 \text{ D}$$

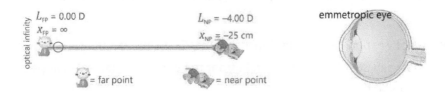

Figure 7-8: Amplitude of accommodation for an emmetropic eye.

Example ☞: Achilles, a -6.00 D myope (∴ far point at 16.6 cm in front of the eye), has a near point at 10 cm. What is his amplitude of accommodation when he is not wearing any spectacles or contact lenses?

Far-point vergence L_{FP} = 1/(−16.6 cm) = 1/(−0.166 m) = −6.00 D. Near-point vergence L_{NP} = 1/(−10 cm) = 1/(−0.10 m) = −10.00 D. Amplitude of accommodation AoA = (−6.00 D) − (−10.00 D) = +4.00 D.

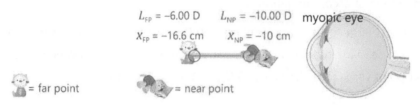

Figure 7-9: Amplitude of accommodation for a −6.00 D myopic eye.

Amplitude of accommodation (AoA):

- the vergence difference between the far point L_{FP} and the near point L_{NP}
- the largest potential increase in optical power that an eye can achieve while adjusting between the far and the near point

Example ☞: Nausicaa, the beautiful daughter of King Alcinous and Queen Arete of the Phaeacians, is a +3.00 D hyperope (∴ far point at 33.3 cm behind the eye) with a near point at 1 m in front of her eye. What is her amplitude of accommodation when she is not wearing spectacle or contact lenses?

Far-point vergence L_{FP} = 1/(+33.3 cm) = 1/(+0.333 m) = +3.00 D. Near-point vergence L_{NP} = 1/(−1 m) = −1.00 D. Amplitude of accommodation AoA = (+3.00 D) − (−1.00 D) = +4.00 D.

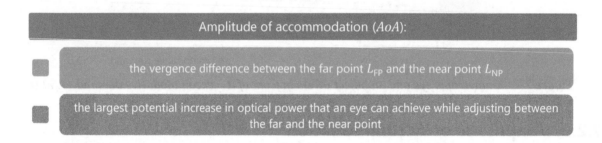

Figure 7-10: Amplitude of accommodation for a +3.00 D hyperopic eye.

Example ☞: When not wearing her prescription, Penelope, Odysseus' faithful wife, can see clearly only when an object is between 20.0 cm and 10.0 cm in front of her eyes. What is Penelope's ametropia and amplitude of accommodation?

Both points are in front of her eyes. She is a myope. The far point is −20.0 cm with vergence −5.00 D. This is her myopia. The near point is −10.0 cm with vergence −10.00 D. Amplitude of accommodation is −5.00 − (−10.00) = +5.00 D.

Example ☞: Penelope is lucky. She found her (correct) spectacles and put them on. What is the farthest and the closest distance that she can now see?

Let us welcome Penelope + correction, a combination that is now emmetropic. With full correction, the far point is effectively at infinity. She still has accommodative amplitude (which is not dependent on worn correction but depends on the optics of the eye) of +5.00 D.

We use Eq. (7.2): Amplitude of accommodation = (far-point vergence) – (near-point vergence) ⇒ +5.00 D = 0.00 D – (near-point vergence) ⇒ Near-point vergence is L_{NP} = –5.00 D.

Thus, her near point when wearing the distance correction is at –20.0 cm.

Example ☞: Penelope is not lucky. She finds her son Telemachus' spectacles (Telemachus is a –7.00 D myope) and put them on. What are the farthest and the closest distances that she can now see?

Penelope now wears an overminused correction; effectively, with this correction, she is a +2.00 D hyperope. Her far point is at +50.0 cm, i.e., half a meter behind her eye. We use Eq. (7.2) to find that the near-point vergence is –3.00 D. Thus, her near point is at –33.3 cm. Note that Penelope now complains of headaches, and not just because of the suitors. She needs to draw constant accommodation. Even at infinity, she needs +2.00 D accommodation.

Accommodation	The ability to adjust power for observation of near objects is an optical requirement.
	The optical power needed to form a clear image from a near object is greater than that required for a distant object. The additional power is provided by accommodation.
	With advancing age, the accommodating ability of the lens diminishes.

Although the decline in accommodative amplitude with age is a common manifestation, independent of the state of emmetropia or ametropia (§ 6.3), it has differing consequences in everyday life.[696] A hyperope needs accommodation even for observing distant objects, while a myope can see close objects without invoking accommodation.

Example ☞: Nymph Calypso, an uncorrected +2.00 D hyperope views a near object at –25.0 cm (i.e., 25.0 cm in front of her eye). The accommodation required to achieve a sharp retinal image (demand) is …

The near object at –25.0 cm has –4.00 D vergence. Calypso has far-point vergence +2.00 D. The accommodation demand is +2.00 – (– 4.00) = +6.00 D.

---

[696] Glasser A, Campbell MC. Biometric, optical and physical changes in the isolated human crystalline lens with age in relation to presbyopia. Vision Res. 1999; 39(11):1991-2015.

Example ☞: Calypso is now corrected with a +1.50 D prescription. She views a near object at −25.0 cm (i.e., 25.0 cm in front of her eye). The accommodation demand for this object is …

The near object at −25.0 cm has −4.00 D vergence. Calypso has far-point vergence +0.50 D (+2.00 − 1.50 of correction). The accommodation demand is +0.50 − (−4.00) = +4.50 D.

An uncorrected <u>myope</u> demands <u>less accommodation</u> compared to an emmetrope or a hyperope. For this reason, many presbyopic myopes simply remove their distance glasses to read instead of using presbyopic correction.

Example ☞: Circe, the beautiful witch-goddess who transforms Odysseus' crew into swine, is an uncorrected 1.50 D myope. She is viewing her magic wand at −50.0 cm (i.e., 50.0 cm in front of her eye). The accommodation demand when viewing this object is …

The magic wand at −50.0 cm yields a −2.00 D vergence. Circe has a far-point vergence of −1.50 D. The accommodation demand is −1.50 − (−2.00) = +0.50 D.

Clinical note 🏥: In order to eliminate the influence of accommodation on the measurement of refractive error, particularly in hyperopia, the accommodative response can be pharmacologically <u>suspended</u> with antimuscarinic (anticholinergic) agents that antagonize (block) the muscarinic acetylcholine receptor, an autonomic nervous system stimulatory neurotransmitter. Thus, the ciliary muscle is paralyzed.

This temporary (transient) neutralization of accommodation is called **cycloplegia**. The most potent cycloplegic agent with the longest lasting action is atropine. Another agent is scopolamine (hyoscine), which has a shorter duration, but its antimuscarinic action is long-lasting. Other agents are cyclopentolate, which is usually used for children, as it is more potent, and tropicamide, used in adults.[697]

To measure the maximum (pharmacologically stimulated) accommodative amplitude,[698, 699] the accommodative response can be pharmacologically <u>stimulated</u> with muscarinic (cholinergic) agonist agents such as pilocarpine, which contract the ciliary muscle.[700, 701]

---

[697] Marron J. Cycloplegia and mydriasis by use of atropine, scopolamine, and homatropine-paredrine. Arch Ophthalmol. 1940; 23:340-50.

[698] Grzybowski A, Schachar RA, Gaca-Wysocka M, Schachar IH, Pierscionek BK. Maximum human objectively measured pharmacologically stimulated accommodative amplitude. Clin Ophthalmol. 2018; 12:201-5.

[699] The pupil constricts significantly after pilocarpine administration; this is unfavorable for prolonged objective accommodation measurements. The use of phenylephrine to predilate the pupil is suggested: Osuin LA, Glasser A. The effects of phenylephrine on pupil diameter and accommodation in rhesus monkeys. Invest Ophthalmol Vis Sci. 2004; 45:215-21.

[700] Koeppl C, Findl O, Kriechbaum K, Drexler W. Comparison of pilocarpine-induced and stimulus-driven accommodation in phakic eyes. Exp Eye Res. 2005; 80(6):795-800.

[701] The primary indication is saliva production stimulator and glaucoma medication. Because pilocarpine is absorbed at the iris pigment epithelium, individuals with a dark iris are more sensitive to the miotic effect of pilocarpine.

7.2.3 Measurement of the Amplitude of Accommodation

An **objective** measurement of the amplitude of accommodation uses a device or technique that measures the ocular power,[702] such as a refractometer,[703] an open-field autorefractor,[704] aberrometry, or retinoscopy.[705] The difference between the minimum (distance) and maximum (near) powers is a true measure of the amplitude of accommodation.

A **subjective** measurement measures the amplitude of accommodation indirectly, by identifying the far and near points. The examinee is presented a target and reports when the target can be held in clear focus.

Subjective tests are more relevant for the task (i.e., to determine how close the examinee can see), as they produce the desired outcome (in this case, the amplitude of accommodation) based on the examinee's reporting of a requested stimulus threshold, which is when the blur condition is just detected. However, subjective tests are influenced by the accommodative triad; there is, simultaneously, accommodation, convergence (initiated by disparity cues), and pupil constriction. Because the constricted pupil increases the depth of field, it increases the perceptual blur tolerance: A greater range of target distances for which no difference in retinal blur is noted, giving a false notion of accommodation. The near point attained is therefore slightly closer, and the measured amplitude of accommodation is slightly larger. In addition, an inherent inaccuracy of the subjective tests is associated with the lag of accommodation.[694]

Measurement of the amplitude of accommodation	
Objective: the optical power difference of the eye between the far and the near points.	Subjective: the vergence difference between the far and near points.
• A device is used to measure the range (increase) of the ocular refractive power.	• The examinee, corrected for distance vision, identifies the near point.

There are three different subjective tests to measure the amplitude of accommodation:

In the **push-up (PU) test**, the examinee, already corrected for distance vision (effectively far point at infinity), is presented with a target (eye chart) that is brought progressively closer. The

---

[702] Wold JE, Hu A, Chen S, Glasser A. Subjective and objective measurement of human accommodative amplitude. J Cataract Refract Surg. 2003; 29(10):1878-88.

[703] Fincham EF. The coincidence optometer. Proc Phys Soc (London). 1937; 49:456-68.

[704] Anderson HA, Stuebing KK. Subjective versus objective accommodative amplitude: preschool to presbyopia. Optom Vis Sci. 2014; 91(11):1290-301.

[705] León A, Estrada JM, Rosenfield M. Age and the amplitude of accommodation measured using dynamic retinoscopy. Ophthalmic Physiol Opt. 2016; 36(1):5-12.

examinee states when the first sustained blur is noted. The PU test has historically been used the most, dating back to the work by American ophthalmologist Alexander Duane.[706]

An alternative subjective technique is the modified push-up (MPU) test, in which an additional minus lens is added over the distance refractive correction. The PU test is then performed through this lens combination. The advantage of the modified push-up test over the conventional push-up test is that the target appears smaller when viewed through the minus lens, so the examinee detects the presence of a blur earlier.[707]

When using techniques such as the RAF rule (the binocular gauge rule or convergence rule) or the Prince rule—techniques that involve a near-point reading card that slides along a ruler—it is desirable to have these rulers be at least 50 cm long to be able to measure the near point along the ruler. For example, plus or minus lenses may be used to maintain the far and the near points on the ruler. A +3.00 D lens fitted on an emmetrope brings the far point from infinity at 1/(3.00 D) = 0.33 m to in front of their eye.

Example ☞: Odysseus, an emmetrope, is fitted with a +3.00 D lens and views a reading card on a 50-cm-long Prince rule. As the target is moved closer, it becomes clear at 33 cm and remains clear until it reaches 12.5 cm. What is the amplitude of accommodation?

The amplitude of accommodation is simply the vergence difference between the two endpoints. The distal point of 33 cm has vergence −3.00 D and the proximal point of 12.5 cm has vergence −8.00 D. Thus, the amplitude of accommodation is −3.00 D − (−8.00 D) = +5.00 D.

Figure 7-11: Gauge (rule) with a sliding target for the measurement of accommodation.

In this example, if Odysseus were not to use the +3.00 D lens, the distal point would be his far point, i.e., infinity, with vergence 0.0 D. The proximal point would be his near point, 20 cm in front of the eye (−0.20 m) with vergence −5.00 D. Thus, AoA is +5.00 D. In principle, AoA is not affected by the addition of the plus lens, which serves to shift the distal and the proximal points on the rule.

[706] Duane A. The accommodation and Donder's curve and the need to revising our ideas regarding them. J Am Med Assoc. 1909:52;1992-6.

[707] Rosenfield M, Cohen AS. Push-up amplitude of accommodation and target size. Ophthalmic Physiol Opt. 1995; 15:231-2.

In the **pull-away** (PA) **test**, also known as push-down test, the target is moved progressively farther away, and the examinee states when the first clear identification of the target is noted.[708] Because of pseudoaccommodation, the push-up and the pull-away tests overestimate the true accommodative amplitude.[709] A possible explanation is that, as a fixed-size object is brought closer, the corresponding retinal image increases in size. The push-up (PU) and the pull-away (PA) tests can be performed monocularly and binocularly.

The **minus lens-to-blur** (MLB) **test**, also known as Sheard's method,[710] is performed (usually monocularly) with the target card presented at 40 cm; progressively, minus lenses are added in –0.25 D steps until the examinee reports the first sustained blur. The examinee is, as in the previous tests, corrected for distance vision. The power of the added lenses divided by the distance value within the phoropter is the amplitude of accommodation. The MLB test may underestimate accommodative amplitude due to retinal image minification by the minus lens.

7.3 CLASSIFICATION OF ACCOMMODATION

7.3.1 Classification on the Basis of Measurement

Accommodation can be classified based on the mode of subjective measurement as **absolute**, **binocular**, and **relative** accommodation.

<u>Absolute</u> accommodation is the measurement of accommodation under monocular viewing conditions. A monocular test eliminates convergence as a limiting factor.

<u>Binocular</u> accommodation is the measurement of accommodation under binocular viewing conditions. This is commonly only tested via the fused cross-cylinder procedure. It is important to remember that the accommodative response is affected by the vergence system; individuals with exophoria have a lower lag of accommodation than individuals with esophoria, who have a much higher lag of accommodation.[711]

<u>Relative</u> accommodation is the amount of binocular accommodation that can be exerted under fixed vergence. It can be negative (or positive) if the examinee can decrease (or increase)

---

[708] Pollock J. Accommodation measurement-clear or blurred? Aust Orthopt J. 1989; 25:20-2.

[709] Ostrin LA, Glasser A. Accommodation measurements in a prepresbyopic and presbyopic population. J Cataract Refract Surg. 2004; 30(7):1435-44.

[710] The test is named after American biophysicist Charles Sheard, Professor of physics and applied optics, and founder of the American Academy of Optometry. See also § 10.5.3.4 Exophoria Management.

[711] Momeni-Moghaddam H, Goss DA, Sobhani M. Accommodative response under monocular and binocular conditions as a function of phoria in symptomatic and asymptomatic subjects. Clin Exp Optom. 2014; 97:36-42.

accommodation while maintaining convergence. It is measured by the magnitude of the maximum plus (or minus) lenses added to maintain vergence.[712] The value of negative (or positive) relative accommodation is the maximum plus (or minimum minus) lenses used until the examinee reports the first blur.[713] Normal values for relative accommodation are at least 2.00 D in either direction, relaxing or stimulating.

Accommodative facility describes how quickly and accurately accommodation can occur. In essence, the accommodative facility is the flexibility of the accommodative system. Accommodative facility is clinically measured with ±2.00 D lens flippers. The examinee wears correction for distance and is asked to observe a near target and to switch focus between the +2.00 D and –2.00 D lenses over one minute. The number of cycles (alternations between the plus and minus lenses) is calculated for this time. This test can be performed both monocularly and binocularly; when performed binocularly, there needs to be a suppression check to ensure that both eyes are actively engaged in the test.

Note ⏰: A complete clinical exam includes the assessment of accommodative function not only as an expression of the amplitude of accommodation but also as an assessment of accommodative lag and fatigue, as well as the accommodative facility.

A decreased accommodative facility is associated with increased difficulty in switching focus between near and far, such as trouble focusing up close after staring far away, or trouble seeing far away after reading up close.

7.3.2 Classification of Involuntary Accommodation

As accommodation is controlled neurologically, it can either be a voluntary, cognitive-induced process, or an involuntary, reflexive type of response. Dr. Gordon G. Heath developed a classification system that breaks the involuntary types of accommodation into four subcategories: reflex, proximal, vergence, and tonic.[714]

Optical **reflex** accommodation may be elicited as an automatic adjustment response to retinal blur by a near object viewed monocularly. This is dependent on the retino-optical cue dioptric stimulus. Reflex accommodation is the largest contributor to accommodation and is considered the normal, involuntary response to blur for maintaining a clear image.

---

[712] In the protocol established by Donders, if the near point is farther than 22 cm, an auxiliary plus lens is be added to image it closer. The power of this lens is added to the result. This 22 cm distance corresponds to an angle of convergence of about 16°.

[713] Taub MB, Shallo-Hoffmann J. A Comparison of three clinical tests of accommodation amplitude to Hofstetter's norms to guide diagnosis and treatment. Optom Vis Dev. 2012; 43(4):180-90.

[714] Heath GG. Components of accommodation. Am J Optom Arch Am Acad Optom. 1956; 33(11):569-79.

On the other hand, accommodation may be elicited by a target that appears to be close to the eye.[715, 716] This response to perceived distance is **proximal** accommodation, which uses primarily spatio-optical cues and is not dependent on the actual dioptric stimulus.[717] In other words, the image formed by this near object may not elicit a retinal blur, even if it is close; just the perception of the object being close elicits proximal accommodation. How can this be the case? An example of proximal accommodation occurs with the use of head-up displays (HUD).

Figure 7-12: (left) Head-up display in a modern airliner (photo by Javier F. Bobadilla used with permission) and (right) in a common passenger car.

HUDs are present in the cockpit of modern airliners such as the Airbus A350 and the Boeing 787. The HUD superimposes flight-related information such as airspeed, heading vector, and altitude over the pilot's line of sight. A HUD reduces the need for constant, alternating transitions between head-up (windshield) and head-down (instrument panel) positions, particularly during a demanding landing, flying under low visibility, and/or at nighttime. This critical flow of fast-paced information is perceived in the more-sensitive central vision (as opposed to peripheral vision), so the need to shift the gaze away from the center is alleviated. The virtual images in the HUD are presented at optical infinity by reflection from a collimated source via a semitransparent beamsplitter. Thus, they do not elicit a retinal blur.

Ocular vergence accommodation describes the accommodative response elicited by binocular retinal disparity.[718] It is the second major contributor to accommodation after reflex accommodation.[719] This is a critical aspect of ocular vergence accommodation, for it gives rise to the convergence accommodation to convergence (CA/C) ratio (§ 7.6).

[715] Wick B, Currie D. Dynamic demonstration of proximal vergence and proximal accommodation. Optom Vis Sci. 1991; 68(3):163-7.

[716] Rosenfield M, Gilmartin B. Effect of target proximity on the open-loop accommodative response. Optom Vis Sci. 1990; 67(2):74-9.

[717] Owens DA. The Mandelbaum effect: evidence for an accommodation bias toward intermediate viewing distances. J Opt Soc Am. 1979; 69:646-52.

[718] Stark L, Kenyon RV, Krishnan VV, Ciuffreda KJ. Disparity vergence: a proposed name for a dominant component of binocular vergence eye movements. Am J Optom Physiol Opt. 1980; 57(9):606-9.

[719] Schor CM, Glenn A. The Fry award lecture: adaptive regulation of accommodative vergence and vergence accommodation. Am J Optom Physiol Opt. 1986; 63(8):587-609.

Finally, there is **tonic** accommodation, which is the accommodative response revealed in the absence of blur, disparity, or proximal inputs, reflecting baseline midbrain neural innervation.

In addition to these four types of accommodation, optical factors, called **optical triggers**, can also trigger a response to accommodation. These optical triggers can be associated with the Stiles–Crawford effect[720] (§ 4.4.2), luminance and contrast,[721] optical vergence,[722, 723] and chromatic aberration.[724, 725, 726, 727]

Chromatic signals provide a directional stimulus to reflex accommodation from both even-error and odd-error cues. An even-error cue, such as a pure defocus blur, is a cue in which the loss of contrast is independent of the direction of the stimulus (i.e., moving toward or away from the eye). An odd-error cue extracts directional information from the stimulus[728] and is considered as being derived from higher-order aberrations. When even-error and odd-error cues are combined, the direction of the stimulus can be determined to guide the eye to either increase or decrease its optical power.[729] Other studies disprove the contribution of monochromatic high-order aberrations to accommodation.[730]

Note 🖳: In clinical practice, proximal accommodation may cause instrument reading errors in devices such as autorefractors.[731]

While the eye looks at a target inside an enclosure that is designed to mimic an object situated at a distance (using collimated light), young individuals, in particular, may display much more minus power during autorefraction than is found in either subjective refraction or in retinoscopy.

[720] Fincham EF. The accommodation reflex and its stimulus. Br J Ophthalm. 1951; (35):381-93.

[721] Rucker FJ. The role of luminance and chromatic cues in emmetropisation. Ophthalmic Physiol Opt. 2013; 33(3):196-214.

[722] Del Águila-Carrasco AJ, Marín-Franch I, Bernal-Molina P, Esteve-Taboada JJ, Kruger PB, Montés-Micó R, López-Gil N. Accommodation responds to optical vergence and not defocus blur alone. Invest Ophthalmol Vis Sci. 2017; 58(3):1758-63.

[723] Marín-Franch I, Del Águila-Carrasco AJ, Bernal-Molina P, Esteve-Taboada JJ, López-Gil N, Montés-Micó R, Kruger PB. There is more to accommodation of the eye than simply minimizing retinal blur. Biomed Opt Express. 2017; 8(10):4717-28.

[724] Graef K, Schaeffel F. Control of accommodation by longitudinal chromatic aberration and blue cones. J Vis. 2012; 12(1):14.

[725] Wang Y, Kruger PB, Li JS, Lin PL, Stark LR. Accommodation to wavefront vergence and chromatic aberration. Optom Vis Sci. 2011; 88(5):593-600.

[726] Kruger PB, Rucker FJ, Hu C, Rutman H, Schmidt NW, Roditis V. Accommodation with and without short-wavelength-sensitive cones and chromatic aberration. Vision Res. 2005; 45(10):1265-74.

[727] Kruger PB, Pola J. Stimuli for accommodation: blur, chromatic aberration and size. Vision Res. 1986; 26(6):957-71.

[728] Metlapally S, Tong JL, Tahir HJ, Schor CM. Potential role for microfluctuations as a temporal directional cue to accommodation. J Vis. 2016; 16(6):19.

[729] Wilson BJ, Decker KE, Roorda A. Monochromatic aberrations provide an odd-error cue to focus direction. J Opt Soc Am A Opt Image Sci Vis. 2002; 19(5):833-9.

[730] Bernal-Molina P, Marín-Franch I, Del Águila-Carrasco AJ, Esteve-Taboada JJ, López-Gil N, Kruger PB, Montés-Micó R. Human eyes do not need monochromatic aberrations for dynamic accommodation. Ophthalmic Physiol Opt. 2017; 37(5):602-9.

[731] Rosenfield M, Ciuffreda KJ. Proximal and cognitively induced accommodation. Ophthal Physiol Opt. 1990; 10(3):252-6.

'Instrument myopia'[732] is a term that describes this proximal accommodation tendency associated with spatial cues generated by the physical location of optical instruments.[733, 734]

Note 💡 : Recall that absolute hyperopia cannot be compensated by accommodation. Consider Nestor, a refractive +4.00 hyperope with 2.50 D AoA. His absolute hyperopia is just 1.50 D.

What triggers accommodation?		
Retinal cues • Reflex: image blur (monocular view) • Vergence: image disparity (binocular view)	Spatial cues (proximal accommodation) • Proximity (object apparent size and distance)	Optical cues • Chromatic aberration • Luminance / contrast

Note ◎ : The concept of 'viewing a near object comfortably' is associated with using half of the amplitude of accommodation. For example, Nestor, a +4.00 hyperope, requires +8.00 D of accommodative response to view a near object at 25 cm in front of his eyes. To do so comfortably, he must have a +16.00 D amplitude of accommodation. Considering his advanced age, this is impossible!

7.3.3 Pseudoaccommodation

Pseudoaccommodation ($\psi\varepsilon\upsilon\delta o$- for false) describes mechanisms that permit acceptable viewing over a range of target distances and that are not brought about by increasing lenticular power.[735] One such mechanism is miosis, the pupil contraction under bright light, which improves near vision by creating a longer depth of field.[736] Another mechanism, proposed by Kepler, is a shift of the lens along the optical axis, contributing about 1.00 to 2.00 D of AoA.

Although not commonly recognized, pseudoaccommodation exists in pseudophakic eyes—eyes that have received an implanted intraocular lens (IOL) to replace the natural crystalline lens, particularly after cataract-removal surgery.[737] Regardless of the IOL design,

---

[732] Salmon TO, van de Pol C. Evaluation of a clinical aberrometer for lower-order accuracy and repeatability, higher-order repeatability, and instrument myopia. Optometry. 2005; 76(8):461-72.

[733] Leibowitz HW, Owens DA. New evidence for the intermediate position of relaxed accommodation. Doc Ophthalmol. 1978; 46(1):133-47.

[734] Ghose S, Nayak BK, Singh JP. Critical evaluation of the NR-1000F auto refractometer. Br J Ophthalmol. 1986; 70(3):221-6.

[735] Pallikaris IG, Kontadakis GA, Portaliou DM. Real and pseudoaccommodation in accommodative lenses. J Ophthalmol. 2011; 2011:284961.

[736] Sergienko NM, Kondratenko YN, Tutchenko NN. Depth of focus in pseudophakic eyes. Graefes Arch Clin Exp Ophthalmol. 2008; 246(11):1623-7.

[737] Nakazawa M. Ohtsuki K. Apparent accommodation in pseudophakic eyes after implantation of posterior chamber intraocular lenses. Am J Ophthalmol. 1983; 96(4):435-8.

whether it is fixed focal length or multifocal, these lenses are placed in the original lens capsule, which still maintains some ability, however slight, to shift its contents back and forth.

Even in the elderly, the ciliary muscle retains some of its ability to contract, and when relaxed, the lens capsule is held under tension.[738, 739, 740] When this tension is relieved (by the contraction of the ciliary muscle), the eye 'accommodates,' by slightly shifting the IOL forward. This provides a small (and perhaps significant when compared to others of the same age without an IOL) amount of accommodative amplitude.[741, 742, 743] Certain advanced IOL designs, such as multifocal IOLs (§ 7.8.4), help in providing pseudoaccommodation.[744]

Other contributions to pseudoaccommodation include corneal aberrations, as they indirectly affect the depth of field of the eye. The most important of these contributions are spherical aberration in normal eyes and coma in eyes with prior laser corneal surgery.[745]

7.4 ANOMALIES OF ACCOMMODATION

Anomalies of accommodation come in several variations, including issues with the stimulation, relaxation, and dynamics of accommodation. Issues with the stimulation are those such as accommodative insufficiency, ill-sustained accommodation (also called accommodative fatigue), and unequal accommodation between the two eyes. Issues with the relaxation of accommodation are found in accommodative excess and accommodative spasm. Issues with the dynamics are found in accommodative infacility, also called accommodative inertia.[746]

Accommodative insufficiency occurs in the presence of insufficient accommodative amplitude compared to the age-matched, expected values; a deficiency of 2.00 D or more is the hallmark finding. Besides true presbyopia, most problems with accommodation are functional in

---

[738] Swegmark G. Studies with impedance cyclography on human ocular accommodation at different ages. Acta Ophthalmol (Copenh). 1969; 47(5):1186-206.

[739] Strenk SA, Semmlow JL, Strenk LM, Munoz P, Gronlund-Jacob J, DeMarco JK. Age-related changes in human ciliary muscle and lens: a magnetic resonance imaging study. Invest Ophthalmol Vis Sci. 1999; 40(6):1162-9.

[740] Park KA, Yun JH, Kee C. The effect of cataract extraction on the contractility of ciliary muscle. Am J Ophthalmol. 2008; 146(1):8-14.

[741] Croft MA, Kaufman PL. Accommodation and presbyopia: the ciliary neuromuscular view. Ophthalmol Clin North Am. 2006; 19(1):13-24.

[742] Atchison DA. Pseudoaccommodation with forward movement of IOLs. J Cataract Refract Surg. 2005; 31(1):11.

[743] Nawa Y, Ueda T, Nakatsuka M, Tsuji H, Marutani H, Hara Y, Uozato H. Accommodation obtained per 1.0 mm forward movement of a posterior chamber intraocular lens. J Cataract Refract Surg. 2003; 29(11):2069-72.

[744] Menapace R, Findl O, Kriechbaum K, Leydolt-Koeppl Ch. Accommodating intraocular lenses: a critical review of present and future concepts. Graefes Arch Clin Exp Ophthalmol. 2007; 245(4):473-89.

[745] Yeu E, Wang L, Koch DD. The effect of corneal wavefront aberrations on corneal pseudoaccommodation. Am J Ophthalmol. 2012; 153(5):972-981.e2.

[746] Ciuffreda, K. Accommodation, the pupil, and presbyopia. In Benjamin WJ, ed. Borish's clinical refraction. St Louis, MO: Butterworrth Heinemann. 2006; 93-144.

nature; their exact etiologies are unknown. At the same time, there are both many systemic conditions and many medications that can negatively affect accommodation. For example, these could be conditions such as diabetes, multiple sclerosis, malnutrition, and nerve palsies, or medications such as anesthesia, parasympatholytic, and tranquilizing drugs.

Trauma or neurogenic disorders may cause permanent insufficiency, and this condition may present unilaterally (usually from trauma or a third-nerve palsy) or bilaterally.[747] Adding plus lenses can provide symptom relief, and vision therapy can eliminate the condition when its etiology is functional, i.e., not from trauma or medication.

Accommodative fatigue (or ill-sustained accommodation) is a measure of the ability to sustain sufficient accommodation over an extended time and can be the first stage of accommodative insufficiency. It is clinically diagnosed via poor repeatability of accommodation measurements, such as poor performance on repeated measurements of amplitude. Practically, this condition results in an increased difficulty in sustaining accommodation during near-point activities.

Accommodative infacility (or **inertia**) is associated with decreased dynamics of accommodation (latency, time constant, and peak velocity). Extra energy and effort are required when one attempts to switch focus between distance and near, and vice versa. As with accommodative insufficiency, accommodative infacility is readily treated with vision therapy.

Accommodative excess has been traditionally described as a higher accommodative response than would be expected for the tested distance, but this diagnosis is rarely found in isolation. Opinions have changed over time, and now this condition is thought of as a subset of accommodative spasm—a condition that is defined by a poor ability to relax the accommodative response. The accommodative spasm can be thought of as the far extreme of accommodative excess in terms of the severe lack of ability to relax accommodation.

Other conditions of accommodation anomalies exist, such as paralysis of accommodation. This is most often pharmacologically induced, but it may be associated with chronic alcoholism or diabetes.

Note ᴏᴏ: The accommodative response, in all of its forms, can be modified via vision therapy. In symptomatic patients, vision therapy can eliminate accommodation issues; in asymptomatic individuals, vision therapy can significantly improve the accommodative dynamic responses.[748, 749]

---

[747] García-Muñoz Á, Carbonell-Bonete S, Cacho-Martínez P. Symptomatology associated with accommodative and binocular vision anomalies. J Optom. 2014; 7(4):178-92.

[748] Vasudevan B, Ciuffreda KJ, Ludlam DP. Accommodative training to reduce nearwork induced transient myopia. Optom Vis Sci. 2009; 86(11):1287-94.

[749] Scheiman M, Cotter S, Kulp MT, Mitchell GL, Cooper J, Gallaway M, Hopkins KB, Bartuccio M, Chung I. Treatment of accommodative dysfunction in children: results from a random clinical trial. Optom Vis Sci. 2011; 88(11):1343-52.

7.5 ACCOMMODATION AND SPECTACLE WEAR

7.5.1 Influence of Refractive Error

As discussed in § 6.6, the spectacle or contact lens that corrects ametropia creates an image from an object at infinity at its secondary focal point. The objective of the optical correction is to make the retina optically conjugate with the location of that image. This is achieved by placing the secondary focal point of the spectacle lens on the far point of the eye.

The simple formula used when calculating the optical power needed for correcting distance ametropia does not consider accommodation, and all attempts are made to minimize the influence of accommodation during clinical subjective refraction. However, the measured refractive status is often influenced by the accommodation; after all, the uncorrected hyperopic eye must accommodate to see in the distance.[750]

Clinical refraction for hyperopia is performed despite a basal amount of accommodation. Therefore, any discussion of either accommodation or vergence must be made knowing the type (myopia, hyperopia, astigmatism) and amount (magnitude) of ametropia.[751]

Example ☞: What is the accommodative demand (magnitude of accommodation required) for an object located 25 cm in front of the eye for (a) a –1.00 D myope, (b) an emmetrope, and (c) a +1.00 D hyperope?

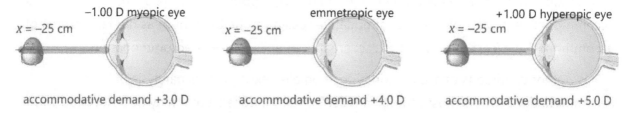

Figure 7-13: Dependence of accommodative demand on ametropia.

Per relationship (7.1), the accommodative demand is the dioptric (vergence) difference between the far point and the point of fixation. The fixation-point vergence is 1/(–0.25 m) = –4.00 D. Therefore,

myopic eye (uncorrected): accommodative demand = –1.00 – (–4.00) = +3.00 D

emmetropic eye: accommodative demand = 0.00 – (–4.00) = +4.00 D

---

[750] Alpern M. Accommodation and convergence with contact lenses. Am J Optom Arch Am Acad Optom. 1949; 26(9):379-87.
[751] When determining the optical correction for ametropias, in addition to the amount of refractive error, age-related considerations (amplitude of accommodation, developmental milestones, binocular vision, and visual acuity) need to be addressed.

hyperopic eye (uncorrected): accommodative demand = +1.00 − (−4.00) = +5.00 D

Note 📷: In this simple example, it is implied that the object distance (0.25 m) is the distance separating the object from the corneal plane.

The geometrical optics professor protests (again!) that we must set the origin of this '0.25 m in front of the eye' distance not at the corneal plane but at the object-space principal plane, which is, on average, about 1.35 mm inside the eye.

The professor is probably right; however, the error because of this slight omission is negligible. A point that is 0.25 m in front of the corneal plane is 0.25135 m in front of the principal plane. Thus, the fixation-point vergence is $L_x = 1/(−0.25135 \text{ m}) = −3.9785$ D, rounded to −4.00 D.

We conclude therefore that the principal plane can be 'acceptably' approximated by the corneal plane.

Example ☞: What is the accommodative demand for a point of fixation located 33 cm in front of the eye (corneal plane) for (a) Antinous, a −3.00 D myope, (b) Odysseus, an emmetrope, and (c) Nausicaa, a +3.00 D hyperope?

Following the procedure in the previous example, the accommodative demand is: (a) 0 D for Antinous, (b) +3.00 D for Odysseus, and (c) +6.00 D for Nausicaa.

In this example, as well as the previous one, we note that, compared to the emmetrope, the uncorrected hyperope requires more accommodation to view an object at the same distance, while the uncorrected myope requires less accommodation.

One interesting consideration is the case of overminusing a person with myopia. The term **overminused** is used to describe the prescription of individuals with myopia with excessive minus spherical power. These individuals must accommodate the additional minus spherical power correction to maintain clarity, so they end up effectively hyperopic.

Example ☞: Amphinomus has a habitual refraction prescription OD −2.50 −0.50×010, OS −2.75 −0.75×170. Cycloplegic refraction reveals OD −1.00 −0.50×010, OS −1.25 −0.75×170. What is the clinical concern?

Antinous is overminused by 1.50 D in both eyes. This minus overcorrection pushes the focal point behind the retina; the retinal blur creates a persistent accommodative demand even for distance vision, which could cause accommodative fatigue.

7.5.2 Accommodation in the Uncorrected and Corrected Hyperope

In addition to the type of ametropia, the accommodative demand is influenced by the type of correction, whether it be contact lens or spectacle correction (including vertex distance).[752]

Uncorrected Hyperope

Nestor is a +4.00 D hyperope fixating at 25 cm (Figure 7-14). Light from the fixation point reaches the eye with vergence = –4.00 D. If the eye is uncorrected (∴ far-point vergence = +4.00 D), then the accommodative demand is, according to relationship (7.1),

Magnitude of accommodation = far-point vergence – fixation-point vergence

Accommodation, uncorrected hyperope: = +4.00 D – (–4.00 D) = +8.00 D.

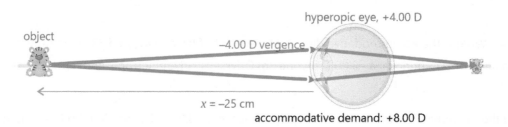

Figure 7-14: Accommodative demand for an uncorrected hyperope.

Contact-Lens-Corrected Hyperope

When corrected, the eye is fixating not on the object but on the image of that object created by the lens: the fixation vergence is altered by the lens. We now consider the vergence of the ray fan that leaves the lens and subsequently reaches the corneal plane. Let's see how.

As illustrated in Figure 7-15, we place a contact lens of +4.00 D power at the corneal plane (vertex distance = 0 mm). This lens images that fixation object at infinity.[753] Said another way, the ray fan, which originates from the fixation point, leaves the contact lens and reaches the eye with vergence 0.0 D. There is no further change in this, as the rays are already at the corneal plane. The fixation point vergence is 0.0 D, and the accommodative demand is:

Magnitude of accommodation = far-point vergence – fixation-point vergence

Contact-lens-corrected hyperope: = +4.00 D – (0.00 D) = +4.00 D.

---

[752] Jiménez R, Martínez-Almeida L, Salas C, Ortíz C. Contact lenses vs spectacles in myopes: Is there any difference in accommodative and binocular function? Graefes Arch Clin Exp Ophthalmol. 2011; 249(6):925-35.

[753] The Geometrical Optics Professor assumes that we are comfortable with the notion that the object vergence is $L = 1/x = 1/(-0.25$ m$) = -4.00$ D. This is added to the contact lens power, so the ray fan leaves the lens with vergence $L' = -4.00 +4.00 = 0.0$ D.

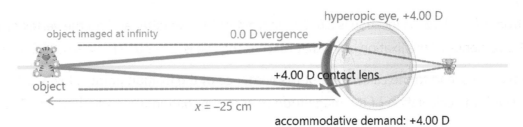

Figure 7-15: Accommodative demand for a contact-lens-corrected hyperope.

Spectacle-Lens-Corrected Hyperope

When the correction is not implemented at the corneal plane but at the spectacle plane (vertex distance ≠ zero), there are three adjustments to the vergence of the fixation point.

The <u>first adjustment</u> is to the power of the spectacle lens. For vertex distance d_v = 15 mm, the power of the spectacle lens is not +4.00 D, but +3.75 D. To calculate the required spectacle lens power, we use relationship (9.7) with the transposition d = –0.015 m (note the minus sign, as the lens is upstream) and the initial power F_o = +4.00 D:

$$\underbrace{F_{u/d\,=\,-15mm}}_{\text{upstream power}} = \frac{F_o}{1 - \underbrace{d}_{\text{transposition (m)}} \cdot \underbrace{F_o}_{\text{initial power}}} = \frac{+4.00}{1 - (-0.015 \cdot 4.00)} = +3.77 \text{ D}$$

This is rounded to +3.75 D. Therefore, this eye has +3.75 hyperopia, at 15 mm vertex.

The <u>second adjustment</u> is to the object location as measured from the spectacle lens plane. While the object is the same distance from the eye, its location is now noted as x = –23.5 cm, as can be easily deduced from the detail presented in Figure 7-16. Because of this designation, the vergence reaching the lens is L = 1/(–0.235 m) = –4.25 D. This is added to the lens power, so the ray fan leaves the lens with vergence L' = –4.25+3.75 = –0.50 D.

Now, for the <u>third adjustment</u>: The leaving-the-lens vergence is not the same as the reaching-the-eye vergence. In general, these two quantities are not equal; the latter is the downstream version of the former, adjusted for the vertex distance.

Here, however, there is minimal difference. To calculate the reaching-the-eye vergence, we can either use Eq (9.7)—discussed in Chapter 9—with transposition d = +0.015 m (note the plus sign because we now move downstream) and L' = –0.50 D. The downstream vergence is therefore L'' = –0.5/[1 – (0.015)·(–0.50)] = –0.5/(1+0.075) = –0.496 D ≈ –0.50 D.

An alternative method is to consider that the vergence reaching the eye is the vergence of the fixation point imaged through the spectacle lens (Figure 7-16). As the fixation point is imaged

2 m in front of the lens, its location is 2.015 m in front of the eye (after adding the vertex distance). Thus, the vergence of the fixation point that reaches the eye is 1/(–2.015 m) = –0.496 D ≈ –0.50 D.

The above steps lead to the calculation of the vergence of the fixation point. Now we can proceed with the calculation of the magnitude of accommodation using relationship (7.1):

Magnitude of accommodation = far-point vergence – fixation-point vergence
Spectacle-lens-corrected hyperope: = +4.00 D – (–0.50 D) = +4.50 D.

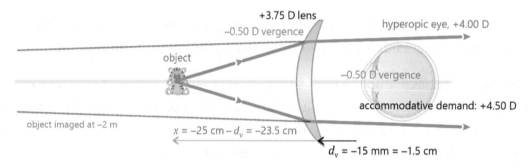

Figure 7-16: Accommodative demand for a spectacle-plane corrected hyperope.

Compare this result to +4.00 D required if that eye is corrected with contact lenses; the spectacled hyperope requires more accommodation: +4.50 D. Another way to say this is <u>the contact-lens-corrected hyperope requires less accommodation</u>.

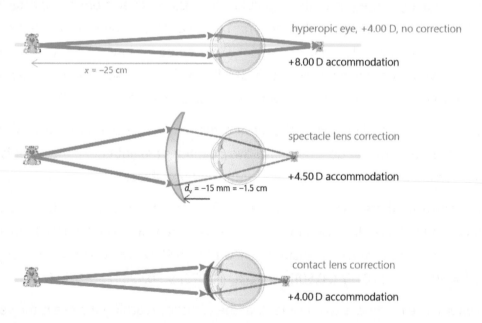

Figure 7-17: In a hyperopic eye, as the vertex distance decreases, the accommodative demand for the same eye–object distance decreases. A hyperope, when viewing a near object, <u>accommodates less</u> when the ametropia is corrected with <u>contact lenses</u> than when it is corrected with spectacles. Compare with Figure 7-24.

Example ☞: Ajax is fully corrected with an Rx +5.50 D, vertex distance 15 mm. What is the accommodative demand when Ajax is fixating on a distance point (assume infinity)?

That's an easy one. By rule, 'fully corrected' means that Ajax is wearing the correction that makes his retina optically conjugate to a point at infinity. Then, we simply invoke Eq. (7.1), far-point vergence L_{FP} = 0.0 D, fixation point ($x = \infty$) vergence L_x = 0.0 D; hence, A = 0.00 D.

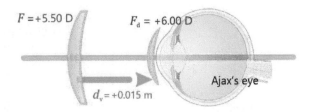

Figure 7-18: Spectacle correction versus contact lens correction for a +5.50 D, vertex 15 mm, hyperope.

What would be the full contact lens correction for Ajax? What is the accommodative demand when Ajax is fixating on a distant point (assume infinity)?

We use Eq. (9.7) with d = +0.015 m (note the plus sign, the contact lens is downstream) and F_o = +5.50 D. Then, F_d = +6.00 D. By rule, 'fully corrected' means that Ajax is wearing the correction that makes his retina optically conjugate to a point at infinity. Then, we, again, invoke Eq. (7.1), far-point vergence L_{FP} = 0.0 D, fixation-point ($x = \infty$) vergence L_x = 0.0 D; hence, A = 0.00 D.

No surprise here. Both the spectacle and the contact lens corrections are vergence equivalent for distance. (This topic is presented in detail in § 9.2.4.).

Example ☞: Ajax, while being fully corrected with spectacles, fixates at a near distance 33.3 cm in front of his spectacles. What is the accommodative demand when Ajax is wearing the Rx: +5.50 D, vertex 15 mm?

(a) Spectacle lens power at a vertex distance of 15 mm = +5.50 D.
(b) Fixation-point location from the lens = −0.333 m; fixation vergence reaching the lens L = −3.00 D.
(c) Vergence leaving the lens L_x' = +2.50 D is produced by adding $L_x + F$.
(d) Fixation-point vergence downstream adjusted to the corneal plane L_x'' = +2.60 D.
Accommodation A = (far-point vergence) − (fixation vergence) = (+6.00 D) − (+2.60 D) = +3.40 D.

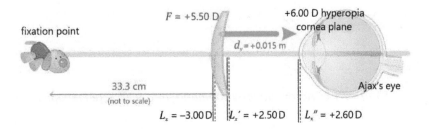

Figure 7-19: Calculation of fixation-point vergence at three different locations.

Example ☞: Ajax, while being fully corrected with contact lenses (+6.00 D), is fixating on the same near point, which is now 34.8 cm in front of his eye. What is the accommodative demand?

This calculation is rather straightforward. The accommodative demand is equal to and opposite in sign to the fixation-point vergence; hence, A = +2.87 D. Note that, in this hyperopic correction, the contact lens correction requires less accommodation (+2.87 D) than the spectacle correction (+3.40 D).

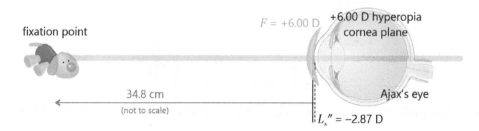

Figure 7-20: Calculation of fixation-point vergence for the contact-lens-correction case.

7.5.3 Accommodation in the Uncorrected and Corrected Myope

Uncorrected Myope

Arete, the Queen of the Phaeacians, is a –4.00 D myope who wishes to read a tablet at 25 cm. Coincidentally, the fixation-point vergence is also = 1/(–0.25 m) = –4.00 D. If uncorrected (∴ far-point vergence = –4.00 D), the accommodative demand is calculated using Eq. (7.1) as follows:

Magnitude of accommodation = far-point vergence – fixation-point vergence

Accommodation, uncorrected myope: = –4.00 D – (–4.00 D) = +0.00 D.

Arete is, apparently, a 'lucky' –4.00 D myope, since she does not need any correction to read comfortably at this 25 cm distance. This is not luck; it is the laws of optics: The object is conveniently located at the far point of her eye, which is conjugate to her retina.

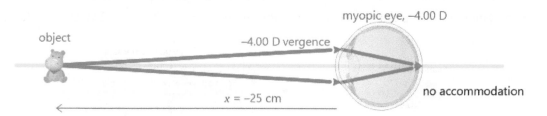

Figure 7-21: Accommodative demand for uncorrected myopia.

Contact-Lens-Corrected Myope

Arete now places a contact lens (CL −4.00 D power) at the corneal plane (vertex distance = 0 mm). The vergence leaving the CL from the fixation point is −4.00 D + (−4.00 D) = −8.00 D.[754] The accommodative demand is equal to and opposite in sign to the fixation point vergence:

Magnitude of accommodation = far-point vergence − fixation-point vergence

Contact-lens-corrected-myope: = −4.00 D − (−8.00 D) = +4.00 D.

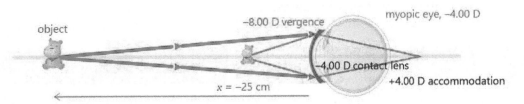

Figure 7-22: Accommodative demand for a contact-lens-corrected myope.

Spectacle-Lens-Corrected Myope

Arete is now considering spectacle correction at a vertex distance d_v = 15 mm. The first adjustment is that the power of the spectacle lens is not −4.00 D but −4.25 D. The second adjustment is that the object is located at a distance x = −23.5 cm (Figure 7-23). For this reason, the vergence reaching the lens is L = 1/(−0.235 m) = −4.25 D. This vergence is added to the lens power, so the rays leave the spectacle lens with vergence L' = −4.25 + (−4.25) = −8.50 D.

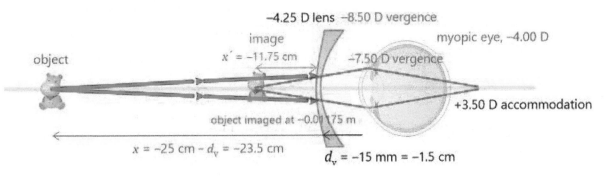

Figure 7-23: Accommodative demand for spectacle-plane corrected myope.

And now, the third adjustment. We recognize that this vergence is <u>not</u> the vergence reaching the eye, it is the vergence leaving the lens. The downstream vergence is therefore L'' = −8.5/[1 −0.015·(−8.50)] = −8.5/(1+0.1275) = −7.538 D ≈ −7.50 D. Alternatively, we calculate that

---

[754] The object vergence is L = 1/x = 1/(−0.25 m) = −4.00 D. This is added to the CL power, so the ray fan leaves the contact lens with vergence L' = −4.00 −4.00 = −8.00 D. Alternatively, the image location of the fixation point through the CL is −12.5 cm.

the fixation point is imaged to 11.75 cm in front of the lens; this distance is 13.25 cm in front of the eye, so the downstream vergence reaching the eye is 1/(–0.1325 m) = –7.50 D. The magnitude of accommodation is calculated using relationship (7.1).

Magnitude of accommodation = far-point vergence – fixation-point vergence
Spectacle-lens-corrected myope: = –4.00 D – (–7.50 D) = +3.50 D.

We recognize that a spectacle-corrected myope requires less accommodation than a fully corrected myope with contact lenses. Conversely, a contact-lens-corrected myope experiences a greater accommodative demand.

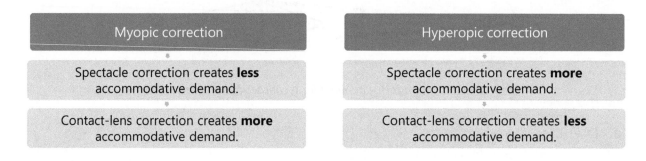

Myopic correction	Hyperopic correction
Spectacle correction creates **less** accommodative demand.	Spectacle correction creates **more** accommodative demand.
Contact-lens correction creates **more** accommodative demand.	Contact-lens correction creates **less** accommodative demand.

Clinical note ⬚: The fact that a contact-lens-corrected myope experiences greater accommodative demand contributes to the fact that myopes transitioning from spectacle correction to contact lenses need presbyopic correction sooner. To the contrary, a hyperope who is approaching presbyopia will experience less near-task difficulty with a full contact-lens correction than with spectacle-lens correction.

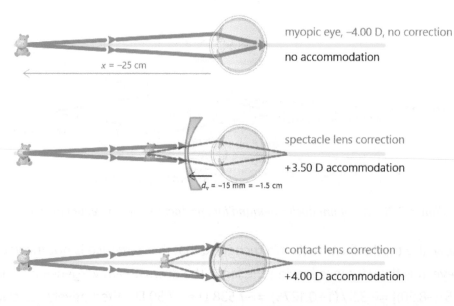

myopic eye, –4.00 D, no correction

no accommodation

$x = -25$ cm

spectacle lens correction

+3.50 D accommodation

$d_v = -15$ mm $= -1.5$ cm

contact lens correction

+4.00 D accommodation

Figure 7-24: In a myopic eye, as the vertex distance is decreased, the accommodative demand for the same eye–object distance increases. A myope, when viewing a near object, <u>accommodates more</u> when the ametropia is corrected <u>with contact lenses</u> than when it is corrected with spectacles. Compare with Figure 7-17.

Example ☞: A fully corrected Achilles is wearing this Rx: −6.50 D, vertex distance 13 mm. What is the accommodative demand when Achilles is fixating on a distance point (assume infinity)?

That's an easy one. By rule, 'fully corrected' means that Achilles is wearing the correction that makes his retina optically conjugate to a point at infinity. Then, we simply invoke Eq. (7.1): far-point vergence L_{FP} = 0.0 D, fixation-point ($x = \infty$) vergence L_x = 0.0 D; hence, A = 0.00 D.

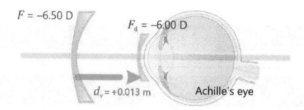

$F = −6.50$ D $F_d = −6.00$ D

$d_v = +0.013$ m   Achille's eye

Figure 7-25: *Spectacle correction versus contact-lens correction for a −6.50 D, vertex 13 mm, myope.*

What would be the full contact-lens correction for Achilles? What is the accommodative demand when Achilles is fixating on a distant point (assume infinity)?

We use Eq. (9.7) with d = +0.013 m (note the plus sign, as the contact lens is downstream) and F_o = −6.50 D. Then, F_d = −6.00 D. Now, regarding the accommodative demand: By rule, 'fully corrected' means that Achilles is wearing the correction that makes his retina optically conjugate to infinity. Then, by Eq. (7.1): far-point vergence L_{FP} = 0.0 D, fixation-point ($x = \infty$) vergence L_x = 0.0 D; hence, A = 0.00 D.

No surprise here. As in the case with Ajax, both the spectacle and the contact-lens corrections are vergence equivalent for distance. Effectively, the fully corrected eye is an 'emmetropic' one, and its far point is at infinity. Again, the aspect that pertains to accommodation is that the two corrections, spectacle and the contact lens, require different accommodation efforts when the eye fixates on a near object.

Example ☞: The fully corrected (using spectacle lenses Rx: −6.50 D, vertex 13 mm) Achilles is fixating on a near point 33.3 cm in front of his spectacles. What is the accommodative demand?

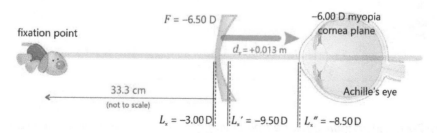

fixation point $F = −6.50$ D   −6.00 D myopia cornea plane

$d_v = +0.013$ m

33.3 cm
(not to scale)   Achille's eye

$L_x = −3.00$ D $L_x' = −9.50$ D $L_x'' = −8.50$ D

Figure 7-26: *Calculation of fixation-point vergence at three different locations.*

(a) Spectacle lens power at the vertex distance of 13 mm = –6.50 D.

(b) Fixation-point location from the lens = –0.333 m; fixation vergence reaching the lens L = –3.00 D.

(c) Vergence leaving the lens L_x' = –9.50 D is produced by adding $L_x + F$.

(d) Fixation-point vergence downstream adjusted to the corneal plane L_x'' = –8.50 D.

Accommodation A = (far-point vergence) – (fixation vergence) = (–6.00 D) – (–8.50 D) = +2.50 D.

Problem-solving strategy to calculate accommodative demand in spectacle correction:

Magnitude of accommodation = far-point vergence – fixation vergence.

Far-point vergence is the reciprocal of the ametropia for that eye.

To calculate fixation-point vergence:

- (a) Check the spectacle lens power at the vertex distance.
- (b) The fixation point location from the lens produces fixation vergence L reaching the lens.
- (c) Vergence leaving the lens L_x' is produced by adding $L_x + F$.
- (d) Leaving-the-lens fixation-point vergence L_x'' is downstream adjusted for the corneal plane.

Example ☞: The fully corrected (using contact lens) Achilles is fixating on the same near point, which is now 34.6 cm in front of his eye's corneal plane. What is the accommodative demand?

This calculation is rather straightforward. The accommodative demand is equal to and opposite in sign to the fixation-point vergence; hence, A = +2.89 D. Note that in this myopic correction, the contact-lens correction requires more accommodation (+2.89 D) than the spectacle correction (+2.50 D).

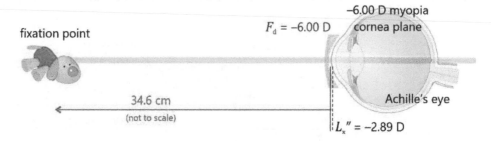

Figure 7-27: Calculation of fixation-point vergence for the contact-lens-correction case.

Advanced practice problems involving accommodation and spectacle wear :

Homer, an +8.00 D hyperope, is holding a +20.00 D lens 2.5 cm in front of his eyes while viewing an object placed 10.0 cm in front of his eyes. What is the accommodative demand experienced by our epic poet?

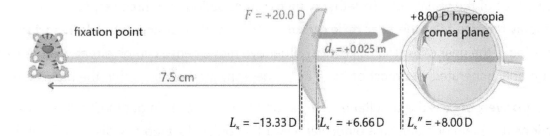

To calculate the accommodative demand, we need the far-point vergence of our hero (+8.00 D) and the vergence reaching the eye from the fixation point (L_x''). Their difference is the accommodative demand.

Calculation of fixation point vergence reaching the eye:

Because vertex is 2.5 cm, fixation point to lens: $x = -7.5$ cm, vergence reaching the lens: $L = -13.33$ D. Vergence leaving the lens $L_x' = +6.66$ D.

Vergence reaching the eye is L_x' vergence downstream adjusted to the corneal plane $L_x'' = +8.00$ D.

Accommodation = far-point vergence – fixation-point vergence = +8.00 D – (8.00 D) = +0.00 D. Homer needs zero accommodation to view this object.

What is Penelope's ametropia if she can clearly and without accommodation view an object 7.2 cm in front of her eyes via a +25.0 D lens held 4.0 cm in front of her eyes?

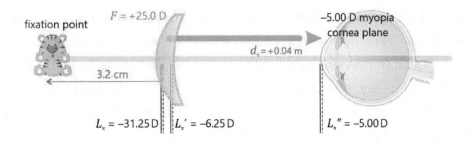

Here we are informed that the accommodative demand is zero; therefore, the vergence reaching the eye equals the uncorrected ametropia of the eye.

Because the vertex is 4 cm, the fixation point to lens: $x = -3.2$ cm, vergence reaching the lens: $L = -31.25$ D. Vergence leaving the lens $L_x' = -6.25$ D.

Vergence reaching the eye is L_x' vergence downstream adjusted to the corneal plane $L_x'' = -5.00$ D.

Penelope is a –5.00 D uncorrected myope.

7.6 CONVERGENCE AND ACCOMMODATION EFFECTS

Accommodation is not the only physiological response to take place when someone is fixating on a near object. Two other responses are engaged: pupillary miosis (constriction) and convergence of the visual axes. Together with accommodation, the three responses are commonly referred to as the **near reflex triad**, synkinetic triad, or **accommodative triad**.[755] Interestingly, the near reflex triad, like most other eye movements, can be either voluntarily or involuntarily generated, but most of the effector neurons are housed within the brainstem.

Convergence is the simultaneous rotation of the two eyes in geometrically opposite directions to obtain or maintain a binocular view of an object located any distance from the eyes. In positive convergence, the eyes rotate inward (nasally), which means the right eye rotates to the left, and the left eye rotates to the right. In divergence, which is negative convergence, the eyes rotate outward (temporally), meaning that the left eye rotates to the left, and the right eye rotates to the right. Thus, while accommodation is the ocular response that creates a monocular clear retinal image from a near object, convergence is the coordinated motor response that brings both eyes to the object of interest to make binocular vision possible. Unlike accommodation, convergence does not usually deteriorate with age.

Just as several cues trigger the accommodative system, several cues also trigger the vergence system. Pertaining to the near reflex triad, the act of convergence when viewing nearby targets is facilitated by both accommodative and fusional vergence responses.

Fusional vergence is driven by **retinal disparity**. Retinal disparity is generated when images fall on retinal locations that do not have a sensory linkage, i.e., are not corresponding points. This stimulates the eyes to align the two viewed images. Accommodative vergence describes the reflexive eye movements in response to accommodation, which occurs in response to retinal blur.[756] Once an eye has responded to and eliminated retinal blur, the accommodative vergence tone is held steady to help keep the eyes in position on the target. Visual processing also uses other perceptual cues, such as proximity, size, texture, overlap, and looming, to help stimulate these vergence responses to near-target viewing.

Convergence is measured in **meter angles** [MA], where 1 MA is the convergence needed to binocularly view an object 1 m away while exerting 1.00 D of accommodation. Meter angles

---

[755] Myers GA, Stark L. Topology of the near response triad. Ophthalmic Physiol Opt. 1990; 10(2):175-81.

[756] Vergence eye movements. In: Leigh RJ, Zee DS. The neurology of eye movements. 5th ed. New York: Oxford University Press; 2015.

are the reciprocal of the working distance, whose value approximately equals the accommodative stimulus [D].

$$\text{Meter Angle [MA]} = \frac{1}{\text{working distance [m]}} = \frac{100}{\text{working distance [cm]}} \qquad (7.3)$$

Example ☞: Penelope is binocularly viewing a target at 8 cm on the median line in front of her eyes. What is her convergence effort, expressed in meter angles?

Convergence effort is 1/0.08 m = 100/8 cm = 12.5 MA.

In emmetropes, the magnitude of accommodation [D] equals the convergence effort required to maintain binocular vision—if the latter is expressed in meter angles.

Example ☞: Odysseus' eyes are converging at a point placed 40 cm on the median line in front of his eyes. What is the accommodation [D] and what is the convergence effort [MA]?

A = (far-point vergence) – (fixation vergence) = (0.00) – (1/–0.4 m) = 0.00) – (–2.5 D) = +2.5 D.
Convergence = 1/0.4 m = 2.5 MA.

Alternatively, convergence can be measured in prism diopters; one **prism diopter** [$^{\Delta}$] is the prism power that deviates a ray by 1 cm over a distance of 1 m (more on this in § 10.1.2). Meter angles can be converted into prism diopters simply by multiplying by the interpupillary distance (IPD or PD), expressed in centimeters.

Thus, the **convergence effort** (expressed in diopters [$^{\Delta}$]) that an emmetrope requires to binocularly fixate on a near object equals the dioptric distance from the object to the center of rotation of the eyes, multiplied by the interpupillary distance:

$$\text{Convergence effort } [^{\Delta}] = \text{IPD [cm]} \times \frac{100}{\text{distance from the center of rotation of the eyes [cm]}} \qquad (7.4)$$

Example ☞: Penelope (IPD = 6.2 cm) is binocularly viewing a target 8 cm in the median line in front of her eyes. What is her convergence effort, expressed in prism diopters?

As discussed in § 2.4.3, the center of rotation of the eye is, on average, 13.5 mm = 1.35 cm inward of the cornea vertex. The 'distance' is the distance from the object of fixation to the center of rotation of the eye. Since the object of fixation is 8 cm in front of the eye, the distance to the center of rotation of her eyes is 8 + 1.35 = 9.35 cm. Convergence = 6.2 · 100/(9.35) = 66.3$^{\Delta}$.

Example ☞: Odysseus' eyes are converging to 40 cm in front of his eyes. The interpupillary distance when the eyes are viewing this point is 6 cm. What is the convergence effort, expressed in prism diopters?

Here, IPD = 6 cm. Since the object of fixation is 40 cm in front of the eye, the distance to the center of rotation of his eyes is 40 + 1.35 = 41.35 cm. Convergence = 6·100/(41.35) = 14.5$^\Delta$.

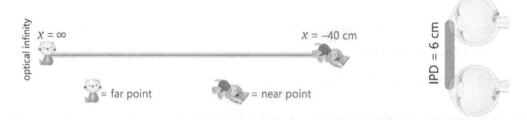

Figure 7-28: Amplitude of accommodation and convergence. The fixation target can be anywhere along the range of clear vision; it is convenient to place the object on the medial plane so that equal angles are formed between each line of sight. Maximum convergence is exerted for the near point of convergence, which can be closer than the near point for clear (monocular) vision.

Note 🐠: Roughly, convergence expressed in prism diopters is about 6× the numerical result obtained with meter angles; alternatively, 1 MA of convergence is about 3$^\Delta$ applied to each eye.

The **near point of convergence** (NPC) is the closest point from a person at which an object is seen binocularly; at the NPC, the lines of sight intersect under the maximum convergence effort. As the NPC can be modified by instructions and target choice, NPC measurements can vary. An NPC value of 5 to 6 cm indicates good vergence performance.[757] The NPC is commonly measured by using either an accommodative target or a penlight while observing through red/green glasses. The NPC measures the closest position in front of the two eyes where convergence is observed; stated differently, it measures the closest position where the lines of sight still maintain interaction.[758]

Likewise, the **far point of convergence** (FPC) is the farthest point from a person at which an object may be seen binocularly or the point to which lines of sight intersect with convergence 'at rest.' The distance between the NPC and FPC is the range of convergence.

Accommodation is intricately linked to convergence; even when testing accommodation monocularly, the covered eye still elicits a convergence response. There are two commonly measured convergence–accommodation responses.

---

[757] Scheiman M, Gallaway M, Frantz KA, Peters RJ, Hatch S, Cuff M, Mitchell GL. Nearpoint of convergence: test procedure, target selection, and normative data. Optom Vis Sci. 2003; 80(3):214-25.

[758] Scheiman M, Wick B. Clinical management of binocular vision: heterophoric, accommodative, and eye movement disorders. 4th ed. Philadelphia, PA: Wolters Kluwer; 2013.

- Accommodation can elicit convergence, measured by the accommodative convergence to accommodation ratio (AC/A ratio).[759] Odysseus (see the preceding example) has AC/A ratio $14.5^{\Delta} \div 2.5$ D $= 5.8^{\Delta}/$D. Normal values for the AC/A ratio are 3^{Δ}:1D to 6^{Δ}:1 D.[760]

- Convergence can elicit accommodation, measured by the convergence-accommodation to convergence ratio (CA/C ratio).[761] Normal values for the CA/C ratio are 0.08 D/$^{\Delta}$ or 0.5 to 0.4 D/MA. [762, 763, 764]

7.6.1 Convergence and Spectacle Wear

We discussed how the type of refractive error (myopia/hyperopia), as well as the type of corrective optics (contact lens or spectacle lens) influences the accommodative demand. The same is true with convergence effects. When observing a near target, the target's image location depends on the type of refractive error and the type of correction being worn.

Example ☞: Eurymachus is a hyperope with Rx +7.75 D at a 15 mm vertex distance. The equivalent contact lens power (0 mm vertex) is +7.00 D. His eyes are fixating on an object 10 cm in front of his eyes.

When wearing a contact lens [Figure 7-29 left], object location from the contact lens is $x = -10$ cm $= -0.10$ m. Vergence reaching the lens is −10.00 D, which is added to the +7.00 D contact-lens power to produce a −3.00 D image vergence reaching the eye. Thus, the image is at $x' = 1/(-3.00$ D$) = -0.33$ m. This is 33.3 cm in front of the eye's corneal plane, or 34.65 cm from the center of rotation of the eye.

When wearing a spectacle lens [Figure 7-29 right], object location from the lens is $x = -8.5$ cm $= -0.085$ m. Vergence reaching the lens is −11.75 D, which is added to the +7.75 D spectacle-lens power to produce a −4.00 D image vergence leaving the spectacle lens. Thus, the image is at $x' = 1/(-4.00$ D$) = -0.25$ m $= -25.0$ cm. This is 25 cm in front of the lens, 26.5 cm in front of the eye's corneal plane, and 27.85 cm from the center of rotation of the eye.

Assuming that IPD = 6.4 cm, the contact lens convergence demand is $6.4 \cdot 100/(34.65) = 18.5^{\Delta}$, while the spectacle lens convergence demand is $6.4 \cdot 100/(27.85) = 23^{\Delta}$.

---

[759] Wybar K. Relevance of the AC-A ratio. Br J Ophthalmol. 1974; 58(3):248-54.

[760] Schor CM. A dynamic model of cross-coupling between accommodation and convergence: simulations of step and frequency responses. Optom Vis Sci. 1992; 69(4):258-69.

[761] Mutti DO, Jones LA, Moeschberger ML, Zadnik K. AC/A ratio, age, and refractive error in children. Invest Ophthalmol Vis Sci. 2000; 41(9):2469-78.

[762] Rosenfield M, Gilmartin B. Assessment of the CA/C ratio in a myopic population. Am J Optom Physio Opt. 1988; 65(3):168-73.

[763] Nonaka F, Hasebe S, Ohtsuki H. Convergence accommodation to convergence (CA/C) ratio in patients with intermittent exotropia and decompensated exophoria. Jpn J Ophthalmol. 2004; 48(3):300-5.

[764] Bruce AS, Atchison DA, Bhoola H. Accommodation–convergence relationships and age. Invest Ophthalmol Vis Sci. 1995; 36(2):406-13.

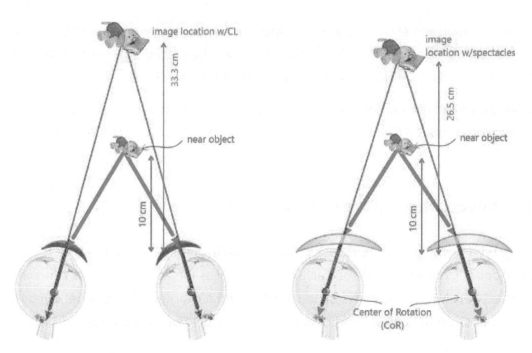

Figure 7-29: Convergence in hyperopia: (left) Contact-lens correction versus (right) spectacle-lens correction.

This example illustrates that, in a hyperope, an image viewed through a spectacle lens is formed closer to the eye than an image viewed through the equivalent contact lens. Thus, the convergence demand for a spectacled hyperope is greater. To the contrary, contact-lens-fitted hyperopic eyes experience reduced convergence demand when fixating on the same target.

Example ☞: Telemachus is a myope with Rx –6.25 D at 15 mm vertex distance. The equivalent contact lens Rx (0 mm vertex) is –7.00 D. He is fixating on an object 10 cm in front of his eyes.

When wearing a contact lens [Figure 7-30 (left)], object location from the contact lens is x = –10 cm = –0.10 m from the lens. The –10.00 D vergence is added to the –7.00 D lens power to produce a –17.00 D image vergence leaving the lens. Thus, the image is located at x' = 1/(–17.00) = –0.0588 m = –5.88 cm in front of the eye's corneal plane, or 7.23 cm from the center of rotation (CoR), which is considered to be 1.35 cm inside the eye (from the corneal plane).

When wearing a spectacle lens [Figure 7-30 (right)], object location from the spectacle lens is x = –8.5 cm = –0.085 m from the lens. Vergence is –11.75 D, which is added to the –6.25 D spectacle-lens power to produce a –18.00 D image vergence leaving the lens. Thus, the image is located at x' = 1/(–18.00) = –0.0555 m = –5.55 cm in front of the lens. This is 7.05 cm in front of the eye's corneal plane and 8.4 cm in front of the eye's center of rotation.

Assuming that IPD = 6.4 cm, the contact-lens convergence demand is $6.4 \cdot 100/(7.23) = 88.5^\Delta$, while the spectacle lens convergence is $6.4 \cdot 100/(8.4) = 76.2^\Delta$.

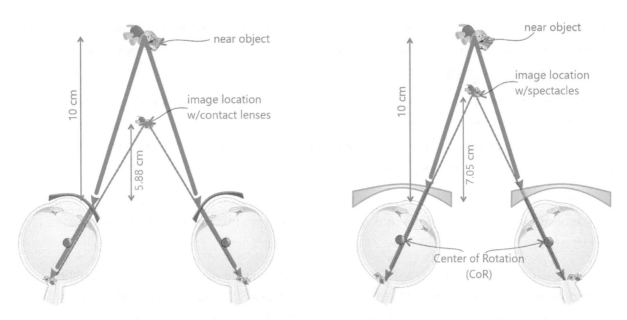

Figure 7-30: Convergence in myopia: (left) Contact-lens correction versus (right) spectacle-lens correction.

The above example illustrates that the image (apparent object) is farther in spectacle correction than in contact-lens correction for a myope. Contact-lens-fitted myopic eyes require an increased convergence effort compared to spectacle-lens-corrected eyes. Hence, the binocular convergence demand for a spectacled myope is less.

Another way to describe this effect uses the terminology of the induced prism (§ 10.5.2). Thus, we can also state that spectacle lenses for the correction of hyperopia create a base-out prism effect when an individual is looking at a near object, which increases the demand for convergence effort. This correction places the near object closer to the eye and requires more outward-muscle-pull effort for proper fusion. On the other hand, spectacle-lens correction of myopia induces a base-in prism effect, which decreases the convergence demand.

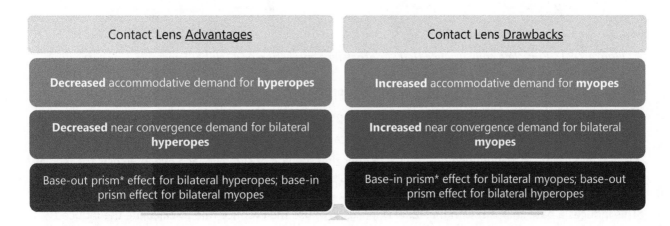

Contact Lens Advantages	Contact Lens Drawbacks
Decreased accommodative demand for **hyperopes**	**Increased** accommodative demand for **myopes**
Decreased near convergence demand for bilateral **hyperopes**	**Increased** near convergence demand for bilateral **myopes**
Base-out prism* effect for bilateral hyperopes; base-in prism effect for bilateral myopes	Base-in prism* effect for bilateral myopes; base-out prism effect for bilateral hyperopes

* More information on base-in and the base-out prism orientations is presented in § 10.5.1.

Example ☞: Eurycleia is a myope with Rx –2.57 D at 11.5 mm vertex distance. The equivalent contact lens Rx (0 mm vertex) is –2.50 D. She is hand-spinning wool 40 cm in front of her eyes. How much less does she converge when observing the spindle using her spectacles if her interpupillary distance is 70 mm?

First, we calculate convergence [$^\Delta$] when she views the spindle at the same distance (this involves several assumptions regarding the presence or lack of accommodative response) without any correction. We use Eq. (7.4): convergence [$^\Delta$] = IPD [cm] · 100 ÷ distance [cm]. Here IPD = 7 cm, distance from the corneal plane = 40 cm, i.e., distance from the CoR = 41.35 cm. Convergence = 7 · 100/(41.35) = 16.92$^\Delta$.

When wearing the contact lens (–2.50 D), the spindle is located 40 cm from the contact lens; the image of the spindle is formed 20 cm from the corneal plane and 21.35 cm from the CoR. Thus, convergence with contact lenses = 7 · 100/(21.35) = 32.78$^\Delta$.

When wearing the spectacle lens (–2.57 D at 11.5 vertex), the spindle is located 38.85 cm from the spectacle lens; the image is formed 19.36 cm in front of the lens (verify with imaging relationships), which is 20.51 from the corneal plane and 21.8 cm from the CoR. Thus, convergence with spectacle lenses = 7 · 100/(21.8) = 32.11$^\Delta$. Eurycleia has a slight advantage of about 0.67$^\Delta$ using a spectacle lens.

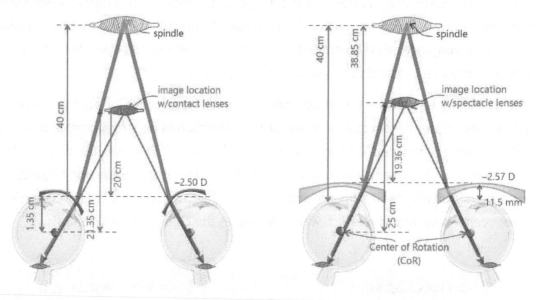

Figure 7-31: Eurycleia convergence (left) Contact-lens correction and (right) Spectacle-lens correction.

There is an additional aspect [discussed in § 10.4 as Prentice's rule, relationship (10.12)] when using spectacles because the eyes turn to gaze while the spectacles do not turn, but are fixed at 13.5 + 11.5 mm = 25 mm from the center of rotation of the eyes (recall that the CoR of the eye is 13.5 mm inside the eye). Using simple similar-triangle geometry, we can infer that the line of sight of each eye intersects the lens at 0.211 cm inward, which is the equivalent of decentering each lens by that amount outward (temporally).

This induces a base-in prism with the –2.50 D lenses. We use the Prentice rule to calculate the induced prism: $P[^\Delta]$ = –2.50 D · 0.211 cm = –0.52$^\Delta$ per eye.

7.7 PRESBYOPIA

7.7.1 Understanding the Problem

The most prevalent optics-related effect in an aging eye is **presbyopia** (πρεσβυ- πρεσβύτερος, elderly, senile & - ὄψις, sight), a gradual decrease in accommodation ability that pushes the near point farther from the eye to the point that near vision is severely compromised.[765]

Early studies by Franciscus Donders,[771] Alexander Duane,[766, 767] and Julius Kaufman[768] revealed a gradual decline in the amplitude of accommodation with age. Young emmetropes can accommodate as close as 10 cm (accommodating demand 10 D), while, over time, emmetropes may need to simply push the newspaper farther away to read.

According to Henry Hofstetter's analysis of these data, the amplitude of accommodation decreases at an average rate of 0.30 D per year, until it reaches 0.50 D at the age of 60, after which it stabilizes.[769] For example, a 40-year-old with an amplitude of accommodation between 5.0 and 8.0 D, with an average of 6.50 D, is expected to drop between 2.50 and 4.00 D, with an average of 3.50 D, at the age of 50.[770]

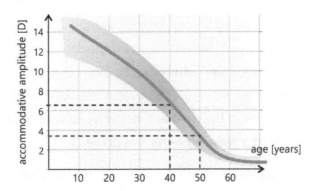

Figure 7-32: Amplitude of accommodation of a human eye, plotted against age. [771]

[765] Beers AP, van der Hiejde GL. Age-related changes in the accommodation mechanism. Optom Vis Sci. 1996; 73(4):235-42.

[766] Duane A. Normal values of the accommodation at all ages. JAMA. 1912; 59(12):1010-3.

[767] Duane A. Studies in monocular and binocular accommodation with their clinical applications. Trans Am Ophthalmol Soc. 1922; 20:132-57.

[768] Kaufman J. Die Absolute und Relative Accommodationsbreite in den Verschiedenen Lebensaltern. Inaugural Dissertation. Georg-August-Universität Göttingen, Germany, 1894.

[769] Hofstetter HW. A comparison of Duane's and Donders' tables of the amplitude of accommodation. Am J Optom and Arch Am Acad Optom. 1944; 21(9):345-63.

[770] Hofstetter HW. Useful age-amplitude formula. Optometric World. 1950; 42-5.

[771] Donders FC. Beiträge zur Kenntnis der Refractions – und Accommodations-anomailen. Albrecht von Graefe's Arvchiv für Ophthalmologie, Band 6. Abtheilung 1, Beriln, 1860. English translation by Moore WD. On the Anomalies of Accommodation and Refraction of the Eye. London, New Sydenham Society, 1864.

A simple formula for the average amplitude of accommodation = 15 – 0.25 × age.

Example ☞: Penelope, with accommodative amplitude of +5.00 D, is probably more than 40 years old.

Accommodative insufficiency is noted if the value is 2.00 D less than this average. This formula, however, has very limited applicability to young, normal subjects.[772] Average values for very young normal subjects are as high as 16.0 D as reported in the literature.[773]

7.7.2 Physiological Etiology

The physiological etiology of presbyopia is quite complex and not completely understood.[774] The accommodative apparatus of the eye fails; this is not disputed. But why?

The onset of presbyopia correlates with several changes relating to anterior segment structures. Most important is that the lens gradually hardens (sclerosis)[113] and thickens,[775] so it becomes increasingly less responsive to the tension applied via the ciliary body / zonular fiber complex. Also, there are also changes in the geometry of the zonular attachments and the elasticity of the capsule and the lens matrix.[776] There are also optical effects, which involve the increase in lens curvature,[106] the graded refractive index, and the magnitude and sign of the spherical aberration. All of the above effects change with advancing age.[777]

While, in the past, the prevailing theory for the presbyopic reduction in accommodative amplitude was the reduced capacity of the lens to accommodate, it is perhaps the reduced capacity of the lens to dissaccommodate,[739] to return to its relaxed state. Then why not lose distance vision instead of losing near vision? The answer lies in the 'lens paradox' (§ 2.2.1.2), which can be explained by changes in the gradient refractive index of the lens with age that result in a lens gradually attaining a reduced refractive power.

Despite the name, the typical presbyope is not an 'aged' person by today's standards; over one billion people worldwide are presbyopes.[778] Presbyopia without optical correction

---

[772] Hashemi H, Nabovati P, Khabazkhoob M, Yekta A, Emamian MH, Fotouhi A. Does Hofstetter's equation predict the real amplitude of accommodation in children? Clin Exp Optom. 2018; 101(1):123-8.

[773] Castagno VD, Vilela MA, Meucci RD, Resende DP, Schneid FH, Getelina R, Nasiloski MR, Fassa AG. Amplitude of accommodation in schoolchildren. Curr Eye Res. 2017; 42(4):604-10.

[774] Adler-Grinberg D. Questioning our classical understanding of accommodation and presbyopia. Am J Optom Physiol Opt. 1986; 63(7):571-80.

[775] Weale RA. Presbyopia. Br J Ophthalmol. 1962; 46(11):660-8.

[776] Gilmartin B. The aetiology of presbyopia: a summary of the role of lenticular and extralenticular structures. Ophthalmic Physiol Opt. 1995; 15(5):431-7.

[777] Glasser A, Campbell MC. Presbyopia and the optical changes in the human crystalline lens with age. Vision Res. 1998; 38(2):209-29.

[778] Holden BA, Fricke TR, Ho SM, Wong R, Schlenther G, Cronje S, Burnett A, Papas E, Naidoo KS, Frick KD. Global vision impairment due to uncorrected presbyopia. Arch Ophthalmol. 2008; 126(12):1731-9.

results in an inability to perform what used to be effortless near tasks at a customary working distance without experiencing visual symptoms.[779] A relaxed emmetropic eye forms the image of a distant object on the retina; whereas, to form a clear image from a near object, the eye needs to adapt to increase the optical power by increasing the optical power of the crystalline lens. In presbyopia, however, the eye cannot properly respond to this 'calling' of optics.

Presbyopia is often classified as a refractive error despite the fact that this effect is a natural evolution of the eye. While it is commonly stated that presbyopia commences after 40 years of age, it begins whenever one's ability to see up close starts to noticeably change.[780] Accommodation decline is a process that begins at birth and progresses over time.

Depending on variations in the working environment, task requirements, nutrition, and pathology,[781] the age at which presbyopia becomes symptomatic varies. For example, hyperopic individuals experience symptoms much earlier than myopic individuals. Additionally, it is common to notice latent hyperopia becoming manifest, causing one to seek both distance and near correction.[782]

7.7.3 The Add Power

Assuming no other refractive error, and depending on the working distance (locations of the near objects of fixation), the eyes of an individual in their mid-40s may need an extra correction of about +1.00 D; a decade later they may need +2.00 D, and well into the early 'silver' years, they may need +3.00 D.

This 'extra' correction, which is <u>always positive</u>, is called the **add** or **addition power**. In spectacles, the prescription for distance correction is not affected, but near correction algebraically increases by the spherical amount (diopters) of add power.

The add power can be implemented as a separate, single vision near prescription (i.e., distance power + add making the near vision Rx), or as part of a segmented prescription, the simplest example of the latter being the bifocal-segmented spectacle lens [Figure 7-33 (right)]. The lens segment (seg) for the near prescription can be one of several shapes, such as a round segment, a half-moon segment called a flat-top, where the entire bottom half of the lens is called an executive bifocal, or it can be part of a progressive addition lens.

---

[779] Patorgis CJ. Presbyopia. In: Amos JF, ed. Diagnosis and management in vision care. Boston: Butterworth, 1987:203-38.

[780] Milder B, Rubin ML. The fine art of prescribing glasses without making a spectacle of yourself, 2nd ed. Gainesville: Triad, 1991:52-3.

[781] Koretz JF, Kaufman PL, Neider MW, Goeckner PA. Accommodation and presbyopia in the human eye: aging of the anterior segment. Vision Res. 1989; 29(12):1685-92.

[782] Weale RA. Epidemiology of refractive errors and presbyopia. Surv Ophthalmol. 2003; 48(5):515-43.

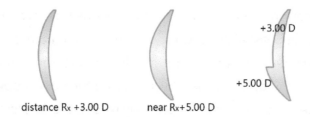

distance Rx +3.00 D   near Rx +5.00 D

Figure 7-33: Examples of single vision prescriptions for (left) distance vision, (center) near vision, and (right) a bifocal segment lens. Add power is +2.00 D.

Practice examples with answers 🛠:

Antinous, a myope with distance Rx −3.00 D and add +2.00 D, needs a near prescription of −1.00 D.
Nausicaa, a hyperope with distance Rx +3.00 D and add +1.50 D, needs a near prescription of +4.50 D.

Often, the add power F_{add} can be simply estimated based on the subject's age; thus, F_{add} increases from +0.75 D for ages 40–42 (for example) to +2.00 for ages up to 55, and up to +2.50 for ages up to 60 years. Add power F_{add} may also be calculated from the difference between the near Rx for the working distance and the distance Rx in the phoropter/trial lens examination.

Example ☞: Polyphemus' distance Rx reads −1.75 −1.25×075. To calculate his near prescription, Polyphemus reports that he can read the desired near-distance text when the trial lens is at +0.25 −1.25×075. What should be the add power?

The add power is the difference between the near and the distance sphere values, which, here, is +2.00 D.

Selection of the add power can be facilitated by the concept of 'comfort.' It is accepted that for individuals to 'comfortably' view a target, they should use no more than half of their amplitude of accommodation (*AoA*), leaving a percentage of the amplitude of accommodation (the other half) in reserve. The rationale is that use of the entire accommodation is not sustainable without discomfort.[783] Thus, for a working (fixation point) distance w_d, the accommodative demand *A* should equal ½ · *AoA*:

$$A = \text{(far-point vergence)} - [1/(-w_d)] = \tfrac{1}{2} \cdot AoA \qquad (7.5)$$

Additionally, we consider a full distance Rx. The far point with this Rx is infinity; with the add power included, the far point with the near Rx becomes $1/(-F_{add})$, or the far-point vergence equals $-F_{add}$. For working distance w_d = 40 cm, Eq. (7.5) becomes

Add power (half-amplitude method): $\qquad F_{add} = (+2.50 \text{ D}) - (\tfrac{1}{2} \cdot AoA) \qquad (7.6)$

---

[783] Millodot M, Millodot S. Presbyopia correction and the accommodation in reserve. Ophthalmic Physiol Opt. 1989; 9(2):126-32.

Example ☞: Laertes has only 1.00 D amplitude of accommodation due to advanced age. What add power does he need to comfortably view the Delphi oracle held 40 cm in front of his eyes?

The add power assumes that Laertes is wearing a proper distance Rx. Therefore, regardless of his refraction status, when wearing the distance Rx, the far point is at infinity. When wearing his add power Rx, the far point is $1/(-F_{add})$. A fixation point at 40 cm has vergence (1/–0.40 m) = –2.50 D, or a dioptric stimulus of +2.50 D. The add power should be: +2.50 D – (½ · AoA) = +2.50 D – (½ · 1.00) = +2.00 D.

The add power alleviates near-vision accommodative demand but <u>does not</u> help <u>distance vision</u>, nor does it alter the <u>range of clear vision</u>, which, dioptrically, <u>remains the same with or without the add power</u>. It is imperative to note that the range of clear vision when one views through the add power shifts closer to the eye by a dioptric amount equal to the add power. When we convert to the <u>linear range of accommodation</u>, this range is <u>smaller</u> when wearing the near correction Rx, and the greater the add power the smaller the linear range.

Example ☞: Laertes, a –1.00 myope, is fitted with add power of +2.00 D. What are the ranges of clear vision with a distance and a near Rx? (Recall that he has 1.00 D amplitude of accommodation.)

When wearing his distance Rx (–1.00 D), effectively, the system 'eye + correction' is emmetropic. This means that his far point is at infinity. The near-point vergence is the difference between the amplitude of accommodation (–1.00 D) and the far-point vergence (0), which is –1.00 D. Thus, the near point is 1.0 m in front of Laertes' eyes (Figure 7-34). The range of clear vision is (∞, –1.0 m).

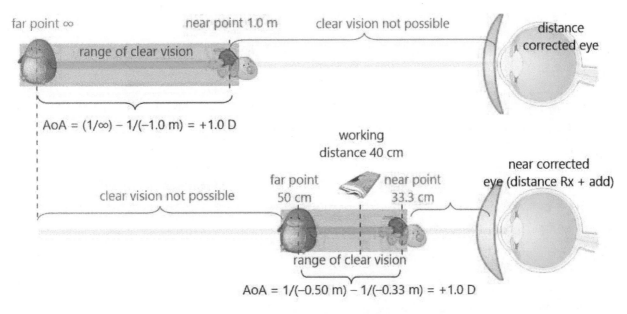

Figure 7-34: Range of clear vision with (top) a distance-vision and (bottom) a near-vision single-spectacle-lens Rx. The range of clear vision equals the amplitude of accommodation (AoA), which, dioptrically, is the same. Both the far point and the near point are shifted by the same dioptric amount (here, by +2.00 D).

The near Rx (distance Rx + add) = +1.00 D. Effectively, the system 'eye + correction' is –2.00 D myopic. The far point is at $1/(–2.00 \text{ D}) = –0.50 \text{ m}$. The near-point vergence is calculated, again, by the difference between the amplitude of accommodation and the far-point vergence, which is –3.00 D.

Thus, when Laertes is wearing the near Rx, the near-point is situated 0.33 m (= 1/3.00 D) in front of his eyes. The range of clear vision is (–0.50 m, –0.33 m); comfortable vision is at –0.40 m, using 0.50 D of accommodation.

A procedure to refine the add power value considers a balance between negative relative accommodation (NRA) and positive relative accommodation (PRA) in such a way that the added power is a dioptric average of NRA and PRA (a detailed discussion of these terms is outside the scope of this textbook).

Example ☞: Telemachus, a 45-year-old war hero, measures a tentative add through the fused cross-cylinder of 1.25 D. His NRA measurement over the cross-cylinder finding is +1.25 D, while his PRA over the cross-cylinder is –0.25D. What would be a tentative add?

The dioptric average of NRA and PRA is ½ × (+1.25 D – 0.25 D) = ½ × (+1.00 D) = 0.50 D.
This balanced value leads to +1.25 D (from the cross-cylinder) + (+0.50 D from a balanced NRA/PRA) = +1.75 D add power.
(This is a very high add-power value for a 45-year-old. Practically speaking, he would likely reject this lens.)

Clinical note ♀ : There is no single add value for any given individual but a range of add values that this person can successfully use for any given task.

There is an adage in clinical practice that "too much plus is as bad as not enough." No matter what technique is used to determine the add value, a trial frame must be used to test the technique on the examinee.

The best algebraic calculations may all be for naught if the examinee feels that the add value being trialed with them is too strong. The "least plus to most functionality" mindset should be adopted unless the examinee has stringent requirements.

7.7.4 Presbyopia Classification

Presbyopia can be classified by type as one of the following:[784]

Incipient presbyopia—also known as borderline, beginning, early, or pre-presbyopia—represents the earliest stage at which symptoms become noticeable. In incipient presbyopia, reading small print requires extra effort. Typically, the patient's history suggests a need for a reading addition, but the subject performs well visually on testing and, given the option, may prefer to remain uncorrected.

Functional presbyopia is associated with gradually declining AoA (stressed to the limits of near-vision accommodative demand), coupled with increased near-task requirements. Due to the continuous gradual accommodation decline, functional presbyopia progresses to **absolute presbyopia**, the condition in which, practically, no accommodative ability remains.

In **premature presbyopia**, the accommodative ability becomes insufficient for the subject's typical near-vision tasks at an earlier than expected due to environmental, nutritional, disease-related, or drug-induced issues.

Nocturnal presbyopia occurs when near-vision difficulties result from an apparent decrease in the amplitude of accommodation in dim light. Increased pupil size and decreased depth of field are usually responsible for this reduction in the range of clear near vision.[785]

7.8 THE MANAGEMENT OF PRESBYOPIA

Presbyopia management is an active field of research and development. This is because presbyopia eventually affects each and every one of us. However, it appears that the proper correction of presbyopia is a prize that is up for grabs. The reason is that, like any problem, it should be treated at its very root. In the case of presbyopia, the main cause is the loss of elasticity of the crystalline lens. Restoration of this elasticity has not been achieved clinically nor at least proven in a laboratory setting.

No possible substitute has the accommodative flexibility of non-presbyopic eyes to restore their ability to quickly switch between clear distance vision and clear near vision. None

---

[784] Kleinstein RN. Epidemiology of presbyopia. In: Stark L, Obrecht G, eds. Presbyopia: recent research and reviews from the third international symposium. New York: Professional Press Books, 1987:12-8.

[785] Glasser A, Kaufman PL. Accommodation and Presbyopia. In: Kaufman PL, Albert A. Adler's physiology of the eye, clinical application, 10th ed. St. Louis: CV Mosby, 2003: 214-5.

of the options available today for managing near vision deficiency addresses the core of the problem, which is nothing less than the irreversible loss of accommodative ability associated with advancing age. Although there are several approaches for managing the visual disability associated with presbyopia, all available modalities are compensatory rather than corrective. For this reason, the available options are, in essence, optical compromises. Like any compromise, these optical compromises entail a transaction, or exchange of goods.

Thus, there is no true treatment for presbyopia. The benefits and losses must be weighed for either option. None of the available techniques can restore the working optical system condition we once had at a young age. Some options for managing presbyopia are presented next.

7.8.1 Spectacle Correction for Presbyopia

In terms of spectacle lenses, there are three options an individual may pursue, each with its own pros and cons.

The first option is a **single vision pair** of spectacles for each different distance, such as single vision computer lenses or single vision near lenses. The benefit of this is that the field of view is only limited by the size of the frame and the corrective power. These spectacles can be very task-specific and are a great option for people who perform a lot of stationary tasks. The obvious downside is that multiple pairs of lenses are therefore required. Typical candidates for wearing spectacles or half-frame reading spectacles are individuals with emmetropia or with a low degree of ametropia (who do not require distance correction). Those with uncorrected myopia whose uncorrected vision meets their near vision needs can generally just remove their distance glasses for near tasks.

Multifocal lenses such as bifocals or trifocals are another option. These are lenses that incorporate specific working distances, such as distant and near, or intermediate and near, or distant and intermediate. The lens inserts may, fortunately, be placed on the lens in the direction of gaze where the insert is needed. The benefit of these lenses is that the insert size is still fairly large; for example, the reading portion of a bifocal may extend across the entire bottom half of the lens (in an executive bifocal) or be a 35 mm insert.

These lenses also are not prone to as many distortions as are progressive addition lenses, so they are much more easily tolerated by individuals with binocular vision disorders or visual-vestibular dysfunctions, and in individuals who have had head injuries. The main downsides are that the lenses are limited in where they are set to focus and that the segments can be very visibly obvious on the lenses.

With the evolution of multifocality, a form of multifocal, progressive power spectacles emerged, which constitutes the third option. The **progressive addition lens** (PAL) attempts to give back to the eyes the ability to see clearly over a range of distances. A PAL has gradients of increasing add power as an individual moves the eyes' gaze from the top of the lens (seeing farther away) down to the bottom of the lens (seeing up close). Differently stated, an individual can view distant, intermediate, and near distances all through this lens without compromising one of those distances, as in a bifocal (which is usually dispensed with a distance and near Rx but without an intermediate Rx).

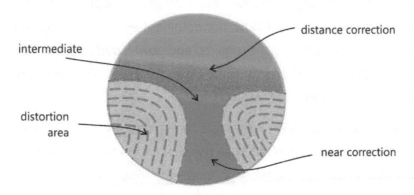

Figure 7-35: Power distribution in a progressive addition lens.

The PAL design, however, does involve significant compromises; to be functional over multiple different target distances, the field of view is significantly decreased when compared to single vision spectacles or bifocal/trifocals. There are two optical centers, the superior center with optical power matched for the distance vision correction and the inferior center with optical power matched for near vision correction. (More accurately, there is no center in the common optical sense, just a continuity of power.) Progressive addition lenses have the additional advantage that the area between the two centers produces the intermediate correction, too. When the individual properly adjusts to the new reality, this option may be almost perfect.

Over time, the designs of PALs have improved, so depending on the design, there may be a significant area on each side (temporal and nasal) of the lens that is unusable due to deliberate distortion (see the distortion areas in Figure 7-35). The word 'deliberate' indicates that the design parameters of the PAL are such that the induced distortion is meant to prevent the eye from using this area, effectively steering the gaze through the near-correction channel. However, this gaze steering can be associated with significant adaptation and comfort issues for the novice wearer, for perhaps up to a few weeks.[786] Other subjects are simply not able to

---

[786] Forkel J, Reiniger JL, Muschielok A, Welk A, Seidemann A, Baumbach P. Personalized progressive addition lenses: correlation between performance and design. Optom Vis Sci. 2017; 94(2):208-18.

tolerate these lenses due to the distortion; however, that being said, as PAL designs have improved, so too has the ability of the population to adapt to wearing this type of lens.

7.8.2 Monovision

Monovision describes the application of a different correction to each eye of the same individual. One eye is corrected for distance vision and the other for near vision. This type of correction thus creates slight anisometropia. Generally, the dominant eye becomes emmetropic (for distance), and the nondominant eye becomes slightly myopic. For example, the dominant eye might be targeted for 0.00 D, i.e., emmetropia, while the fellow, nondominant eye can be targeted for – 0.75 D myopia. This nondominant eye, having the required add power, performs the short distance vision tasks. Monovision thus can offer sharp vision for both distances. The reported rates of success with monovision correction range from 60 to 80%.[787]

Monovision is successful when individuals can voluntarily use the eye corrected for distance while viewing distant objects, and can use the eye corrected for near vision while performing near tasks. In doing so, the brain ignores the input from the eye that is not appropriately corrected for a given distance. Additionally, because an individual can voluntarily focus at near ranges with one eye while the other eye is blurred (due to being focused at distance), the brain is again able to ignore the information coming in through the blurred eye.

Monovision can be applied with laser refractive procedures, contact lenses (see § 7.8.3),[788] or IOL implantation following cataract-removal surgery.[789]

A limitation of monovision is that, when the required addition is more than 1.75 D, clear intermediate vision (objects at 1 m to 3 m) is problematic, particularly in its binocular aspect. In such a case, the nondominant eye is targeted for a large 'myopia' correction of −1.75 D, while the dominant eye is targeted for emmetropia. This relatively large disparity between the two eyes may lead to vision discomfort, sometimes negatively affecting activities of daily living such as driving and reading, and they may lead to the development of binocular dysfunctions associated with stereoscopic perception and spatial disorientation.[790, 791, 792]

---

[787] Evans BJ. Monovision: a review. Ophthalmic Physiol Opt. 2007; 27(5):417-39.

[788] Durrie DS. The effect of different monovision contact lens powers on the visual function of emmetropic presbyopic patients (an American Ophthalmological Society thesis). Trans Am Ophthalmol Soc. 2006; 104:366-401.

[789] Baikoff G, Matach G, Fontaine A, Ferraz C, Spera C. Correction of presbyopia with refractive multifocal phakic intraocular lenses. J Cataract Refract Surg. 2004; 30(7):1454-60.

[790] Burge J, Rodriguez-Lopez V, Dorronsoro C. Monovision and the misperception of motion. Curr Bio. 2019; 15(5):2586-92.

[791] Collins M, Goode A, Brown B. Distance visual acuity and monovision. Optom Vis Sci. 1993; 70(9):723-8.

[792] McGill E, Erickson P. Stereopsis in presbyopes wearing monovision and simultaneous vision bifocal contact lenses. Am J Optom Physiol Opt. 1988; 65(8):619-26.

7.8.3 Contact Lenses for Presbyopia

Since contact lenses are worn on the eye, the options for presbyopic correction are not the same as for spectacles. Single vision contact lenses are not easily removed or applied for changing visual distances, so, unlike spectacles, 'reading' contacts are not typically an option. As discussed in § 7.8.2, monovision entails the use of one contact lens for distance vision on one eye and another contact lens for near vision on the fellow eye.[793]

Contact lenses with multifocal designs are commonplace solutions for presbyopes who prefer not to wear glasses over their distance-vision contacts. The downside to this option is that multifocal lenses form two foci of light that inevitably are shared by both the distant and the near part of the object field. As a result, there is often decreased contrast sensitivity.

For rigid contact lenses, the options are similar to those for spectacles when comparing bifocals to progressive lenses. The two basic rigid contact lens designs are based on either alternating/translating vision or simultaneous vision.

The alternating-vision design was introduced first and follows the philosophy implemented in a bifocal spectacle lens: The near-vision addition portion is at the bottom of the contact lens (Figure 7-36). The issue with the implementation of this design in contact lenses is that, to use the near segment, the lower part of the lens needs to be in front of the pupil, so the contact lens must move on the surface of the eye, usually by the lens resting on the lower lid and rising as the eye moves downward for near gaze. An application that allows contact lens translating movements is not easy to implement; such lenses are usually not well tolerated by the wearer.

Figure 7-36: Optical principles of a bifocal contact lens.

[793] Callina T, Reynolds TP. Traditional methods for the treatment of presbyopia: spectacles, contact lenses, bifocal contact lenses. Ophthalmol Clin North Am. 2006; 19(1):25-33.

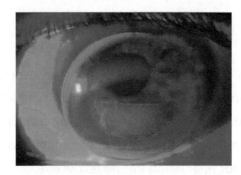

Figure 7-37: Fluorescein imaging of a bifocal rigid contact lens.

Multifocal designs offer acceptably sharp vision by the simultaneous presentation of distance and near images (and sometimes intermediate images), represented by varying degrees of corrective power across the lens [Figure 7-38 (right)]. Simultaneous-vision lens designs achieve this by positioning the distance- and near-vision-correction-lens portions concurrently over different pupillary areas, similar to a bullseye target [Figure 7-38 (left)].[794]

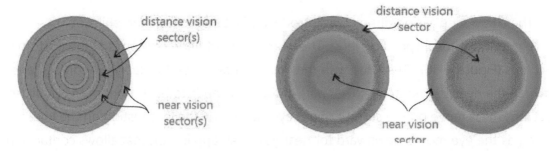

Figure 7-38: Architectures of multifocal contact lens designs: (left) The concentric design and (right) the design with varying degrees of corrective power across the lens.

Because when looking at targets through the distance sector or the near sector of the lens the object needs to be at the proper distance to be clearly focused on a sharp retinal image, viewing the same target through a different part of the pupil results in a blurry, out-of-focus image. This is a common issue in multifocal designs: Contrast may be somewhat reduced. Sometimes subjects report 'ghosting' or shadows around images due to the juxtaposition of multiple different lens powers in such close proximity, or they may sense a reduced contrast and reduced acuity, especially in low-contrast, low-light environments.[795]

As the simultaneous-vision design has proved to be successful, lens designers have created two major types, each implemented in both soft lenses and rigid lenses. The first major

---

[794] Josephson JE, Caffery BE. Monovision vs. bifocal contact lenses: crossover study. J Am Optom Assoc. 1987; 58(8):652-4.
[795] Back A, Grant T, Hine H. Comparative visual performance of three presbyopic contact lens corrections. Optom Vis Sci. 1992; 69(6):474-80.

type, called the center-near design, employs near vision correction in the central portion of the lens and distance vision correction in the peripheral portion of the lens (Figure 7-39). In such lenses, the power of the lens progressively becomes more positive (or less negative) from the peripheral sector to the central sector (Figure 7-40).

Figure 7-39: Examples of contact lenses with a center sector for near vision (center-near) correction.

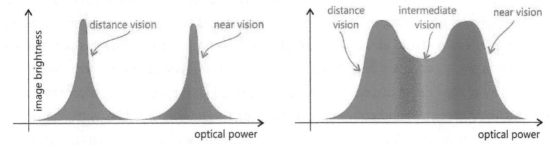

Figure 7-40: Distribution of optical power in (left) bifocal and (right) progressive designs.

The simultaneous-vision design is based on the miosis effect, an aspect of the near reflex triad (§ 7.1.2): When the eye focuses up close, the pupil constricts and the eye must accommodate to see clearly. With a smaller pupil, the central optical zone is what the pupil looks through, which explains the name 'center-near' design [Figure 7-41 (left)]. When the eye relaxes and fixates in the distance, it is no longer accommodating and the pupil dilates [Figure 7-41 (right)], allowing for vision through the lens' peripheral optical zones, which are designed for distance vision.

Figure 7-41: Principle of operation of the center-near contact lens design.

A concern with this design is that, for acceptable distance vision on a sunny day, sunglasses are needed to offset the miosis brought about by the bright sunlight. Without sunglasses, the wearer might look through the center-near sector. The sunglasses permit adequate mydriasis (pupil dilation) to allow the wearer to use the distance vision peripheral zone.

The design with the distance vision correction at the center of the lens, directly in front of the pupil, reverses the main drawback to the other lens type (the challenge of wearing center-near contact lenses in bright light). Therefore, the center-distance contact lens offers improved distance clarity, but at the expense of the wearer's near vision.

However, although presbyopia is defined through a loss of near vision, contact lens wearers are more likely to accept a compromise to their near vision than to their distance vision. This is likely because they have come to terms with having a reduction in the ability to see up close; not completely improving their near vision difficulties is likely not as dramatic as having distance vision affected. From an early age, individuals become accustomed to sharp distance vision, so even a slight reduction in distance acuity might bring about more discomfort than a slight reduction in near vision acuity. Generally, if the pupil is relatively large, a center-near lens will be more likely accepted, and conversely, if the pupil is relatively small (as is the general trend in older-age individuals), perhaps it is best to use a contact lens with a center-distance design.

A variation in contact lens design is the aspheric contact lens design, which incorporates a gradually changing curvature of the contact lens surface, producing an add power effect similar to that achieved by progressive addition spectacle lenses. Aspheric transitions are often incorporated into the intermediate zones (Figure 7-42). An aspheric bifocal lens, considered a version of the simultaneous vision design, effectively forms a series of superimposed images of the object of regard. Although image contrast is reduced, a sharp retinal image will be formed when the object is within the focusing range of the distance and near portions of the lens.

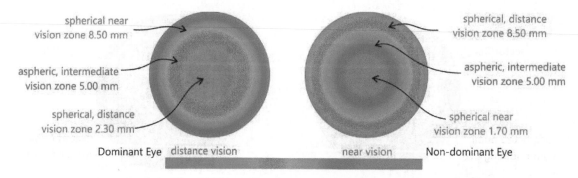

Figure 7-42: Combination of (left) center-distance and (right) center-near correction in contact lenses for the dominant eye and the fellow non-dominant eye. This is considered a modified monovision application.

An alternative design is called the concentric-design simultaneous vision. A lens of this type is constructed with a small circular central zone surrounded by another, annular optical zone. From the center to the edge of the lens there are many optical zones that alternate between distance correction and near correction. Either the distance correction [Figure 7-43 (left) and (center)] or the near correction [Figure 7-43 (right)] can be in the central zone, the former being more common.

Figure 7-43: Distribution of optical power in a contact lens where the center is for distance correction, with (left) two concentric zones and (center and right) multiple, alternating concentric zones.

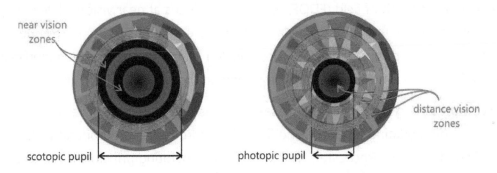

Figure 7-44: Principle of operation of contact lenses with concentric-design simultaneous vision.

These designs are the most popular, but others do exist, such as the diffraction contact lens, in which a concentric circular pattern creates a diffraction effect to provide for near focus, and the central part of the lens provides for distance vision via traditional refraction. Subjects may experience ghosting of images and difficulty with low light illumination; as with the other simultaneous vision lenses, these contact lenses may reduce contrast sensitivity.

7.8.4 Presbyopia Surgical Management Options

The most common surgical option for presbyopia is implantation of intraocular lenses (IOLs) with multifocal, extended depth of focus/field, or accommodating mechanisms. These premium IOL options are generally for patients who are subject to cataract removal surgery and wish to have reduced spectacle dependence after surgery. Although less common, it is possible for patients to opt to have their clear lens removed to get a premium presbyopia-correcting IOL (refractive lens exchange). IOLs can also be implanted in a monovision modality, which is perhaps the most common presbyopic surgical correction of all!

Other, more recent presbyopia surgical management options include procedures that allow for modification of the corneal surface in a way that achieves multifocality. The two main approaches involve either modifying the depth of focus or changing the central corneal curvature, as in using a power component or a spherical aberration component.

Multifocal IOLs apply principles similar to those applied in the contact lens designs. Alternating rings of distance and near (and sometimes intermediate) zones provide simultaneous vision. The same can be achieved with a diffractive design. Multifocal IOLs have side effects similar to those of multifocal contact lenses, including glare and halos; one downside is that they are not easily removed (once implanted). Another issue is the reduced contrast for the subject and for the examiner trying to image the retina.

By applying increased spherical aberration or a small aperture to the IOL,[796] the lens can provide an extended depth of field (EDOF) for improved focus at near vision while maintaining distance vision.[797] In fact, the range of clear vision in this case tends to be more continuous than when using a multifocal design. The EDOF designs do not, however, provide magnification for near objects since there is no near-power component in the lens.

Accommodating IOLs come the closest to attaining some form of restoration of the eye's natural accommodating function. The first FDA-approved accommodating IOL was the Crystalens (Bausch + Lomb, Rochester, New York).[798] Its operating principle is based on the forward translation of the optic part of the IOL during accommodation. It depends on the integrity of the lens capsule and zonular system to allow the hinges of the IOL to flex the lens forward when the ciliary muscle contracts, thereby increasing the optical power of the eye (recall that the effective power of a lens system is dependent on the element separation, § 2.3.2). Another approach employed in the Synchrony IOL (Visiogen, Abbott Medical Optics, Santa Ana, California) uses two lens components that move apart from each other and forward in the eye during the accommodation effort, again increasing the power of the eye.[799] More advances are being made to incorporate fluid components into the IOL that act to change the curvature of the central optic zone and increase power during the accommodation effort.

---

[796] currently under FDA trials.

[797] Bellucci R, Cargnoni M, Bellucci C. Clinical and aberrometric evaluation of a new extended depth-of-focus intraocular lens based on spherical aberration. J Cataract Refract Surg. 2019; 45(7):919-26.

[798] Zamora-Alejo KV, Moore SP, Parker DG, Ullrich K, Esterman A, Goggin M. Objective accommodation measurement of the Crystalens HD compared to monofocal intraocular lenses. J Refract Surg. 2013; 29(2):133-9.

[799] McLeod SD, Vargas LG, Portney V, Ting A. Synchrony dual-optic accommodating intraocular lens: Part 1: Optical and biomechanical principles and design considerations. J Cataract Refract Surg. 2007; 33(1):37-46.

Accommodating IOLs are a great advance but are not without drawbacks. So far, all of these designs depend on an intact capsule and zonule system and the proper functioning of their components. For instance, the hinge haptics of the Crystalens sometimes push the optic part of the IOL backward instead of forward during the accommodation effort, and a phenomenon known as Z syndrome sometimes left the IOL in a tilt position inside the eye.[800] The Synchrony IOL is a more complicated design with the two lens components and requires a slightly larger incision for implantation than a standard one-piece IOL; it stands to reason that the larger, fluid-filled IOLs may also require more surgical skill to be successfully implanted.

Other attempts to restore accommodation include the use of a femtosecond laser to break up adhesions within the crystalline lens, allowing the lens to bulge. Most of these attempts have been unsuccessful, however.

An alternative treatment is surgical modification of the **asphericity** of the cornea (§ 2.1.4) via a refractive laser procedure. Corneal asphericity corresponds to a +0.25 µm root mean square (RMS) of positive spherical aberration (for a 6.0 mm optical zone)[72] and is constant with age (excluding any pathology). This is not the case for the spherical aberration of the crystalline lens (§ 2.1.4.1), which at a young age has approximately the same magnitude but opposite sign, resulting in almost zero ocular spherical aberration (lenticular asphericity).[108] The principle of this treatment is that the spherical aberration induced by asphericity provides the required add power for the presbyopic correction added over the central pupil area (Figure 7-45).

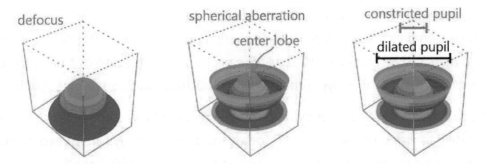

Figure 7-45: Three-dimensional wavefront illustrations corresponding to (left) defocus and (center) spherical aberration. (right) Defocus resembles the center lobe of the spherical aberration. The center lobe in the center and right images represents the wavefront-related add power resulting from spherical aberration.

A certain amount of spherical aberration for a particular pupil diameter has the advantage that, when the pupil constricts upon fixating at a near object, the pupil-center

---

[800] Mohebbi M, Afshan AB, Inanloo B, Nabavi A. Lens exchange for management of accommodative intraocular lens tilting. Taiwan J Ophthalmol. 2019; 9(1):46-48.

spherical aberration acts as the necessary add. The same logic applies to multifocal contact lenses incorporating wavefront design.[801] The leading surgical option is PresbyLASIK,[802] which results in a combination of a controlled spherical aberration with ametropia management. The optical principle relies on a characteristic of spherical aberration: For a small pupil diameter, the (negative) spherical aberration has almost the same effect as the defocus control, so a slightly aspheric surface provides additional correction for photopic and mesopic vision.

Laser treatment of the cornea intended to correct hyperopia has the advantage that it naturally results in increased corneal aberration (more negative Q-value, § 2.1.4), and, as it is applied in a presbyopic subject (probably of more than 40 years of age), it will naturally compensate for the age-related changes in crystalline lens asphericity.

Intracorneal **onlays** and **inlays** are alternative modalities to address presbyopia and, to some degree, refractive error. This is achieved through adding specifically designed and shaped material rather than corneal tissue removal or permanent corneal reshaping as in laser ablative or tissue-removing procedures. Because onlays and inlays are additive and do not remove tissue, the capacity for reversal/removal is preserved[803] if the application is not effective or if other correction types are desired. Onlays are superimposed on the cornea, while inlays are implanted in the stroma.

Because of the need to be implanted, inlays require an intracorneal pocket; while this is, indeed, an additional surgical step, it is also the inlays' ultimate advantage over onlays, as their application has a higher degree of stability and predictability. The intracorneal pocket is prepared using special high-precision surgical tools or a femtosecond laser. The initial step of the technique resembles the SMILE procedure of creating an intrastromal pocket. The pocket creation step may also be combined with a LASIK procedure in the case of a need to correct for refractive error, such as myopia, hyperopia, or astigmatism, in addition to presbyopia treatment.

Intracorneal inlays have recently begun to make inroads, and are considered a safe and viable alternative to vision correction.[804, 805] Today, the available inlays are of two main types, depending on their function. The first type involves elements that increase the optical power being placed over the optical zone; this results in a multifocal cornea. The second type is essentially a pinhole in front of the pupil that limits the entrance pupil of the eye. The principle

---

[801] Katsoulos C, Karageorgiadis L, Vasileiou N, Mousafeiropoulos T, Asimellis G. Customized hydrogel contact lenses for keratoconus incorporating correction for vertical coma aberration. Ophthalmic Physiol Opt. 2009; 29(3):321-9.

[802] Epstein RL, Gurgos MA. Presbyopia treatment by monocular peripheral presbyLASIK. J Refract Surg. 2009; 25(6):516-23.

[803] Lindstrom RL, Macrae SM, Pepose JS, Hoopes PC. Corneal inlays for presbyopia correction. Curr Opin Ophthalmol. 2013; 24(4):281-7.

[804] Alió JL. Intracorneal inlays. J Refract Surg. 2016; 32(2):139.

[805] Srinivasan S. Corneal inlays for spectacle independence: Friend or foe? J Cataract Refract Surg. 2016; 42(7):953-4.

of operation of the first type is to alter the anterior surface of the cornea by inserting material with a refractive index that is same as that of the stroma to locally increase corneal thickness.[806] The locally increased corneal thickness translates to a modified corneal curvature and therefore a modified power. To provide the add power needed for near vision correction, which essentially is a hyperopic-type correction, a center-zone inlay of lenticule shape is implanted.[807]

An example of the first type of inlay is the Raindrop (ReVision Optics, Lake Forest, California), previously known as Vue +/ PresbyLens. This is a transparent, hydrogel-based mini inlay lens (with a refractive index the same as that of the cornea) that resembles a small plus power contact lens but with a diameter of 1.5 to 2.0 mm and a center thickness of about 32 μm.[808]

Because the inlay lens is thicker at the center, it serves to increase the central curvature of the anterior cornea, hence increasing the optical power over the center of the pupil, and offering add power when vision is through the center zone of 1.5 to 2.0 mm. The optical power is unaffected for the mid-periphery. In this way, the eye acquires multifocal properties.

The US FDA approved the Raindrop inlay for implantation in the cornea to improve near vision in presbyopes in June 2016. The Raindrop is usually implanted monocularly and has shown effectiveness in the treatment of presbyopia for emmetropic eyes.[809] Recently (March 2019), the FDA issued a class 1 recall for it, so it was available only temporarily in the US.[810]

Other designs of corneal inlays include the Flexivue (Presbia, Los Angeles, California)[811] and the ICOLENS (Neoptics AG, Hünenberg, Switzerland).[812] These designs implement a multifocal power addition approach (as opposed to the single-power approach of the Raindrop), similar to the correction of presbyopia with contact lenses with a central distance segment.

An example of the second type of inlay is the KAMRA corneal inlay (originally developed by AcuFocus, Irvine, California, currently manufactured by CorneaGen, Seattle, Washington). The

---

[806] The same optical power addition effect can be achieved with the use of material with a larger refractive power. In this case, the (unavoidable) increase in corneal thickness plays a secondary role in the refractive effect.

[807] In theory, a myopic-type correction would work if the inlay shape were thinner (or of a lower refractive index) at the center and thicker (or of higher refractive index) at the mid-periphery edge. However, a significantly larger-diameter inlay would be required.

[808] Gutierrez Amoros C. Surgical correction of presbyopic ametropia with non-refractive transparent corneal inlay and an implantable collamer Lens. J Refract Surg. 2016; 32(12):852-4.

[809] Moarefi MA, Bafna S, Wiley W. A review of presbyopia treatment with corneal inlays. Ophthalmology and therapy. 2017; 6(1):55-65.

[810] FDA. RVO 2.0, Inc. recalls raindrop near vision inlay due to risk of increased risk of corneal haze. Medical Device Recalls. www.fda.gov/MedicalDevices/Safety/ListofRecalls/ucm632670.htm. March 5, 2019

[811] Malandrini A, Martone G, Canovetti A, Menabuoni L, Balestrazzi A, Fantozzi C, Lenzetti C, Fantozzi M. Morphologic study of the cornea by in vivo confocal microscopy and optical coherence tomography after bifocal refractive corneal inlay implantation. J Cataract Refract Surg. 2014; 40(4):545-57.

[812] Konstantopoulos A, Mehta JS. Surgical compensation of presbyopia with corneal inlays. Expert Rev Med Devices. 2015; 12(3):341-52.

KAMRA is a small-sized (3.8 mm) disk of a thickness of 5 μm, with a small round opening (1.6 mm) at its center (Figure 7-46). The material is an opaque, biocompatible polymer called Kynar®.[813] The KAMRA ring is placed intrastromally in front of the pupil. As in all of such corneal implants, the ring should be centered on the first Purkinje reflection (§ 2.3.1).[814, 815]

The KAMRA principle of operation is to limit the pupil diameter to 1.6 mm. This small pupil provides an increased depth of field, thus improving perceptual sharpness over a larger range of fixation distances (§ 3.4.2); i.e., the eye can perceive sharper images over a relatively larger range in front of the eye, so it requires less accommodative response.

To evaluate the safety and efficacy of the KAMRA inlay, the US FDA reviewed the results of three clinical studies and approved it for implantation in the cornea to improve near vision in presbyopes in April 2015. Studies of the KAMRA corneal inlay have shown effectiveness in the improvement of reading performance and near and intermediate visual acuity.

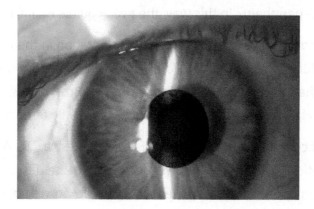

Figure 7-46: Eye with a KAMRA corneal inlay (image courtesy of Dr. Corina van der Pol, used with permission).

These studies also showed that the KAMRA inlay has a minimal effect on distance visual acuity and contrast sensitivity.[816] The implantation of a KAMRA inlay is combinable with other refractive and ocular procedures, such as cataract refractive surgery and IOL implantation,[817] and with laser procedures, including radial keratectomy[818] and LASIK.[819]

---

[813] Arlt EM, Krall EM, Moussa S, Grabner G, Dexl AK. Implantable inlay devices for presbyopia: the evidence to date. Clin Ophthalmol. (Auckland, NZ). 2015; 9:129.

[814] Jalali S, Aus der Au W, Shaarawy T. AcuFocus corneal inlay to correct presbyopia using femto-LASIK. One-year results of a prospective cohort study. Klin Monbl Augenheilkd. 2016; 233(4):360-4.

[815] Naroo SA, Bilkhu PS. Clinical utility of the KAMRA corneal inlay. Clin Ophthalmol. (Auckland, NZ). 2016; 10:913-9.

[816] Waring GO. Correction of presbyopia with a small aperture corneal inlay. J Refract Surg. 2011; 27(11):842-5.

[817] Tan TE, Mehta JS. Cataract surgery following KAMRA presbyopic implant. Clin Ophthalmol. (Auckland, NZ). 2013; 7:1899.

[818] Mulet ME, Alió JL, Knorz MC. Hydrogel intracorneal inlays for the correction of hyperopia: outcomes and complications after 5 years of follow-up. Ophthalmology. 2009; 116(8):1455-60.

[819] Tomita M, Kanamori T, Waring IV GO, Yukawa S, Yamamoto T, Sekiya K, Tsuru T. Simultaneous corneal inlay implantation and laser in situ keratomileusis for presbyopia in patients with hyperopia, myopia, or emmetropia: six-month results. J Cataract Refract Surg. 2012; 38(3):495-506.

7.9 LOW VISION

7.9.1 Low-Vision Definitions

Visual impairment encompasses conditions of reduced vision that cannot be corrected within the range of normal vision by spectacle glasses or contact lenses. Visual impairment is a broad term that includes:

- **Partial sightedness** indicates some type of visual problem in which the affected individual might need some special training.
- **Low vision** indicates visual impairment ranging from moderate to profound and is not necessarily limited to distance vision.
- **Legal blindness** is a legal term (without specific medical or functional implications) that applies to individuals with best-corrected visual acuity of 20/200 or less in the better eye, or a visual field (§ 4.1.3) of less than 20 deg in the better eye.

Note 👤: The placement of this visual impairment section in a chapter dedicated to presbyopia does not suggest that low or near vision is the only aspect of vision that matters to the affected presbyopic individuals. A comprehensive low-vision examination includes visual acuity determination as part of a broader visual function testing, intending to select the appropriate near or low-vision aid for the affected individual.[820, 821]

An individual with low vision may be unable to read a newspaper at a normal viewing distance, even when corrected with spectacle glasses or contact lenses. According to the International Council of Ophthalmology (ICO),[822] individuals with low vision have a residual vision that can be enhanced by vision enhancement aids, such as a magnifying lens, contrast enhancement devices, or a telescopic aid that they may require adaptations for habitual activities.

Affected individuals may be classified as functionally blind if their residual vision alone is insufficient for reliable task performance. These individuals benefit from the use of vision

---

[820] Lovie-Kitchin JE, Feigl B. Assessment of age-related maculopathy using subjective vision tests. Clin Exp Optom. 2005; 88(5):292-303.

[821] Lovie-Kitchin JE. Low Vision. In: Rosenfield M, Logan N, Edwards K, eds. Optometry: Science, Techniques and Clinical Management. New York: Elsevier, Chapter 30, 475-97, 2009.

[822] Report prepared for the International Council of Ophthalmology 29th International Congress of Ophthalmology Sydney, Australia, April 2002. Retrieved from www.icoph.org/downloads/visualstandardsreport.pdf.

substitution skills (Braille, white cane, voice output, etc.); however, their residual vision may still be useful as an adjunct to their blind skills.

According to the World Health Organization (WHO), visual impairment is classified based on the best spectacle-corrected vision in the better eye, as shown in Table 7–1.

Table 7–1: Visual impairment classification according to the World Health Organization based on the best spectacle-corrected vision in the better eye.

Best spectacle-corrected vision in the better eye	Visual Impairment Classification
20/30 to 20/60	mild vision loss / near-normal vision
20/70 to 20/160	moderate visual impairment / moderate low vision
20/200 to 20/400	severe visual impairment / severe low vision
20/500 to 20/1 000	profound visual impairment / profound low vision
Worse than 20/1 000	near-total visual impairment / near total blindness
no light perception	total visual impairment

The importance of low-vision testing cannot be overestimated. The world population is getting older, so the number of people at risk for visual impairment is ever increasing. Also, the prevalence of chronic age-related eye diseases, such as age-related macular degeneration, glaucoma, and diabetic retinopathy, appears to be increasing at an alarming rate; the incidence rates have approximately quadrupled with each decade of advancing age.[823]

Another low-vision population, mostly due to amblyopia and strabismus, is children aged 0–18 years. This is 3% to 7% of the global low-vision population.[824, 825] Low-income families in underdeveloped nations may be at a higher risk of having these conditions. Additionally, cortical visual impairment and cerebral visual impairment (CVI) have become the most frequently occurring conditions for vision loss in young children, often resulting from perinatal conditions. CVI is now the most frequently occurring vision loss condition in young children; this points to the fact that the brain is as important as the eyes for visual functioning.

---

[823] Rudnicka AR, Kapetanakis VV, Jarrar Z, Wathern AK, Wormald R, Fletcher AE, Cook DG, Owen CG. Incidence of late-stage age-related macular degeneration in American whites: Systematic review and meta-analysis. Am J Ophthalmol. 2015; 160(1):85-93.e3.

[824] Brandão AO, Andrade GM, Vasconcelos GC, Rossi LD, Saliba GR. Instruments for evaluation of functionality in children with low vision: a literature review. Arq Bras Oftalmol. 2017; 80(1):59-63.

[825] Ghaderi S, Hashemi H, Jafarzadehpur E, Yekta A, Ostadimoghaddam H, Mirzajani A, Khabazkhoob M. The prevalence and causes of visual impairment in seven-year-old children. Clin Exp Optom. 2018; 101(3):380-385.

Conditions that affect the visual development of young children demonstrate just how important the growing brain is to vision; it has been stated that problems of vision development are problems of human development.[826]

7.9.2 Traditional Semi-Quantitative Tests for Low Vision

Some very basic quantitative tests have traditionally been used for low vision if the examinee is not able to read any of the optotypes on an acuity chart. One test is the **counting fingers** (CF) test, which determines the examinee's ability to count fingers at any given distance. The result is notated in the following way: CF @ "x distance"; for example, CF 1' means that the individual was able to see the projected number of fingers held one foot from their face.

If the examinee shows little or no success with counting fingers, we use the **hand motion** (HM) test, also at a certain distance. HM is the ability of the examinee to detect the movement of the examiner's hand when it is held close to the examinee's eyes. This test works because there are many different neurological visual pathways; the ability to process target motion and detect movement is carried along a visual pathway other than the one that processes target detail (acuity resolution).

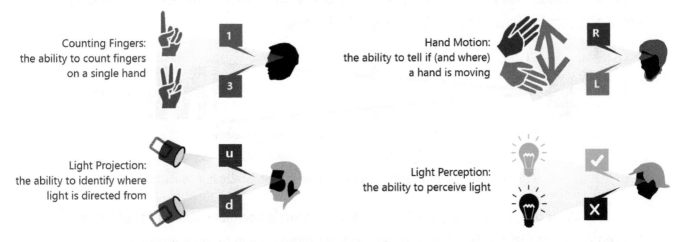

Counting Fingers: the ability to count fingers on a single hand

Hand Motion: the ability to tell if (and where) a hand is moving

Light Projection: the ability to identify where light is directed from

Light Perception: the ability to perceive light

Figure 7-47: Counting fingers, hand motion, light projection, and light perception: a semi-quantitative scale for reporting low vision.

Then there is **light projection** (LProj). Holding a penlight at a distance of about 50 cm in front of the examinee, the examiner asks the examinee to either point to the light source or describe where light is coming from (up, out, straight ahead, down and out, etc.).

---

[826] Richard AI. Causes of blindness and low vision in Bayelsa State, Nigeria: a clinic-based study. Nig Q J Hosp Med. 2010; 20(3):125-8.

Lastly, **light perception** (LP) and no light perception (NLP) test the ability to perceive some light or no light, respectively. No light perception, especially when in both eyes, is generally considered a state of total blindness. If there is no light perception, the only other available tests are electrodiagnostics, such as the visually evoked potential (VEP), which determines whether any information goes to the visual cortex.

These tests are crude, inaccurate, and lack a strict scientific basis. Hand motion, as performed, is more of a visual field test. Eleanor E. Faye, Director of the Lighthouse Low Vision Services, has stated: *"The commonly used term 'finger counting' is a vague, negative, inaccurate and careless vision test. A numerical designation for everything except light projection and light perception is more accurate and psychologically more positive for practitioner and patient."*[827]

7.9.3 Handheld Low-Vision Card Tests

Alternatives to the crude tests can consist of moving the eye chart much closer to the examinee (1 m away). This may provide a more reliable measurement, down to 20/800. Special eye charts for the evaluation of visual acuity in low vision present a more meaningful alternative. The metric for low-vision determination is the **M-unit**, denoted simply by M or M print). As initially defined by Louise Sloan, 1.0 M-unit (1.0 M) is the overall dimension of the letter subtending an angle of 5 arcmin at a distance of 1 m (height 1.454 mm).[828]

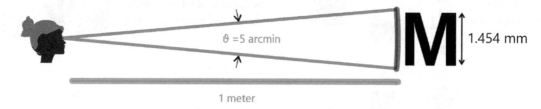

Figure 7-48: Definition of 1 M-unit (angle and letter size not to scale).

Thus, at one meter away, the 1.0 M-unit represents a decimal visual acuity of 1.0 or Snellen 20/20, or logMAR 0.0. This is based on the simple similar-triangle analogy:

$$\text{Test distance/M-unit} = 20 \text{ ft/Snellen letter size} \tag{7.7}$$

Thus, for a test distance of 1 m and M-unit = 1.0, the equivalent visual acuity is Snellen 20/20.

[827] Faye EE. Clinical low vision, 2nd ed. Boston: Little Brown & Co., 1994
[828] Sloan L, Brown D. Reading cards for selection of optical aids for the partially sighted. Am J Ophthalmol. 1963; 55(6):1187-99.

Example ☞: What is the M-unit acuity that corresponds to a 1.0 M sized optotype (1.454 mm) <u>just</u> being read at a near distance of 40 cm?

We use the simple analogy: Test distance/M-unit = 20 ft/Snellen letter size, which yields a Snellen letter size = 50, or Snellen vision of 20/50 or +0.4 logMAR.

A **Feinbloom flip chart** was created for testing the partially sighted by the pioneering optometrist William Feinbloom, who developed special tests for low vision and established visual rehabilitation techniques. In this chart, the optotypes are large-size numerals. Individual pages of the chart display one to seven numbers and are portable, to be used at any distance, thus allowing for a large testing range from 20/10 to 20/14 000. Typically, when testing with a Feinbloom chart, the test begins at 5 or 10 ft instead of the traditional 20 ft. The chart that Feinbloom found most suitable was the H591 Snellen chart (Bausch + Lomb AMA rating chart).[829]

The **Berkeley Rudimentary Vision Test** (BRVT) is a simple test for assessing severely impaired vision beyond the limits of the letter charts.[830] The test was developed after the World Blind Cricket Council asked Dr. Bailey to join an advisory committee on rules and methods to classify the vision of athletes participating in Blind Cricket competitions. Its advantages include ease of use, portability, no electric power requirement, and *in situ* administration.

The test adds 12 quantitative increments between the lowest acuity level measurable with a standard eye chart and the light perception test. It consists of three handheld card-pairs. Each card-pair has two 25 cm square cards hinged together so that there are four panel faces (Figure 7-49). The cards display four single tumbling E targets (STE cards), four grating targets, a white field projection test, and a black/white discrimination test.

The STE cards consist of a single tumbling E target (introduced in § 3.4.4). The largest E and the smallest E—the largest (around 15 cm high) is noted as 100 M, and the smallest (around 4 cm high) is noted as 25 M—are on the outside, while the two intermediate sizes (63 M and 40 M) are on the inside. The recommended protocol is to present the STE cards at a distance of 1 m (100 cm), where acuity ranges from logMAR = 2.0 to 1.4 (equivalent to 20/2000 to 20/500) in increments of 0.20 log units.

If the orientation of the largest E cannot be recognized at 1 m, the cards are brought to 25 cm. There should be at least four presentations at each size level when the examinee is close to the threshold. At 25 cm, the STE acuity becomes logMAR 2.6 to 2.0 (20/8000 to 20/2000). On failure to identify the orientation of the largest E at 25 cm, testing proceeds with the second pair.

---

[829] Feinbloom W. Introduction to the principles and practice of sub-normal vision correction. J Am Optom Assoc. 1935; VI: 3-18.

[830] Bailey IL, Jackson AJ, Minto H, Greer RB, Chu MA. The Berkeley rudimentary vision test. Optom Vis Sci. 2012; 89(9):1257-64.

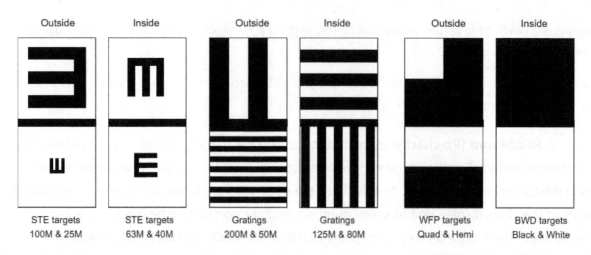

Outside	Inside	Outside	Inside	Outside	Inside
STE targets 100M & 25M	STE targets 63M & 40M	Gratings 200M & 50M	Gratings 125M & 80M	WFP targets Quad & Hemi	BWD targets Black & White

Figure 7-49: The three card-pairs of the Berkeley Rudimentary Vision Test. (left) Single tumbling E card-pair. (center) Grating acuity card-pair. (right) Basic vision card-pair (see discussion below for acronym definitions). Image courtesy of Dr. I. L. Bailey.

The second card-pairs have square-wave gratings. Just as in the single E cards, the panels are grouped: The largest and the smallest (200 M and 50 M, respectively) gratings are on the outside, and the two intermediate sizes (125 M and 80 M) are on the inside. In other words, these optotypes are twice as large as their counterparts in the STE cards. They are presented at 25 cm, and the grating acuity range is logMAR 2.90 to 2.30 (20/16000 to 20/4000) in steps of 0.20 log units. Close to the threshold, there should be at least six presentations.

The third card-pair has two tests, the white field projection (WFP) and the black-white discrimination (BWD). For the WFP, one panel has a white quadrant on a black background and its partner panel is divided into a black half and a white half. Both panels can be presented in four different orientations, and the examinee's task is to identify the location of the white field. For both panels, there should be a minimum of four presentations, with at least one in each of the four orientations. This card-pair should be presented at 25 cm. At this distance, the cards subtend an angle of 53° such that the white quad-field is 26°×26° and the white hemifield is 26°×53°.

If the subject is unable to consistently identify the location of the white field, the black-white discrimination (BWD) test is administered. One panel is all white and the other is all black. The two card faces are presented at 25 cm, and the examinee's task is to identify whether the panel presented is black or white. If the subject cannot reliably tell the black from the white, then the BRVT testing is concluded, and the light perception (LP) test is administered.

7.9.4 Vision Testing with Gratings

The determination of visual acuity in infants is complicated by the ability to understand and follow test requirements, which requires developed cognitive function. Although infants have central cones present at birth, the anatomy of the fovea, which permits high-resolution acuity, does not fully develop until at least around 30 months of age.[831] This may be attributed to incomplete development and specialization of the photoreceptors and synapses in the retinal layers, and incomplete myelination of the upper visual pathways. Visual function that enables adequate resolution to play with toys is reached at about 6 months.[832] Thus, it is more suitable to test infant vision using gratings, which are presentations of black and white stripes without any recognizable form. Gratings come in varying densities, i.e., in varying spatial frequencies.

The **Teller Acuity Cards**® and the **Keeler Acuity Card** test are specialized pediatric vision tests that use gratings instead of optotypes. Infants can typically resolve around 10 cycles per degree, where 'resolving' means preferentially looking toward cards presented with this spatial frequency size. Thus, the task is to identify the direction of lines when the cards are presented at different distances. The Teller acuity test is a preferential looking test. Infants are shown a gray card with a grating on one side; if the infant spends more time looking at the grating than at the gray side, it is assumed that the infant can see the grating.

Figure 7-50: (left) Simplified grating paddles for pediatric vision testing. (right) Keeler cards, printed with a circular patch to avoid identification of the grating by its edge.

The benefit of using cycles per degree to report visual acuity is that the signal resolution in optical engineering is often measured in terms of spatial frequencies, so human vision can readily be matched to optical instrumentation. Many test patterns have sections of grid patterns to test resolution using such terms. This metric is also applicable when employing the notion of cut-off frequency using the MTF functions.[663]

---

[831] Anstice NS, Thompson B. The measurement of visual acuity in children: an evidence-based update. Clin Exp Optom. 2014; 97(1):3-11.

[832] Gwiazda J, Wolfe JM, Brill S, Mohindra I, Held R. Quick assessment of preferential looking acuity in infants. Am J Optom Physiol Opt. 1980; 57(7):420-7.

7.10 NEAR VISION

Although similar techniques are involved in the evaluation of distance vision and near vision (just at different working distances), the evaluation of near vision is significantly more complex. At the near distance, the binocular visual system and executive cognitive function must be taken into consideration, rather than just the optical resolution. An examiner must consider fixation, oculomotor skills (saccades/pursuits), accommodation, and vergence skills, all while considering whether the examinee has the necessary language and visual perceptual skills to process what is being read.

Reading skill is different from just recognizing letters. The simple recognition of a letter involves mostly optical resolution. To resolve a 20/200 letter, there is demand of just rudimental optical resolution, as opposed to the recognition of a 20/20 letter, which demands increased optical resolution. On the other hand, the act of reading accesses a much larger retinal area and involves the entire visual cortex and far more complicated cerebral processing tasks.

The evaluation of reading is important for several reasons: On one hand, it is used to monitor the progress of visual rehabilitative programs, for example, in adults undergoing rehabilitation due to an acquired brain injury. On the other hand, it may help elucidate the functional impairment of ophthalmic diseases in ways that the simple measurement of acuity cannot. Near vision testing and the evaluation of reading skills are related but not identical. Near vision refers to the physical viewing distance, whereas reading refers to the task performed at that distance. Naturally, there is some overlap between these terms, as most tests involve reading text on cards held at a near distance. Thus, letter chart acuity and reading acuity are two different measurements—a distinction that must be documented accordingly.

The historic near vision charts include the Jaeger, the Nieden, and the Parinaud charts. The Jaeger near vision chart consists of short paragraphs (blocks) of text in various type sizes of successively smaller text, generally ranging in size from J10 (large print on the top block) to J1 (very small print on the lower block). When testing with the Jaeger chart, it is important to document whether near or distance vision correction was used and that the testing was performed both monocularly and binocularly.

The **Jaeger chart** is named after Eduard Jäger von Jaxtthal. It originally contained seven paragraphs, each printed in successively smaller font sizes; the smallest paragraph that could be read determined near visual acuity. The typeface on a modern Jaeger eye chart usually ranges from J10 (14-point type using Times New Roman font) to J1 (approximately 3-point type, Times New Roman). The J1 on a Jaeger card is considered the near vision equivalent of 20/20 distance acuity. Some Jaeger charts have an additional paragraph labeled "J1+", with even smaller text than the J1 text. Common newsprint generally ranges in size between J7 (10-point type) and J10 (14-point type), which are the equivalent of 20/70 and 20/100, respectively, on a distance eye chart.

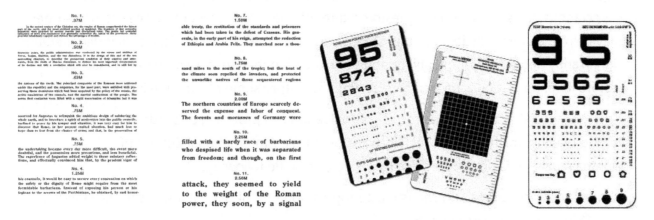

Figure 7-51: (left) Jaeger cards. (right) Rosenbaum cards.

Unfortunately, modern Jaeger charts are not standardized, and the actual letter sizes on different Jaeger cards might vary, depending on the manufacturer. The print size for a given point notation can vary considerably, depending on the chosen font.

Attempts to introduce the logarithmic scale were made by Louise Sloan[828] and Charles Henry Keeler.[833] Sloan's cards used continuous text paragraphs of different lengths; the type utilized a standard typewriter font. The smallest print size was 1.0 M-unit, increasing as follows: 1.0 M, 1.5 M, 2.0 M, 2.5 M, 3.0 M, 4.0 M, 5.0 M, 7.0 M, and 10 M, in an approximately logarithmic progression.

The Keeler A numbers introduced a simple logarithmic basis, each being 80% of the acuity of the previous 'A' numbers. A standard acuity of 20/20 is designated as A.1, while the next grade, A.2, represents an acuity of 80%, and the A.3 grade, an acuity of 64%. This provides the magnification necessary to effect the desired degree of acuity improvement.

The Rosenbaum Pocket Vision Screener (Rosenbaum card) can provide up to a 20/800 distance equivalent. The test uses single letters to be more comparable to distance letter acuity.

---

833 Raiford MB. Keeler low-vision aids. Am J Ophthalmol. 1969; 67(4):542-6.

7.10.1 Standardized Reading Chart Tests

Considerable improvement has been made in the treatments for vision-threatening conditions such as the removal of cataract and implantation of premium IOLs[834] and for retinal degenerations that offer safe and durable outcomes.[835] This, in turn, has led to increased expectations of visual functionality restored through medical procedures; while cataract surgery may help to restore functionality, this is not always the case. For example, macular degeneration significantly degrades reading ability, and there are no one-step, easy treatments that can restore it; rehabilitation is necessary to attempt to restore some of what the individual lost.

Standardized reading performance evaluation can provide a dependable method for testing reading ability. The Visual Function Committee / International Council of Ophthalmology has produced guidelines that specify the following:[836]

- The print sizes of reading charts must progress logarithmically, analogous to the standards of visual acuity measurements.
  The test conditions, optotypes, and chart designs used should be calibrated.
- The test distance must be specified in all instances.
- Continuous text materials are desirable for reading charts.
- The typeset material should be based on the distance at which the height of lower-case letters such as "o," "m," and "x" subtends five arcmin.

Mathematical models described in EN:ISO 8596[246] facilitate the development of standardization and calibration of such tests. These tests develop 'sentence optotypes,' whose print size has a logarithmic progression.

A known challenge to these reading tests is that, because they contain lower-case letters, accurate estimation of letter size might be an issue. The logReading Acuity Determination (**logRAD**) is considered the reading acuity equivalent of logMAR measure for research purposes. Adoption of the logRAD print size[837] would help develop reading acuity as a standardized reading parameter in vision assessment.[838]

---

[834] Alió JL, Plaza-Puche AB, Piñero DP, Amparo F, Jiménez R, Rodríguez-Prats JL, Javaloy J, Pongo V. Optical analysis, reading performance, and quality-of-life evaluation after implantation of a diffractive multifocal intraocular lens. J Cataract Refract Surg. 2011; 37(1):27-37.

[835] Schlottmann PG, Alezzandrini AA, Zas M, Rodriguez FJ, Luna JD, Wu L. New treatment modalities for neovascular age-related macular degeneration. Asia Pac J Ophthalmol (Phila). 2017; 6(6):514-9.

[836] Colenbrander A. Consilium Ophthalmologicum Universale Visual Functions Committee, Visual Acuity Measurement Standard. Ital J Ophthalmol. 1988; 11:5-19.

[837] Radner W. Ophthalmic reading charts: Part 2: Current logarithmically scaled reading charts. Ophthalmologe. 2015; 113(12):1029-35.

[838] Radner W. Reading charts in ophthalmology. Graefes Arch Clin Exp Ophthalmol. 2017; 255(8):1465-82.

The standardized reading charts include the Bailey–Lovie Word Reading Chart, the Oculus Reading Probe II (Oculus Corporation, Deleware, the Colenbrander English Continuous Text Near Vision Cards (Precision Vision, Woodstock, Illinois), the MNread Charts (Precision Vision), the SKread Charts (Precision Vision), and the Radner Reading Charts (Precision Vision).

Some tests also measure reading speed and allow for determination of reading parameters such as reading acuity, reading speed based on reading acuity, critical print size, reading score, and logMAR/logRAD ratio. In addition to being used in clinical settings, these tests are used in research, providing insight into the reading performance of subjects under vision rehabilitation. In several research studies, they are either part of the methodology or are the very objective of the investigation.

The Bailey–Lovie Word Reading Chart [Figure 7-52 (right)] uses unrelated, long words to assess ability that may require more than one fixation. Text is arranged in a logarithmic size progression and is standardized by controlling the typeface (Times Roman), spacings, the number of words per row and making each group of words of approximately equal difficulty.[839]

Figure 7-52: (left) The word reading chart proposed by Bailey and Lovie in 1980.[840] (right) Bailey–Lovie text charts for assessing near visual acuity. These charts use sentences from the MNRead corpus.[841] Image courtesy of Dr. Jan E. Lovie-Kitchin.

The use of four-, seven-, and ten-letter words at each size level was based on the observation that, in individuals with age-related macular degeneration (AMD), the word length can affect the ability to read the word. The words and word order were selected to have the first letters of the words evenly distributed over the whole alphabet. The examinee is asked to read aloud all words, from the 80-point size to the smallest size possible, while reading is recorded.

The **Oculus Reading Probe II** (Oculus Optikgeräte GmbH, Wetzlar, Germany) is an innovative example of calibrating an already well-recognized reading chart with modern

---

[839] Law FW. Standardization of reading types. Br J Ophthalmol. 1951; 35(12):765-73.

[840] Bailey IL, Lovie JE. The design and use of a new near-vision chart. Am J Optom Physiol Opt. 1980; 57(6):378-87.

[841] MNRead-History. Retrieved from vision.psych.umn.edu/~gellab/MNREAD/ Accessed 02/10/2020.

standards. The test uses long paragraphs from books, such as Rudyard Kipling's *The Jungle Book*. The print sizes increase logarithmically from decimal acuity 1.0 to 0.04.

The **Colenbrander English Continuous Text Near Vision Cards** (Precision Vision, Woodstock, Illinois) were developed by Dr. August Colenbrander. These cards are logarithmically scaled and available in 12 languages. They are designed for use at 40 cm (a cord is mounted on the cards) and cover decimal acuity from 0.063 to 1.25. The test sentences have 44 characters, including spaces and a different number of words (nine to 11 words). These reading cards are also available as mixed-contrast cards on which high and low contrast (20% Weber) are presented side-by-side on the same card.

The **Minnesota Low-Vision Reading Test**, introduced by Drs. Steve Mansfield[842] and Gordon Legge,[843] is a test for assessing the reading performance of the visually impaired. Officially called "Printed cards for measuring low-vision reading performance," the cards are known as MNread printed cards or **MNread test**.

In its computerized version (Figure 7-53), short sentences with a fixed format of 4 lines of 13 fixed-width characters each are displayed in large print on a computer display for a pre-set duration. Then the examiner reduces the presentation duration until the subject makes reading errors. Reading speed is given as the number of words read divided by the reading time. MNread has been developed in several other languages[844, 845] and is available as an iPad app.[846]

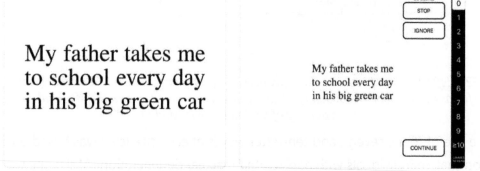

Figure 7-53: MNread test electronic application screenshots.

[842] Mansfield JS, Legge GE, Bane MC. Psychophysics of reading XV. Font effects in normal and low vision. Invest Ophthalmol Vis Sci. 1996; 37(8):1492-501.

[843] Legge GE, Ross JA, Luebker A, LaMay JM. Psychophysics of reading. VIII. The Minnesota low-vision reading test. Optom Vis Sci. 1989; 66(12):843-53.

[844] Mataftsi A, Bourtoulamaiou A, Haidich AB, Antoniadis A, Kilintzis V, Tsinopoulos IT, Dimitrakos S. Development and validation of the Greek version of the MNREAD acuity chart. Clin Exp Optom. 2013; 96(1):25-31.

[845] Castro CT, Kallie CS, Salomão SR. [Development and validation of the MNREAD reading acuity chart in Portuguese]. Arq Bras Oftalmol. 2005; 68(6):777-83.

[846] App Store Review. Retrieved from: itunes.apple.com/us/app/mnread/id1196638274?ls=1&mt=8 Accessed 02/10/2020.

The **Pepper Visual Skills for Reading Test** (VSRT) is another handheld-card test. It was developed to assess the reading performance of adult readers who were reading efficiently before the onset of a macular disease, such as diseases that create central scotomas that inhibit efficient reading. The Pepper test can assess visual word recognition, saccadic eye movement control, return sweep eye movement control, and effective positioning of the scotoma in relation to the words to be read.[847, 848]

The **SKread Test**, an updated version of the Pepper test, was developed by Drs. Donald C. Fletcher, Manfred MacKeben, and co-workers at the Smith-Kettlewell Eye Research Institute (San Francisco, California). The test evaluates the functional visual status of low vision subjects and provides information about the location of scotomas that are interfering with visual ability.[849] The SKread test uses 2 handheld charts, each with 14 paragraphs consisting of the same number of words and letters displayed in 3 lines, using the same format as the MNread test. The text is high-contrast black type on a white background; type sizes range from 8× larger than newsprint down to 0.4 M-units, which is less than half the size of newsprint.

The SKread test uses a series of common, random words that do not form meaningful sentences. The words and letters are chosen to be easily confused or misread; this aspect facilitates erroneous readings, which in turn can reveal the presence and/or location of a scotoma. The type of errors made by subjects with central scotoma depends on the location of the scotoma relative to the retinal area used for fixation. For example, individuals with a dense scotoma to the right of fixation make more 'right errors' by missing letters at the end of words, while those with a scotoma to the left of fixation make more 'left errors' by missing letters at the beginning of words.

The Radner test, developed by Wolfgang Radner, is also available in several different languages and provides sentences that are rigorously and linguistically standardized;[850] for example, paragraphs were constructed so that words with the same number of syllables were in the same position in the text in all paragraphs. These series of tests provide several different reading parameters from a single examination in subjects with normal to low vision.[851]

---

[847] Stelmack J, Stelmack TR, Fraim M, Warrington J. Clinical use of the Pepper visual skills for reading test in low vision rehabilitation. Am J Optom Physiol Opt. 1987; 64(11):829-31.

[848] Baldasare J, Watson G, Whittaker S, Miller-Shaffer H. The development and evaluation of a reading test for low vision individuals with macular loss. J Vis Impair Blind. 1986; 80:785-89.

[849] MacKeben M, Nair UK, Walker LL, Fletcher DC. Random word recognition chart helps scotoma assessment in low vision. Optom Vis Sci. 2015; 92(4):421-8.

[850] Radner W, Radner S, Diendorfer G. Integrating a novel concept of sentence optotypes into the RADNER Reading Charts. Br J Ophthalmol. 2017; 101(3):239-43.

[851] Stifter E, Konig F, Lang T, Bauer P, Richter-Muksch S, Velikay-Parel M, Radner W. Reliability of a standardized reading chart system: variance component analysis, test-retest and inter-chart reliability. Graefes Arch Clin Exp Ophthalmol. 2004; 242(1):31-9.

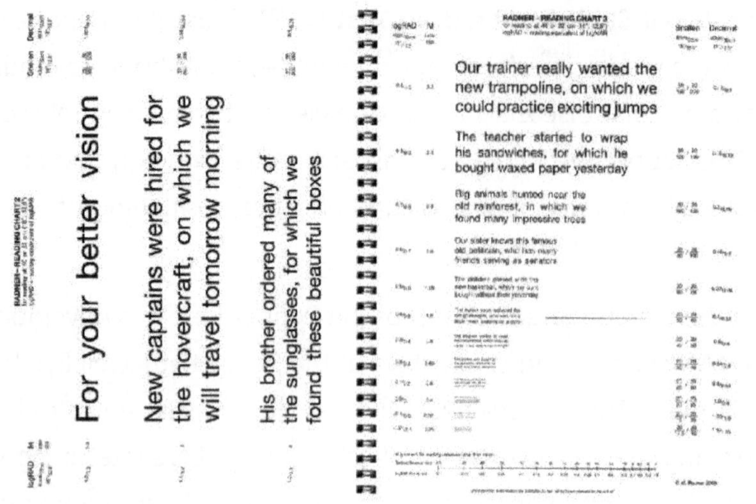

Figure 7-54: Images from the Radner reading chart. Note the logarithmic print size progression.

Other reading tests include the **International Reading Speed Texts** (IReST) test, which provides long standardized segments for a more accurate assessment. This test is available in a booklet form and uses long paragraphs for analyzing speed and fluency of reading in low-vision subjects. It consists of paragraphs of text (about 130 words per text) that are equivalent to the reading demands encountered in daily life, with the same difficulty, content, and linguistic characteristics in the different languages.[852]

The Keeler reading test types use long paragraphs, but do not come with a recommended reading distance nor a logarithmic progression. The Eschenbach and Zeiss reading tests use long paragraphs and also provide a logarithmic progression of the print size.

---

[852] Trauzettel-Klosinski S, Dietz K, IReST Study Group. Standardized assessment of reading performance: the new international reading speed texts IReST. Invest Ophthalmol Vis Sci. 2012; 53(9):5452-61.

7.11 ACCOMMODATION AND PRESBYOPIA QUIZ

Casting (poetic license, Homer's *Odyssey*), by order of refractive error reported at the corneal plane.

<u>Hyperopes</u>: Eurymachus +7.00; Ajax +6.00; Nestor +4.00; Nausicaa +3.00; Calypso +2.00; Diomedes +1.25.

<u>Emmetropes</u>: Odysseus

<u>Myopes</u>: Laertes –1.00; Circe –1.50; Tiresias –2.00; Eurycleia –2.50; Antinous –3.00; Arete –4.00; Penelope –5.00; Achilles –6.00; Telemachus –7.00.

Parts of this quiz require knowledge of vertex power conversions (§ 9.2.4) and astigmatic prescriptions (§ 8.2.1).

Accommodation

1) Which of the following heroes requires less accommodative demand when viewing a target at 50 cm in front of his/her eyes?

   a) Nestor (+4.00 hyperope)
   b) Calypso (+2.00 hyperope)
   c) Laertes (–1.00 myope)
   d) Tiresias (–2.00 myope)

2) Odysseus, an emmetrope, views the tip of his bow placed 50 cm in front of his cornea. What is the accommodative demand?

   a) –4.00 D
   b) –2.00 D
   c) –0.50 D
   d) +0.50 D
   e) +2.00 D
   f) +4.00 D

3) When Odysseus accommodates, the refractive power of his eyes increases because his eyes' ...

   a) corneal curvature increases
   b) axial length decreases
   c) lenticular curvature flattens
   d) lenticular power increases

4) As Odysseus is accommodating, these <u>two pairs</u> of cardinal points are <u>decreasing</u> their separation (compared to their separation in a relaxed eye):

   a) principal point *P* from nodal point *N*
   b) principal point *P* from principal point *P′*
   c) nodal point *N* from nodal point *N′*
   d) principal point *P′* from focal point *F′*

5) As Odysseus is stringing his bow, he is also accommodating to see the tip of his arrow. What <u>two</u> effects are taking place in his eye?

   a) ciliary muscle contracts

   b) ciliary muscle relaxes
   c) zonular tension increases
   d) zonular tension decreases

6) What changes occur in the Purkinje reflex images during accommodation?

   a) no change in P_1 and P_3
   b) no change in P_1 and P_2
   c) P_1 and P_2 move away from the cornea
   d) P_1 and P_2 become smaller
   e) P_3 and P_4 become smaller
   f) P_3 and P_4 become larger

7) Circe's far point is 66.6 cm, while her near point is 8 cm. What is her amplitude of accommodation?
   a) 1.50 D
   b) 11.00 D
   c) 12.50 D
   d) 14.00 D

8) Nestor has a far point 25 cm behind his eye. He is trying to read a scroll at 25 cm in front of his eye. What is the accommodative demand?

   a) no accommodative demand
   b) +0.50 D
   c) +2.00 D
   d) +4.00 D
   e) +6.00 D
   f) +8.00 D

9) Laertes is a –1.0 D myope. He is trying to reach his sword at 2.5 feet (≈ 75 cm) in front of his eyes. What is his accommodative demand?
   a) +1.33 D
   b) +1.00 D
   c) +0.33 D
   d) –0.33 D
   e) no accommodative demand

10) Laertes' shield is 3 feet (≈ 100 cm) in front of his eyes. What is the accommodative demand when he is fixating on his shield?

a) +1.33 D
b) +1.00 D
c) +0.33 D
d) −0.33 D
e) no accommodative demand

11) The shortest distance at which Laertes can read the inscription on his signet ring is 33.3 cm. What is his amplitude of accommodation?

a) 2.00 D
b) 3.00 D
c) 6.00 D
d) 7.00 D
e) 8.00 D
f) 10.00 D

12) What is the accommodative demand before and after Laertes fits the +2.00 D lenses for a fixation point 20 cm in front of his eyes?

a) before: +4.00 D; after: +4.00 D
b) before: +5.00 D; after: +3.00 D
c) before: +2.00 D; after: +4.00 D
d) before: +4.00 D; after: +2.00 D

13) Diomedes is a +1.25 D uncorrected hyperope viewing a chessboard at 57 cm in front of his eyes. What is the accommodative demand?

a) +0.50 D
b) +1.25 D
c) +1.75 D
d) +3.00 D
e) +4.00 D

14) Seer Tiresias is a −2.00 myope. What is his accommodative demand when he fixates on the seer stone held 16.6 cm in front of his eyes?

a) +1.00 D
b) +2.00 D
c) +4.00 D
d) +5.00 D
e) +6.00 D
f) +8.00 D

15) How far in front of his eyes should Tiresias place his seer stone in order not to exert any accommodative response?

a) infinity
b) 2.0 m
c) 1.0 m

d) 0.5 m
e) 0.25 m

16) Nymph Calypso is a hyperope with a far point 50 cm behind her eye. When she gazes at Odysseus, who is just 1 m away, what is her accommodative demand?

a) +1.00 D
b) +2.00 D
c) +3.00 D
d) +4.00 D
e) +6.00 D
f) +8.00 D

17) What is Odysseus' accommodating demand when he gazes back at nymph Calypso (1 m away)?

a) +1.00 D
b) +2.00 D
c) +4.00 D
d) +5.00 D
e) +6.00 D
f) +8.00 D

18) While on the island of Ogygia, Calypso and Odysseus fixate on the same object the same distance from each. To do so, Calypso is exerting 3× the accommodating effort of Odysseus. What is the distance of that target?

a) infinity
b) 2.0 m
c) 1.0 m
d) 0.5 m
e) 0.25 m

19) After a long 8 years, Calypso is ordered by the Olympian gods to let Odysseus leave the island of Ogygia. As he sails away, she waves goodbye to him. What is her accommodating demand?

a) +1.00 D
b) +2.00 D
c) +4.00 D
d) +5.00 D
e) +6.00 D
f) +8.00 D

20) Which hero requires 3.00 D of accommodation when viewing a target at 20 cm?

a) Nestor (+4.00 hyperope)
b) Calypso (+2.00 hyperope)
c) Laertes (−1.00 myope)
d) Tiresias (−2.00 myope)

21) Achilles, a −6.00 myope, requires +2.00 D of accommodation to read a scroll describing an oracle about his heel. How far from his eyes is the scroll?
   a) 6 cm
   b) 12.5 cm
   c) 16.6 cm
   d) 25 cm
   e) 50 cm

22) Achilles won a not-so-perfect war prize for bravery: a set of −2.00 D contact lenses. While wearing them, he reads that scroll again. How far from his eyes should he hold the scroll if he wants to use the same +2.00 D of accommodation as in Q 21?

   a) 6 cm
   b) 12.5 cm
   c) 16.6 cm
   d) 25 cm
   e) 50 cm

23) Telemachus is a −7.00 D myope. If he cannot see clearly when an object is less than 6.90 cm from his eye, what is his amplitude of accommodation?
   a) 4.5 D
   b) 7.0 D
   c) 7.5 D
   d) 14.5 D

24) The treasure trove had more −2.00 D contact lens sets; several of our heroes experiment with them. Telemachus is the newest victim. While wearing them, what is the closest distance he can clearly see (with maximum accommodation)
   a) 6.90 cm
   b) 8.00 cm
   c) 12.50 cm
   d) 14.28 cm

25) The closest distance (maximum accommodation) that our hero, fitted with −2.00 contact lenses, can see clearly is 10.00 cm. If his/her amplitude of accommodation is 7.00 D, who is our hero?
   a) Laertes (uncorrected −1.00)
   b) Tiresias (uncorrected −2.00)
   c) Arete (uncorrected −4.00)
   d) Penelope (uncorrected −5.00)

26) Back to Q 25. Our hero now removes the contact lenses. The far and the near points are now ...
   a) far point 20.0 cm, near point 8.33 cm

   b) far point 33.3 cm, near point 8.33 cm
   c) far point 5.0 cm, near point 12.0 cm
   d) far point 20.0 cm, near point 10.0 cm

27) Ajax, a +6.00 D hyperope, is wearing a +4.00 D contact lens. He is playing chess with Achilles, with the board located 25.00 cm in front of his eyes. How much accommodation does Ajax require?
   a) 2.00 D
   b) 4.00 D
   c) 6.00 D
   d) 8.00 D

28) Telemachus is about to read a secret engraving. He is, as we know, a −7.00 D myope, referenced to the corneal plane. Luckily, being a member of the royal court, he has both the contact lens −7.00 D correction and the equivalent spectacle lens correction @ 13 mm vertex distance. Before we begin, what is the proper spectacle lens power?
   a) −6.41 D
   b) −7.00 D
   c) −7.07 D
   d) −7.70 D

29) Telemachus starts experimenting with no correction. What distance from his eyes should he hold the engraving to require no accommodation?
   a) 1.43 cm
   b) 14.3 cm
   c) 1.43 m
   d) infinity

30) Telemachus is back wearing the contact lens prescription, holding the engraving at a distance just 8 cm in front of his eyes (the corneal plane). What is the accommodative demand?
   a) 5.50 D
   b) 7.00 D
   c) 10.50 D
   d) 12.50 D

31) Not quite happy with the contact lenses, Telemachus tries the spectacle lens correction (refer to Q 28). Still holding the engraving 8 cm in front of his eyes (the corneal plane), what is the accommodative demand?
   a) 5.50 D
   b) 7.00 D
   c) 10.50 D
   d) 12.50 D

32) Nausicaa is wearing her proper contact lens correction (recall, she is a +3.00 hyperope), while hanging Odysseus' clothing 50 cm away. What is her accommodative demand?

a) +1.92 D
b) +2.00 D
c) +2.14 D
d) +3.00 D
e) +5.00 D
f) +700 D

33) What would have been Nausicaa's spectacle lens correction at a 12 mm vertex distance?

a) +2.00 D
b) +2.89 D
c) +3.00 D
d) +3.11 D

34) Wearing the spectacle correction identified in Q 33, what would be Nausicaa's accommodative demand when she gazes 50 cm from her corneal plane?

a) +1.92 D
b) +2.00 D
c) +2.14 D
d) +3.00 D
e) +5.00 D

35) Diomedes, a +1.25 hyperope, is fitted with a +0.75 contact lens. What is his accommodative demand when viewing a target 10 cm from his corneal plane?

a) 9.75 D
b) 10.0 D
c) 10.5 D
d) 11.25 D

36) Which hero demands more accommodation [D] than the same numerical convergence [MA] when viewing the same fixation point 40 cm in front of their eye, placed on the medial plane?

a) Nausicaa (+3.00 hyperope)
b) Odysseus (emmetrope)
c) Circe (–1.50 myope)
d) Penelope (–5.00 myope)

37) Laertes, an uncorrected –1.00 myope, is fixating on a medial plane target placed 50 cm in front of his eyes. What is the accommodative demand [D] and the convergence effort [MA]?

a) 4 D; 2 MA
b) 1 D; 1 MA
c) 1 D; 2 MA

d) 2 D; 1 MA

38) Back to Q 37. When expressed in [$^\Delta$], what is Laertes' convergence effort (approximately)?

a) 2^Δ
b) 4^Δ
c) 6^Δ
d) 8^Δ
e) 12^Δ

39) Calypso, an uncorrected +2.00 hyperope, is fixating on a medial plane target placed 50 cm in front of her eyes. What is the accommodative demand [D] and the convergence effort [MA]?

a) 4 D; 2 MA
b) 1 D; 1 MA
c) 1 D; 2 MA
d) 2 D; 1 MA

40) Which hero experiences increased convergence demand when wearing his/her spectacles instead of wearing his/her contact lenses and fixating at the same distance?

a) Nestor (+4.00 hyperope)
b) Calypso (+2.00 hyperope)
c) Tiresias (–2.00 myope)
d) Arete (–4.00 myope)

41) Which of the following myopic heroes experiences increased accommodative demand when he/she is wearing his/her contact lenses?

a) Tiresias (–2.00 myope)
b) Arete (–4.00 myope)
c) Penelope (–5.00 myope)
d) Achilles (–6.00 myope)

42) Eurymachus is a +7.00 D hyperope with a 15.0 D amplitude of accommodation. What is his near point when he is not wearing correction?

a) 15 cm
b) 14.2 cm
c) 12.5 cm
d) 8 cm

43) When not wearing correction, what amount of accommodation does Eurymachus use to fixate at infinity?

a) 0.00 D
b) 7.00 D
c) 8.00 D
d) 15.00 D

44) Bonus question from Greek Mythology: Which of the following axioms has been grossly misrepresented by the careless individual who put these quiz questions together?

a) Odyssey's heroes were all emmetropes.
b) Calypso never let Odysseus leave.
c) Seer Tiresias was blind.
d) Laertes was not part of the epic tale.

Presbyopia & Near Vision

45) Laertes, a –1.00 myope (= distance Rx), is using a +2.00 D add power. What is his near Rx?

a) –3.00
b) –1.00
c) +1.00
d) +2.00
e) +3.00

46) Which of the following does not change when Laertes switches from his distance Rx to his near Rx?

a) amplitude of accommodation
b) accommodating demand at 20 cm
c) location of near point
d) location of far point

47) What are Laertes' far and near points when he is wearing his distance Rx? His amplitude of accommodation is only 2.00 D.

a) far point ∞; near point 0.5 m
b) far point ∞; near point 1 m
c) far point ∞; near point 2 m
d) far point 0.5 m; near point 0.25 m
e) far point 1 m; near point 0.5 m
f) far point 1 m; near point 0.33 m

48) Laertes wears near Rx +1.00 (distance Rx –1.00, AoA 2.00 D). What are his far and near points when wearing his near Rx?

a) far point ∞; near point 0.5 m
b) far point ∞; near point 1 m
c) far point 2.0 m; near point 0.5 m
d) far point 1 m; near point 0.5 m
e) far point 1 m; near point 0.33 m
f) far point 0.5 m; near point 0.25 m

49) Nausicaa, a hyperope with distance Rx +3.00 D and add +1.50 D, needs a near Rx of …

a) +1.50
b) +3.00
c) +4.50
d) +6.00

50) Nausicaa's amplitude of accommodation is 2.5 D. When she is wearing the distance Rx of +3.00 D, her near point is …

a) 20 cm
b) 25 cm
c) 33.3 cm
d) 40 cm
e) 66 cm

51) When Nausicaa is wearing near Rx of +4.50 D, her far and near points are …

a) far point 66.6 cm; near point 25 cm
b) far point ∞; near point 25 cm
c) far point 40 cm near point 25 cm
d) far point ∞; near point 66.6 cm

52) Odysseus, an emmetrope, cannot produce a clear image if it is any closer than 80 cm from his eyes. What add power will help him fixate with maximum accommodation at 25 cm in front of his eyes?

a) 1.25 D
b) 1.75 D
c) 2.25 D
d) 2.75 D

53) Wearing the near Rx (Q 52), what is the farthest that Odysseus will be able to fixate with zero accommodation?

a) 25 cm
b) 36.36 cm
c) 40 cm
d) 80 cm
e) Infinity

54) How does Odysseus' dioptric range of clear vision compare between the distance and the near Rx?

a) distance range: 1.25 D; near range: 1.25 D
b) distance range: 0.80 D; near range: 0.25 D
c) distance range: ∞; near range: 0.25 D
d) distance range: 4 D; near range: 2.75D

55) How does Odysseus' linear range of clear vision compare between the distance and the near Rx?

a) distance: ∞ to 80 cm; near: ∞ to 25 cm
b) distance: ∞ to 25 cm; near: 25 cm to 0 cm
c) distance: ∞ to 80 cm; near: 36.6 cm to 25 cm
d) distance: ∞ to 36.6 cm; near: 36.6 to 25 cm

56) Amphinomus' OD distance Rx is −1.00 −0.50×010. He needs add power +2.50 OU. What should be his single vision near Rx (OD)?

    a) −1.00 −0.50×010
    b) +1.50 −0.50×010
    c) +2.50 −0.50×010
    d) +1.25 −0.75×010

57) Amphinomus' OS distance Rx is −1.25 −0.75×170. What should be his single vision near Rx (OS)?

    a) +1.25 −0.75×170
    b) +1.50 −0.75×170
    c) +2.50 −0.50×170
    d) −1.00 −0.50×170

58) An accommodative amplitude of 1.25 D is indicative of an individual about ____ years old.

    a) 35
    b) 45
    c) 55
    d) 65

59) Eurycleia of Ithaca is left with only 0.50 D AoA. What add power does she need to comfortably view her spindle, which is 40 cm away?

    a) +0.50 D
    b) +1.75 D
    c) +2.00 D
    d) +2.25 D

60) When corrected for distance, Antinous has a near point at 40 cm. What add should he be prescribed to comfortably view a target at the same distance?

    a) −1.25 D
    b) 0.00 D
    c) 1.25 D
    d) 1.75 D

61) Antinous is a −3.00 myope, as we already know. According to Q 60, what should be his near Rx?

    a) 1.25 D
    b) 0.00 D
    c) −1.25 D
    d) −1.75 D

62) What is Tiresias' amplitude of accommodation if he is using just half of this amplitude to focus on the seer stone at 12.50 cm in front of his eyes?

    a) 0.00 D
    b) 6.00 D
    c) 8.00 D
    d) 10.00 D
    e) 12.00 D

63) Using the answer to Q 62, how far from Tiresias' eyes is the closest point to which he can bring the seer stone to clearly see it (maximum accommodation; disregard depth of field)?

    a) 6 cm
    b) 7.14 cm
    c) 8.33 cm
    d) 14 cm

64) Using the answer to Q 63, what add should be prescribed to Tiresias for a normal working distance of 40 cm?

    a) 0.00 D
    b) 0.50 D
    c) 1.00 D
    d) 2.00 D

65) Ajax, when fully corrected for distance, has a near point of 25 cm. What add should he be prescribed for a normal working distance of 40 cm?

    a) 0.00 D
    b) 0.50 D
    c) 1.00 D
    d) 2.00 D

66) Penelope, a −5.00 myope fitted with a −4.00 D lens, has a near point of 1 ft (≈ 33 cm). What is her amplitude of accommodation?

    a) +1.00 D
    b) +2.00 D
    c) +3.00 D
    d) +4.00 D

67) Back to Q 66. When Odysseus returns, he restores order and provides the proper distance Rx and near Rx for his wife. What will the add power and the near Rx be (working distance = 40 cm)?

    a) add power: 1.50 D; near Rx: −3.50 D
    b) add power: 1.50 D; near Rx: −6.50 D
    c) add power: 1.00 D; near Rx: −4.00 D
    d) add power: 1.00 D; near Rx: −5.50 D

68) What is Circe's (a −1.50 D myope) far point when she is wearing her near Rx (+0.50 D)?

    a) 2.00 m in front of her eye
    b) 0.66 m in front of her eye
    c) 0.50 m in front of her eye
    d) 2.00 m behind her eye
    e) 0.66 m behind her eye
    f) 0.50 m behind her eye

7.12 ACCOMMODATION AND PRESBYOPIA SUMMARY

Accommodation

When fixating at the **far point**, the eye is 'relaxed,' or 'not accommodating;' i.e., there is no increase in the optical power of the crystalline lens. The retina is conjugate to the far point. The **near point** is the closest point at which an object can be placed and still form a sharp image on the retina. To achieve this, the eye accommodates at its largest capacity; i.e., the crystalline lens achieves its maximum power. Between the two points, which define the range of clear (or sharp) vision, accommodation can range from zero (the far point) to maximum (the near point).

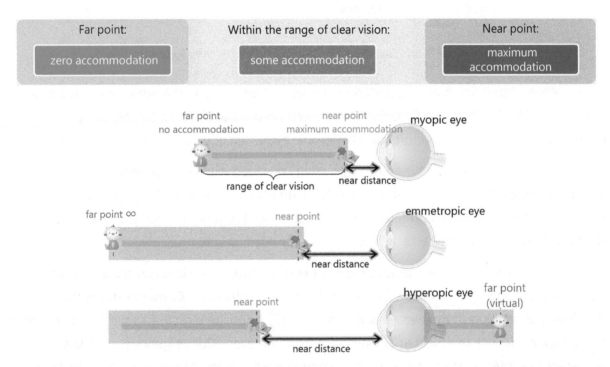

Figure 7-55: Near and far points in myopia (top), emmetropia (middle), and hyperopia (bottom).

When an object is placed anywhere between the far and the near points (range of clear vision), the eye is subject to the dioptric stimulus to accommodation, referred to as the fixation point vergence L_x. The accommodative demand (the stimulus magnitude of accommodation) is

Magnitude of Accommodation A = (far-point vergence L_{FP}) − (fixation-point vergence L_x)

The magnitude of accommodation represents the increase in optical power that the eye needs to make the fixation point optically conjugate to the retina. For an emmetropic eye, it is simply the fixation-point vergence.

The closest an object can be placed and still be seen with relative clarity is the near point, where the eye is subject to the maximum stimulus to accommodation (the near-point vergence L_{NP}). The accommodative demand is the largest (this amount is the amplitude of accommodation AoA) and represents the maximum increase in optical power that the eye needs in order to make the near point optically conjugate to the retina.

Amplitude of Accommodation AoA = (far-point vergence L_{FP}) – (near-point vergence L_{NP})

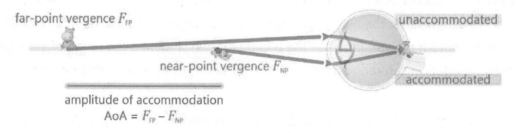

Figure 7-56: Definition of the amplitude of accommodation.

When determining accommodation, it is important to know the refractive status of the eye, i.e., to identify where the far point is. The accommodative demand for the same target will be less for a myopic eye and more for a hyperopic eye when compared to an emmetropic eye.

A hyperopic eye accommodates less when corrected with contact lenses (in general, with a reduced vertex distance) than when corrected with spectacle lenses. A myopic eye accommodates more when corrected with contact lenses (in general, a reduced vertex distance) than when corrected with spectacle lenses.

When fixating at a near object, the **near reflex triad**, which involves accommodation, convergence, and pupillary miosis (pupil constriction), is activated. **Convergence** is the simultaneous rotation of the two eyes in geometrically opposite directions to obtain or maintain the binocular view of an object at any distance from the eyes. Convergence is measured in **meter angles** [MA], which is the amount of convergence needed to see an object 1 m away while exerting 1.00 D of accommodation. Meter angles are equivalent to the reciprocal of the working distance, whose value approximately equals the accommodative stimulus:

$$\text{Meter Angle [MA]} = \frac{1}{\text{working distance [m]}} = \frac{100}{\text{working distance [cm]}}$$

Thus, the **convergence effort** (expressed in prism diopters [$^\Delta$]) that an emmetrope requires to fixate binocularly at a near object equals the dioptric distance from the object to the center of rotation of the eyes, multiplied by the interpupillary distance.

$$\text{Convergence effort } [^{\Delta}] = \text{IPD [cm]} \times \frac{100}{\text{distance from the center of rotation of the eyes [cm]}}$$

The near point of convergence (NPC) is the closest point at which an object may be seen binocularly; the NPC can be closer than the near point of accommodation (for example, 10 cm).

The eyes of a myope wearing spectacles will binocularly converge less than when that individual is wearing contact lenses. The eyes of a hyperope wearing spectacles will binocularly converge more than when that individual is wearing contact lenses.

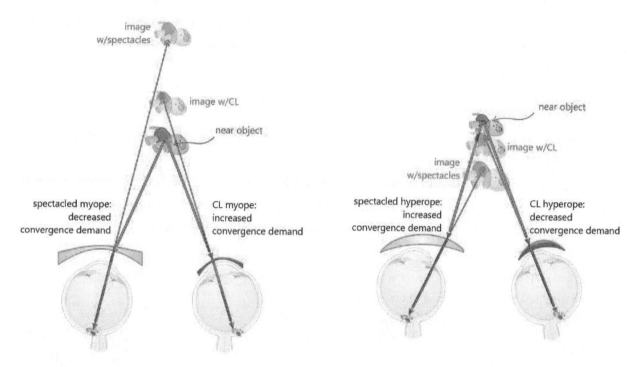

Figure 7-57: Near-vision binocular convergence: spectacle lens versus contact lens correction for (left) myopia and (right) hyperopia.

Presbyopia

Presbyopia manifests as a gradual decrease in accommodative ability. From infancy, the accommodative amplitude decreases with age at an average rate of 0.3 D per year until it stabilizes at around 60 years of age, with roughly 0.5 D of remaining amplitude:

Average Amplitude of Accommodation: $\qquad 15 - 0.25 \times \text{age}$ $\qquad\qquad$ (7.8)

The working distance for an individual with presbyopia dictates the extra plus power that they will need for comfortable near vision; this extra plus power is referred to as an **add** or

addition of plus over their distance refractive state. When providing an add in spectacles, the distance prescription is never affected; instead, the near prescription is commonly dispensed as the algebraic combination of the distance prescription with a spherical amount of plus power. Note that when an add is included, this should be obtained as a positive difference between the front vertex power of the spectacle lens.

The selection of the add power can be facilitated by the concept of 'comfort'. In order for an individual to 'comfortably' view a target, he/she should be using no more than half of his/her amplitude of accommodation, leaving a percentage of the amplitude of accommodation (the other half) in reserve. The rationale for this principle is that the use of the entire accommodation is not sustainable without discomfort. Traditionally, the working distance of 40 cm is considered (as this is where near visual function is routinely evaluated) and the accommodative stimulus is 2.50 D.

Empirical Formula for Add Power: $F_{add} = (2.50\ D) - (\frac{1}{2} \cdot AoA)$ (7.9)

When using an add power, both the far and the near point are shifted by the same dioptric amount closer to the eye, equal to the add power. Thus, when a fully corrected for distance presbyope uses the add power, the far point is the reciprocal of the add power, and the near point is shifted by a dioptrically equal amount. The dioptric range of clear vision does not change; however, the linear range of clear power is often significantly shorter.

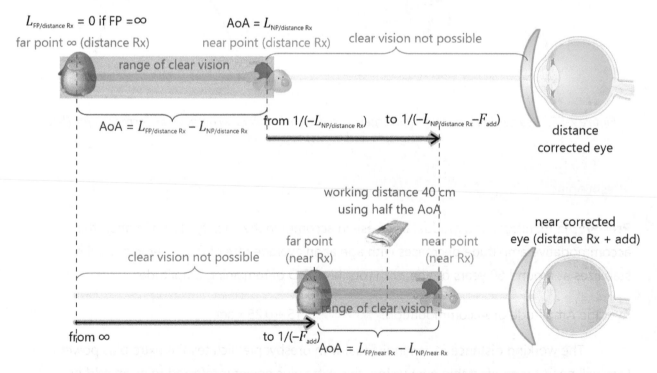

Figure 7-58: Vergence diagram for a distance-corrected eye (top) and a near-corrected eye (bottom).

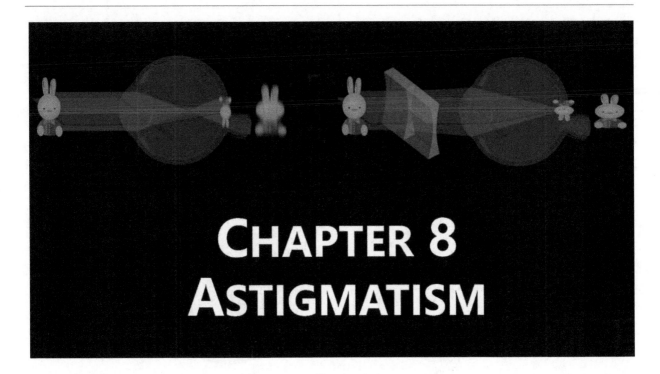

CHAPTER 8
ASTIGMATISM

8.1 GEOMETRY AND CLASSIFICATION OF ASTIGMATISM

An implicit assumption up to now has been that the corneal surface is part of a perfect sphere. Regardless of the cross-section orientation, the cornea is assumed to produce circular cross-sections: If we imagine that we intersect the cornea along the horizontal, the vertical, or any other oblique orientation, the cross-section yields circular surfaces of equal, fixed radii of curvature.

These radii of curvature are generally smaller in myopia (steeper cornea) and larger (flatter cornea) in hyperopia. In any case (either emmetropia, myopia, or hyperopia), the points of focus corresponding to any two individual corneal cross-sections coincide—just not always on the retina.

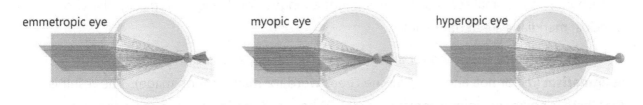

Figure 8-1: Ray convergence along two distinct meridians for an emmetropic, myopic, and hyperopic eye. The points of focus corresponding to any two cross-sections coincide.

8.1.1 Meridians

The cross-section planes just described are called meridian planes, and their intersection with the corneal surface are meridians. The **meridian** is defined similarly to geographic meridians. It is a virtual line passing through the pupil center, just as the geographical meridians pass through the poles of the earth.

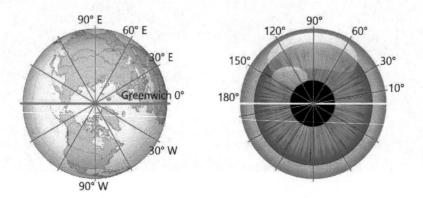

Figure 8-2: Meridians in geography and the optics of the eye.

The meridians are reported in degrees (°) and have values from 0° to 180° in a counter-clockwise direction (standard ISO 8429:1986) for both eyes. In visual optics and the profession of eye care, the value of 0° is not used, so the horizontal meridian is referred to as 180°. The vertical meridian is referred to as 90°. Clock hours are also used in denoting meridian values but less often than degrees. The horizontal meridian at 180° crosses the 3 o'clock and 9 o'clock positions, while the vertical meridian at 90° is at the 12 o'clock position.

The cornea is not part of a spherical surface, but an ellipsoid surface. We can 'dissect' the ellipsoid along two perpendicular cross-sections, one along the greater diameter and one along the smaller diameter (corneal toricity, § 2.1.4.2). These are the two **principal meridians**. The **steep** meridian has the greatest curvature (shortest radius of curvature), and the **flat** meridian has the smallest curvature (largest radius of curvature). The steep meridian corresponds to the largest optical power and the shortest focal length; the flat meridian corresponds to the smallest optical power and the longest focal length. Typically, the two principal meridians are at right angles.

This different optical power along the two meridians, also known as toricity, causes **astigmatism** (α- for not, and -$\sigma\tau\acute{\iota}\gamma\mu\alpha$, the Greek word for mark or spot image). The result is that there is no image point (stigmatic image). Where one meridian is at a sharp focus, the other forms a line.

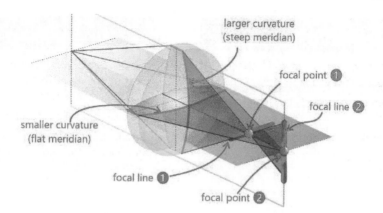

Figure 8-3: Astigmatism is caused by different lens curvatures between the two principal meridians.

In myopia/hyperopia, focusing is rather simple: Rays in any meridian converge at the same point. In astigmatism, focusing is rather complicated; as illustrated in Figure 8-3, rays in the steep meridian focus at focal point 1, while rays in the flat meridian focus at focal point 2.

Because the rays in the flat meridian plane do not focus at point 1, at this location, these rays form line ❶. Accordingly, at point 2, line ❷ is formed because the steep meridian is defocused. The 3-D shape formed by connecting the rays between these two focal lines defines the **Sturm conoid**, named after the Swiss-French mathematician Jacques Charles François Sturm. The interval between the two focal lines is **Sturm's interval**, which can be expressed either linearly, as the axial (longitudinal) separation between the two focal lines, or dioptrically, as the vergence difference between the two focal lines (simply, the difference in power between the two principal meridians, which as we will see, is the magnitude of astigmatism).

The **circle of least confusion** is the smallest cross-section within Sturm's interval; it is therefore formed in the space between the two focal lines. [The moniker 'circle' is a simplification—often its shape is not a circle (disk).] It lies at the dioptric midpoint (average vergence) between the two focal lines, i.e., the average power between the two principal meridians. Its location therefore is found as the reciprocal of this vergence.

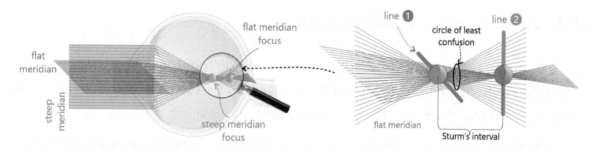

Figure 8-4: Ray convergence for an astigmatic eye along the two principal meridians. The focal points corresponding to the two meridians do not coincide. Compare with Figure 8-1. The red and blue lines indicate the focal lines corresponding to the most powerful (steep) and least powerful (flat) meridians, respectively.

Defocus Refractive Error	Astigmatic Error
• Expresses the inability of the ocular system to focus the image from a distant object on the retina.	• Expresses the inability of the ocular system to focus parts of the image that correspond to different meridians on the retina.
• The optically conjugate image is formed at a single spot but away from the retina.	• No clear optically conjugate image is ever formed.
• Results from power disparity in relation to what is needed for the axial length of the eye (emmetropic power).	• Results from a differential distribution of refractive power along the two principal meridians.

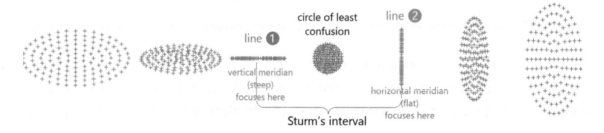

Figure 8-5: Through focus spot diagrams in astigmatism. The circle of least confusion is between the two focal lines at their dioptric midpoint.

Example ☞: Once upon a time in a land far away, Dorotea holds a lens (in the air). This lens has power +2.00 D @ the horizontal meridian and +8.00 D @ the vertical meridian. Where is the circle of least confusion, and what is the expanse of Sturm's interval?

The dioptric midpoint between the two extremes is +5.00 D = ½·(+2.00+8.00), the average of the two principal meridian sphere values in Doroteas' lens. The circle of least confusion lies at the reciprocal of this dioptric power, which is 1/(+5.00 D) = +20 cm = 0.20 m.

The dioptric Sturm's interval, <u>the difference</u> between the two sphere values, is 6.00 D (= 8.00 – 2.00). The linear Sturm's interval is the axial separation between the two focal lines: The vertical meridian forms a horizontal line at 1/(+8.00 D) = +0.125 m, while the horizontal meridian forms a vertical line at 1/(+2.00 D) = +0.50 m. Therefore, the linear expanse of Sturm's interval is 0.375 m (= 0.50 – 0.125).

8.1.2 Classification of Astigmatism

The first distinction of astigmatism is <u>refractive</u>—astigmatism is classified by the <u>location</u> of the <u>two focal lines</u> (Sturm conoid) <u>with respect to the retina</u>. It is assumed that no accommodation (relaxed eye) is taking place. This results in five types of astigmatism:

Simple myopic astigmatism occurs when one focal line [the red line in Figure 8-6 (left)] lies on the retina, while the other (the blue line) lies before the retina. In **compound myopic** astigmatism, both focal lines lie before the retina; i.e., they are both myopic but to different degrees.

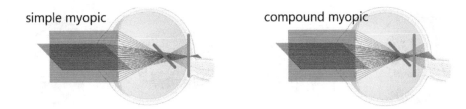

Figure 8-6: (left) Simple myopic and (right) compound myopic astigmatism. Red and blue lines indicate focal lines corresponding to the steepest (most optical power) and flattest (least optical power) meridians, respectively.

Simple hyperopic is the astigmatism in which one focal line [blue line in Figure 8-7 (left)] is on the retina and the other (red) is beyond the retina. In **compound hyperopic** astigmatism, both focal lines are located beyond the retina, as shown in Figure 8-7 (center).

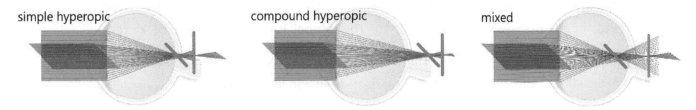

Figure 8-7: (left) Simple astigmatism, (center) compound hyperopic astigmatism, and (right) mixed astigmatism.

In **mixed** astigmatism, one focal line is before the retina [blue line in Figure 8-7 (right)] and the other (red) is beyond the retina. The conoid of Sturm straddles the retina. The circle of least confusion is close to, or on, the retina, the latter occurring in purely symmetric, equally mixed astigmatism. Thus, mixed astigmatism usually correlates to better visual acuity than the other types.

The second distinction of astigmatism is based on the <u>distribution of the meridional power</u> relating to the <u>orientation of the focal lines</u>. In **'with-the-rule'** (WTR) astigmatism, the most powerful, steep meridian is vertical (90 ± 30°). Then, the first focal line is horizontal (just as in all of the examples shown above), which occurs when the vertical meridian is focused while the horizontal meridian (with less power) is not yet focused. If the steep meridian is horizontal (180° ± 30°), we have **'against-the-rule'** (ATR) astigmatism, in which the first focal line is vertical.

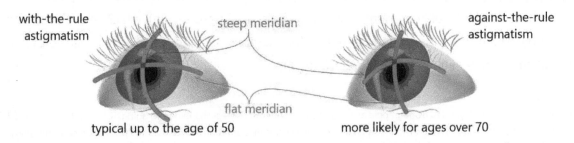

Figure 8-8: Corneal astigmatism at a younger age is typically with-the-rule (left), while it is more likely to be against-the-rule in older age (right).

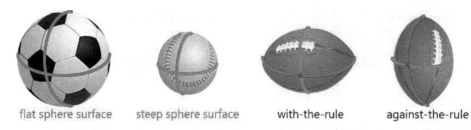

flat sphere surface   steep sphere surface   with-the-rule   against-the-rule

Figure 8-9: Flat spherical, steep spherical, with-the-rule (WTR), and against-the-rule (ATR) surfaces. WTR astigmatism can be conceptualized as vertical overpower, while ATR can be seen as horizontal overpower.

These names derive from the fact that, during adulthood, the average cornea is steeper in the vertical meridian by about 0.50 D compared to the horizontal. Simply said, with-the-rule rules! The with-the-rule dominance gradually decreases with age, and then it reverses until an average age of 70 years.[853, 854] It is more likely that elderly individuals have an increased incidence of against-the-rule astigmatism.[855] The football is (finally) ready to be kicked!

The orientation of the steep meridian (red color) and the flat meridian (blue color) can help in visualizing the 'rule' type of astigmatism, as shown in Figure 8-10.

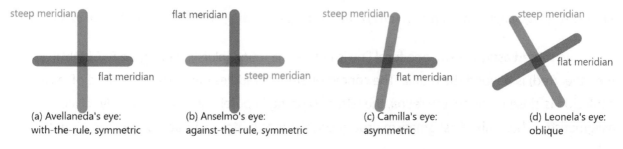

(a) Avellaneda's eye: with-the-rule, symmetric   (b) Anselmo's eye: against-the-rule, symmetric   (c) Camilla's eye: asymmetric   (d) Leonela's eye: oblique

Figure 8-10: Steep and flat principal meridians in several types of astigmatism orientation and symmetry.

Astigmatism is considered **oblique** if the orientation of either principal meridian is between 30° to 60°. The with-the-rule, against-the-rule, and the oblique classification reflect the rotational orientation of the power meridians and the subsequent rotation of the Sturm conoid.

The distinction between with-the-rule, oblique, and against-the-rule relates to the orientation of the focal lines. Avellaneda's eye [Figure 8-10(a)] and Anselmo's eye [Figure 8-10(b)] differ in the focal line orientations (with- and against-the-rule), which are related to a rotation by 90°. If the rotation had been less, for example, 45°, the result would be the oblique astigmatism seen in Leonela's eye [Figure 8-10(d)].

---

[853] Hayashi K, Hayashi H, Hayashi F. Topographic analysis of the changes in corneal shape due to aging. Cornea. 1995; 14(5):527-32.

[854] Fledelius HC, Stubgaard M. Changes in refraction and corneal curvature during growth and adult life. A cross-sectional study. Acta Ophthalmol (Copenh). 1986; 64(5):487-91.

[855] Kanellopoulos AJ, Asimellis G. Distribution and repeatability of corneal astigmatism measurements (magnitude and axis) evaluated with color light emitting diode reflection topography. Cornea. 2015; 34(8):937-44.

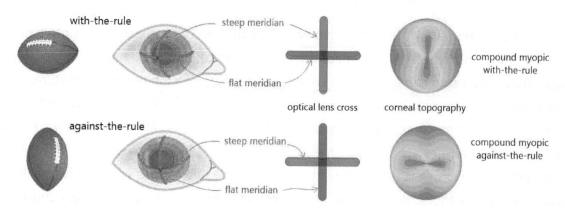

Figure 8-11: *The four illustrative representations of (top) with-the-rule astigmatism and (bottom) against-the-rule astigmatism: shape of the football, meridians, lens cross, and bow-tie pattern in corneal topography.*

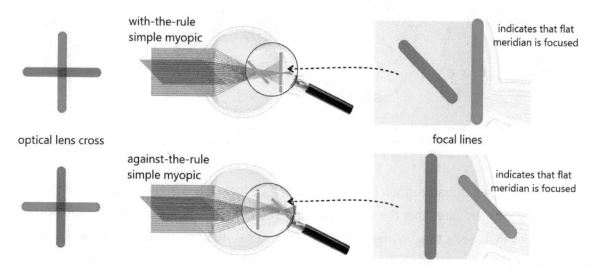

Figure 8-12: *Simple myopic astigmatism (top) with-the-rule and (bottom) against-the-rule. The two forms differ by a rotation of the lens cross (and the corresponding focal lines defining the Sturm conoid) by 90°.*

Food for thought 🍽 :

The distinction between myopic, hyperopic, and mixed type relates to the <u>axial placement of the focal lines</u> (Sturm conoid) with respect to the retina. Both examples in Figure 8-12 are simple myopic. If we rotate the lens cross by 90°, they are still the same in terms of refractive power, but are of the opposite-rule type.

Note 🔍 : Astigmatism cannot be classified according to the criterion of axial length—there is no axial astigmatism. This is because the axial length in each eye has a single value, the same for the two principal meridians, so the axial length in one eye cannot be longer or shorter than in the other eye.

A third distinction of astigmatism is based on symmetry. If the principal meridians are perpendicular to each other (90°), then astigmatism is **regular** or **symmetric**. If the principal meridians deviate from being at right angles, we have an **irregular** or **asymmetric** astigmatism.

Corneal topography[67] 2-D maps project the distribution of corneal power onto a disk of about 8 to 9 mm in diameter. These maps are color-coded to a diopter range. Warmer (red) colors indicate increased curvature, while cooler colors (blue) indicate reduced curvature. The tell-tale sign of astigmatism is the <u>hourglass</u> or bow-tie pattern—a figure-8 with warmer colors indicating increased curvature. Thus, the pattern orientation aligns with the steep meridian; the flat meridian is usually perpendicular to the steep one, connecting the bluer areas.[856] The bow-tie symmetry reflects aspects of astigmatism that cannot be determined with simple manifest measurement or traditional keratometry. It has been assumed so far that the extent and/or orientation of each part of the hourglass pattern is the same. This is not always the case.

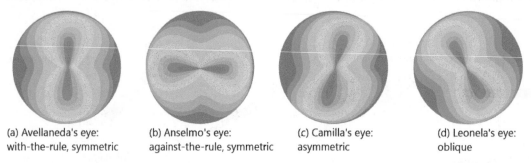

(a) Avellaneda's eye: with-the-rule, symmetric (b) Anselmo's eye: against-the-rule, symmetric (c) Camilla's eye: asymmetric (d) Leonela's eye: oblique

Figure 8-13: Hourglass patterns associated with the principal meridians indicated in Figure 8-10.

Camilla's eye curvature map [Figure 8-13 (c)] may look like symmetric astigmatism, but it is not. A closer look indicates that the two principal meridians are not perpendicular. The hourglass pattern shows that, while the flat meridian is horizontal, the steep meridian is slightly oblique, thus not forming right angles. Figure 8-14 presents more cases of asymmetric astigmatism: In Lothario's eye map, the pattern is skewed. The top part of Policarpa's map suggests superior steepening, while Periandro's map shows steepening toward the inferior section.

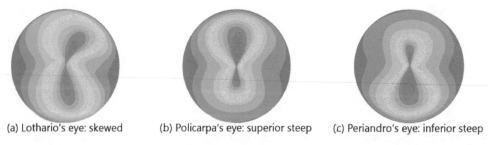

(a) Lothario's eye: skewed (b) Policarpa's eye: superior steep (c) Periandro's eye: inferior steep

Figure 8-14: Various forms of asymmetric astigmatism demonstrated in topography.

When asymmetric or irregular astigmatism is present, often the determination of the (orientation) overriding meridian is not possible, so this representation is not applicable. The 'plus'- and 'minus'-cylinder forms cannot properly describe asymmetric astigmatism. The two

---

[856] *Ocular Imaging* § 4.3.4 Axial, Tangential and Refractive Power Maps.

meridians might not be perpendicular to each other, or their orientation might not be consistent. In skewed astigmatism, for example, the two meridians can be different in the center and in the periphery. It's possible that the meridian corresponding to the 3 to 5 mm optical zone annulus differs from the meridian corresponding to a center 3 mm optical zone.

This brings up the question of the optical zone: for example, what is the implication of irregular astigmatism at the periphery if it is regular in the better part of the center 3 mm? Determination of central zone astigmatism is the most important and provides the best possible representation of astigmatism for two reasons: This zone affects the most-sensitive photopic vision, and the estimate of peripheral astigmatism is often based on less-reliable data.

8.2 MAGNITUDE AND AXIS OF ASTIGMATISM

Astigmatism can be conceptualized as a gradual variation in optical (refractive) power between two extremes, the minimum (along the flat meridian) and the maximum (along the steep meridian). Thus, astigmatism is a bivariate quantity consisting of a modulus, which determines the magnitude, and an axis, which determines the orientation.

The amount or **magnitude** of astigmatism is the difference between the powers of the two principal meridians (expressed in diopters). The **axis** of astigmatism is the orientation of the meridian with the least optical power. It is expressed in degrees from 0° (reported as 180) up to 179°; the degree sign is not used, just three digits. The 'zero' value is horizontal and increases in a counter-clockwise direction. In Figure 8-15, King Policarpo's eye power (see Figure 8-14) ranges from 63.50 D along the vertical meridian to 60.50 D along the horizontal meridian, with intermediate values in between. The magnitude of astigmatism is 60.50 − 63.50 = −3.00 D. The axis is @ 180°, denoted by ×180.[857] Perpendicular to this, @ 90°, is the power meridian with the greatest power (63.50 D). We just described the **minus**, or **negative**, **cylinder**, which is the most commonly used convention.

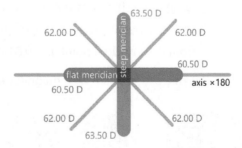

Figure 8-15: The magnitude of this astigmatism is −3.00 D, and the axis is 180.

---

[857] In many textbooks, the term 'axis meridian' is used in lieu of axis. This, however, may lead to confusion. See editorial by Rosen M. Axis or Meridian? J Cataract Refract Surg. 2011; 37(10):1743.

There is also the **plus**, or **positive**, **cylinder** convention, in which the magnitude is the smallest meridian power minus the greatest meridian power. The axis is the orientation of the meridian with the <u>greatest optical power</u>. In the example of Figure 8-15, the plus-cylinder component is written as +3.00×090.

King Policarpo's astigmatism presents the more-frequent with-the-rule astigmatism. Pedro Alonso, on the other hand (to be discussed in Figure 8-21), has a less-frequent against-the-rule astigmatism, as the horizontal meridian has more power than the vertical. In this case, the minus cylinder is expressed as –3.00×090 and the plus cylinder is expressed as +3.00×180.

Example ☞: Avellaneda's eye has an axial length of 23.82 mm and a refractive index of 1.336. The power along the vertical meridian (90°) is +62.00 D and along the horizontal (180°) is +58.00 D. In this eye:

• The focal length (from the principal point to the retina) is 23.82 – 1.6 mm = 22.22 mm = 0.0222 m. The reference emmetropic optical power is 1.336/0.0222 m = +60.00 D. This is a hypothetical power: <u>If</u> the eye had this much power along all meridians, it would be <u>emmetropic</u> (it does <u>not</u> and it is <u>not</u>).

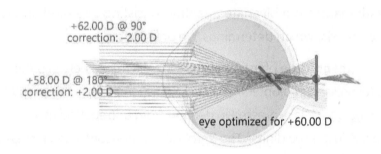

+62.00 D @ 90°
correction: –2.00 D

+58.00 D @ 180°
correction: +2.00 D

eye optimized for +60.00 D

Figure 8-16: Mixed, with-the-rule astigmatism of –4.00 D magnitude.

• The vertical meridian is –2.00 <u>myopic</u>, which means that it has +2.00 D <u>more power</u> than the emmetropic reference. Thus, a vertically oriented beam <u>focuses before the retina</u> (red dot; horizontal blue line) at 1.336/62 D = 0.02155 m = 21.55 mm from the principal point, i.e., 0.67 mm to the left of the retina.

• The horizontal meridian is +2.00 <u>hyperopic</u>, which means that it has –2.00 D <u>less power</u> than the emmetropic eye. Thus, a horizontally oriented beam <u>focuses after the retina</u> (blue dot; vertical red line) at 1.336/58 D = 0.02303 m = 23.03 mm from the principal point, i.e., 0.81 mm to the right of the retina.

• Avellaneda's eye has mixed, with-the-rule astigmatism with magnitude –4.00 D and axis ×180.

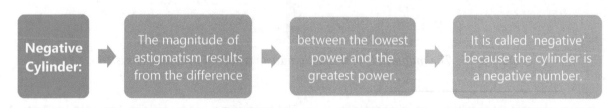

Negative Cylinder: ➡ The magnitude of astigmatism results from the difference ➡ between the lowest power and the greatest power. ➡ It is called 'negative' because the cylinder is a negative number.

Prevalence studies over large populations suggest that almost a quarter of human eyes have 0.50 D or less of astigmatism, while 40 % have astigmatism between 1.00 D and 1.50 D, and about 25 % of eyes have more than 1.50 D of astigmatism.[858] Thus, astigmatism is considered the most common refractive error following myopia and hyperopia.[859, 860] Genetic disposition appears to play a role,[861] while other factors associated with astigmatism development include eyelid pressure, extraocular muscle tension,[862] and visual feedback.[863] High astigmatism is associated with the development of amblyopia in young individuals.[864] Hereditary factors have been linked to astigmatism as well.[865]

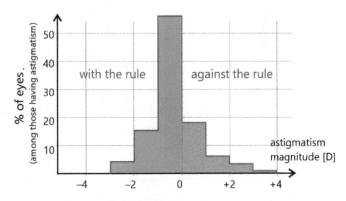

Figure 8-17: Typical population distribution of astigmatic error. Astigmatism magnitude is the difference in refractive power between the two principal meridians: the flat one minus the steep one. With-the-rule astigmatism has a negative magnitude, while against-the-rule astigmatism has a positive magnitude.

8.2.1 Astigmatic Prescriptions

Several conventions are used for denoting an astigmatic prescription. These can be based on the optical lens cross, the plus and minus cylinder, or the (less-used) crossed-cylinder. Rules have been established to help convert from one convention to another.

[858] Hashemi H, Fotouhi A, Yekta A, Pakzad R, Ostadimoghaddam H, Khabazkhoob M. Global and regional estimates of prevalence of refractive errors: systematic review and meta-analysis. J Curr Ophthalmol. 2018; 30(1):3-22.

[859] Hoffer KJ. Biometry of 7,500 cataractous eyes. Am J Ophthalmol. 1980; 90(3):360-68.

[860] Ferrer-Blasco T, Montés-Micó R, Peixoto-de-Matos SC, González-Méijome JM, Cerviño A. Prevalence of corneal astigmatism before cataract surgery. J Cataract Refract Surg. 2009; 35(1):70-5.

[861] Pärssinen O, Kauppinen M, Kaprio J, Koskenvuo M, Rantanen T. Heritability of refractive astigmatism: a population-based twin study among 63-to 75-year-old female twins. Invest Ophthalmol Vis Sci. 2013; 54(9):6063-7.

[862] Read SA, Collins MJ, Carney LG. The influence of eyelid morphology on normal corneal shape. Invest Ophthalmol Vis Sci. 2007; 48(1):112-9.

[863] Read SA, Collins MJ, Carney LG. A review of astigmatism and its possible genesis. Clin Exp Optom. 2007; 90(1):5-19.

[864] Abrahamsson M, Sjöstrand J. Astigmatic axis and amblyopia in childhood. Acta Ophthalmol. 2003; 81(1):33-7.

[865] Dirani M, Islam A, Shekar SN, Baird PN. Dominant genetic effects on corneal astigmatism: the genes in myopia (GEM) twin study. Invest Ophthalmol Vis Sci. 2008; 49(4):1339-44.

The **optical lens cross** (or, simply, optical cross or power cross) is a schematic representation that simply denotes the two individual spherical (correction) powers along the two principal meridians. The two correction powers correspond to the power values of the corrective lens as they are read off of a lensometer wheel. In the example of Figure 8-16, the cross is −2.00 along the 90° (denoted as @ 90°) and +2.00 along the 180°, as is also shown in Figure 8-18 (a).

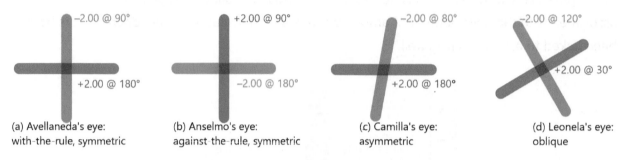

(a) Avellaneda's eye: with-the-rule, symmetric

(b) Anselmo's eye: against-the-rule, symmetric

(c) Camilla's eye: asymmetric

(d) Leonela's eye: oblique

Figure 8-18: Lens cross in several types of astigmatism symmetry (all of mixed astigmatism). Compare to Figure 8-10. (a) Avellaneda's eye is WTR, symmetric; (b) Anselmo's eye is ATR, symmetric; (c) Camilla's eye has asymmetric astigmatism; (d) Leonela's eye has oblique astigmatism.

Practice examples with answers ⚒: The optical lens crosses for the examples shown in Figure 8-18 are:

(a) Avellaneda's eye has with-the-rule astigmatism: +2.00 D @ 180° / −2.00 D @ 90°

(b) Anselmo's eye has against-the-rule astigmatism: −2.00 D @ 180° / +2.00 D @ 90°

(c) Camilla's eye has asymmetric astigmatism: −2.00 D @ 180° / +2.00 D @ 80°

(d) Leonela's eye has oblique astigmatism: +2.00 D @ 30° / −2.00 D @ 120°

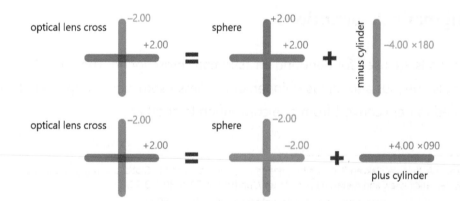

Figure 8-19: Optical lens cross, minus Rx, and plus Rx forms of Avellaneda's astigmatism.

The **minus-cylinder** and the **plus-cylinder Rx** forms are two different prescriptions that describe the <u>same corrective lens</u>. They present sphere power [D], cylinder power [D], and axis (three digits preceded by the ×sign). In the minus form (preferred by optometrists), the cylinder power is negative; in the plus form, the cylinder power is positive. For example, the minus Rx form of +2.00 −4.00×180 means that the sphere is +2.00 D, the cylinder is −4.00 D, and the axis is ×180.

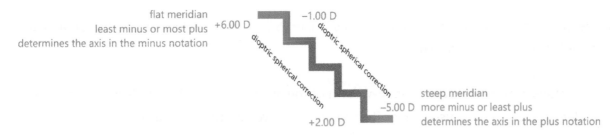

Figure 8-20: Flat meridian and steep meridian visualization in the form of dioptric correction.

To derive the <u>minus-cylinder</u> form <u>from the lens cross form</u>, we follow these steps: Start with <u>the most plus</u> (or least minus) sphere power meridian; this is the sphere value. Pedro Alonso's astigmatism, shown in Figure 8-21, has an optical lens cross −1.00 D @ 180° / +2.00 D @ 90°, so we start from the +2.00 D. Then calculate the dioptric step, which is the algebraic difference required to arrive at the other meridian (since we started from the most plus, this step is expected to be negative (going down the ladder in Figure 8-20). This gives the minus cylinder. In Pedro Alonso's case, it is −3.00. The axis is the meridian of the first step, which is ×090.[866]

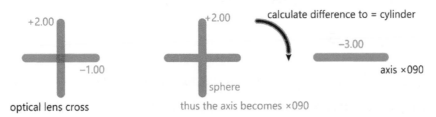

Figure 8-21: Producing the minus Rx prescription form +2.00 −3.00×090 from the optical lens cross.

To derive the <u>plus-cylinder</u> form <u>from the lens cross form</u>, the process differs only in that we start with <u>the least plus</u> (or most minus) sphere power meridian, which in Pedro Alonso's case is −1.00 D. The (plus) cylinder power is +3.00, and the axis is ×180.

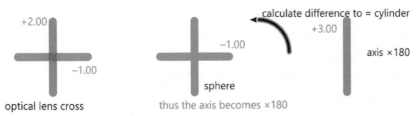

Figure 8-22: Same case as in Figure 8-21, producing the plus Rx prescription form −1.00 +3.00×180.

Example ☞: The minus- and plus-cylinder forms for the astigmatism examples in Figure 8-18 are:

Minus Rx: (a) +2.00 −4.00×180, (b) +2.00 −4.00×090, (c) not defined/applicable, and (d) +2.00 −4.00×030.

Plus Rx: (a) −2.00 +4.00×090, (b) −2.00 +4.00×180, (c) not defined/applicable, and (d) −2.00 +4.00×120.

---

[866] Remember, the axis is 'married' to the sphere. Once you determine the sphere, write down the axis as well. The axis is the meridian whose power you just used for the sphere value.

In the asymmetric case (c), there is no true minus or plus Rx form (is not defined/applicable) because the two meridians are not perpendicular.

Power transposition is the re-writing of the astigmatic prescription from the minus-cylinder Rx form to the plus-cylinder Rx form, and vice versa. The steps are:

1. Add the sphere and cylinder power values (it is an algebraic addition, so mind the possible − sign on either of them). This is the new sphere value. The minus-cylinder form of the example above is +2.00 −4.00×180. Then, the new sphere value is −2.00.

2. Flip the sign of the cylinder. The new cylinder value is +4.00.

3. Rotate the axis by 90° by adding or subtracting 90 from the axis to keep the value between 1 and 180. Here, the new axis is ×090. Therefore, the plus-cylinder form is −2.00 +4.00×090.

Sum:
Add sphere and cylinder to produce the new sphere value.

Sign:
Flip the sign of the cylinder and retain its power.

Axis:
Rotate the axis by 90° (add or subtract, keep between 0° and 180°).

Practice examples with answers ⚒ :

Astigmatism by type, in the form of negative (minus) cylinder Rx prescription:

Rutilio has simple myopic astigmatism: 0.00 −0.50×180 (instead of 0.00, we may simply write plano)

Reionoso has compound myopic astigmatism: −1.00 −0.75×180

Ricote has simple hyperopic astigmatism: +0.50 −0.50×180

Ana Félix has compound hyperopic astigmatism: +2.00 −0.50×180

Tosilos has mixed astigmatism: +0.50 −1.00×180

Transposition to positive- (plus) cylinder Rx prescription:

Rutilio's simple myopic astigmatism: −0.50 +0.50×090

Reionoso's compound myopic astigmatism: −1.75 +0.75×090

Ricote's simple hyperopic astigmatism: 0.00 +0.50×090

Ana Félix's compound hyperopic astigmatism: +1.50 +0.50×090

Tosilos' mixed astigmatism: −0.50 +1.00×090

Conversion to optical lens cross:

Rutilio's simple myopic astigmatism: −0.50 @ 90° / 0.00 (plano) @ 180°

Reionoso's compound myopic astigmatism: −1.75 @ 90° / −1.00 @ 180°

Ricote's simple hyperopic astigmatism: 0.00 (plano) @ 90° / +0.50 @ 180°

Ana Félix's compound hyperopic astigmatism: +1.50 @ 90° / +2.00 @ 180°

Tosilos' mixed astigmatism: −0.50 @ 90° / +0.50 @ 180°

Note 📎 : In all the above examples, the astigmatism type is with-the-rule. In the minus-cylinder notation, the with-the-rule axis is close to 180. In the plus-cylinder notation, the with-the-rule axis is close to 090.

Example ☞: What is Marcela's type of astigmatism if her prescription is –2.00 –1.00×180?

This prescription corrects along the 180° –2.00 D, and along the 90° –3.00 D. It is compound myopic because both meridians are myopic. It is with-the-rule because the steep meridian is vertical and therefore requires the largest (the most minus) correction.

Example ☞: What is Luzmán's type of astigmatism if his prescription is +0.50 –1.50×180?

This prescription corrects @ 180° +0.50 D, and @ 90°, –1.00 D. It is mixed because one meridian (the horizontal) is hyperopic and the other (the vertical) is myopic (for those still in doubt, the plus-cylinder form is –1.00 +1.50×090). It is with-the-rule because the steep meridian is vertical and therefore requires the largest (the most minus) correction.

Useful note 🧍 : In mixed astigmatism, the sphere and cylinder have opposite signs in <u>both</u> plus and minus forms.

Case 1: Lucinda's minus Rx prescription is +0.50 –1.25×180.
This transposes to the plus Rx –0.75 +1.25×090. Yes, it is mixed astigmatism; note the opposing signs of the sphere and cylinder in both forms. The 1.25 D conoid span straddles the retina. Those still in doubt can look at the optical lens cross: +0.50 @ 180° / –0.75 @ 90°.

Case 2: Juan Haldudo's minus Rx prescription is +0.75 –0.50×180.
Before rushing to classify this as mixed astigmatism, we note that it transposes to +0.25 +0.50×090. This is compound hyperopic, not mixed astigmatism. The entire 0.50 D conoid span is behind the retina. Those still in doubt can look at the optical lens cross: +0.75 @ 180° / +0.25 @ 90°.

Useful note 🧍🧍 : In simple myopic or hyperopic astigmatism, there is a plano sphere in one of the two forms, while in the other Rx form, the sphere and cylinder are of equal magnitude and opposite sign.

Case 1: Simple myopic astigmatism has a plano sphere in the minus-cylinder Rx. Rutilio's Rx, for example, is 0.00 –0.50×180, which becomes –0.50 +0.50×090 in the plus Rx form.

Case 2: Simple hyperopic astigmatism has a plano sphere in the plus-cylinder Rx. Ricote's Rx, for example, is 0.00 +0.50×090, which becomes +0.50 –0.50×180 in the minus Rx form.

The **crossed-cylinder form** is an alternative, less frequently used convention for describing astigmatism. It is the counterpart of the lens cross, in which two perpendicularly aligned cylinder values (hence, crossed-cylinder) are used instead of sphere values. This form is never used in prescribing spectacle lenses; however, it helps in explaining the function of a toric lens. If two cylinders with perpendicular axes are combined, a spherocylindrical lens results.

Consider, for example, a cylinder +2.00×090 combined with a cylinder +3.00×180. In the crossed-cylinder form, this is written as +2.00×090 / +3.00×180 and can be spoken as 'plus two axis ninety in combination with plus three axis one-eighty.' This combination creates an astigmatic power distribution similar to what can be achieved with an optical lens cross that reads +2.00 @ 180° / +3.00 @ 90°. Thus, a simple way to move between these two notations is to simply cross the meridian power values (using × to denote cylinder).

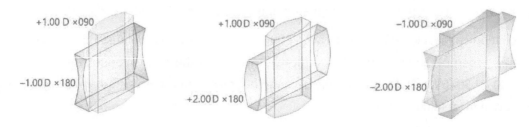

Figure 8-23: 3-D representation examples of the crossed-cylinder form: (left) +1.00×090 / –1.00×180, (center) +1.00×090 / +2.00×180, and (right) –1.00×090 / –2.00×180.

Example ☞: What is the crossed-cylinder form when the optical lens cross is +3.00 @ 135° / –1.00 @ 45°?

This (oblique) astigmatism converts to the crossed-cylinder form: +3.00 ×045 / –1.00 ×135.

Example ☞: What is the crossed-cylinder form for this minus-cylinder prescription form: –2.00 –1.00×180?

We convert to optical lens cross: –2.00 @ 180° / –3.00 @ 90°. This with-the-rule compound myopic astigmatism can be expressed in crossed-cylinder form as –3.00 ×180 / –2.00 ×090.

8.2.2 Spherical Equivalent

The **spherical equivalent** (SE) is a spherical power that produces a focal point coincidental to the circle of least confusion of a spherocylindrical lens. Thus, the spherical equivalent is considered the dioptric vergence for the circle of least confusion. Hence, the spherical equivalent equals the algebraic sum of the sphere and half the cylindrical value, i.e., sphere + (½·cylinder). The axis simply disappears because the spherical equivalent is ... spherical.

Spherical Equivalent (SE): $SE = F_s + (½ \cdot F_c)$ (8.1)

where F_s is the sphere power and F_c is the cylinder power.

Note 🗎 : This formula for spherical equivalent works with either plus or minus Rx prescription form. It is, however, important to keep tabs on the algebraic signs!

Practice examples with answers ⚒ :

Case A: Sancho Panza's Rx is –2.50 –1.00×180; SE is –2.50 + [½ · (–1.00)] = –2.50+(–0.50) = –3.00 D.

Case B: Dapple's Rx is –2.00 +2.00×090; SE is –2.00 + [½·(+2.00)] = –2.00+(+1.00) = –1.00 D.

Note 🪪: The spherical equivalent is independent of the choice of minus or plus Rx notations.

Sancho Panza's plus-cylinder Rx: –3.50 + 1.00×090; SE: –3.50 + [½·(+1.00)] = –3.50 + (+0.50) = –3.00 D.

Dapple's minus-cylinder Rx: 0.00 –2.00×180; SE: 0.00 + [½·(–2.00)] = 0.00 + (–1.00) = –1.00 D.

Note ◉ : SE can also be computed by the average of the two spherical powers in the lens cross.

Sancho Panza's lens cross: –2.50 @ 180° / –3.50 @ 90°; SE: ½· [–2.50 + (–3.50)] = –3.00 D.

Dapple's lens cross: (plano) @ 180° / –2.00 @ 90°; SE: ½· [0.00+ (–2.00)] = –1.00 D.

In a trial lens or phoropter refraction examination, if we simply increase the cylinder in the typical spherocylindrical formulation, the spherical equivalent is affected: A half sphere must be compensated (e.g., +0.25 D) per each cylinder diopter change (e.g., –0.50 D) to <u>keep the placement of the circle of least confusion on the retina.</u>

Example ☞: During the phoropter test, we place a –2.00 –1.50×180 in front of Marcela's eye. Subsequently, during the examination, the cylinder changes to –0.50×180. What should the new spherical power be to keep the placement of the circle of least confusion on the retina?

Cylinder power changes from –1.50×180 to –0.50×180; this means that the <u>change</u> in cylinder power is +1.00 D. We therefore need to compensate by adding –0.50 D sphere, making the new sphere power –2.50 D.

Note 📑 : Mixed astigmatism usually has a (near) zero SE. Zero occurs for equally mixed astigmatism only.

Example ☞: Ambrosio's Rx is –1.00 +2.00×090. SE = –1.00 + [½ · (+2.00)] = –1.00 + (+1.00) = 0.00 D. Lens cross: –1.00 @ 90° / +1.00 @ 180°; SE (average of the two powers) = ½·[–1.00 + (+1.00)] = 0.00 D. This is equally mixed astigmatism.

Example ☞: Grisóstomo's Rx is –0.75 +1.25×180. SE = –0.75 + [½·(+1.25)] = –0.75 + 0.625 = –0.125 D. Lens cross: –0.75 @ 180° / +0.50 @ 90°; SE (average of the two powers) = ½·[–0.75 + (+0.50)] = –0.125 D. This is mixed but not equally mixed astigmatism.

8.3   The Seat of Astigmatism

It has been implied throughout the preceding text that astigmatism is due to the cornea: We talk about corneal meridians with different optical (refractive) powers, as in Figure 8-24. This corneal toricity (§ 2.1.4.2) causes **corneal astigmatism** and is indeed quantitatively the largest astigmatism component in the eye, but is <u>not the only one</u>. Typically, we measure corneal toricity using keratometry or corneal topography.

Example ☞ : What is the contribution of corneal toricity in Antonia's eyes, shown in Figure 8-24?

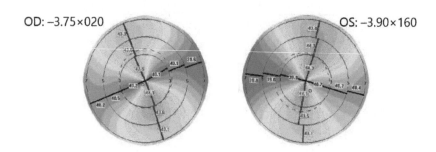

OD: –3.75×020   OS: –3.90×160

Figure 8-24: Right (OD) and left (OS) eye corneal topographies of the same person. This is slightly oblique, with-the-rule astigmatism. (Numeric values on the topography maps indicate corneal power). Such right and left eye enantiomorphism, or mirror symmetry, is common.

Right eye (OD). The average (within the center 3 mm optical zone) steep meridian power (red line) is 43.90 D @ 110°, and the average flat meridian (blue line) power is 40.15 D @ 20°. The magnitude of astigmatism due to corneal toricity is the difference between the smallest power (40.15 D) and the greatest (43.9 D), which produces a magnitude of –3.75 D; the axis is along the meridian with the weakest power: –3.75×020.

Left eye (OS). The average steep meridian (red line) power is 44.20 D @ 70°, and the average flat meridian (blue line) power is 40.30 D @ 160°. Thus, the magnitude of astigmatism due to corneal toricity is –3.90×160.

Note ✉: Corneal topography can help in assessing the type of astigmatism that relates to the meridian power distribution (WTR, ATR, or oblique). The refractive aspect, which determines whether astigmatism is myopic, hyperopic, etc., cannot be evaluated by topography alone because the spherical component, whose determination requires knowledge of the axial length of the eye, is not provided by topography.

Note ♀ : In Figure 8-24. we see that Antonia's OD astigmatism axis is ×020 and the OS axis is ×160. This is an example of mirror symmetry, known as enantiomorphism,[867] which is notable in oblique astigmatism. In enantiomorphism, there is a strong symmetry between the right- and left-eye axes; another example is the case of OD axis ×010, OS axis ×170. The sum of the two astigmatism axes is often very close to 180.

---

[867] Dunne MC, Elawad ME, Barnes DA. A study of the axis of orientation of residual astigmatism. Acta Ophthalmol (Copenh). 1994; 72(4):483-9.

There is also **internal astigmatism**, which is mainly produced by a contribution from the anterior surface of the crystalline lens. Sources for internal astigmatism are the posterior cornea and the crystalline lens; thus, internal astigmatism can be attributed to two sources, the **posterior cornea** and **phakic** or **lenticular astigmatism**.[868] If the cylinder measured by manifest refraction matches what is produced by corneal toricity alone, then there is no internal astigmatism—the astigmatism is (purely) anterior corneal astigmatism. If not, we assume that there is internal astigmatism.

The aggregate of all contributions is the **refractive, total, ocular,** or **manifest astigmatism**, which is what is measured in manifest refraction and is written in the prescription. The rays, in simple words, on their way to form the distorted retinal image, are subject to total ocular astigmatism, regardless of its origin. The image does not 'split' the origin of astigmatism. In contrast, several ocular imaging devices can indicate the seat of astigmatism, albeit indirectly: Corneal topography measures anterior toricity, while manifest refraction measures manifest astigmatism. Their difference can be attributed to internal astigmatism.

Example ☞ : What is Antonia's OD internal astigmatism, considering the corneal topography in Figure 8-24, if the manifest refraction is –3.25 –3.75×020?

As discussed following the data in Figure 8-24, the cylinder due to corneal toricity is –3.75×020. It is identical to the cylinder measured by manifest refraction. Thus, there is <u>no</u> internal astigmatism in this eye.

Example ☞ : Princess Felesinda has manifest refraction –2.50 –1.75×180. The keratometric measurements (called K-readings) are 44.20 D @ 180° and 46.45 D @ 90°. Determine the internal astigmatism.

Corneal toricity is the difference between the two K-readings: (44.20 – 46.45) = –2.25 D. The axis is ×180, corresponding to the flatter meridian. Thus, corneal toricity is –2.25×180. Since the cylinder, measured by manifest refraction, is –1.75×180, there is an offset 'cancellation' by +0.50×180. This can be attributed to internal astigmatism, arising mainly from the lens contribution.

Lenticular astigmatism can be caused by lenticular toricity, the difference in curvature between the crystalline lens meridians (§ 2.1.4.2). Additional contributions are a tilted or decentered lens with respect to the optical axis. In a healthy and normal eye, lenticular astigmatism contributes to about ≈ +0.50×180 or –0.50×090. Larger amounts of lenticular astigmatism can be pathologic; individuals with diabetes may develop lenticular astigmatism because high and fluctuating blood sugar levels can affect the shape and form of the lens.[863]

---

[868] Anstice J. Astigmatism: Its components and their changes with age. Am J Optom Physiol Opt. 1971; 48(12):1001-6.

Posterior corneal astigmatism is caused by posterior corneal surface toricity. Corneal topography (usually Placido)[67] measures astigmatism that is due solely to the anterior cornea. If no distinction is mentioned, then 'corneal' astigmatism is 'anterior corneal' astigmatism. Recently, however, devices that can image the anterior and the posterior cornea surfaces individually have been developed. The Orbscan, Pentacam, and Cassini[869] can separately measure astigmatism resulting from the anterior and the posterior corneal surfaces. Thus, we have the clinical tools to distinguish between anterior-surface and posterior-surface corneal astigmatism.

Figure 8-25: Individual contributions to total (manifest) astigmatism.

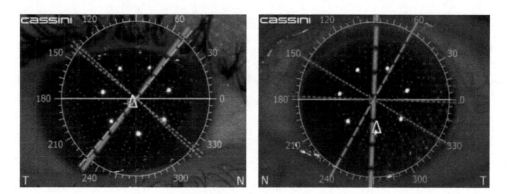

Figure 8-26: Anterior and posterior corneal astigmatism imaged via the Cassini topographer. The bold red dashed line is anterior steep meridian, the blue dashed line is anterior flat meridian, and the orange lines show the principal meridians corresponding to posterior astigmatism.

In healthy, normal corneas, posterior corneal astigmatism is ≈ 12.5% of the anterior astigmatism. It is mainly against-the-rule[46] (meaning that WTR anterior corneal astigmatism is reduced), which is primarily the case in young adults.[870, 871] To the contrary, if anterior corneal astigmatism is ATR, then posterior astigmatism leads to increased astigmatism.[872] This ATR

[869] *Ocular Imaging* § 4.4.2 The Cassini Topographer.

[870] Montalbán R, Piñero DP, Javaloy J, Alió JL. Correlation of the corneal toricity between anterior and posterior corneal surfaces in the normal human eye. Cornea. 2013; 32(6):791-8.

[871] Koch DD, Ali SF, Weikert MP, Shirayama M, Jenkins R, Wang L. Contribution of posterior corneal astigmatism to total corneal astigmatism. J Cataract Refract Surg. 2012; 38(12):2080-7.

[872] Sano M, Hiraoka T, Ueno Y, Itagaki H, Ogami T, Oshika T. Influence of posterior corneal astigmatism on postoperative refractive astigmatism in pseudophakic eyes after cataract surgery. BMC Ophthalmol. 2016; 16(1):212.

nature of posterior corneal astigmatism can be attributed to the fact that, although the two corneal surfaces mimic each other, the anterior surface is facing a lower refractive index (left, air; right, cornea), while the posterior surface is facing a higher refractive index (left, cornea; right, aqueous), although with significantly less difference in absolute values (§ 2.2.2). It is the same reason that the posterior corneal surface has a negative power and the anterior surface has positive power: The sign of the difference between the refractive indices is the opposite.[873]

However, the axes of anterior and posterior astigmatism are not always parallel. Figure 8-26 (left) shows a near-perfect alignment of the anterior and posterior oblique astigmatism axes. In the right image, we note a significant difference between the anterior and posterior astigmatism axes. In this case, simulated keratometry data, which are obtained based only on anterior measurements, would report astigmatism of −3.25×178, whereas proper consideration of anterior and posterior toricity yields −2.25×150.

Food for thought 🧁 : What if the two astigmatism components do not line up? What if the corneal principal meridians lie along the 180° − 90°, but lenticular astigmatism has meridians along the 30°–120°?

The combination of astigmatism with axis misalignment is mathematically challenging. A solution can be provided by vector decomposition of astigmatism in vector terms. This involves the use of power vectors, which are discussed in § 9.5.4 and § 9.5.5.

The clinical significance of posterior corneal and lenticular astigmatism attains relevance during refractive surgery; the challenge in maximizing the outcome lies in the determination of the true anterior-surface corneal astigmatism.

Laser refractive surgery modifies the anterior corneal component of astigmatism and can completely eliminate (although perhaps it should not) corneal (anterior, that is) astigmatism; thus, residual astigmatism is determined by posterior corneal and lenticular astigmatism. This is why some amount of residual anterior corneal astigmatism may be desired. In other words, the surgical decision might be to leave some residual corneal astigmatism that will balance the existing posterior cornea and lenticular astigmatism.

In cataract surgery, it is critical to select the proper toric IOL power. The magnitude and axis are determined by the existing corneal astigmatism (and possible modification of it with accurate surgical incisions), aiming for minimal postoperative ocular astigmatism.

---

[873] Rozema JJ, Hershko S, Tassignon MJ; for EVICR.net, Project Gullstrand Study Group. The components of adult astigmatism and their age-related changes. Ophthalmic Physiol Opt. 2019; 39(3):183-93.

8.4 EFFECT OF ASTIGMATISM ON VISION

Astigmatism affects the retinal image and subsequently reduces vision in a way that differs from simple ametropia.[874] In myopia or hyperopia, the retinal image is composed of circular blur projections, so the defocused image has a symmetrical blur (Figure 6-51). In astigmatism, the retinal blur is no longer symmetrical. Being elliptic in nature, it varies in its orientation; at the limits of Sturm's conoid, blur patches degenerate into lines.

Mixed astigmatism has the least detrimental effect on visual acuity compared to other types. This is because the two focal lines are straddling the retina, one slightly in front and the other past the retina. Thus, the circle of least confusion is very close (or even lies on) the retina. Even today, the effect of astigmatism on visual acuity is the subject of many research studies. Generally, the effect depends on the type of astigmatism, its magnitude, and its axis. Moreover, there are confounding variables in this quite complex problem, such as age, corneal and lenticular astigmatism, and status of accommodation.[875]

It is not clear whether the axis orientation affects visual acuity, and if so, which orientation has the most detrimental effect. Some studies indicate that the axis orientation does not influence visual acuity,[876] while other studies suggest that ATR and oblique astigmatism affect visual acuity more adversely than equal-magnitude WTR.[877, 878, 879] Interestingly enough, some studies suggest that ATR astigmatism may affect visual acuity less adversely than WTR astigmatism,[880] while other studies single out oblique (from WTR or ATR) astigmatism as the one that leads to the most adverse effects in visual acuity.[881] Recent studies conclude that the drop in visual acuity is associated with axis orientation, with the least affected being the 90° orientation, i.e., ATR astigmatism.[882, 883]

---

[874] Raasch TW. Spherocylindrical refractive errors and visual acuity. Optom Vis Sci. 1995; 72(4):272-5.

[875] Remón L, Monsoriu JA, Furlan WD. Influence of different types of astigmatism on visual acuity. J Optom. 2017; 10(3):141-8.

[876] Remón L, Tornel M, Furlan WD. Visual acuity in simple myopic astigmatism: influence of cylinder axis. Optom Vis Sci. 2006; 83(5):311-5.

[877] Miller AD, Kris MJ, Griffiths AC. Effect of small focal errors on vision. Optom Vis Sci. 1997; 74(7):521-6.

[878] Wolffsohn JS, Shah Bhogal G. Effect of uncorrected astigmatism on vision. J Cataract Refract Surg. 2011; 37(3):454-60.

[879] Alpins NA. New method of targeting vectors to treat astigmatism. J Cataract Refract Surg. 1997; 23(1):65-75.

[880] Trindade F, Oliveira A, Frasson M. Benefit of against-the-rule astigmatism to uncorrected near acuity. J Cataract Refract Surg. 1997; 23(1):82-5.

[881] Kobashi H, Kamiya K, Shimizu K, Kawamorita T, Uozato H. Effect of axis orientation on visual performance in astigmatic eyes. J Cataract Refract Surg. 2012; 38(8):1352-8.

[882] Mathur A, Suheimat M, Atchison DA. Pilot study: effect of the age on visual acuity with defocus and astigmatism. Optom Vis Sci. 2015; 92(3):267-1.

[883] Serra PM, Cox MJ, Chisholm CM. The effect of astigmatic axis on visual acuity measured with different alphabets in Roman alphabet readers. Clin Optom (Auckl). 2018; 10:93.

8.4.1 The Astigmatic (Clock) Dial

The fixed **astigmatic dial** is a practical device that helps in determining the axis of astigmatism and measuring its magnitude. The fixed aspect is due to the non-rotational nature of the presented target. The dial consists, in general, of lines radiating from the center. The most frequently used example is the **clock dial**, introduced by John Green in 1866, which is composed of triplets of spokes spaced by 30° intervals.[884]

The clock dial consists of twelve triplets of lines, each oriented along with the dials of the hour [Figure 8-27 (left)]. Thus, the lines in the clock dial can be identified by the clock position; for example, the 2 o'clock position is the 30° meridian. Each group consists of three lines (hence the triplet lines), and, within each group, the spacing and width of the individual lines are designed to be resolved by a person with visual acuity of at least 20/30.

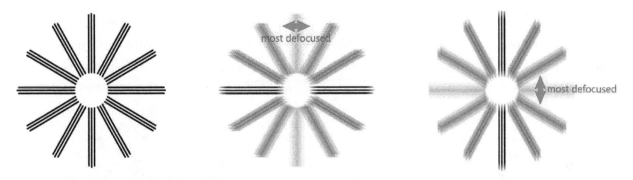

Figure 8-27: (left) The entire clock dial appears to be equally clear in the case of emmetropia; (center) the horizontal line (3 o'clock line) appears to be more clear when the astigmatic axis is 090; (right) the vertical line (12 o'clock line) appears to be more clear when the astigmatic axis is 180.

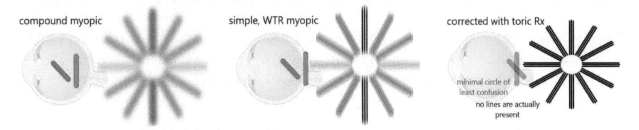

Figure 8-28: Clock dial clinical application. (left) Uncorrected compound myopic WTR astigmatism. Both focal lines are in front of the retina; no clock dial group of lines appears to be clear. (center) With proper spherical power, the vertical focal line is brought to the retina; the vertical group of clock dial lines appears to be more clear—effectively, this renders the case of simple myopic astigmatism. (right) With the application of the proper spherocylindrical correction, Sturm's interval collapses, bringing both focal lines to the retina; all clock dial line groups appear to be equally clear.

---

[884] Green J. On a new system of tests for the detection and measurement of astigmatism. Trans Am Ophth Soc. 1867-1868; 4-5:131.

When using the astigmatic dial, the appropriate spherical (plus or minus) power is placed on the retina of the examinee so that the astigmatism becomes simple myopic; then the most forward focal line of Sturm's interval is placed on the retina [example shown in Figure 8-28 (center) and Figure 8-30]. This means that only one group of clock dial lines becomes clear because this group corresponds to the focal line that is closest to (and best if directly on) the retina. The group of clock dial lines that is most blurred corresponds to the focal line that is the farthest from the retina. The meridian that parallels the most blurry (hence, the faintest) line or the meridian that is perpendicular to the best focused (hence, the darkest and most prominent) line denotes the astigmatic axis. The magnitude of astigmatism can be determined by adding a cylinder in 0.25 D steps until Sturm's interval collapses [Figure 8-28 (right)] and all groups of lines appear equally clear.

Example ☞: What is the clock dial examination process in Señora Arbolea's compound, ATR hyperopic astigmatism with Rx +1.00 +2.00×180?

The optical (power) cross of Arbolea's prescription is +1.00 @ 180° / +3.00 @ 90°. It is compound hyperopic (both powers positive). The steep meridian is horizontal (hence, ATR). Without any trial lens correction, this astigmatism creates two focal lines behind the retina, with the circle of least confusion dioptrically between the two; the astigmatic clock dial appears to be blurry.

example Rx: +1.00 +2.00×180

+3.00
+1.00

against-the-rule
compound hyperopic
uncorrected astigmatism

circle of least confusion

Figure 8-29: Clock dial application in ATR-compound hyperopic astigmatism, with no correction applied.

Step 1 is to add a sphere amount (either on a trial lens or a phoropter), with the intent of bringing the flat meridian to focus on the retina. This requires the use of +3.00 D; now the lens cross of the combination (correction + eye) is –2.00 @ 180° / plano @ 90°. Astigmatism becomes simple myopic (still ATR).

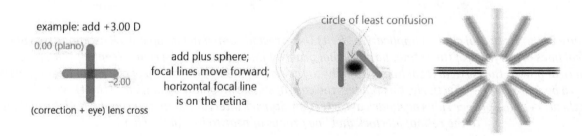

example: add +3.00 D

0.00 (plano)
–2.00

(correction + eye) lens cross

add plus sphere;
focal lines move forward;
horizontal focal line
is on the retina

circle of least confusion

Figure 8-30: Clock dial application in ATR-compound hyperopic astigmatism with spherical correction applied to bring the focus of the flat meridian to the retina.

In this combination, Sturm's interval has not changed (it is 2.00 D with or without the addition of sphere), nor has the circle of least confusion changed in shape or size. The benefit is that we can visualize the axis—it is 90° (the vertical meridian) because it is the meridian that parallels the blurriest (hence, the faintest) line. Alternatively, the axis is visualized as the meridian that is perpendicular to the best focused (hence, the darkest and most prominent) line, which, in this case, is horizontal.

Step 2 is to add the required cylinder to collapse Sturm's integral to the retina. This requires the eventual use of –2.00×090; now the combination (correction + eye) 'lens cross' is plano @ 180° / plano @ 90°. Astigmatism is eliminated, both 'lines' are focused on the retina (in reality, they disappear), and the circle of least confusion is on the retina and attains a minimum size. All lines on the dial appear sharp and clear (careful observation will reveal a meridional compression along the axis of astigmatism!).

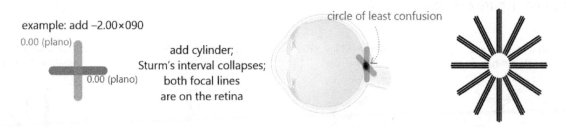

Figure 8-31: Clock dial application in ATR-compound hyperopic astigmatism, cylinder correction applied to bring the focus of the steep meridian on the retina.

A known limitation of the clock dial is that the 30° spacing between groups of lines does not allow for fine discrimination of the axis. Other fixed dials are the **sunburst** or **fan dial**, the **Lancaster's dial**,[885] and **Verhoeff's supplementary dial**.[886] The sunburst dial consists of individual spoke-lines angularly spaced by 10° intervals. Lancaster's dial consists of a 50 cm diameter target composed of spoke lines spaced by 10° intervals; the lines are 20 cm long and about 2 arcmin wide. Verhoeff's dial simply consists of two adjustable sets of lines, the principal meridians.

8.4.2 Effect of Astigmatism on Letter Legibility

In simple myopic WTR astigmatism, vertically oriented image features appear to be defocused, as they correspond to myopic vision, while horizontal features appear to be focused. Thus, there is a vertically defocused aspect to the retinal image. A compound myopic WTR astigmatism also has a vertical defocus, but it is more like a vertical ellipse. This affects optotype perception.

---

[885] Lancaster WB. Subjective tests for astigmatism, especially astigmatic charts. Trans Am Acad Ophth. 1915; 167.
[886] Verhoeff FH. Two new astigmatic charts. Ophth Rec. 1899; 8:541.

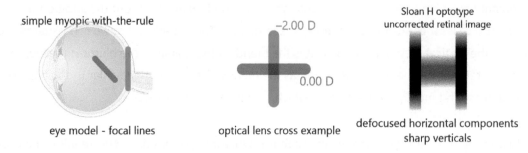

Figure 8-32: Effect of simple myopic, with-the-rule astigmatism on the perception of the Sloan H optotype.

Vertical and horizontal features are defocused differently. In the letter H, for instance, simple WTR astigmatism [Figure 8-32 and Figure 8-33(a)] causes a horizontal line defocus. A compound WTR myopic astigmatism brings additional defocus, while the horizontal line is more defocused [Figure 8-33(b)].

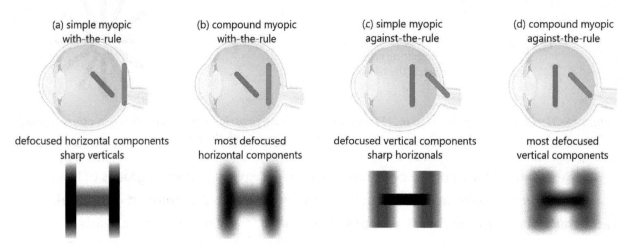

Figure 8-33: Effect of the type of astigmatism on retinal image meridional defocus.

To the contrary, ATR astigmatism stretches the retinal image along the horizontal lines, which do not suffer from this deformation; a horizontal line is still a clearly formed horizontal line but is just blurry at the edges. Vertical lines, however, when stretched horizontally, exhibit notable blur [Figure 8-33(c)]. Thus, ATR astigmatism results in vertical defocus. Therefore, images with predominant vertical features are affected more in ATR astigmatism.

Example ☞: What is Dapple's vision (recall, Rx 0.00 –2.00×180)?

Dapple has WTR simple myopic astigmatism. The steep meridian is vertical, –2.00 D myopic. The projected blur on the retina is a vertical ellipse, almost a vertical line. Dapple sees horizontal features as blurry and misses horizontal gaps but can still clearly see vertical details. Dapple will likely confuse the letters F and P. On the other hand, using a target with mainly vertical strokes (for example, the letter H) Dapple will 'suffer' less when identifying the optotypes.

Figure 8-34: The 20/160 Snellen letters F and P as seen by Dapple, with Rx 0.00 –2.00×180.

Example ☞: What is the vision type of Rocinante, whose prescription is 0.00 –2.00×090?

This is ATR simple myopic astigmatism. The steep meridian is –2.00 D myopic @ 180°. The blur projected onto the retina is a horizontal ellipse, almost like a horizontal line. Rocinante sees vertical features as fuzzy but can still clearly see horizontal details.

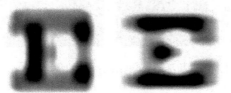

Figure 8-35: Simulated perception of the 20/200 Snellen letter E with (left) Dapple's vision with-the-rule 0.00 –2.00×180 and (right) Rocinante's vision against-the-rule 0.00 –2.00×090.

The effects of hyperopic astigmatism, on the other hand, can be harder to predict. The reason is that accommodation is also involved. Simple hyperopic astigmatism may produce effects similar to those of mixed astigmatism when an adequate amount of accommodation is drawn, which leads to both astigmatic focal lines moving closer to the retina. However, this does not affect the line orientation classification: WTR astigmatism remains WTR!

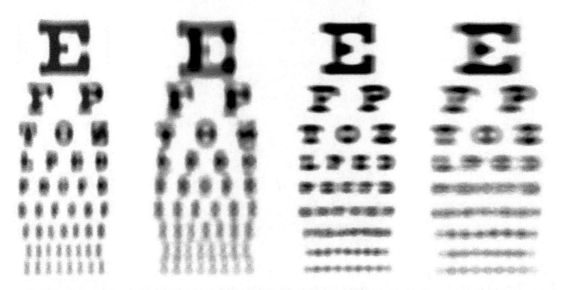

Figure 8-36: Effect of simple myopic astigmatism on visual acuity as demonstrated on a Snellen eye chart. From left to right: WTR astigmatism (left) –1.50×180 and (second from left) –2.00×180; ATR astigmatism (third from left) –1.50×090 and (right) –2.00×090. Compare with Figure 6-51.

In general, the with-the-rule astigmatism, vertically oriented blur has less impact on reading than an equal amount of against-the-rule, horizontally oriented blur. The spacing between letters in a text is typically tighter than the spacing between lines; thus, adjacent letters will run together in against-the-rule astigmatism, as shown in Figure 8-36 (right).

Figure 8-37: Vision simulation with simple myopic astigmatism: (left) WTR and (right) ATR.

These effects are also illustrated in the vision simulation shown in Figure 8-37. In WTR astigmatism, the letter I appears to be elongated vertically but is very legible, as are (in general), all of the vertical strokes. In ATR, however, the vertical stokes appear severely defocused. For example, a letter I spreads horizontally and almost merges with its neighboring letters.

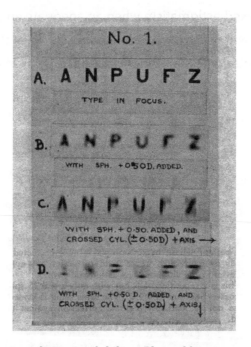

Figure 8-38: Effect of astigmatism on letter readability. Blurred letters are more easily recognizable when their vertical parts (as opposed to their horizontal parts) are brought to focus in WTR astigmatism.[887]

---

[887] Williamson-Noble FA. A possible fallacy in the use of the cross-cylinder. Br J Ophthalmol. 1943; 27(1):1-12.

8.5 CORRECTION OF ASTIGMATISM: PRINCIPLES

The origin of the correction of astigmatism dates back to the 19th century with the work of George Biddell Airy. An astigmat himself, Airy presented the cylinder lenses for astigmatism correction at the Cambridge Philosophical Society in 1825.[888] The term 'cylinder' reflects the different value of the refractive error (and therefore of the correction) between the two principal meridians. The astigmatic correction must address the different ametropia (myopia or hyperopia) along the two principal meridians. The corrective lens power must be determined separately for each of the two principal meridians. This requires overlaying two different lenses, which is a practical challenge!

8.5.1 Toric Lens Correction

The lens that combines spherical and cylindrical correction is a **toric lens** (§ 9.5), also called spherocylindrical, which is neither spherical nor cylindrical, but a combined shape. Using the axis and refractive meridian of the cylinder lens, along the axis meridian, the toric lens power equals the spherical power alone, while along the refractive meridian, the toric lens power equals the algebraic sum of the spherical and cylindrical powers.

Toric spectacle correction follows the same optical principles of far point conjugacy as in myopia or hyperopia. This correction places an object at infinity at the far point of that eye, now taking into account the different far points for the two principal meridians.

Consider the case of Cardenio, with two distinct far points in front of his eye: one along the horizontal meridian at 1.0 m (noted as −1.0 m) and the other along the vertical meridian at 50 cm (noted as −0.5 m). These two far points are distinct because Cardenio has different ametropias along the horizontal meridian and along the vertical meridian!

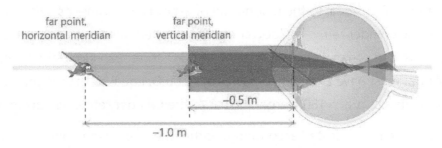

Figure 8-39: Cardenio's uncorrected, with-the-rule, compound myopic eye.

---

[888] Levene JR. Sir George Biddell Airy, FRS (1801-1892) and the discovery and correction of astigmatism. Notes and Records of the Royal Society of London. 1966; 21(2):180-99.

Cardenio's eye (Figure 8-39) has with-the-rule, compound myopic astigmatism. The defocus along the horizontal meridian is −1.00 D, while along the vertical it is −2.00 D. Thus, the lens that corrects the horizontal defocus has power −1.00 D @ 180°, and the lens that corrects the vertical defocus has power −2.00 D @ 90°.

The **toric lens** that corrects this astigmatism has a different optical power and a different focal length along the two principal meridians. The optical lens cross Rx is −1.00 D @ 180° and −2.00 D @ 90°. The minus form Rx is −1.00 −1.00×180, and the plus form Rx is −2.00 +1.00×090.

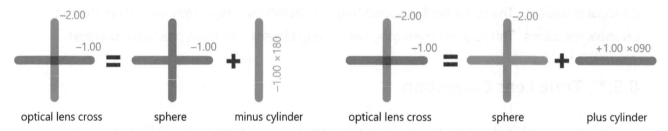

optical lens cross   sphere   minus cylinder   optical lens cross   sphere   plus cylinder

Figure 8-40: Optical lens cross, minus cylinder, and plus cylinder forms corresponding to the toric lens that corrects the astigmatism shown in Figure 8-39.

Consider now the correction of Dulcinea del Toboso, whose astigmatism is compound hyperopic and requires correction of +2.00 D along the vertical meridian and +3.00 D along the horizontal meridian. The astigmatism magnitude is −1.00 D, the difference in optical power between the horizontal and vertical meridians. The axis is ×180 because Dulcinea's eye has the least optical power along the horizontal meridian (requiring the most plus correction). The minus Rx is +3.00 −1.00×180, and the plus Rx form is +2.00 +1.00×090. Sometimes the numbers are preceded by S or DS, denoting the spherical correction (sphere), and C or DC, denoting the cylinder.

In Dulcinea's prescription, we can make a +2.00 D correction anywhere and can make an additional +1.00 D correction along the horizontal meridian. So, a plus cylinder must have a refractive power of 1.00 D, equal to the magnitude of astigmatism, while its axis is at ×090, perpendicular to the cylinder refractive/power meridian. Alternatively, we can make a +3.00 D correction anywhere and can make an 'additional' −1.00 D correction along the vertical meridian. So, a minus cylinder must have a refractive power of −1.00 D, equal to the magnitude of astigmatism, while its axis is at ×180, perpendicular to the cylinder refractive/power meridian.

A toric lens can be fabricated according to either the plus or the minus Rx form (§ 9.5.2). With the application of this toric lens, the conoid of Sturm is eliminated, and the circle of least confusion becomes, ideally, a point focused on the retina.

8.5.2 Correction with the Spherical Equivalent

When prescribing astigmatic toric contact lenses, one consideration is that the contact lens must be fitted with the minimization of lens rotation in mind, a problem that does not apply to spectacle correction, as these lenses are mounted in a fixed way on the frame.

Rotation of the axis of the contact lens from its intended orientation results in a loss of visual acuity. For each one degree (1°) of error in a toric lens rotational alignment, there is a 3.3 % decrease in the correction of astigmatism, or a 30% decrease in astigmatic correction per 10° of lens rotation.[889] A soft toric contact lens fit is successful if it can achieve and maintain the intended corrected visual acuity. Thus, axis rotation and instability of the contact lens may be detrimental to achieving the proper correction; a rotation of the lens by 30° essentially cancels the benefit of correcting astigmatism with a toric lens.

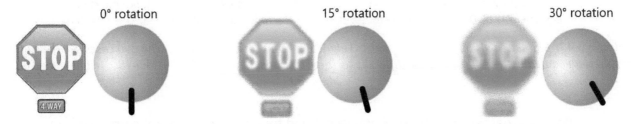

0° rotation   15° rotation   30° rotation

Figure 8-41: Deterioration of the image as a result of the rotation of a toric lens.

A prescription of spherical equivalent (as opposed to a toric correction) aims to place the circle of least confusion on the retina.[890] Thus, the spherical power prescribed is the spherical equivalent (§ 8.2.2). This approach has the advantage that the correction is free of rotational error—there is no cylinder (and, therefore, no axis) to worry about being rotated. There are certain limitations, however. A prescription of spherical equivalent is practically effective only for astigmatism of a magnitude up to 0.75 D, and in some cases, 1.00 D.

Parameters that influence the success of a spherical equivalent correction are the magnitude of the cylinder, the pupil size, and the lens design. For large cylinders, the size of the circle of least confusion is still rather significant, so vision correction using the spherical equivalent is noticeably less effective than vision correction using a spherocylindrical lens.[891]

---

[889] Pujol J, Arjona M, Arasa J, Badia V. Influence of amount and changes in axis of astigmatism on retinal image quality. J Opt Soc Am A Opt Image Sci Vis. 1998; 15(9):2514-21.

[890] Morgan PB, Efron N. Prescribing soft contact lenses for astigmatism. Cont Lens Anterior Eye. 2009; 32(2):97-8.

[891] Morgan PB, Efron SE, Efron N, Hill EA. Inefficacy of aspheric soft contact lenses for the correction of low levels of astigmatism. Optom Vis Sci. 2005; 82(9):823-8.

As a rule, if the cylinder correction is greater than 1.00 D, the spherical equivalent contact lens prescription will likely produce less than optimal correction. Strictly speaking, the spherical equivalent is less than optimum for any toric correction, but the question of whether the accompanying loss of vision will cause a problem is more pertinent to large cylinders.

On the other hand, the benefit of fitting a toric contact lens with less than 0.50 D of cylinder (if available) is negated by the real possibility of lens rotation. In such cases, the spherical equivalent is preferred.

| spherical equivalent −3.00 D | toric correction −2.50 −1.00×180 | | spherical equivalent −3.00 D | toric correction −2.00 −2.00×180 |

Figure 8-42: Simulated vision using the spherical equivalent and toric correction. The two cases use the same spherical equivalent (−3.00 D) but use different toric corrections: (left) Rx −2.50 −1.00×180; (right) Rx −2.00 −2.00×180.

Both approaches, the spherical equivalent and toric spherocylindrical correction, bring the circle of least confusion to the retina. However, in addition, toric spherocylindrical correction collapses Sturm's interval to the retina, producing the smallest possible expanse of the circle of least confusion.

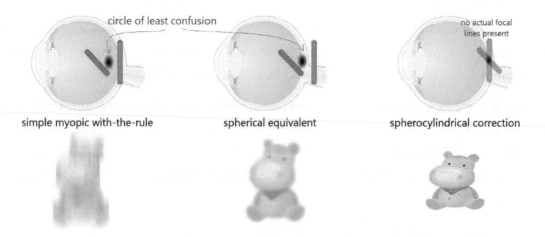

Figure 8-43: (top) Focal lines and (bottom) simulation of the retinal image in (left) uncorrected, simple myopic with-the-rule astigmatism, (center) astigmatism corrected with the spherical equivalent, and (right) astigmatism corrected with a toric spherocylindrical lens. In both the spherical equivalent and the toric corrections, the circle of least confusion is on the retina. However, there can be significant qualitative differences between the results of these two types of corrections.

Figure 8-44: (top) Uncorrected astigmatism of magnitude –2.00 with the axis at (left) 180, (center) 045, and (right) 090. (bottom) Vision corrected with spherical equivalent –1.00. Simulations created by Costas Katsoulos using the Sarver and Associates VOL-Pro simulation software; images reprinted with permission.

8.5.3 Distortion in the Corrected Retinal Astigmatic Image

The uncorrected astigmatic retinal image of a point is a blur ellipse. The shape, size, and degree of blur are all dependent on the pupil shape and diameter, and the type of astigmatism.[892] A cylindrical correction clears this blur ellipse and restores image clarity. In an uncorrected retinal image, the prevailing defocus (long ellipse axis) is along the meridian with the greater ametropia. Consider with-the-rule, simple myopic astigmatism, where the vertical meridian is myopic, while the horizontal meridian is emmetropic. The image, in this case, is defocused along the vertical meridian [Figure 8-45 (left)].

The required correction of this astigmatism is a cylinder lens with a horizontal axis, or, equivalently, a vertical power (refractive) meridian. However, this comes at a price, as there is anamorphic distortion in the corrected image. As discussed in § 9.3, the corrected myopic image is minified (condensed). The greater the amount of corrected myopia the more minified the corrected image. The parameter describing the retinal image size reduction is spectacle magnification; in myopic corrections, it can be shown (see data in Figure 9-26) that the retinal image decreases by about 1.25% per one diopter of refractive error.

Therefore, the most-blurred part of the astigmatic image before the image is corrected becomes the most condensed part after the image is corrected. In the case of WTR simple myopic astigmatism, the corrected image [Figure 8-45 (right)] is minified along the vertical refractive meridian (i.e., perpendicular to the horizontal cylinder axis) but not along the horizontal meridian.

---

[892] Charman WN, Voisin LI. Optical aspects of tolerances to uncorrected ocular astigmatism. Optom Vis Sci. 1993; 70(2):111-7.

uncorrected
astigmatic
image

corrected
astigmatic
image

Figure 8-45: WTR simple myopic astigmatism: (left) uncorrected and (right) fully corrected image.

Thus, when using an astigmatism-correcting cylinder spectacle lens, the corrected image is distorted asymmetrically; the unequal powers of the principal meridians result in differing meridional magnifications. This anamorphic distortion induces **meridional aniseikonia**.[893] The corrected (monocular) retinal image is magnified (or minified) disproportionally in one direction—the direction requiring the most correction. The perceived images are altered in shape, such as the short/fat bunny in Figure 8-45 (right) and the letter H in Figure 8-46. This distortion may also result, for obliquely oriented shapes, in declination/tilt. Each cylinder diopter produces approximately 0.4° of image tilt.

The severity of the distortion in the corrected image is dependent on the magnitude of the cylinder and its placement with respect to the eye (vertex distance, § 9.2.4)—the two parameters that mainly determine spectacle magnification (§ 9.3).

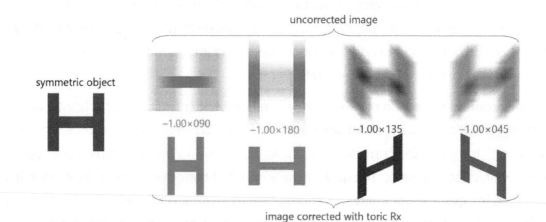

uncorrected image

symmetric object

−1.00×090 −1.00×180 −1.00×135 −1.00×045

image corrected with toric Rx

Figure 8-46: (left) Symmetric object and (right) image distortion due to asymmetric meridional magnification from a toric lens. (top) The uncorrected retinal image and (bottom) the corrected retinal image, which may be magnified disproportionally in one direction. The image may appear to be taller (−1.00×090), shorter (−1.00×180), or tilted (−1.00×135 or −1.00×045).

Example ☞: What is the relative meridional distortion when Hidalgo Don Quixote de la Mancha's astigmatism is fully corrected with a −5.50×090 cylinder placed at a 15 mm vertex distance?

[893] Guyton DL. Prescribing cylinders: the problem of distortion. Surv Ophthalmol. 1977; 22(3):177-88.

Don Quixote's astigmatism is simple myopic ATR. There is emmetropia along the vertical meridian, hence there is no vertical retinal blur. The image is blurred horizontally due to the –5.50 D myopic power. The cylinder lens placed at a vertex distance of 15 mm in front of an eye results in a meridional asymmetry between the two magnifications.

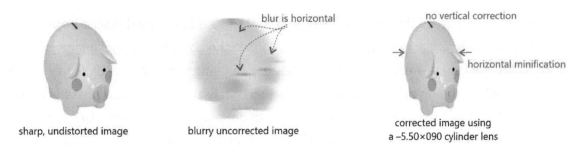

Figure 8-47: Meridional distortion when correcting ATR astigmatism using a –5.50×090 cylinder lens (distortion not presented to scale).

While there is no image size change along the vertical meridian, the F = –5.50 D power along the refractive /power meridian horizontally minifies the corrected image. To calculate the amount of magnification, we use the power factor at vertex distance d_v = 15 mm, employing relationship (9.16). [Material on spectacle magnification is presented in § 9.3.1.]

Power factor (with power – 5.50 D, vertex 15 mm) is 1/[1 – ($d_v \cdot F$)] = 1/[1– (0.015 · –5.50)] = 1/1.082 ≈ 0.9237. This means that the corrected image contracts along the horizontal meridian by about 1 – 0.923 = 7.63 %, resulting in a distorted corrected image that is compressed along the horizontal meridian.

Such monocular meridional asymmetric magnification can be alleviated by placing the corrective lens at a shorter vertex distance. This results in reduced distortion; because both spectacle magnification meridional values grow closer to unity, their difference is smaller, so the asymmetry between the two meridional magnifications also becomes smaller. A contact lens correction, for example, is considered to have a zero vertex distance[894] and results in zero power factor magnification and meridional distortion.

Example ☞: Don Quixote places the same corrective –5.50×090 cylinder lens at a shorter vertex distance of 7 mm. What is the relative meridional distortion?

Power factor (with power – 5.50 D, vertex 7 mm) is 1/[1 – ($d_v \cdot F$)] = 1/[1– (0.007 · –5.50)] = 1/1.04 ≈ 0.961. This means that the corrected image contracts along the horizontal meridian by about 1 – 0.961 = 3.7 %, resulting in a less distorted corrected image. The asymmetry between the two meridians (0% vertical

---

[894] Not exactly! The Optics Professor rises in angry protest (again!). Technically, all distances should be referenced to the object space principal plane, which is 3 mm inside the eye. Strictly speaking, even a contact lens is actually placed at some finite distance in front of the entrance pupil of the eye. Thus, the actual vertex distance for a contact lens is probably 4 mm. For simplicity, however, we often consider a zero value for the vertex distance of a contact lens.

minification and 3.7 % horizontal minification) will be less when the same corrective lens is placed closer to the eye. A brief note is in order here: As discussed in § 9.2.4, when placed at a 7 mm vertex distance, the required effective power for achieving the same refractive effect as a −5.50×090 correction placed at a 15 mm vertex distance would be −5.75 D, resulting in a 3.8 % minification.

We conclude that a cylinder (and, likewise, a toric) lens placed any distance from (in front of) the eye causes differential meridional magnification, so the corrected retinal image is distorted. There are very few exceptions to this result, one being the rare case of purely simple astigmatism, in which the myopic/hyperopic part is also purely axial. We could possibly apply Knapp's rule (§ 6.6.5), but this is not a likely scenario. In general, a contact lens will have much less distortion than other types of lenses due to the zero vertex power.

This asymmetric monocular magnification, however, is not the main problem associated with spectacle-corrected astigmatism. The main problem is that this asymmetric distortion, under binocular vision, leads to spatial perception alteration. Consider the correction of Montesinos' oblique astigmatism OD −1.00×045 and OS −1.00×135. The retinal images of a vertically oriented S-letter, observed at some distance, will be tilted toward each other at the top by about 0.4° (an accentuated version is illustrated in Figure 8-48). Under binocular fusion, the (single) image of the vertical letter may appear to be inclined toward the observer.

This error in stereoscopic spatial localization may be intolerable by Montesinos and other individuals, and is apparently unproportional to the small amount of monocular tilt that causes it. This is particularly the case in oblique distortion in one or both eyes, which causes more-distressing binocular symptoms than vertical or horizontal distortion. Moving objects present with even more-severe spatial perception errors, as spatial clues are not properly processed.

uncorrected OD −1.00×135 uncorrected OS −1.00×045 corrected OD −1.00×135 corrected OS −1.00×045

Figure 8-48: (left) Uncorrected and (right) toric-lens-corrected images. The two corrected monocular images appear to be tilted when viewed binocularly, leading to a false stereopsis perception.

It is often thought, erroneously, that in oblique astigmatism the defocused retinal image is tilted, and that astigmatic correction straightens up the retinal image. In reality, the opposite occurs. The defocused retinal images [Figure 8-48 (left)] are not tilted—it is the direction of defocus that is tilted (has an inclination along the axis), and, by correcting defocus, the corrected images become tilted [Figure 8-48 (right)]!

These effects are also illustrated in Figure 8-49 and Figure 8-50. The object (left) is viewed as shown in the blurred image (center). In simple myopia, say −1.00, the image is slightly defocused due to a small blur circle. This image, when corrected, is uniformly minimized (right).

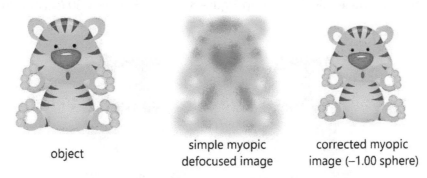

object   simple myopic
              defocused image   corrected myopic
                                     image (−1.00 sphere)

Figure 8-49: Simulation of the effects of correcting myopic refractive error. (left) Object, (center) uncorrected simple myopic image, and (right) spectacle-corrected image with −1.00 sphere Rx.

We now assume WTR astigmatism of the form −1.00×180 [Figure 8-50 (second from left)]. When looking at this defocused, uncorrected image, the circle of least confusion is now elliptic because the blur in the uncorrected image is maximized along the orthogonal-to-the-astigmatism-axis meridian (i.e., along the 90°). The spectacle-corrected image (third from left) appears to be vertically squeezed because it is minimized along the direction of most defocus.

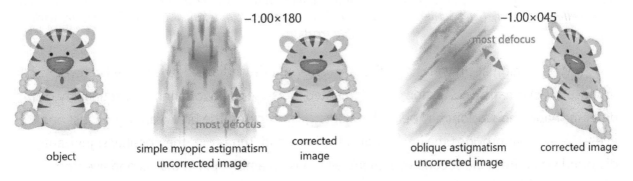

object   simple myopic astigmatism
              uncorrected image   corrected
                                       image   oblique astigmatism
                                                    uncorrected image   corrected image

Figure 8-50: Simulation of the effects of WTR and oblique astigmatism. (left) Object, (second from left) uncorrected simple WTR myopic image, (center) spectacle-corrected WTR myopic image, (second from right) uncorrected oblique astigmatic image, and (right) spectacle-corrected image.

We now assume oblique astigmatism of the form −1.00×045 [Figure 8-50 (second from right)]. When looking at this defocused, uncorrected image, the circle of least confusion is now elliptic, but there is no true inclination in the retinal image; the impression is derived because the blur (defocus) in the uncorrected image is maximized along the orthogonal-to-the-astigmatism-axis meridian (i.e., along the 135°). The spectacle-corrected image (right) now appears inclined or slanted because it is minimized along the most defocused direction.

The same effect is also demonstrated in the eye chart image simulations shown in Figure 8-51. There is no perceivable inclination in the uncorrected perception, either: It is the defocus blur that is slanted, not the image itself. With the full spectacle cylinder correction, however, the image may become sharp but noticeably tilted [as in Figure 8-48 and Figure 8-50 (second from right)].

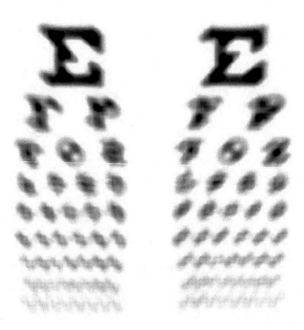

Figure 8-51: Effect of simple myopic oblique astigmatism on monocular visual acuity, as demonstrated on a Snellen eye chart. (left) Astigmatism –2.00×045 and (right) astigmatism –2.00×135. Compare with Figure 8-36.

When astigmatism varies significantly in magnitude and axis between the two eyes, if full monocular astigmatism correction is implemented, because the two monocular retinal images differ in shape, their fusion may be problematic. In such cases, the brain can rely on just one eye—the eye that provides the less-distorted vision—and 'tunes out' the possibly significantly distorted vision from the second eye, eventually causing amblyopia in the second eye from disuse, particularly in children. This is not the only challenge that astigmatism spectacle correction might need to address. An astigmatic eye that is fully corrected on the spectacle plane will have a differential in the dioptric stimulus to accommodation (§ 7.2.1) between the principal meridians.

To compensate for these effects, clinical wisdom suggests that, to the extent possible, a minus-cylinder lens (posterior toric surface) should be fitted at the closest possible vertex distance. A contact lens is preferred because the meridional magnification error is the least possible. Thus, to lessen the apparent distortions, a compromise should be sought between maintaining adequate CDVA and reducing the cylinder power.

Figure 8-52 illustrates a not-so-rare case of enantiomorphic oblique astigmatism. While such magnitudes are not common, and typically the obliqueness is in the range of 10° to 15°, this example illustrates *in extremis* the problem with fully correcting oblique astigmatism. The binocular image perception of the corrected image leads to spatial perception alterations.

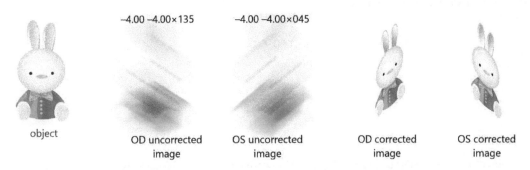

Figure 8-52: Uncorrected and fully corrected image perception for OD –4.00 –4.00×135 and OS –4.00 –4.00×045. This is the case of enantiomorphic oblique astigmatism.

Now consider the case of different types of astigmatism, for example, Ginesillo de Parapilla's astigmatism: OD –4.00 –4.00×180 and OS –4.00 –4.00×090. This is rather unique, as the right eye is with-the-rule, and the left eye is against-the-rule. Such conditions do not occur naturally, but rather are a likely outcome of ocular surgery that resulted in postoperative astigmatism. Such large amounts of astigmatism may be a result of suture placement after a corneal transplant, for example, or a traumatic eye injury. The two (monocular) corrected images are significantly and disproportionally distorted; Ginesillo's perceptual adaptation to such a different monocular meridional distortion is likely to be very difficult.

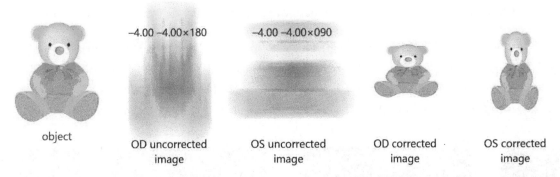

Figure 8-53: Uncorrected and fully corrected image perception for OD –4.00 –4.00×180 and OS –4.00 –4.00×090. This is the case where one eye is with-the-rule and the other eye is against-the-rule.

Finally, consider the not-so-rare case of same-axis-but-different-magnitude astigmatism, such as Maese Pedro's astigmatism: OD –1.00 –0.50×180 and OS –1.00 –3.00×180 (Figure 8-54). Astigmatism in both eyes is with-the-rule but with a notable difference in cylinder magnitude.

While cylinder magnitude differences of up to 1.50 D are not uncommon, cylinder magnitude differences of 3.00 D and greater are quite rare. Again, this example serves to illustrate *in extremis* the problem with fully correcting different magnitudes of astigmatism: The corrected monocular images are disproportionally distorted, and the resultant binocular image perception leads to depth perception alterations.

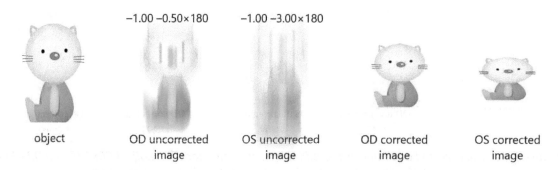

Figure 8-54: Uncorrected and fully corrected image perception for OD eye –1.00 –0.50×180 and OS eye –1.00 –3.00×180—the case of same-axis (here 180) but-different-magnitude WTR astigmatism. This example is further discussed in § 9.3.1, where we learn that retinal image minification is 2.25% for OD and 6.00% for OS.

Clinical Pearl 🧠 : Where should the best astigmatic correction be applied?

The obvious answer would be as close as possible to the seat of astigmatism. If the seat of astigmatism and the surface upon which the correction is applied are spaced by some distance, the full correction will still result in residual, secondary astigmatism, which is a high-order aberration.

Since secondary astigmatism is a high-order aberration (these concepts are presented in *Ocular Imaging*, Volume 5 of this series), residual amounts can be present even if the magnitude of the astigmatic correction is calculated correctly per the spherocylindrical part, which corresponds to a low-order aberration.

If the astigmatism is corneal (which is the most prevalent type; significant lenticular astigmatism does occur, but rarely), the optimal solution is laser refractive surgery or contact lenses. If spectacle or intraocular lens correction is selected, the larger the distance of the correcting lens from the cornea (vertex distance / effective lens position) the larger the residual secondary astigmatism.

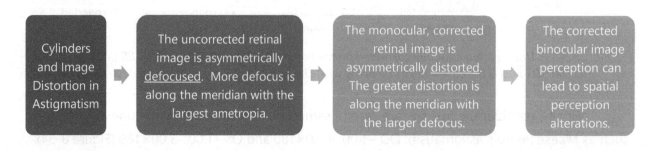

8.6 STOKES LENS AND JACKSON CROSS-CYLINDER

Introduced by Edward Jackson in 1887, the cross-cylinder <u>examination</u> or **Jackson cross-cylinder** (JCC) **test** is a <u>procedure</u> for the refined determination of the magnitude and axis of astigmatism. The origin of lens used in this procedure, which today is known as the JCC lens, can be traced back to an idea conceived in 1849, known as the **Stokes lens.**[895]

Sir George Gabriel Stokes, an Irish mathematician and later a Professor of Mathematics at Cambridge University and President of the Royal Society (UK), described what he called an astigmatic lens as follows: *"Conceive a lens ground with <u>two cylindrical surfaces of equal radius</u>, one concave and the other convex, with their <u>axes crossed</u> at right angles; call such a lens an astigmatic lens; ... and a line parallel to the axis of the convex surface the astigmatic axis."* The Stokes lens, thus, is a combination of two equal-in-magnitude and opposite-in-sign ($F_1 = -F_2$) cylinder lenses, placed at right angles. This can be realized by placing the flat surfaces of a planoconvex lens and a crossed planoconcave lens in contact with each other.

While astigmatism is traditionally presented as sphere and cylinder, the Stokes lens offers an intrinsic description of astigmatism as the <u>semi-difference of the principal sphere powers</u> (which is half, not the full cylinder power). Astigmatism according to Stokes is defined as

$$\text{Astigmatism = Spherical equivalent + Stokes lens components} \qquad (8.2)$$

where the Stokes lens components are ±half the 'cylinder' of the traditional Rx, with each of the two components being 90° apart: one at the Rx axis, and the other at the crossed axis.

Example ☞: Describe the following astigmatism Rx according to Stokes −1.75 −0.50×180.

Solution: First, calculate the spherical equivalent, which, in this case is −2.00. Then, halve the cylinder power for the first component, initially keeping the same axis as in the Rx, here −0.25×180 (or +0.25 @ 180° if you use the sphere power lens cross). The other 'half' cylinder lines up with the crossed-cylinder and has a flipped sign, becoming +0.25×090 (−0.25 @ 90° in the sphere power expression). Thus, the two forms are

Crossed-cylinder form: (Spherical equivalent −2.00) + (Stokes lens −0.25×180 / +0.25×090)

Lens cross form: (Spherical equivalent −2.00) + (Stokes lens +0.25 @ 180° / −0.25 @ 90°)

This way, the Stokes lens component represents the real essence of astigmatism; the sphere effect and the cylinder effect are completely disengaged. For example, in the two Stokes

[895] Stokes GG. On a mode of measuring the astigmatism of a defective eye. Rep Br Assoc. 1849; 2:10-1.

astigmatism expressions, (−2.00) + (−0.25×180 / +0.25×090) and (−2.00) + (−0.75×180 / +0.75×090), the sphere effect is the same, but astigmatism increases.

So, what is the relationship between the Stokes lens and the Jackson cross-cylinder (JCC)? Stokes gets credit for inventing the Stokes lens. However, Edward Jackson, Professor at the Department of Ophthalmology at the University of Colorado, is credited with introducing this lens in the refraction routine, although he was not the first to do so. William S. Dennett, a New York ophthalmologist and member of the American Mathematical Society, published a version of the technique (in 1885)[896] two years before Jackson did in the same journal (in 1887),[897] the *Transactions of the American Ophthalmological Society*. The established use of the JCC for the determination of astigmatism is predicated in that work. Initially, the technique aimed to discover the presence (or not) of astigmatism; a fine tuning determines the axis as well. However, it was not until William H. Crisp's work in 1931, almost 50 years later,[898] that the technique was brought to the attention of professionals, popularizing the procedure.

The JCC lens is a low-power Stokes lens with either 0.25 or 0.50 D cylinder powers (or with 0.12, 0.37, 0.75, and 1.00 D). The JCC lens can be best described by the crossed-cylinder form, which is the most closely related form and can best conceptually describe JCC power.

Figure 8-55: Four handheld JCC lenses with (left to right) 1.00, 0.75, 0.50, and 0.25 D cylinder powers.

Example ☞: JCC at the primary orientation. Case 1: ±0.25 JCC; Case 2: ±0.50 JCC.

Crossed-cylinder forms. Case 1: −0.25×180 / +0.25×090; Case 2: −0.50×180 / +0.50×090.

Lens cross forms. Case 1: +0.25 @ 180° / −0.25 @ 90°; Case 2: +0.50 @ 180° / −0.50 @ 90°.

Minus-cylinder prescription forms. Case 1: +0.25 −0.50×180; Case 2: +0.50 −1.00×180.

Plus-cylinder prescription forms. Case 1: −0.25 +0.50×090; Case 2: −0.50 +1.00×090.

Note 1 ✐ : In either the minus- or the plus-cylinder Rx form, the sphere component in the JCC (as in any Stokes lens) is half and of opposite power to the cylinder. The <u>spherical equivalent is always zero</u>.

[896] Dennett WS. The Stokes' lens for measuring astigmatism. Trans Am Ophthalmol Soc. 1885; 4:106-10.

[897] Jackson E. Trial set of small lenses and a modified trail frame. Trans Am Ophthalmol Soc. 1887; 4:595-8.

[898] Crisp WH. The cross-cylinder tests, especially in relation to the astigmatic axis. Trans Ophthal Soc UK. 1931; 1:495.

In the primary JCC orientation (Figure 8-56), the +.50 mark (if present, in black or white) is at the 12 o'clock position and reads left to right; the red –.50 mark is at the 9 o'clock position and reads down to up. The marks are on the front surface (facing the examiner). In this orientation, the optical lens cross form is +0.50 @ 180° (+0.50 D power along the horizontal meridian) / –0.50 @ 90° (–0.50 D power along the vertical meridian). The JCC axis in this orientation is the horizontal line. If this JCC lens is placed in front of a lensometer, its power reads –0.50 +1.00×090.

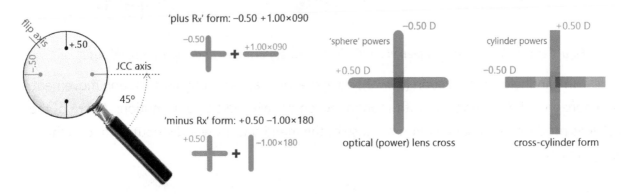

Figure 8-56: (left) A ±0.50 JCC lens in its <u>primary orientation</u>, showing (second from left) the plus and minus Rx forms, as well as (second from right) the optical lens cross and (right) the cross-cylinder forms. The +.50 and –.50 marks on the lens itself correspond to the crossed-cylinder, which is perpendicular to the lens cross. The JCC is mounted in a round ring with its handle at 45° from the axis. A twirl of the stem handle changes the cross-cylinder lens to the flipped position (Figure 8-57 left); the back surface is now the front, and the marks are interchanged.

The JCC is used clinically to subjectively determine refractive astigmatism (cylinder power and axis). The lens can be flipped by a simple twirl of the stem handle between the thumb and the index finger. When flipped, the lens undergoes a rotation of 180° about the flip axis. As the back surface is brought to the front of the examiner, the red and white marks trade places, and the principal meridians alternative rapidly. When flipped, the positive power meridian, which is horizontal in the primary orientation, becomes vertical; the negative power meridian, which is vertical in the primary orientation, becomes horizontal. Effectively, the flip is akin to a swift 90° turn.

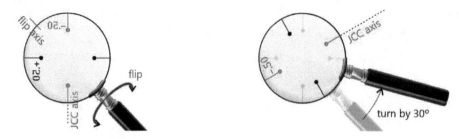

Figure 8-57: The two operations of a Jackson cross-cylinder lens per the primary orientation shown in Figure 8-56. (left) Flipped around the flip axis and (right) turned around the optical axis (perpendicular to the page).

Distant objects viewed through the JCC lens in the primary position appear elongated (expanded) horizontally and minified (shortened) vertically (Figure 8-58). This anamorphic meridional distortion is due to the lens's positive horizontal and negative vertical powers.

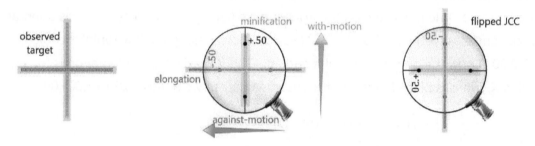

Figure 8-58: (left) Target as seen via a JCC in its (center) primary and (right) flipped positions.

In handheld neutralization (§ 9.7.2), objects exhibit apparent against-motion movement with horizontal JCC motion and with-motion movement with vertical JCC motion. A turn of the JCC lens produces a scissors motion because of the meridional power distribution due to the astigmatic lens.

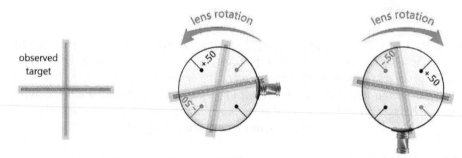

Figure 8-59: Scissors motion in a rotating JCC lens.

The JCC test starts on the premise that the circle of least confusion is on the retina; this is assured when the best subjective refraction correction is presented in front of the eye. The JCC lens has a zero spherical equivalent; therefore, when this lens is placed in front of the eye, the location of the circle of least confusion is the same, regardless of the lens orientation.[899]

---

[899] Jackson E. How to use the cross cylinder. Am J Ophthalmol. 1930; 13(4):321-3.

If there is astigmatism, there is also a retinal blur because the two focal lines are separated by Sturm's interval. Even if the circle of least confusion is still on the retina, a shorter interval results in improved vision, while a longer interval results in worsening vision. With a collapsed (expanded) Sturm's interval, the focal lines move closer together (farther away), and the circle of least confusion is reduced (increased) in size. This is exactly what the JCC does when it is placed in front of the eye: Depending on its orientation (primary, flipped, or turned), it displaces the two focal lines simultaneously in opposite directions, expanding or contracting the initial interval of Sturm. The circle of least confusion remains on the retina, varying only in diameter. Hence, the astigmatic error can be increased or decreased and is thus determined[900] when the examinee is asked to notice the perceived difference when the JCC is flipped or turned.

Example ☞: Consider Tosilos' with-the-rule, mixed astigmatism +0.50 −1.00×180. Recall that the optical lens cross is −0.50 @ 90° / +0.50 @ 180°. In this case, the circle of least confusion is on the retina, and we are ready to apply a ±0.25 JCC lens.

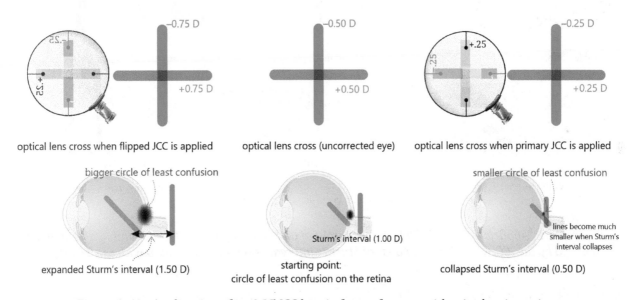

optical lens cross when flipped JCC is applied   optical lens cross (uncorrected eye)   optical lens cross when primary JCC is applied

bigger circle of least confusion   smaller circle of least confusion

Sturm's interval (1.00 D)   lines become much smaller when Sturm's interval collapses

expanded Sturm's interval (1.50 D)   starting point: circle of least confusion on the retina   collapsed Sturm's interval (0.50 D)

Figure 8-60: Application of a ±0.25 JCC lens in front of an eye with mixed astigmatism.

In the 'flipped' position [Figure 8-60 (left)], the compound (eye and JCC) optical lens cross is − 0.75 @ 90° / +0.75 @ 180°. Sturm's interval expands from 1.00 D to 1.50 D, the circle of least confusion is enlarged, and vision deteriorates. Tosilos reports 'worse.'

When the JCC is applied in the primary position [Figure 8-60 (right)], the compound (eye and JCC) optical lens cross corresponds to −0.25 @ 90° / +0.25 @ 180°. Sturm's interval collapses from 1.00 D to 0.50 D, the circle of least confusion gets smaller, and vision improves. Tosilos reports 'better.' When the JCC is placed

---

[900] Jackson E. The astigmic lens (crossed cylinder) to determine the amount and principal meridians of astigmia. Ophthalmol Rec. 1907; 17:378-83.

with its axis parallel to the axis of refractive astigmatism, a maximum of perceived difference is identified by the examinee when the lens is flipped, and 'better' is reported when the JCC axis aligns with the Rx axis.

Example ☞: What happens when we apply a ±0.50 JCC in front of Sansón Carrasco's emmetropic eye?

In the flipped position [Figure 8-61 (left)], the compound (eye and JCC) optical lens cross is −0.50 @ 90° / + 0.50 @ 180°. This expands Sturm's interval from 0.00 D to 1.00 D. The circle of least confusion is enlarged, vision deteriorates, and Sansón reports 'worse.'

In the primary application [Figure 8-61 (right)], the compound (eye and JCC) lens cross is +0.50 @ 90° / −0.50 @ 180°. This, again, expands Sturm's interval from 0.00 D to 1.00 D. Likewise, the circle of least confusion is enlarged (compared to the non-application), vision deteriorates, and Sansón reports 'worse.'

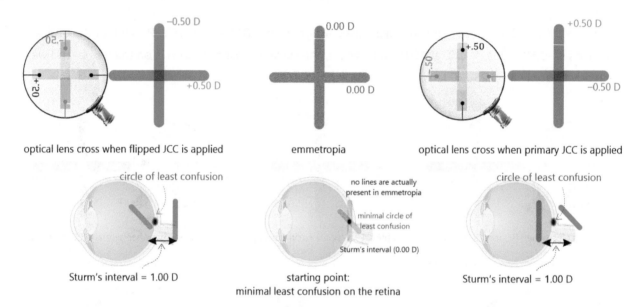

optical lens cross when flipped JCC is applied   emmetropia   optical lens cross when primary JCC is applied

circle of least confusion   no lines are actually present in emmetropia   circle of least confusion

minimal circle of least confusion

Sturm's interval (0.00 D)

Sturm's interval = 1.00 D   starting point: minimal least confusion on the retina   Sturm's interval = 1.00 D

Figure 8-61: Application of a ±0.50 JCC lens in front of an emmetropic eye. The amount of astigmatism induced by the JCC, which is the expanse of Sturm's interval, is the same (= 1.00 D with this ±0.50 JCC).

Clinical note 👥: It is often said that the two positions (flipped and primary) produce a similar 'worse' effect when presented in front of an emmetropic eye, i.e., in general, an eye whose circle of least confusion has been brought to the retina (the neutral point). The accepted notion is that the two images are 'equally' blurred between the two positions (primary and flipped).

Indeed, Sturm's interval, as well as the placement and size of the circle of least confusion, is in both cases identical; thus, the 'amount' of blur is equal. However, the two positions (primary and flipped) have a 90° difference in the retinal image blur orientation, which may be confounded by accommodation and/or the toric Rx applied (if needed to bring the circle of least confusion to the retina). Because the flipped JCC leads to a rotation of the focal lines from the with-the-rule effect to against-the-rule, a different defocus is developed, depending on the orientation of the prevailing features in the presented target.

8.7 ASTIGMATISM QUIZ

Classification of Astigmatism

1) With fixed magnitude and axis, and no accommodation, which astigmatism type brings one focal line in front of and the other behind the retina?

   a) simple myopic
   b) simple hyperopic
   c) mixed
   d) compound myopic
   e) compound hyperopic

2) When one focal line is in front of and the other is behind the retina, which two of the following are true?

   a) The best uncorrected visual acuity is afforded.
   b) The spherical equivalent is close to zero.
   c) The focal lines collapse on each other.
   d) The corrected retinal image has no distortion.

3) Altisidora's power along the vertical meridian is 63.00 and along the horizontal meridian is 61.00. This astigmatism has the following characteristics:

   a) with-the-rule, cylinder –2.00 D
   b) against-the-rule, cylinder +2.00 D
   c) with-the-rule, cylinder 63.00 D
   d) against-the-rule, cylinder 61.00 D
   e) mixed, cylinder 61.00 D

4) Belirifonte's astigmatic prescription is –1.00 –1.50×180. Sturm's interval spans ...

   a) 2.75 D
   b) 2.50 D
   c) 1.75 D
   d) 1.50 D
   e) 1.00 D
   f) 0.50 D

5) Grantaire's lens cross is –1.00 @ 180° / –1.50 @ 90°. Sturm's interval spans ...

   a) 2.50 D
   b) 1.50 D
   c) 1.00 D
   d) 0.50 D

6) What is the dioptric equivalent of Arminador's circle of least confusion in Rx –2.00 –1.50×180?

   a) –3.50 D
   b) –2.75 D
   c) –2.00 D
   d) –1.75 D
   e) –1.50 D
   f) –0.50 D

7) If Sturm's interval collapses, then the focal lines ...

   a) are brought closer together
   b) are closer to the retina
   c) are separated further away
   d) rotate by 90°

8) If Sturm's interval collapses, then the circle of least confusion becomes ...

   a) larger
   b) smaller
   c) a line along the steep meridian
   d) a line along the flat meridian

9) What type is Clareo's astigmatism (0.00 +0.75×090)?

   a) simple hyperopic, against-the-rule
   b) compound hyperopic, against-the-rule
   c) simple hyperopic, with-the-rule
   d) compound hyperopic, with-the-rule

10) Clodio's astigmatism (+0.50 –1.50×165) is ...

   a) mixed, with-the-rule
   b) mixed, against-the-rule
   c) compound myopic, with-the-rule
   d) compound myopic, against-the-rule
   e) compound hyperopic, with-the-rule
   f) compound hyperopic, against-the-rule

11) What type is Friston's astigmatism (–1.50 –0.50×090)?

   a) mixed, with-the-rule
   b) mixed, against-the-rule
   c) compound myopic, with-the-rule
   d) compound myopic, against-the-rule
   e) compound hyperopic, with-the-rule
   f) compound hyperopic, against-the-rule

12) Dapple's astigmatism (0.00 –2.00×180) is ...

   a) with-the-rule simple myopic; steep meridian is vertical, –2.00 D
   b) against-the-rule simple myopic; steep meridian is horizontal, –2.00 D

c) with-the-rule simple myopic; steep meridian is horizontal, –2.00 D

d) against-the-rule simple myopic; steep meridian is vertical, +2.00 D

13) Jack's astigmatism (–2.00 +2.00×090) is ...

a) with-the-rule simple myopic; steep meridian is vertical, –2.00 D

b) against-the-rule simple myopic; steep meridian is horizontal, –2.00 D

c) with-the-rule simple hyperopic; steep meridian is horizontal, –2.00 D

d) against-the-rule simple hyperopic; steep meridian is vertical, +2.00 D

14) Leonela's lens cross (+2.00 @ 30°/ –2.00 @ 120°) is...

a) oblique astigmatism

b) asymmetric astigmatism

c) compound hyperopia

d) with-the-rule astigmatism

15) What is Leonela's axis of astigmatism (use minus Rx)?

a) ×–030

b) ×030

c) ×–120

d) ×120

e) ×330

16) What is Vivaldo's astigmatism (+1.00 –1.00×090)?

a) with-the-rule simple hyperopic

b) against-the-rule compound myopic

c) with-the-rule mixed

d) against-the-rule mixed

e) with-the-rule simple hyperopic

f) against-the-rule simple hyperopic

17) Which of the following prescriptions indicates compound hyperopic astigmatism (two correct)?

a) +1.00 –0.75×090

b) +1.00 +0.50×030

c) –0.50 +1.50×180

d) –0.50 +0.50×120

e) +1.00 –1.25×010

18) Back to Q 17. Which of these astigmatisms has the greatest span of Sturm's interval?

a) A   b) B   c) C   d) D   e) E

19) Enantiomorphism, or mirror imaging, describes a pair of objects that relate to each other as the right hand relates to the left. If the right eye has

cylinder –1.50×030, then, the left eye may have cylinder ...

a) –1.50×030

b) –1.50×150

c) +1.50×030

d) +1.50×150

20) Select the bow-tie topography shape and lens cross that describe against-the-rule astigmatism:

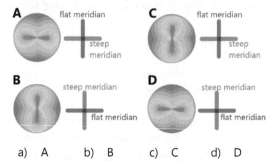

a) A   b) B   c) C   d) D

21) The steep meridian in a lens cross describes the one with the (three correct—check Figure 8-20) ...

a) most minus correction (if both –)

b) least minus correction (if both –)

c) most plus correction (if both +)

d) least plus correction (if both +)

e) the minus correction (if one +, the other –)

f) the plus correction (if one +, the other –)

22) What is the plus Rx form of this lens cross?

a) +4.00 –1.00×180

b) +4.00 –3.00×180

c) +4.00 +1.00×090

d) +1.00 +3.00×090

e) +1.00 +4.00×090

23) What is the minus Rx form in Q 22?

a) +4.00 –1.00×180

b) +4.00 –3.00×180

c) +4.00 –3.00×090

d) +1.00 +3.00×090

e) +1.00 +4.00×090

24) Back to Q 22. Which meridian is the steepest?

a) @ 90°; it has the most corrective power

b) @ 90°; it has the least plus corrective power

    c)   @ 180°; it has the most plus corrective power

    d)   @ 180°; it has the most corrective power

25) Back to Q 22. What is the type of astigmatism?

    a)   WTR compound hyperopic

    b)   WTR simple myopic

    c)   ATR compound hyperopic

    d)   ATR simple myopic

    e)   WTR mixed

26) Back to Q 22. What is Sturm's interval?

    a)   1.00 D

    b)   3.00 D

    c)   4.00 D

    d)   5.00 D

27) What is unusual about this lens cross +0.25 @ 10° / −1.50 @ 80°?

    a)   Nothing is unusual!

    b)   Both power signs should be either − or +.

    c)   The meridians are not perpendicular.

    d)   The flat power cannot be +0.25.

28) In compound myopic astigmatism, the most minus corrective power is along the ...

    a)   flat meridian

    b)   steep meridian

    c)   bisector between flat and steep

    d)   perpendicular to steep meridian

29) What is the plus Rx form of this lens cross?

    a)   +1.00 −4.00×070

    b)   +1.00 −4.00×020

    c)   +1.00 −4.00×160

    d)   +1.00 +4.00×160

    e)   −3.00 +4.00×070

    f)   −3.00 +1.00×070

    g)   +1.00 +4.00×020

30) Back to Q 30. What is the minus Rx form?

    a)   +1.00 −4.00×070

    b)   +1.00 −4.00×020

    c)   +1.00 −4.00×160

    d)   +1.00 +4.00×160

    e)   −3.00 +4.00×070

    f)   −3.00 +1.00×070

31) Back to Q 30. What is the type of astigmatism?

    a)   WTR compound hyperopic

    b)   WTR simple myopic

    c)   ATR compound hyperopic

    d)   ATR simple myopic

    e)   WTR mixed

32) Back to Q 30. Which meridian is the flat one?

    a)   @ 20°

    b)   @ 70°

    c)   @ 160°

    d)   @ −20°

33) Back to Q 30. What is Sturm's interval?

    a)   1.00 D

    b)   3.00 D

    c)   4.00 D

    d)   5.00 D

34) In this Rx (plano) −1.25×180, where is the vertical focal line formed (state dioptric values)?

    a)   −1.25 D (in front of the retina)

    b)   0.00 D (on the retina)

    c)   +0.625 D (behind the retina)

    d)   +1.25 D (behind the retina)

Prescriptions and Forms

35) Sancho's Rx is −2.50 −1.00×180. The spherical equivalent is ...

    a)   −3.50 D

    b)   −3.00 D

    c)   −2.50 D

    d)   −2.00 D

    e)   −1.50 D

    f)   −1.00 D

36) The spherical equivalent for Florisea's Rx (+1.50 −1.00×090) is ...

    a)   −1.00 D

    b)   −0.50 D

    c)   +0.50 D

    d)   +1.00 D

37) During phoropter refraction examination, you just added a −0.50 D cylinder. To maintain the circle of least confusion on the retina (and pass your practical), you should compensate by adding ...

    a)   −0.50 D sphere

b)   +0.50 D sphere

c)   −0.25 D sphere

d)   +0.25 D sphere

e)   +0.50 D cylinder

f)   +0.25 D cylinder

38) Sancho de Azpeitia (+1.00 +3.00×180) is
     undergoing cycloplegic refraction. A +4.00 D trial
     lens is fitted on the phoropter. This brings ...

     a)   the steep meridian focus on the retina

     b)   the circle of least confusion on the retina

     c)   one line in front of and the other behind the retina

     d)   the flat meridian focus on the retina

     e)   both focal lines in front of the retina

39) Back to Q 38. What sphere power is needed to
     focus Sancho's steep meridian on the retina?

     a)   +1.00 D

     b)   +2.00 D

     c)   +3.00 D

     d)   +4.00 D

40) Back to Q 38. What sphere power is needed to place
     Sancho's circle of least confusion on the retina?

     a)   +2.00 D

     b)   +2.50 D

     c)   +3.00 D

     d)   +3.50 D

41) Felesindos' lens cross is −0.50 @ 90° and +0.50 @
     180°; the minus- and plus-cylinder Rx forms are ...

     a)   +0.50 −1.00×090 and −0.50 +1.00×180

     b)   +0.50 −1.00×180 and −0.50 +1.00×090

     c)   +0.50 +1.00×180 and −0.50 −1.00×090

     d)   plano +1.00×180 and −0.50 −1.00×090

     e)   +0.50 −1.00×090 and plano +1.00×090

42) Andrés' lens cross is −1.75 @ 90° / −1.00 @ 180°;
     the minus- and plus-cylinder Rx forms are ...

     a)   −1.00 −0.75×180 and −1.75 +0.75×090

     b)   −1.00 −0.75×090 and −1.75 +0.75×180

     c)   −1.75 −0.75×090 and −1.00 +0.75×180

     d)   −1.75 −0.75×180 and −1.00 +0.75×090

43) Arnaldo's plus Rx form of +3.50 −1.25×140 is ...

     a)   +2.25 +1.25×140

     b)   +2.25 +1.25×050

     c)   +2.25 −1.25×050

     d)   +3.50 +1.25×140

     e)   −3.50 +1.25×050

44) Anselmo's plus Rx form of −1.00 −0.75×010 is ...

a)   −1.75 +0.75×100

b)   +1.75 +0.75×100

c)   −1.75 −0.75×010

d)   −1.75 −0.75×100

e)   +1.00 +0.75×110

f)   −1.00 +0.75×010

45) Andrés' minus Rx form of −1.75 +0.75×090 is ...

     a)   +1.75 +0.75×090

     b)   +1.75 +0.75×180

     c)   −1.75 −0.75×090

     d)   −1.75 +0.75×180

     e)   +1.00 +0.75×180

     f)   −1.00 −0.75×180

46) Auristela's spherical equivalent for the lens cross
     −0.75 @ 180° / +0.50 @ 90° is ...

     a)   −1.25 D

     b)   −0.75 D

     c)   −0.50 D

     d)   −0.25 D

     e)   −0.125 D

     f)   +0.50 D

47) The spherical equivalent for Constanza's lens
     cross +0.50 @ 180° / −0.50 @ 90° is ...

     a)   −1.00 D

     b)   −0.50 D

     c)   −0.25 D

     d)   −0.125 D

     e)   0.00 D

     f)   +0.50 D

48) The spherical equivalent in a Stokes lens ...

     a)   is always zero

     b)   is twice the cylinder power

     c)   is half the cylinder power

     d)   depends on the spherical component

49) Two correct cross-cylinder Stokes expressions are:

     a)   −0.25×180 / +0.25×090

     b)   −0.50×180 / +0.25×090

     c)   −0.25×180 / +0.75×090

     d)   −0.75×180 / +0.75×090

50) Don Fernando's astigmatism −1.50 −1.00×180
     according to Stokes cylinder lens cross is ...

     a)   SE −1.75 + (−0.25×180 / +0.25×090)

     b)   SE −2.00 + (−0.50×180 / +0.50×090)

     c)   SE −2.00 + (−0.25×180 / +0.25×090)

     d)   SE −2.50 + (−0.25×180 / +0.25×090)

51) Luciandra's astigmatism −1.75 −0.50×180 according to Stokes cylinder lens cross is ...

    a)   SE −1.75 + (−0.25×180 / +0.25×090)

    b)   SE −2.00 + (−0.50×180 / +0.50×090)

    c)   SE −2.00 + (−0.25×180 / +0.25×090)

    d)   SE −2.25 + (−0.25×180 / +0.25×090)

52) A ±0.25 JCC lens in the primary orientation can be described in minus- and plus-cylinder Rx forms as ...

    a)   +0.25 −0.50×180 and −0.25 +0.50×090

    b)   −0.25 −0.50×090 and −0.25 +0.50×180

    c)   +0.50 −1.00×090 and −0.50 +1.00×180

    d)   +0.50 −0.25×180 and −0.50 +0.25×090

53) Rx +0.50 −1.00×180 corresponds to a (all at the primary orientation) ...

    a)   ±0.25 JCC

    b)   ±0.50 JCC

    c)   ±0.75 JCC

    d)   ±1.00 JCC

54) Maritornes' manifest refraction is +0.75 −1.50×010. What is Sturm's dioptric interval?

    a)   0.50 D

    b)   0.75 D

    c)   1.00 D

    d)   1.50 D

    e)   2.50 D

55) Back to Q 54. Where is the circle of least confusion in Maritornes' eye (dioptrically)?

    a)   −0.75 D (in front of the retina)

    b)   0.00 D (exactly on the retina)

    c)   +0.75 D (behind the retina)

    d)   +1.50 D (behind the retina)

56) What is the lens cross form in Maritornes' eye?

    a)   +0.75 @ 10° / −1.50 @ 100°

    b)   +0.75 @ 10° / +1.50 @ 100°

    c)   +0.75 @ 10° / +0.75 @ 100°

    d)   +0.75 @ 10° / −0.75 @ 100°

57) A ±0.50 JCC lens, the axis at 10° is placed in front of Maritornes' eye. What is the (eye + JCC) lens cross?

    a)   +0.25 @ 10° / −1.50 @ 100°

    b)   +0.25 @ 10° / −0.25 @ 100°

    c)   +0.75 @ 10° / +0.25 @ 100°

    d)   +0.75 @ 10° / −0.25 @ 100°

58) Back to Q 57. What is Sturm's dioptric interval in the combined Maritornes' eye + JCC ?

    a)   0.50 D

    b)   0.75 D

    c)   1.00 D

    d)   1.50 D

    e)   2.50 D

59) Back to Q 58. Where is the circle of least confusion in this combination (dioptrically)?

    a)   −0.25 D (in front of the retina)

    b)   0.00 D (exactly on the retina)

    c)   +0.50 D behind the retina

    d)   +0.75 D behind the retina

60) We now flip the JCC in front of Maritornes' eye as in Q 54. Where is the circle of least confusion (dioptrically)?

    a)   −0.25 D (in front of the retina)

    b)   0.00 D (exactly on the retina)

    c)   +0.50 D (behind the retina)

    d)   +0.75 D (behind the retina)

61) Back to Q 60. What is Sturm's dioptric interval in the combined Maritornes' eye + JCC?

    a)   0.50 D

    b)   0.75 D

    c)   1.00 D

    d)   1.50 D

    e)   2.50 D

62) Back to Q 60. What is the resultant (Maritornes' eye + JCC) lens cross?

    a)   +1.25 @ 10° / −1.50 @ 100°

    b)   +0.25 @ 10° / −0.25 @ 100°

    c)   +1.75 @ 10° / +0.25 @ 100°

    d)   +1.25 @ 10° / −1.25 @ 100°

63) A JCC is placed in front of an astigmatic eye wearing the best spectacle correction. The circle of least confusion ...

    a)   moves behind the retina

    b)   remains on the retina

    c)   moves in front of the retina

    d)   depends on whether the JCC is in the primary or the flipped position

64) In Durandarte's manifest Rx −0.50 −1.00×180, we present a ±0.50 JCC (primary position, axis 180°). What is the combined (eye + JCC) lens cross?

    a)   −1.00 @ 180° / −1.50 @ 90°

    b)   −2.00 @ 180° / −1.00 @ 90°

    c)   plano @ 180° / −2.00 @ 90°

    d)   −1.00 @ 180° / −1.00 @ 90°

Effects on Vision and Correction of Astigmatism

65) The following <u>two</u> true statements regarding posterior corneal astigmatism are:

 a) It does not contribute to ocular astigmatism.
 b) Its magnitude is about 12.5% of the anterior astigmatism.
 c) In most eyes, it is mainly against-the-rule.
 d) The anterior and posterior astigmatism axes form 45° with each other.

66) Select the correct description of Dapple's vision with prescription 0.00 −2.00×180:

 a) strong defocus of horizontal elements, good focus of vertical elements
 b) good focus of horizontal elements, strong defocus of vertical elements
 c) weak defocus of both horizontal and vertical elements
 d) strong defocus of both horizontal and vertical elements

67) In an uncorrected compound myopic WTR astigmatic eye, the vertical group of clock dial lines appears …

 a) very clear, unlike the other lines, which are blurry
 b) somewhat blurry, but less than the other lines
 c) clear, just like the other lines
 d) equally blurry as the other lines
 e) more blurred than the other lines

68) In simple myopic WTR astigmatic eye, the vertical group of clock dial lines appears …

 a) very clear, while the other lines are blurry
 b) somewhat blurry, but less than the other lines
 c) clear, just as the other lines
 d) equally blurry as the other lines
 e) more blurred than the other lines

69) You are reading a line drawing with the most detail located along the vertical lines. Which astigmatism type will affect you most?

 a) oblique
 b) against-the-rule
 c) with-the-rule
 d) mixed

70) Toric lens correction entails … (three correct)

 a) placement of both far points (along the two principal meridians) at infinity

 b) placement of the circle of least confusion on the retina
 c) eliminating distortion from the corrected images
 d) use of average spherical power to compensate for meridional variation
 e) placement of both focal lines on the retina

71) Spherical equivalent correction entails… (two correct)
 a) placement of both far points (along the two principal meridians) at infinity
 b) placement of the circle of least confusion on the retina
 c) eliminating distortion from the corrected images
 d) use of average spherical power to compensate for meridional variation
 e) placement of both focal lines on the retina

72) The far point in Sanchica's eye −2.50 −1.50×180 is …
 a) 25 cm in front, both meridians
 b) 40 cm in front, both meridians
 c) 66.6 cm in front, both meridians
 d) 25 cm in front for the vertical, 40 cm in front for the horizontal meridian
 e) 25 cm in front for the horizontal, 40 cm in front for the vertical meridian

73) Teresa's anterior corneal topography readings are 42.50 @ 10° and 44.25 @ 100°. What is the contribution of anterior corneal astigmatism?
 a) −0.25×100
 b) −1.50×010
 c) −1.50×100
 d) −1.75×010
 e) −2.00×010
 f) 42.50×010
 g) 42.50×100

74) Teresa's manifest prescription is −2.50 −1.50×010. Which two of the following statements are true?
 a) Most of the astigmatism is due to lens toricity.
 b) Most of the astigmatism is due to corneal toricity.
 c) There is no net contribution to astigmatism due to the internal eye optics.
 d) The cornea and lens contribute the same type of astigmatism.
 e) The lens is partially counteracting the corneal contribution.

75) Back to Q 74. What is Teresa's interior astigmatism?

   a) −0.25×100
   b) −1.50×010
   c) −1.50×100
   d) −1.75×010
   e) −2.00×010
   f) −2.50×010

76) What would be Teresa's spherical equivalent?

   a) −4.00 D
   b) −3.25 D
   c) −2.50 D
   d) −1.50 D
   e) −1.50×010
   f) −2.50×100
   g) −3.25×100

77) What would be Teresa's toric correction?

   a) −2.50 −1.50×010
   b) −3.25 D (no cyl)
   c) −1.50 −2.50×010
   d) −2.50 −1.50×100

78) Which of the following would be the most likely candidate to prescribe the spherical equivalent?

   a) −1.50 −2.50×010
   b) −2.50 −1.50×045
   c) −1.50 −2.50×100
   d) −1.50 −0.50×030
   e) (plano) −2.00×180

79) Maria Zoraida's anterior corneal topography reveals 43.25 @ 10° and 45.25 @ 100°. What is the contribution of corneal astigmatism?

   a) 43.25×010
   b) −2.00×010
   c) +2.00×010
   d) 45.25×100

80) The data presented in Q 79 enable us to determine that Maria has _____ astigmatism.
   a) myopic
   b) hyperopic
   c) mixed
   d) with-the-rule
   e) against-the-rule

81) Back to Q 79. Maria's manifest prescription is −3.25 −2.00×010. This suggests that ...

   a) most of astigmatism is due to lens toricity
   b) most of astigmatism is due to corneal toricity

   c) there is no net contribution to astigmatism by the internal eye optics
   d) the cornea and lens have same type of astigmatism
   e) the lens partially offsets the corneal contribution

82) Ginés' Rx is −0.50 +0.50×180. Which sphere power brings the circle of least confusion to the retina?

   a) −0.50 D
   b) −0.25 D
   c) 0.00 D
   d) +0.25 D
   e) +0.50 D

83) The power in a −1.50×180 cylinder lens is ...

   a) −1.50 D @ 180°
   b) −1.50 D @ 90°
   c) +1.50 D @ 180°
   d) +1.50 D @ 90°

84) The corrected astigmatic retinal image is asymmetrically distorted in ...

   a) with-the-rule astigmatism, compressed mostly vertically
   b) with-the-rule astigmatism, compressed mostly horizontally
   c) with-the-rule astigmatism, compressed both horizontally and vertically
   d) against-the-rule astigmatism, compressed mostly vertically

85) Toric lens correction of the Rx −3.00 −4.50×100 results in the (monocular) corrected retinal image, being _____ compressed (minified).

   a) only horizontally
   b) mostly horizontally
   c) mostly vertically
   d) only vertically

86) Where is the steep meridian in the eye in Q 85?

   a) @ 110°
   b) @ 100°
   c) @ 90°
   d) @ 10°

87) Tomé Cecial's eye has K-readings of 43.00 D @ 10° and 44.75 D @ 100°. What is the residual astigmatism when Tomé wears hard contact lenses with Rx −0.75 −1.50×010 (use lens cross)?

   a) −0.25×010
   b) −0.25×100
   c) −0.75×010
   d) −0.75×010

Then

Below.

8.8 ASTIGMATISM SUMMARY

Definitions and Classification of Astigmatism

The two **principal meridians**, the **steep** meridian and the **flat** meridian, are the two radial orientations through the pupil center that correspond to the greatest and smallest ocular optical powers. Usually, the two principal meridians are at right angles to each other.

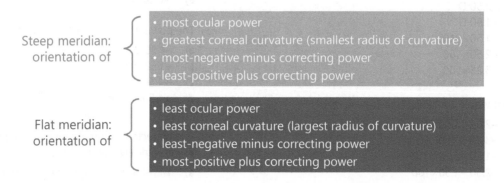

Steep meridian: orientation of
- most ocular power
- greatest corneal curvature (smallest radius of curvature)
- most-negative minus correcting power
- least-positive plus correcting power

Flat meridian: orientation of
- least ocular power
- least corneal curvature (largest radius of curvature)
- least-negative minus correcting power
- most-positive plus correcting power

This toric optical power distribution causes **astigmatism**: When the steep meridian is in focus, the flat meridian is still defocused, forming a focal line (horizontal blue in Figure 8-62); when the flat meridian is in focus, the steep meridian has defocused, forming a steep focal line (perpendicular red in Figure 8-62). The separation between the two lines, known as Sturm's interval, spans a dioptric difference that is a measure of astigmatism (simply called cylinder).

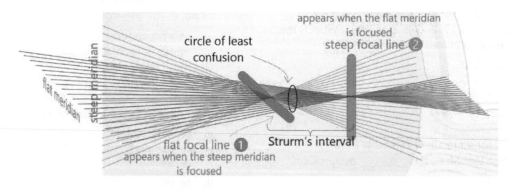

Figure 8-62: Focal lines and Sturm's interval.

Astigmatism can be classified by the location of the focal lines (w/respect to the retina) in the myopic (simple or compound), hyperopic (simple or compound), and mixed types.

Figure 8-63: Astigmatism classification based on the location of the focal lines.

A second classification is based on the rotational orientation of the focal lines (distribution of power) in with-the-rule, oblique, and against-the-rule (Figure 8-64) astigmatisms.

Figure 8-64: Astigmatism classification based on the orientation of the focal lines.

Finally, astigmatism can be classified according to the qualitative (symmetry) relationship between the principal meridians as being either symmetric or irregular (e.g., skewed, inferior steep, superior steep, etc.) For example, the principal meridians may not be perpendicular. This classification can be better understood using the bow-tie pattern symmetry in corneal topography axial curvature maps.

The amount or **magnitude** of astigmatism is the difference between the optical (refractive) powers of the two principal meridians. The **axis** of astigmatism is the orientation of the meridian with the <u>least optical power</u>—this is the **minus**, or **negative cylinder**, which is the most often used convention. In the **plus**, or **positive cylinder** convention, the magnitude is the difference between the least meridian power and the greatest meridian power, and the axis is the orientation of the meridian with the <u>greatest optical power</u>.

The Description of Astigmatism

The **optical lens cross** is a representation of the two individual spherical powers (the spherical correction needed) along the two principal meridians. The highest-powered (steep) meridian requires more minus (or less plus) correction than the lower-powered (flat) meridian.

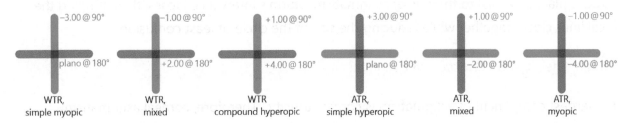

Figure 8-65: Optical lens cross for various types of astigmatism. What is common among all cases?

The **minus cylinder** and the **plus cylinder** are two different prescription forms that denote the sphere power, cylinder power, and axis in degrees. In the minus form, the cylinder power is negative; in the plus form, the cylinder power is positive. To produce the minus-cylinder form from the lens cross:

- Start from the flat meridian and denote the power, which is the sphere power F_s, and the axis, which is the orientation along the flat meridian (recall that the axis is 'married' to the sphere).
- Take the power difference between the flat and the steep meridians to obtain the cylinder power F_c. This is how to produce a minus cylinder.

Power transposition is the re-writing of the astigmatic prescription from the minus-cylinder form to the plus-cylinder form, and vice versa. The steps are the following:

- Add the sphere and cylinder power values (this is an algebraic addition, so mind the possible – sign on either of them). This is the new sphere value.
- Flip the sign of the cylinder.
- Change the axis by 90°, by adding or subtracting 90 (to be maintained between 1 and 180).

The **spherical equivalent** (SE) is a spherical power that produces a focal point coincidental to the circle of least confusion formed by a spherocylindrical lens with sphere power F_s and cylinder power F_c. Thus, the spherical equivalent is considered the dioptric vergence of the circle of least confusion.

Spherical Equivalent (SE): $$SE = F_s + (½ \cdot F_c)$$

The **crossed-cylinder form** is an alternative, less often used, form to describe astigmatism. It is the counterpart of the lens cross, in which the values of two perpendicularly aligned crossed-cylinders are used instead of the sphere values.

The **Jackson cross-cylinder** (JCC) lens is a low-power Stokes lens (such as 0.50 D cylinder powers) that can be best described by the crossed-cylinder form, having two cross-cylinders of equal and opposite power at right angles. Its spherical equivalent is zero, so it does not reposition the circle of least confusion, but only expands or collapses Sturm's interval. When a JCC is placed parallel to the axis of astigmatism, Sturm's interval collapses, thus bringing the focal lines closer together while reducing the size of the circle of least confusion.

Origin, Effects, and Correction of Astigmatism

The largest component of astigmatism is corneal toricity. Therefore, corneal astigmatism accounts for most of what is measured clinically as manifest astigmatism. Within the cornea, there is anterior corneal astigmatism, which can be measured with corneal topography, and posterior corneal astigmatism, which requires an independent measurement of the posterior surface curvature with dedicated instruments for that purpose. Also, there is internal astigmatism, mainly due to lens toricity or tilt.

To estimate the contribution of anterior cornea toricity to astigmatism, we select the flat meridian, being the one with the weakest corneal power; this is the axis, which is 180 in Figure 8-66 (left) and 030 in Figure 8-66 (right). The power difference between the flat and steep meridians is the magnitude of astigmatism, which is –1.50 for Figure 8-66 (left) and –3.00 for Figure 8-66 (right).

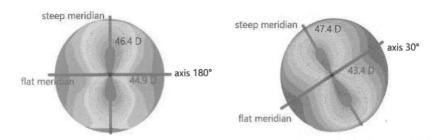

Figure 8-66: Astigmatism resulting from corneal toricity: (left) Magnitude –1.50 D, axis 180 and (right) magnitude –3.00 D, axis 030.

The effects of astigmatism on vision are distinguished from spherical (defocus) error by the axis orientation.

With-the-rule astigmatism (flat meridian/axis close to 180) primarily affects the horizontal parts of an optotype, which appear more blurry. When corrected, these parts are subject to more minification, resulting in a meridionally distorted image that appears as vertically squeezed.

Against-the-rule astigmatism (flat meridian/axis close to 090) primarily affects the vertical parts of an optotype, which appear more blurry. When corrected, these parts are subject to more minification, resulting in a meridionally distorted image that appears as horizontally minified.

Figure 8-67: Effects of astigmatism on a defocused uncorrected image and an image corrected with the proper toric Rx: (left) with the rule and (right) against-the-rule.

CHAPTER 9
OPHTHALMIC LENS OPTICS

9.1 SOME HISTORICAL FACTS

Vision-correcting glasses are one of humankind's most important inventions. We do not know exactly who to thank for their invention. Several individuals claim to have invented spectacles, but the definitive historical evidence is clouded by unfounded information.[901, 902]

Due to the highly technical nature of crafting spectacles, their invention likely happened in northern Italy sometime during the 14th century, either in Veneto or Tuscany; in these regions, at the time, intricate glassmaking was elevated to unparalleled levels. The earliest depiction of spectacle glasses in art dates back to 1352 and was found in a fresco created by Tomaso Barisini (better known as Tommaso da Modena) in the Chapter House of the Seminario, which is attached to the Basilica San Nicolò of the Treviso Cathedral (Veneto, Italy).[903]

It's possible that the invention of spectacles can be credited to either Salvino D'Armato or the Dominican friar Alessandro della Spina.[904]

---

[901] Ronchi V. Perche non si ritrova l'inventore degli Occhiale? Rivista di Oftalmologia. 1946; (1):140.

[902] The Invention of Spectacles. Retrieved from www.college-optometrists.org/the-college/museum/online-exhibitions/virtual-spectacles-gallery/the-invention-of-spectacles.html.

[903] Eyeglasses Through the Ages. Retrieved from www.antiquespectacles.com/history/ages/through_the_ages.htm.

[904] Timeline of Eyeglasses. Retrieved from https://www.aao.org/museum-of-vision.

In his treatise *De Iride* (1220–1235), the English statesman and scholastic philosopher Robert Grosseteste mentions the use of optics to "read the smallest letters at incredible distances." However, the first reference to a lens that helps vision comes from the English philosopher and Franciscan friar Roger Bacon, a.k.a. Doctor Mirabilis, in his book *Opus Majus* (1266). Bacon certainly understood the optics needed for spectacle construction, and Spina mentioned an anonymous lens inventor who purposely did not want his identity revealed. If that inventor was indeed Bacon, it is obvious why he chose to remain in obscurity: He spent a majority of his 80 years of life imprisoned for the scientific ideas he espoused. If he had revealed that he was the inventor spectacles, it is much more likely that he would have faced even more trouble than he already did.

D' Armato's supporters claim, as proof of his claim to spectacle invention, a memorial plaque interred in the St. Maria Maggiore church, Florence, Italy, that has the inscription: "*Here lies Salvino D' Armato Armati from Florence, inventor of spectacle glasses. May God forgive his sins. Year of God 1317.*" (It is not clear, however, if the mentioned invention is among these 'sins.') Unfortunately, it is likely that this plaque was a family prank (its inscription having been driven by pride), rather than a true historical marker.[905]

Figure 9-1: (left) A plaque claiming that Salvino D' Armato Armati is the inventor of spectacle glasses. (right) A portrait of Cardinal Fernando Niño de Guevara by El Greco (Δομήνικος Θεοτοκόπουλος), c. 1600, is among the early depictions of an individual wearing spectacle glasses.

In 1623 in Seville, Spain, the Jacobin priest Benito Daza de Valdes discussed contemporary spectacle lenses and frames in both technological and utilitarian detail, in his book *Uso de los Antoios Para todo Genero de Vistas* (*Use of Spectacles for all Kinds of Sight*).[906] This was an impressive feat considering the era in which it was written. This uniquely authentic book is considered by many to be the first book of clinical optometry because de Valdes

---

[905] Rosen E. The invention of eyeglasses. J Hist Med Allied Sci. 1956; 11:13-46 & 83-218. doi:10.1093/jhmas/XI.1.13.

[906] Hofstetter HW. Optometry of Daza de Valdes (1591-ca. 1636). Am J Optom Physiol Opt. 1988; 65(5):354-7.

proposed procedures similar to today's methods of optometric analysis, including methods such as those used today in prescribing for presbyopia.

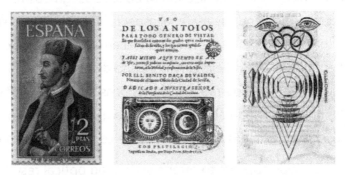

Figure 9-2: (left) Benito Daza de Valdés (1592–1634) on a postage stamp, (center) the cover of his book, and (right) a sketch from that book.

Benjamin Franklin, one of the most resourceful Founding Fathers of the United States of America, is credited with the invention of the bifocal spectacles in 1784. Being myopic himself, he could not tolerate changing spectacles once he also became presbyopic, so he requested that his optician slice both of his glasses in half and glue the two halves together, placing the distance half on top and the reading half on the bottom. He dubbed this invention 'double spectacles.'

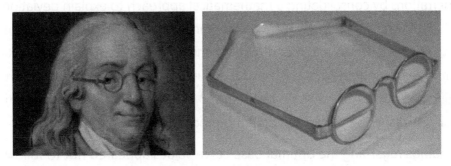

Figure 9-3: (left) Founding father Benjamin Franklin and (right) a replica of his bifocal spectacles.

Spectacle design is a testament to the evolution of ophthalmic optics over time. Historical lenses were of primitive design; they had a front surface that was a flat form of zero power, with the entire power ground onto the other surface. Their significant drawback was that such flat-form lenses allowed only about a 10° area of clear vision around the lens center due to excessive off-axis aberrations such as oblique astigmatism.[907]

---

[907] *Geometrical Optics* § 8.3.3 Oblique / Radial Astigmatism.

Contemporary spectacle lenses, regardless of their frame design, are all meniscus in a bent shape with a plus-powered, convex front surface called the base curve (§ 9.4.3). This design offers many advantages, one of which is the minimization of oblique astigmatism. A good lens design that includes both the geometrical and the material aspects helps to reduce several other forms of aberrations in addition to correcting the spherocylindrical error. These include spherical, chromatic, and field aberrations such as field curvature and distortion.[908] This design allows for an extended field over which clear (non-aberrated) vision is possible—up to 60° wide. The science— and perhaps art—of designing the optimal lens shape for a given prescription that offers the least amount of aberration over a wide field is referred to as the corrected curve theory.

The bent meniscus shape appears to offer a very good optical result in most cases. Its origin is attributed to the work of the English physicist William Hyde Wollaston, who in 1803 designed a meniscus lens, called a periscopic lens, to improve image quality by reducing peripheral distortions. This lens design can create images with a focal plane curvature that corresponds to the curvature of the macula; in this way, the field curvature of the image matches the curvature of the retina (§ 4.1.1), thus offering a good match between the formed image plane and the receiving photosensitive surface.

Wollaston's work was mainly empirical, given the primitive understanding of aberrations at the time. The German mathematician Philip Ludwig von Seidel was the first to formulate the concept of aberrations by consolidating a mathematical approach to explain deviations he simply called 'errors.' In the late 1800s, the French oculist Franz Ostwalt[909] applied aberration theory formulations to spectacle lenses and found that a meniscus could compensate for astigmatism. The front bent-meniscus ophthalmic lens was subsequently perfected with the construction of a forward-bulging periscopic (punctal) spectacle lens.[910] Several fabrication labs, such those at the Carl Zeiss Co. in Germany, led by Moritz von Rohr, produced these improved lenses.

The findings regarding the optimal base curve values appeared not to follow a coherent model. The Wollaston-recommended curves were far too steep compared to those suggested by Ostwalt's work. The connection between the two findings was identified much later by the famous Danish ophthalmologist Marcus Hans Eric Tscherning.[911] Tscherning's analysis showed that there is indeed a mathematical model describing the entire span of best-form base curves, and that their plot with respect to the Rx power forms a well-defined ellipse (§ 9.4.3.1).

---

[908] *Ocular Imaging* § 5.2 Classification of Aberrations

[909] Ostwalt F. Ueber periskopische Gläser. (On Periscope Glasses.) V. Graefe's Arch. XIVI, 3. In Ophthalmic Review, a Record of Ophthalmic Science. William George Sym, ed. Edinburgh, 1899.

[910] Percival AS. Prescribing Spectacles. Br J Ophthalmol. 1924; 8(5):229-32.

[911] Norn M, Jensen OA. Marius Tscherning (1854–1939): his life and work in optical physiology. Acta Ophthalmol Scand. 2004; 82(5):501-8.

9.2 LENS POWER AND VERGENCE

9.2.1 Curvature and Surface Power

Any part of a spherical surface, whether it is reflective or refractive, has a **radius of curvature** r, defined as the vector drawn from that surface toward the geometric center of the circle that inscribes this surface. The radius of curvature is measured by its length, and it has an algebraic sign, reflecting its vector nature. The sign is positive if the vector points to the right and negative if it points to the left, assuming that the light is propagating to the right. Often, the radius of curvature is expressed in millimeters; for example, the average radius of the cornea is about 7.7 mm (§ 2.1.1). However, when calculating power, as well as in keratometry,[124] it is important to convert the values of radius of curvature to meters.

Curvature C is reciprocal to the radius of curvature ($C = 1/r$) and describes how curved or bent a surface is. A surface with a short radius of curvature has a large curvature, while a surface with a long radius of curvature has a small curvature. Both curvature and radius of curvature have the same algebraic sign. When the radius is expressed in meters, the curvature has units of optical power, or diopters [1 D = m^{-1}].

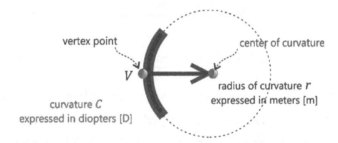

Figure 9-4: The reciprocal relationship between curvature and radius of curvature.

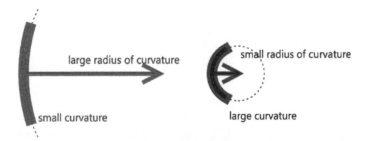

Figure 9-5: (left) Small curvature is associated with a large radius of curvature. (right) Large curvature is associated with a short radius of curvature.

Example ☞: A surface with a radius of curvature r = +0.5 m has curvature C = 1/(+0.5 m) = +2.0 D, while a surface with a radius of curvature r = +25 mm = +0.025 m has curvature C = 1/(+0.025 m) = +40.0 D.

9.2.1.1 Power of a Single Spherical Refracting Interface

A single spherical refracting interface (SSRI) is the simplest (save for the flat surfaces) optical surface. It separates two media that have different refractive indices: n before the interface (incident side, object-space) and n' after the interface (refracted side, image-space). An SSRI has a radius of curvature r and curvature ($C = 1/r$). The power F of this interface is the difference between the two refractive indices around the interface divided by the radius of curvature.[912]

Single Spherical Refracting Interface Power:
$$F[\text{D}] = \frac{n' - n}{r\,[\text{m}]}$$
(9.1)

Here, the radius of curvature r must be converted to meters.

     The object-space (primary) focal length f is the reciprocal of the surface power multiplied by the object-space refractive index n: $f = n/F$. The image-space (secondary) focal length f' is the reciprocal of the surface power multiplied by the image-space refractive index n': $f' = n'/F$.

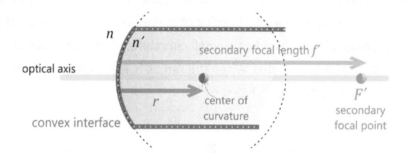

Figure 9-6: Convex SSRI radius of curvature and the secondary focal point.

     The importance of the SSRI power relationship is that it is used to compute the powers of the individual front and back surfaces of a lens, which, in turn, are used to compute the lens power. As we will see, there are several versions of what we call lens power in a thick lens, such as the nominal power, the equivalent power, and the two vertex powers (front and back).

Note: ✍ Because the power of an SSRI is proportional to the difference between the two refractive indices, the same surface may have a different power if the surrounding medium is different (e.g., instead of air, there is water).

Example ☞: A glass (crown glass, $n'_{\text{glass}} = 1.523$) spherical surface has power, when preceded by air, of $F = -6.00$ D. If this glass is submerged in water ($n_{\text{water}} = 1.333$), what would be its power?

---

[912] *Geometrical Optics* § 1.2.4.2 Optical Power of an SSRI.

The surface power is proportional to the difference between the refractive index (n') after the interface and the refractive index (n) before the interface. In air, this difference is $n'_{glass} - n_{air}$ = 1.523 − 1.0 = 0.523. In water, the difference is $n'_{glass} - n_{water}$ = 1.523 − 1.333 = 0.190. The radius of curvature is the same in both cases—we do not need to calculate it.[913] The power when the SSRI is submerged in water is simply proportional to the ratio 0.190/0.523 = 0.363; new power = (−6.00 D)·0.363 = −2.18 D.

9.2.2 Nominal and Equivalent Lens Power

9.2.2.1 The Nominal Lens Power

In a thin lens, we can ignore the lens thickness and simply add the two surface powers together. The **nominal lens formula** is none other than the concept of the simple algebraic addition of the front and back surface powers to produce the **nominal lens power**, ignoring the effect of the lens thickness. In ophthalmic lenses, front refers to away from the eye and back means close to the eye. The nominal lens power is a convenient approximation that is valid for thin lenses.

Example ☞: What is the power of the lens Courfeyrac fabricated if we ignore the center thickness?

We use the nominal lens formula. A thin lens with a front surface power +6.00 D and back surface power −8.00 D would make a −2.00 D nominal lens power, which almost equals the thick lens equivalent power.

9.2.2.2 The Equivalent Lens Power

Because no lens is ideally thin, if the lens material has a refractive index n and the surfaces are separated by a distance t (always positive), the **equivalent power** F_e in air becomes

$$\text{Equivalent Power of a Thick Lens:} \quad F_e = \frac{n-1}{r_1} + \frac{1-n}{r_2} - \frac{t}{n}\left(\frac{n-1}{r_1}\right)\cdot\left(\frac{1-n}{r_2}\right) = F_1 + F_2 - \frac{t}{n}F_1 \cdot F_2 \quad (9.2)$$

where F_1 and F_2 are the surface powers of the spherical interfaces (SSRIs) of the first lens surface (front power or **base curve power**) and the second lens surface (back surface power), respectively. The separation between these surfaces is the **lens thickness** t.

The equivalent power addresses the questions: What is the power if we had a thin lens instead of this thick lens? What power would we use in the imaging relationships? The answer is in Eq. (9.2), which is known as Gullstrand's relationship. This equation is significant because

---

[913] It looks like you just went through the calculations. It is −8.71 cm, right?

the optical elements in the human eye are thick lenses (recall the use of this relationship in the discussion of corneal power § 2.1.3 and lenticular power § 2.2.1).

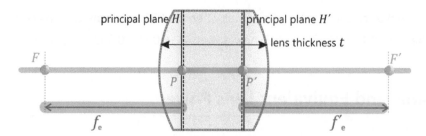

Figure 9-7: Equivalent focal length in a thick lens.

Assuming (so far) that the lens is surrounded by air, the **equivalent focal length** (distance) f_e is reciprocal to the equivalent optical power:

Equivalent Focal Length (in air):
$$f_e \text{ [m]} = \frac{1}{F_e \text{ [D]}}$$
(9.3)

Example ☞: Courfeyrac fabricated a thick lens with front surface power +6.00 D, back surface −8.00 D, and 4 mm center thickness, made of crown glass (n_{glass} = 1.523). What is the equivalent power of this lens?

The third term in relationship (9.2) is $-(t/n)\cdot F_1 \cdot F_2$ = −(0.004m/1.523)·(+6.00 D)·(−8.00 D) = +0.126 D. The equivalent power is +6.00 −8.00 D +0.12 D = −1.88 D.

The equivalent focal length(s) is measured from the lens principal plane(s),[914] which may be located inside or outside the lens proper (such as in meniscus lenses); for this reason, the equivalent focal length is not a practical concept. Instead, we primarily use the front and back focal lengths of a thick lens (§ 9.2.5).

9.2.3 Vergence: Upstream and Downstream Power

Waves emitted by any point or by an extended source are, by nature, diverging. Therefore, the vergence of a diverging ray bundle from just about any source or object is negative. Further, as light propagates away from the source, its wavefront curvature, and therefore its vergence, becomes less negative. This is because vergence is defined as the reciprocal of the distance l from that particular point in space multiplied by the refractive index n of the medium.

Example ☞: Brujon measures a point source radiating to the right (Figure 9-8). What is the vergence at A (0.1 m to the right of the source) and at B (0.5 m to the right of the source)? Propagation is in air.

---

[914] *Geometrical Optics* § 6.2.1 Principal Points and Principal Planes.

Brujon measures at location A, 0.1 m after the source, a radius of curvature of −0.1 m. The sign is negative because the point of convergence is to the left. Vergence at A has magnitude $1/(-0.1\,\text{m}) = -10.0\,\text{D}$. At point B, which is 0.5 m after (to the right of) the source, the wavefront radius of curvature is −0.5 m. Vergence at location B is also negative, with magnitude $1/(-0.5\,\text{m}) = -2.0\,\text{D}$.

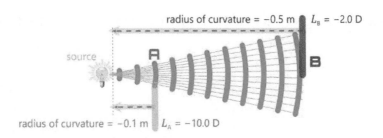

Figure 9-8: Vergence at different locations away from a source.

The farther the light waves are from the source the longer the distance representing the wavefront radius of curvature and the smaller the vergence magnitude because the wavefront curvature flattens. Vergence is reduced such that, at an infinite distance from the source, it becomes zero. We need to keep in mind, therefore, that the value of <u>vergence changes as the wavefront propagates</u>.

The calculation of vergence at different points involves the notions of downstream and upstream vergence. Vergence calculated at a point that has traveled with the stream, along the direction of light propagation, is called **downstream**. Vergence calculated at a point that travels against the stream, in a direction against that of light propagation, is called **upstream**.

Example ☞: Now Brujon measures a ray bundle at location A, which is converging to point B, located 20 cm to the right (Figure 9-9). What is the vergence Brujon measures at A? What is the vergence at location C, located 70 cm to the right of A? Consider propagation in air.

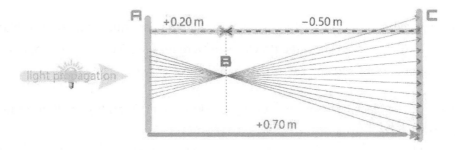

Figure 9-9: As the beam converges and then diverges, the vergence value flips its algebraic sign.

At location A, the ray bundle needs +0.2 m to converge. The sign is positive because the point of convergence is to the right, along the direction of light propagation. Vergence at A has magnitude $1/(+0.2\,\text{m}) = +5.0\,\text{D}$.

At location C, the ray bundle is diverging. It appears that the origin, the point of convergence, is 0.5 m before C, against the direction of light propagation. Thus, the ray bundle needs –0.5 m to converge. Vergence at C has magnitude 1/(–0.5 m) = –2.0 D.

Example ☞: What about the vergence at location D, which is 10 cm from A, and at location E, which is 45 cm from A?

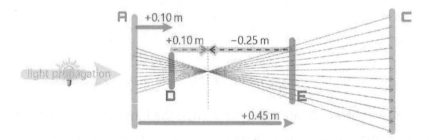

Figure 9-10: The magnitude of vergence is greater closer to the point of convergence.

At location D, the ray bundle needs +0.1 m to converge. The sign is positive because the point of convergence is still to the right. Hence, vergence at D has magnitude 1/(+0.1 m) = +10.0 D. It is more positive than the vergence at A.

At location E, the ray bundle is diverging; the point of origin is located 0.25 m before it (–0.25 m). Hence, vergence at E has magnitude 1/(–0.25 m) = –4.0 D. It is more negative than at C (which is –2.0 D).

Note ♥ : D is downstream of A, and E is downstream of A but upstream of C. The concepts of downstream and upstream are relative—we must always state in relation to what point.

Example ☞: Jehan is measuring the wavefront curvature exiting an aperture of an optical 'black box' with vergence L = –5.0 D. He wants to know the downstream vergence at 30 cm to the right if there is air between the black box and the screen. Let us help him find the answer.

The wavefront exiting the black box (shown in orange in Figure 9-11) is diverging. It originates from a point within the black box.

The wavefront reaching the screen (shown in dark green in Figure 9-11) propagates (farther) downstream by d = +30 cm = +0.3 m.

Therefore, the wavefront reaching the screen also originates from the same point as the wavefront exiting the black box. The difference between the two wavefronts is the radius of curvature, or the convergence distance, which is now larger by the separation between the aperture of the black box and the screen.

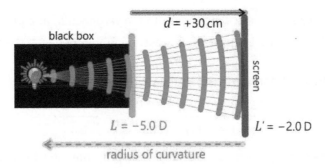

Figure 9-11: Computation of downstream vergence from a known value at a given point.

At the black-box aperture, the radius is the reciprocal of the vergence at this point, which is 1/(−5.0 D) = −0.2 m.

At the screen, the radius of curvature is increased by 0.3 m, becoming −0.5 m. Thus, the directional distance of the screen to the source is now half a meter and points to the left.

We inform Jehan that the vergence at this point is $L' = 1/(−0.5 \text{ m}) = −2.0$ D.

A formula that provides the downstream vergence when the initial vergence is known is

Downstream Vergence (air): $$L' = \frac{L}{1 - d \cdot L}$$ (9.4)

where L' is the vergence at a point located d (meters) downstream of the initial vergence L. The distance d is positive since it is along the direction of light propagation. The more generalized expression that includes the fact that the space between is filled with a medium with refractive index n is

Downstream Vergence (medium with n): $$L' = \frac{L}{1 - \dfrac{d}{n} \cdot L} = \frac{1}{\dfrac{1}{L} - \dfrac{d}{n}}$$ (9.5)

In the example above, vergence is $L = −5.0\,$D, and we seek vergence L' at $d = +0.3\,$m downstream (note the + sign!). If propagation is in air, downstream vergence is

$$L' = \frac{L}{1 - d \cdot L} = \frac{-5.0 \text{ D}}{1 - (+0.3 \text{ m}) \cdot (-5.0 \text{ D})} = \frac{-5.0 \text{ D}}{1 + 1.5} = \frac{-5.0 \text{ D}}{2.5} = -2.0 \text{ D}$$

This is exactly the result calculated with the initial analytical considerations.

Note ⊕: Relationship (9.4) can be used for the computation of <u>upstream vergence</u>. The formula is almost identical; the only difference is that distance d is negative since it is against the direction of light propagation.

Example ☞: Jean Prouvaire wants to calculate the upstream vergence L' at a location 30 cm to the left of a point that has vergence $L = -2.0$ D. Let us help him, assuming that between the two points there is air.

The vergence for an upstream distance $d = -0.3$ m (note the – sign!) is

$$L' = \frac{L}{1-d \cdot L} = \frac{-2.0 \text{ D}}{1-(-0.3 \text{ m}) \cdot (-2.0 \text{ D})} = \frac{-2.0 \text{ D}}{1-0.6} = \frac{-2.0 \text{ D}}{0.4} = -5.0 \text{ D}$$

We observe that this is the same problem as was previously presented in which Jehan was measuring downstream vergence—hey, the plot thickens...Jean and Jehan are the same person!

9.2.4 Effective (Downstream) Power and Vertex Distance

The downstream (and upstream) vergence effects have implications for the relationship between a spectacle lens worn on a frame at a vertex distance in front of the eye and the required optical correction when the position of the corrective lens on the frame is accounted for.

Spectacle lenses are worn in a frame situated in front of the wearer's face, physically separated from the corneal plane. This separation distance is called the **vertex distance** d_V measured between the back surface of the spectacle lens and the anterior cornea. When a spectacle lens is placed a vertex distance from the eye, vergence effects are exerted.

For example, at location A in Figure 9-12, the beam just after the lens has a vergence of +1.0 D, which means that the point of focus is situated 1 m to the right of the lens. At location B (distance to focus +0.5 m), vergence is +2.0 D, and at point C (distance to focus +0.25 m), vergence is +4.0 D. This describes the **effective downstream power** F_d of a lens. In order for a lens placed at B to have the same effect (to converge the beam to the secondary focal point F') as it had in point A, it must have an effective power of $F_{d=0.5} = +2.0$ D. If the lens is placed at C, it would need an effective power of $F_{d=0.25} = +4.0$ D.

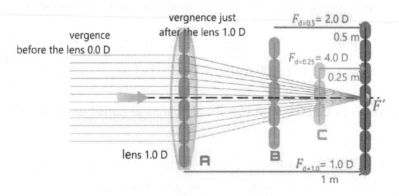

Figure 9-12: Downstream optical power.

In the simple approach introduced in § 6.6.1 (correction of myopia), the power of a corrective lens equals the degree of myopia/hyperopia. However, this is an approximation, albeit a very good one, given that this is the logic behind contact lenses (§ 9.3) and refractive laser surgeries, since, in both of these methods, the lens 'touches' the eye. Spectacle lenses do not touch the eye, but sit at a vertex distance, usually, of 12 to 15 mm. This distance is affected by the globe and orbit shape (e.g., deep-set eyes have a larger vertex) and by the shape of the mounting frame. Contact lenses are prescribed with zero vertex distance.

Here is an example of a corrective lens with optical power +10.00 D, placed at a distance of 15 mm in front of the eye (Figure 9-13). A collimated beam (initial vergence 0 D) just after the lens obtains vergence of +10.00 D. To correct the +10.00 hyperopia, the rays need to converge at the far point M_R, which is also the focal point of the lens $F' = SM_R = 100$ mm.

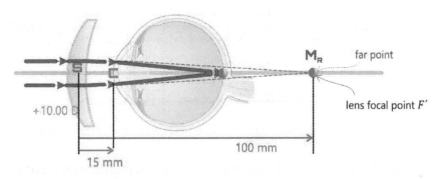

Figure 9-13: A plus-powered corrective lens at 15 mm vertex distance.

For a lens to correct the +10.00 hyperopia when in contact with the cornea, i.e., at point C, the effective power must be the reciprocal of distance CM_R = 100 − 15 mm = 85 mm (the far point of the eye, M_R, is the same!) The power of that lens in contact with the eye is the **effective downstream power** F_d = 1/(0.085 m) = +11.76 D.

In a myopic eye (Figure 9-14), the corrective spectacle lens has power −10.00 D, and the distance to focus is CM_R = −100 + (−15) mm = −115 mm. For a lens to correct the −10.00 D when in contact with the cornea, i.e., at point C, the optical power is F_d =1/(−0.115 m) = −8.70 D.

In general, for a lens to have the same convergence effect when transposed (shifted) to position d, the effective focal length at the new location f_d must be

$$f_d = f_o - d \qquad (9.6)$$

where f_o is the focal length of the lens in the initial position, and d is the distance to the new position. This relationship, when presented in terms of optical power, takes the form

Downstream Power:

$$\underbrace{F_d}_{\text{effective downstream power}} = \cfrac{F_o}{1 - \underbrace{d}_{\text{transposition [m]}} \cdot \underbrace{F_o}_{\text{initial optical power}}} \qquad (9.7)$$

where we follow the Cartesian sign convention, and distances are expressed in meters. A downstream transposition (to the right, since we are considering light traveling to the right) is positive, and an upstream transposition (to the left) is negative. Note the identical forms of the downstream power Eq. (9.7) and the downstream vergence Eq. (9.4). This form is also used for upstream vergence F_u, the only difference being that the transposition becomes negative (always expressed in meters).

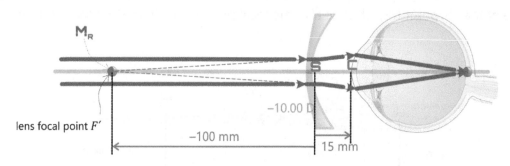

Figure 9-14: A minus powered corrective lens at 15 mm vertex distance.

The examples in Figure 9-13 and Figure 9-14 verify this relationship. For $F_o = +10.0$ D and $d = +0.015$ m, downstream optical power is $F_d = +10.0/[1 - 0.015\cdot(+10.0)] = 11.76$ D, and for $F_o = -10.0$ D, downstream optical power is $F_d = (-10.0)/[1 - 0.015\cdot(-10.0)] = -8.70$ D.

It is therefore clear that the lens with Rx power +10.00 D at vertex distance 15 mm, when in contact with the eye, needs an effective downstream power +11.76 D. This is the reason that, particularly in cases of <u>hyperopia</u> greater than 4.00 D, <u>contact lenses are higher in power</u> and <u>spectacle lenses are lower in power</u>.

Example ☞: Mlle Gillenormand requires a $F = +10.00$ D contact lens to correct her hyperopic error. If Inspector Javert is using a trial frame at 25 mm, he will measure an Rx of what power?

This is a case of upstream power; the power mounted on the frame is upstream compared to the corneal plane. We use Eq. (9.7) with $d = -0.0025$ m and $F_o = +10.0$ D. Then, $F_u = (+10.0)/[1 - (-0.025)\cdot(+10.0)]$ = +8.0 D. Thus, the prescription power mounted on the trial frame is $F_u = +8.0$ D.

Accordingly, a lens with Rx −10.00 D at vertex distance 15 mm has, when in contact with the eye, an effective power of −8.70 D. This is why, particularly in cases of <u>myopia</u> greater than −4.00 D, <u>contact lenses are lower in power</u> and <u>spectacle lenses are higher in power.</u>

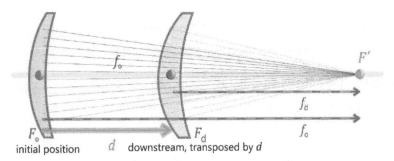

Figure 9-15: Effective focal length of a lens transposed by a distance d along the optical axis (downstream transposition).

For this reason, any prescription (even the Rx for contact lenses or refractive correction, written with the traditional format of prescription glasses) should always indicate the vertex distance, as if the subject were wearing spectacles. Thus, the hyperopia in Figure 9-13 is written as +10.00 (vertex 15 mm) and the myopia in Figure 9-14 is written as –10.00 (vertex 15 mm). The optical power of a spectacle lens fitted at a different vertex distance may need to be compensated to achieve the same intended correction.

Vertex distance:	
is important when converting between contact lens and spectacle Rx	becomes significant if the spectacle Rx is ±4.00 D or more

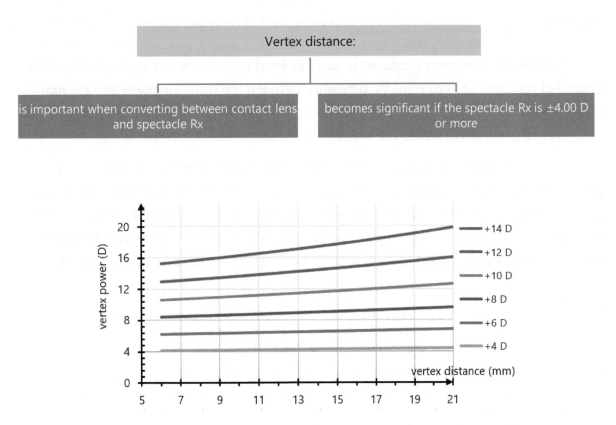

Figure 9-16: Vertex-adjusted power for a plus lens versus vertex distance for several Rx powers.

Examples ☞:

Inspector Javert wears spectacle Rx +3.25 D @ 10 mm vertex. The equivalent contact lens Rx is +3.25 D.

Monseigneur Bienvenu wears spectacle Rx −3.25 @ 10 mm vertex distance. This is equivalent to contact lens Rx −3.25 D (in both cases, there is no change due to rounding to the nearest 0.25 D).

Félix Tholomyès wears spectacle Rx +5.50 @ 8 mm vertex. This is equivalent to contact lens Rx +5.75 D. Gueulemer wears spectacle Rx −5.50 @ 8 mm vertex. This is equivalent to contact lens Rx −5.25 D.

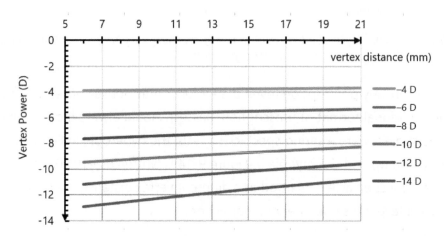

Figure 9-17: Vertex-adjusted power for a minus lens versus vertex distance for Rx powers from −4.0 D to −14.0 D.

A different outcome is produced in cases of small refractive errors or cases of a vertex distance of less than 12 mm. Here the difference between the vertexed power and the non-vertexed power is <u>not clinically significant</u> because the ophthalmic lenses are fabricated in 0.25 D increments, and the two values would round to the same dioptric power values.

The above discussion suggests that for the same prescription, contact lenses and spectacle lenses may have a different optical power. By tradition, the Rx written is associated with a individual's spectacle power; thus, it is the contact lens prescriptions that may differ from the dispensed spectacle prescription. Again, this difference is clinically significant in cases of large refractive errors (greater than ± 4.00 D) and/or in cases with a large vertex distance.

Notes 🖻 : It should be emphasized that the standard dispensed prescription always refers to the spectacle prescription, and, for this reason, it should always include the tested vertex distance.

The omission of the vertex distance may result in an incorrect power calculation for contact lens fitting, laser vision correction, or even IOL implantation. This is why the vertex distance should always accompany the spectacle Rx.

Because the change in power is dependent on the power itself, when vertexing a spherocylindrical Rx, the two powers along the principal meridians should be <u>vertexed independently</u>. Thus, the prescription must first be converted to the lens cross.

Example 📋 : In general, for hyperopia, the contact lens power is greater than the spectacle power (more plus), and for myopia, the contact lens power is less than the spectacle lens power (less minus). Let us use a round Rx number, 10.0 D. A hyperopic Rx of +10.0 D at 15 mm vertex has a contact lens power $L' =$ 10.0/[1 − 0.015×10] = +11.75 (Figure 9-13). A myopic Rx of −10.0 at 15 mm vertex has a contact lens power $L' = -10.0/[1 − 0.015×(−10)] = −8.75$ D (Figure 9-14)—after rounding to the nearest 0.25 D.

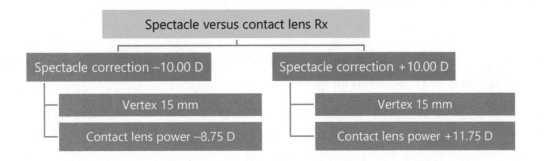

Note 🔖 : The geometrical optics professor protests (again!). He claims that we must consider the magnitude (therefore, the necessary correction) of ametropia not at the spectacle plane or the corneal plane (vertex distance = 0), but at the object-space principal plane, which is, on average, 1.35 mm inside the eye. In other words, true ametropia should be measured from the principal plane of the eye.

We respond that this is not practical. The best approximation of the degree of ametropia is the power of the contact lenses (placed at the corneal plane) and not the power of the spectacle lenses (which are placed at some non-zero vertex distance). However, historically, spectacle lenses were developed centuries before contact lenses. Therefore, the established norm is that the optical power of the spectacle lenses placed at a certain vertex distance is used to express the degree of ametropia in the prescription.

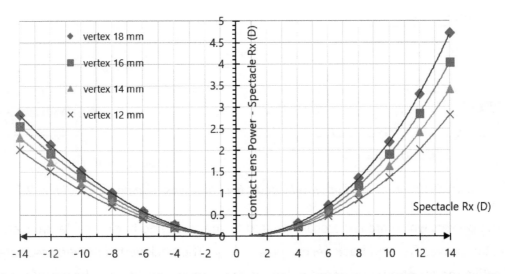

Figure 9-18: Difference in contact lens power versus spectacle (Rx) power at different vertex distances.

Example ☞: Fauchelevant wants to switch from a spectacle prescription +6.00 –4.00×180 @ 12 mm to contact lenses. What should be the contact lens Rx?

The lens cross is +6.00 @ 180° and +2.00 @ 90°, vertex distance 12 mm. Using $d = +0.012$ m in relationship (9.4), +6.00 becomes +6.47 D, rounded to +6.50 @ 180°, while +2.00 becomes +2.05, which practically remains +2.00 @ 90°. The new lens cross is therefore +6.50 @ 180° and +2.00 @ 90°, and Fauchelevant's contact lens prescription becomes +6.50 –4.50×180.

Example ☞: Please help Euphrasie switch from a spectacle prescription of –4.25 +1.75×090 at a vertex distance of 12 mm to a contact lens prescription.

The lens cross for Euphrasie's Rx is –2.50 @ 180° and –4.25 @ 90°. Using $d = +0.012$ m in Eq. (9.4), –2.50 D power remains –2.50 @ 180° (–2.43, to be exact), while –4.25 D becomes –4.00 @ 90° (–4.04 D, to be exact). The new lens cross is –2.50 @ 180° and –4.00 @ 90°, and the contact lens Rx becomes –4.00 +1.50×090.

9.2.5 Front and Back Vertex Lens Power

In addition to the equivalent power and the equivalent focal lengths, which are measured from the principal planes, in a thick lens we have:

• the **front focal distance** (length), *FFD* or *FFL*, the distance along the optical axis from the primary focal point F in object space to the vertex V of the front lens surface.

• the **back focal distance** (length), *BFD* or *BFL*, the distance along the optical axis from the vertex V' of the back optical surface to the secondary focal point F' in image space.

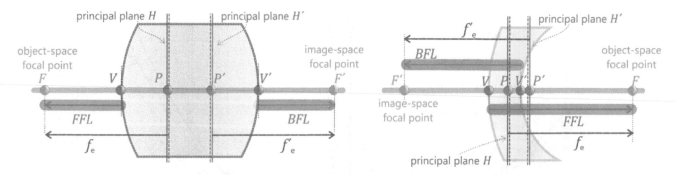

Figure 9-19: Front and back focal lengths in a thick lens. Compare with Figure 9-7.

The powers which are reciprocally related to the front and back focal lengths are the **front vertex power** F_{FVP} and **back vertex power** F_{BVP}. The back vertex power, associated with the corrective (prescription) power of the lens, is the vergence exiting the back surface of a thick lens (in image space) if a collimated pencil of rays enters the lens from the front (object space). Their significance is very practical since they are regularly measured by lensometers without the need to know (by mathematical calculations) the locations of the principal planes.

The <u>front vertex power</u> is also known as the '<u>neutralizing</u>,' or 'front neutralizing' power, since it is the vergence (of opposite sign) of a beam incident on the lens, which, upon exiting the lens becomes collimated (zero optical power). What we measure when we neutralize the lens, facing outward, is the front vertex power.

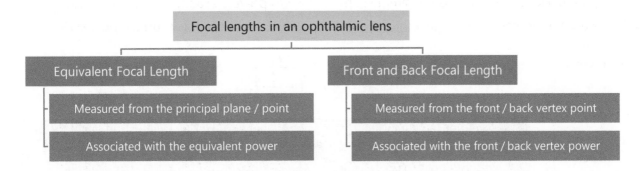

Much like the equivalent optical power, the back and front vertex powers are affected by the lens thickness. Recall that the equivalent power is not equal in magnitude to the nominal power by virtue of the third term in Gullstrand's formula. The same is true for the back and the front vertex powers: Their values are not the same as the nominal power, either. The thicker the lens (and, often, the more the surface curvatures differ) the more noticeable this difference is.

In examples that we will soon see, a thick (6 cm—very thick, indeed), biconvex lens has nominal power +20.0 D, equivalent power +16.0 D, and back and front vertex powers +26.66 D. Another example of a 3 mm thick meniscus lens (this is a more realistic example of an ophthalmic lens) that has nominal power is +5.00 D, equivalent power +5.10 D, front vertex power +5.05 D, and back vertex power +5.20 D. Obviously, these differences are not as dramatic as in the very thick lens; however, they do bear significance, even in a typical-thickness ophthalmic lens. The powers can be identical to the simple sum of the two surface powers of the two SSRIs that form the lens (nominal power) only in the case of zero thickness.

The question that arises is, why are these values different? Let's examine the back vertex power, which is the sum of the two powers at the back surface: (1) the power of the first (anterior) surface F'_1 (i.e., the vergence of a collimated beam leaving the first SSRI) upon reaching the second interface traveling through the lens thickness and (2) the power of the second surface F_2 (as is). Likewise, the front vertex power is the sum of two powers: (1) the power of the first surface F_1 (as is) and (2) the power of the back surface F'_2 upon reaching the first interface traveling through the lens thickness.

To calculate the primed power F'_1, we use the downstream vergence relationship (9.5), in which the original vergence L is the front surface power F_1 (base curve, § 9.4.3). F'_1 is now adjusted at a downstream distance equal to the lens thickness t. The medium between is none other than the lens material, with refractive index n.

Downstream-Adjusted Front Surface Power F'_1 (lens thickness t, index n): $\quad F'_1 = \dfrac{F_1}{1 - \dfrac{t}{n} \cdot F_1}$

Then, the back vertex power is the simple sum of the two powers exactly at the back vertex. These are the downstream-adjusted front surface power F'_1 and the back surface power F_2:

Back Vertex Power: $\qquad\qquad\qquad F_{BVP} = \dfrac{F_1}{1 - \dfrac{t}{n} \cdot F_1} + F_2 \qquad\qquad\qquad$ (9.8)

Back Vertex Power {
- is the vergence of an incident collimated beam upon leaving the image-plane back surface of a thick lens.
- is the sum of the back surface power F_2 and the downstream-adjusted front surface power F'_1.
- can be measured with standard methods (e.g., with a lensometer).
- is the power value reported in corrective spectacle lenses.

We can calculate the front vertex power following a similar logic. The justification is simple. It is, again, the sum of two powers: the front surface power F_1 is not adjusted (it is already there!), but the back surface power F'_2 is downstream-adjusted. To calculate F'_2, we use the same formula as Eq. (9.5), in which t is the lens thickness. It is again downstream because now light travels from right to left and, thus, from the back lens surface to the front lens surface.

Front Vertex Power: $\qquad\qquad\qquad F_{FVP} = F_1 + \dfrac{F_2}{1 - \dfrac{t}{n} \cdot F_2} \qquad\qquad\qquad$ (9.9)

Once the front vertex power F_{FVP} and the back vertex power F_{BVP} are established, we can compute the front focal length (FFL) and the back focal length (BFL), which are reciprocally related to the refractive index of the front medium and the back medium, respectively.

Front Focal Length and Front Vertex Power: $\qquad F_{FVP} = \dfrac{n_F}{FFL} \implies FFL = \dfrac{n_F}{F_{FVP}} \qquad$ (9.10)

Back Focal Length and Back Vertex Power: $\qquad F_{BVP} = \dfrac{n_B}{BFL} \implies BFL = \dfrac{n_B}{F_{BVP}} \qquad$ (9.11) where n_F (also noted as n) and n_B (also noted as n') are the refractive indices in front of (before the first element, in general) and at the back of the thick lens (after the last element, in general), respectively.

Front Vertex Power {
- Is the—opposite sign—beam vergence entering the object-space front surface of a thick lens such that the beam leaving the lens is collimated (producing an image at infinity).
- Is the sum of the front surface power F_1 and the downstream-adjusted back surface power F'_2.
- Can be measured with the front surface of the lens against the lensometer stop.
- Is the power typically measured by hand neutralization and used for referencing add power in presbyopic prescriptions.

Example ☞: Brevet fabricates a symmetric biconvex glass (n= 1.5) lens, 6 cm thick at the center, with front surface power F_1 = +10 D and back surface power F_2 = +10 D. The lens is surrounded by air. Calculate the equivalent power, the front and back vertex powers, and the corresponding focal lengths.

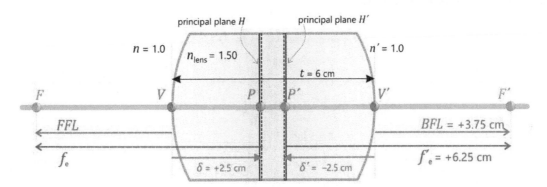

Figure 9-20: BFL, FFL, and equivalent focal lengths in a symmetric biconvex glass lens 6 cm thick. The principal planes are located using the quantities δ and δ'.

Nominal power: $F = F_1 + F_2 = +10.0\ D + 10.0\ D = +20.0\ D$.

Equivalent and vertex powers:

$$F_e = F_1 + F_2 - \frac{t}{n}F_1 \cdot F_2 = +10\ D + 10D - \frac{0.06\ m}{1.5} \cdot (+10\ D) \cdot (+10\ D) = +20\ D - 4\ D = +16.0\ D.$$

$$F_{FVP} = F_1 + \frac{F_2}{1 - \frac{t}{n} \cdot F_2} = +10\ D + \frac{+10\ D}{1 - \frac{0.06\ m}{1.5} \cdot (+10\ D)} = +10\ D + \frac{+10\ D}{1 - 0.04 \cdot 10} = +10\ D + 16.66\ D = +26.66\ D.$$

$$F_{BVP} = \frac{F_1}{1 - \frac{t}{n} \cdot F_1} + F_2 = \frac{+10\ D}{1 - \frac{0.06\ m}{1.5} \cdot (+10\ D)} + 10\ D = \frac{+10\ D}{1 - 0.04 \cdot 10} + 10\ D = +16.66\ D + 10\ D = +26.66\ D.$$

Note that the two vertex powers are equal in magnitude but differ in equivalent power.

Equivalent focal length: $f'_e = 1/F_e = 1/(+16\ D) = +0.0625\ m = +6.25\ cm$.

$FFL = 1/F_{FVP} = 1/(+26.66\ D) = +0.0375\ m = +3.75\ cm$; $BFL = 1/F_{BVP} = 1/(+26.66\ D) = +0.0375\ m = +3.75\ cm$.

Note ✏ : In the example of Figure 9-20, the two vertex powers (and, by association, the back and front focal lengths) are equal in magnitude. This is solely because the two surfaces are symmetric; i.e., they have the same surface power.

In a typical ophthalmic lens, however, the two vertex powers (and their associated focal lengths) are <u>not</u>, in principle, of <u>equal magnitude</u>. Even if the medium is the same on both sides of the lens, the two surfaces are rarely symmetric ($r_1 \neq r_2$, which implies that $F_1 \neq F_2$), so the two vertex powers are not equal in magnitude, and their differences are particularly pronounced in high-power thick lenses.

Example ☞: Bamatabois is experimenting with a meniscus glass ($n = 1.5$) lens, 3 mm thick at the center. Front surface power (base curve) is $F_1 = +10.0\ D$ and back surface power is $F_2 = -5.0\ D$. Calculate the equivalent, front, and back vertex powers.

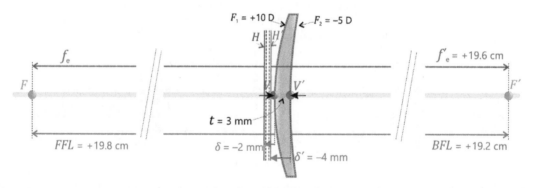

Figure 9-21: BFL, FFL, and equivalent focal length in a plus meniscus ophthalmic lens of 3 mm thickness.

Nominal power: $F = F_1 + F_2 = +10.0\ D - 5.0\ D = +5.0\ D$.

Equivalent power:

$$F_e = F_1 + F_2 - \frac{t}{n} F_1 \cdot F_2 = +10.0\ D - 5.0\ D - \frac{0.003\ m}{1.5} \cdot \left(+10.0\ D\right) \cdot \left(-5.0\ D\right) = +5.0\ D + 0.1\ D = +5.10\ D.$$

Front vertex power:

$$F_{FVP} = F_1 + \frac{F_2}{1 - \dfrac{t}{n} \cdot F_2} = +10\ D + \frac{-5\ D}{1 - \dfrac{0.003\ m}{1.5} \cdot -5\ D} = +10\ D + \frac{-5\ D}{1 + 0.002 \cdot 5} = +10\ D + \frac{-5\ D}{1.01} = +10\ D - 4.95\ D = +5.05\ D.$$

Back vertex power:

$$F_{BVP} = \frac{F_1}{1 - \dfrac{t}{n} \cdot F_1} + F_2 = \frac{+10\ D}{1 - \dfrac{0.003\ m}{1.5} \cdot +10\ D} - 5\ D = \frac{+10\ D}{1 - 0.002 \cdot 10} - 5\ D = \frac{+10\ D}{0.98} - 5\ D = 10.20\ D - 5\ D = +5.20\ D.$$

Note 🔊: In the previous typical ophthalmic meniscus lens example, the two vertex powers are slightly different in magnitude and also differ from the nominal and equivalent powers.

Example ☞: Montparnasse made a hemispherical planoconvex lens oriented with the flat surface facing image space. What are the equivalent, front, and back vertex powers and focal lengths? Radius of curvature r = +10 cm; refractive index n = 1.5. The lens is placed in the air.

The hemispherical lens has a thickness equal to the convex surface radius of curvature: $t = r$ = +10 cm. Surface powers: $F_1 = (n-1)/r_1 = (1.5-1)/(+0.1 \text{ m}) = +5.0 \text{ D}$ and $F_2 = (n-1)/r_2 = (1-1.5)/(\infty) = 0 \text{ D}$.

Nominal power: $F = F_1 + F_2 = +5.0 \text{ D} + 0.0 \text{ D} = +5.0 \text{ D}$.

Equivalent power: $F_{e \text{ planoconvex}} = F_1 + F_2 - \dfrac{t}{n} F_1 \cdot F_2 = +5 \text{ D} + 0 - \dfrac{t}{n} \cdot (+5 \text{ D}) \cdot 0 = +5.0 \text{ D}$.

Equivalent focal length: $f'_e = 1/F_e = 1/(+5.0 \text{ D}) = +0.20 \text{ m} = +20 \text{ cm}$.

Front vertex power: $F_{FVP} = F_1 + \dfrac{F_2}{1 - \dfrac{t}{n} \cdot F_2} = +5 \text{ D} + \dfrac{0}{1 - \dfrac{0.01 \text{ m}}{1.5} \cdot (0 \text{ D})} = +5.0 \text{ D}$.

Front focal length: $FFL = 1/F_{FVP} = 1/(+5.0 \text{ D}) = +0.20 \text{ m} = +20 \text{ cm}$.

Back vertex power: $F_{BVP} = \dfrac{F_1}{1 - \dfrac{t}{n} \cdot F_1} + F_2 = \dfrac{+5 \text{ D}}{1 - \dfrac{0.10 \text{ m}}{1.5} \cdot (+5 \text{ D})} + 0 \text{ D} = \dfrac{+5 \text{ D}}{1 - 0.333} = \dfrac{+5 \text{ D}}{0.66} = +7.5 \text{ D}$.

Back focal length: $BFL = 1/F_{FVP} = 1/(+7.5 \text{ D}) = +0.20 \text{ m} = +13.33 \text{ cm}$.

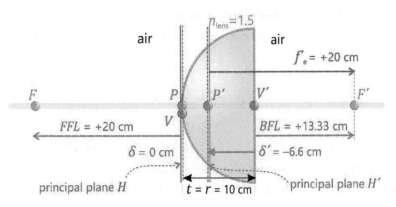

Figure 9-22: BFL, FFL, and equivalent focal length in a 10 cm thick hemispheric planoconvex glass lens.

9.2.5.1 The True Plano Lens, the Equi-sided Lens, and the Concentric Lens

A thin lens with a front surface power +6.00 D and back surface power −6.00 D would make a 0.00 D lens, which is called a **plano lens**. In general, a plano lens is any lens with zero power. However, the details can be truly deceiving upon examining the complicated nature of the equivalent and Rx power of such a lens. Let's dig in.

Example ☞: Cambronne's lens has +6.00 D and back surface power −6.00 D. The lens is made of crown glass (n = 1.523) with center thickness 2.2 mm. What are the equivalent, front, and back vertex powers?

We might be tempted to classify Cambronne's lens as a plano lens. Not so fast.
Surface powers: F_1 = +6.00 D, F_2 = −6.00 D.
Nominal power: $F = F_1 + F_2$ = 0.00 D. Does this value make it a lens plano? No, because we have not yet considered the fact that the lens has a non-zero thickness.
Equivalent power: $F_e = F_1 + F_2 − (t/n)·(F_1·F_2)$ = +6.00 −6.00 − 0.00144·(−36) = +0.0520 D.
Front vertex power $F_{FVP} = F_1 + F_2/[1−(t/n)·(F_2)]$ = +6.00 −6.00/[1− 0.00144·(−6)] = +0.0515 D.
Back vertex power $F_{FVP} = F_1/[1−(t/n)·(F_1)] + F_2$ = +6.00/[1− 0.00144·(+6)] −6.00= +0.0524 D.

We realize therefore that Cambronne's lens is <u>not</u> exactly <u>a true plano lens</u>. This lens, having the same (but opposite sign) powers, is called an **equi-sided lens**.

A true plano lens must have a slightly steeper back surface curvature to produce zero power. Take, for example, Listolier's lens from the example below. With a base curve of +6.00 D, the lens is ground to a back surface power of −6.0525 D. This lens does not sound like a plano lens, but its powers are zero, so it is a true plano lens.

Example ☞: Listolier's lens has +6.00 D and back surface power −6.0525 D. The lens is also made of crown glass (n = 1.523) with the same center thickness of 2.2 mm. What are the equivalent, front, and back vertex powers?

Surface powers: F_1 = +6.00 D, F_2 = −6.0525 D.
Nominal power: $F = F_1 + F_2$ = −0.0525 D.
Equivalent power: $F_e = F_1 + F_2 − (t/n)·(F_1·F_2)$ = +6.00 −6.0525 − 0.00144·(−36.315) = +0.00 D.
Front vertex power $F_{FVP} = F_1 + F_2/[1−(t/n)·(F_2)]$ = +6.00 −6.0525/[1− 0.00144·(−6.0525)] = +0.00 D.
Back vertex power $F_{FVP} = F_1/[1−(t/n)·(F_1)] + F_2$ = +6.00/[1− 0.00144·(+6)] −6.0525= +0.000 D.

A third type of lens that toys with the concept of 'zero' power is the **concentric lens**, in which the two centers of curvature coincide. This can be realized if the difference between the two (front surface and back surface) radii of curvature equals the lens center thickness.[915]

Example ☞: Fameuil's lens has +6.00 D and back surface power –6.153 D. The lens material is crown glass (n = 1.523), and center thickness is 2.2 mm. What are the equivalent, front, and back vertex powers?

Surface powers: F_1 = +6.00 D, F_2 = –6.153 D.
Nominal power: $F = F_1 + F_2$ = –0.153 D.
Equivalent power: $F_e = F_1 + F_2 - (t/n)\cdot(F_1\cdot F_2)$ = +6.00 –6.153 – 0.00144·(–36.918) = –0.1 D.
Front vertex power $F_{FVP} = F_1 + F_2/[1–(t/n)\cdot(F_2)]$ = +6.00 –6.153/[1– 0.00144·(–6.153)] = –0.1 D.
Back vertex power $F_{FVP} = F_1/[1–(t/n)\cdot(F_1)] + F_2$ = +6.00/[1– 0.00144·(+6)] –6.0525= –0.1 D.

Fameuil's lens is a concentric lens because the two radii of curvature (front r_1 = +0.0872 m and back r_2 = +0.0850 m) differ by the exact amount of the lens thickness t = 0.0022 m.

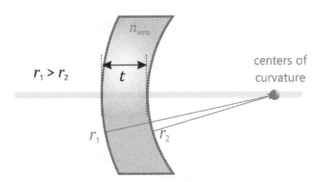

Figure 9-23: Design of a concentric lens.

However, neither of this lens' powers is zero. So, why do we even bother? The answer is that it has zero prism effect, which relates to the fact that the two centers of curvature are coincident. There are other interesting properties of concentric lenses. One concentric design, called the Maksutov concentric lens, is used in parallel space for the correction of the spherical aberration of telescope objectives, with a limited impact on any of the primary aberrations. Other variations of the concentric lens design include the **size lens**,[916] which is used in the prescription of aniseikonia.

---

[915] Rosin S. Concentric lens. J Opt Soc Am. 1959; 49(9):862-4.
[916] *Geometrical Optics* § 6.1.2 Specialty Lenses.

9.3 CORRECTED IMAGE AND SPECTACLE MAGNIFICATION

9.3.1 Corrected Retinal Image in Ametropia

Any correction, with either spectacles or contact lenses, affects the retinal image size. A notable exception is for axial ametropia corrected with the application of Knapp's rule (§ 6.6.5), in which case the corrected image size is not affected.

Spectacle magnification is the ratio of the image size h' in a corrected eye to the image size h in a noncorrected eye, where the images are of the same object at the same location. This term is used regardless of the correction type, with either spectacles or contact lenses. Spectacle magnification is thus the ratio of the two image sizes: with and without correction.

The calculation of spectacle magnification can be challenging if no detailed ocular dimensions and optical parameters of the eye are available. Retinal image size (the emmetropic case is presented in § 6.2.2 and the ametropic case is in § 6.5.2) is determined by the angle ϑ subtended by the visual axis with the optical axis from the edge of the object. The clinical counterpart of the visual axis is the line of sight, which is the chief ray connecting the fixation point to the center of the entrance pupil, as shown in Figure 9-24.

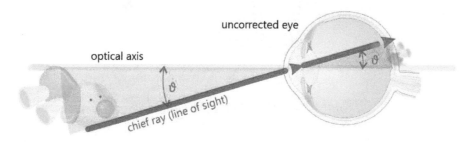

Figure 9-24: The angle ϑ subtended by the chief ray with the optical axis in an uncorrected eye.

However, since spectacle magnification is the ratio of two image sizes formed in the same eye, knowledge of these dimensions is not necessary. The key is that the angle at the fixation point determines the retinal image size, per relationship (6.3), so the image ratio is an angle ratio. Spectacle magnification is therefore an <u>angular magnification.</u>

Spectacle Magnification: $\dfrac{\text{retinal image size with correction}}{\text{retinal image size without correction}} = \dfrac{\vartheta'}{\vartheta}$ (9.12)

where angle ϑ' is formed by the corrected image and increases with a plus-powered and decreases with a minus-powered corrective lens. So, a plus-powered spectacle lens produces an increased retinal image size, while a minus powered spectacle lens produces a decreased image size (minification).

To model this effect, we trace a chief ray directed at the eye at an angle ϑ. This ray is incident on a plus lens of back vertex power F_{BVP} (prescription Rx) placed at a vertex d_v. At the lens, the ray bends, forming an angle ϑ'. Geometrical analysis in Figure 9-25 leads to Eq. (9.13).

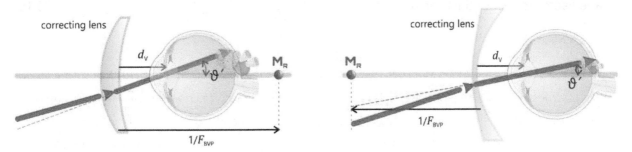

Figure 9-25: Spectacle magnification geometry in (left) a plus-lens correction and (right) a minus-lens correction. The angle ϑ' inside the eye is altered by the presence of the lens at distance d_v in front of the eye.

Spectacle Magnification (thin lens):
$$M = \frac{1}{1 - \left(\underbrace{d_v}_{\text{vertex distance}} \cdot \underbrace{F_{BVP}}_{\text{lens vertex power}} \right)}$$
(9.13)

Note ✒: There are several variations to the above relationship. Despite the strenuous protest by the optics professor, this formula ignores/disregards the purely optical consideration of using distance d_v from the center of the corrective lens to the <u>entrance pupil of the eye</u>, not the vertex distance, which is an approximation. Often, the entrance pupil of the eye is about 3 mm inside the eye, past the cornea.

So far, the physical lens thickness t has been ignored—the lens was considered thin. If we include aspects of a thick lens, spectacle magnification can be presented as[917]

Spectacle Magnification (thick lens):
$$M = \underbrace{\frac{1}{1 - \left(\frac{t \cdot F_1}{n} \right)}}_{\text{shape factor}} \cdot \underbrace{\frac{1}{1 - \left(d_v \cdot F_{BVP} \right)}}_{\text{power factor}}$$
(9.14)

where F_1 is the front surface lens power (base curve), t is the lens center thickness (expressed in meters), and n is the refractive index of the lens material.

The new factor [shown in red in Eq. (9.14)] is the lens **shape factor**. The lens shape factor is always > 1.0, staying barely above 1.0 for most minus and low plus lenses, considering that the base curve in ophthalmic lenses is convex, and thickness can only be positive! The

---

[917] Rabbetts RB. Bennett and Rabbett's Clinical Visual Optics 4th Edition, § 13. Subsidiary effects of correcting lenses. Butterworth-Heinemann; 2007.

shape factor is important <u>only in large plus corrections</u> with large (front) base curve power and/or significant lens thickness t.

Shape Factor (effect of thick lens):
$$\frac{1}{1-\left(\frac{t\cdot F_1}{n}\right)} \approx 1+\left(\frac{t\cdot F_1}{n}\right)$$
(9.15)

Note 📋 : Plus lenses have a fixed (small, non-zero) edge thickness. As per the discussion in § 9.4.4, their center thickness is variable, depending on (increasing with) lens power, (increasing with) lens diameter, and (decreasing with) lens material refractive index. On the other hand, minus lenses have a fixed (small, non-zero) center thickness. Their edge thickness is variable, depending on (increasing with) lens power, (increasing with) lens diameter, and (decreasing with) lens material refractive index.

The second factor [shown in blue in Eq. (9.14)] is the lens **power factor**. The lens power factor is, essentially, the thin lens spectacle magnification, which is dependent on the corrective power of the lens (back vertex power F_{BVP} = Rx power) and the distance of the lens from the 'seat of the ametropia' (vertex distance d_v). The magnification M resulting from the power factor is always >1.0 for a plus-powered lens and is always <1.0 for a minus-powered lens.

Power Factor:
$$\frac{1}{1-\left(d_v\cdot F_{BVP}\right)} \approx 1+\left(d_v\cdot F_{BVP}\right)$$
(9.16)

The spectacle magnification resulting from the power factor can also be expressed either as a rational number or as percentage.

Spectacle Magnification (%): $M\,(\%) = (M-1)\cdot 100 = d_v\,[m]\cdot F_{BVP}\cdot 100 = d_v\,[cm]\cdot F_{BVP}$ (9.17)

Example ☞: What is the spectacle magnification for Bahoral's spectacle lens Rx = +1.00 D with base curve power +6.00 D, vertex distance 12 mm, center thickness 3.00 mm, and made of glass with n = 1.5?

Implementing Eq. (9.14), the shape factor is 1.012146, and the power factor is 1.012146 (coincidentally!). Bahoral is experiencing spectacle magnification M = 1.024439. Expressed in (%), $M\,(\%) = (M-1)\cdot 100$ = 2.44%.

Example ☞: Azelma wears spectacle lens Rx = +5.00 D with base curve +8.00 D, vertex distance 12 mm, center thickness 7.20 mm, and made of glass with n = 1.5. What is the spectacle magnification experienced?

Implementing Eq. (9.14), the shape factor is 1.0399, and the power factor is 1.0638. So, the spectacle magnification is M = 1.106. Expressed in (%), $M\,(\%) = (M-1)\cdot 100$ = 10.6%.

Example ☞: In an attempt to reduce spectacle magnification for the same prescription worn by Azelma (Rx = +5.00 D), monsieur Thénardier suggests that his daughter use a reduced base curve +6.00 D, a reduced vertex distance 10 mm, and a higher refractive index glass with n = 1.8 (which also reduces the center thickness to about 4.50 mm). Is the monsieur Thénardier correct in his suggestion?

The new shape factor is 1.0152, and the new power factor is 1.0526 (this changes very little). Spectacle magnification is M = 1.068. Expressed in (%), M (%) = (M − 1)·100 = 6.86%. Yes, Thénardier was right.

Spectacle magnification therefore is influenced by lens type, power, and vertex distance. A large vertex distance results in increased magnification (in plus lenses) and increased minification (in minus lenses). The data presented in Figure 9-26 indicate that the power factor (blue line) contributes significantly more (about 10×) to spectacle magnification than the shape factor (red line). However, since the power factor is dependent on the refraction parameters (vertex distance d_v and Rx power F_{BVP}), the shape factor can be used to adjust the spectacle magnification by using a different base curve (F_1) and/or different lens thickness t and refractive index n.

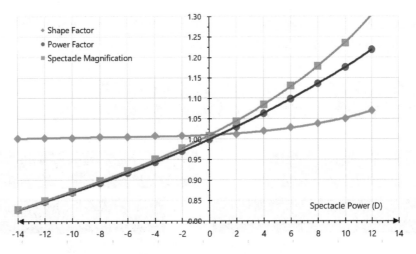

Figure 9-26: Dependence of spectacle magnification (vertical axis)—and the shape factor and power factor components of speckle magnification—on lens prescription power for vertex power d_v = 15 mm. Base curve and lens center thickness are chosen over typical values (Vogel's rule) for the spectacle power.

A plus lens magnifies, while a minus lens minifies (has magnification less than one, a.k.a. minification.)

The greater the lens power the more a plus lens magnifies and the more a minus lens minifies.

Vertex distance influences magnification; away from the eye, magnification increases; closer to the eye, magnification decreases.

Spectacle magnification in refractive ametropia is nearly proportional to the amount of refractive error, as demonstrated by the data illustrated in Figure 9-26, where the curve is nearly linear. For plus corrections, spectacle magnification increases by about 2.5% per diopter of refractive error. For minus corrections, spectacle magnification decreases by about 1.25% per diopter of refractive error.

Note 🖉: In contact lens correction, the power factor is almost unity (≈ 1.0), and spectacle minification is negligible. Exact calculations should use the value of 3 mm as the 'vertex distance' in Eq. (9.13). This is important in high myopia, as a better (corrected) visual acuity is achieved with contact lenses due to less retinal image minification (spectacle magnification is closer to 1.0).[918]

Example ☞: Madame Thénardier wears –12.00 spectacles at 13 mm vertex distance. Considering only a power factor magnification, what would be different if she were to switch to a contact lens Rx?

The spectacle magnification experienced by Mme Thénardier is calculated using Eq. (9.16) or the simplified version, Eq. (9.17): Power factor ≈ 1+ [0.016 · (–12.00)] = 1 – 0.192 = 0.808 or 19.2% minification. Here we are using an 'enhanced' vertex distance concept, which is that the lens-to-corneal-plane distance + corneal-plane-to-principal-plane distance = 13 + 3 = 16 mm. This enables use of a 3 mm 'vertex distance' for the contact lens:

The contact lens Rx for Mme Thénardier would be –10.38 D. Using, again, the simplified version, Eq. (9.17), Power factor ≈ 1+ [0.003 · (–10.38)] = 1 – 0.031 = 0.96886 or 3.1% minification.

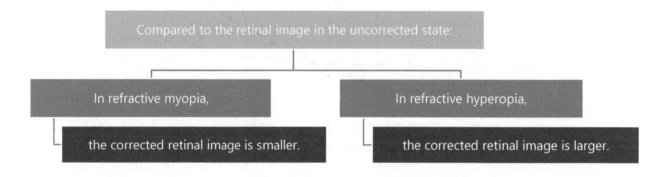

We realize that there are significant retinal image size changes when a spectacle lens correction is applied. This has implications for corrected visual acuity. A high myope, such as Mme Thénardier, when corrected with spectacle lenses, may experience a significant reduction in the corrected image size. The letters from the logMAR = 0.0 line appear smaller than they do to an emmetrope and may therefore not be seen. However, the details are complicated, as the nature of ametropia (being axial or refractive) is a compounding factor that affects the size of the corrected image.

[918] Collins JW, Carney LG. Visual performance in high myopia. Curr Eye Res. 1990; (9):217-23.

Figure 9-27: Corrected retinal image size variation by type of ametropia. Compare with Figure 6-44.

In addition, when correcting astigmatism (as discussed in § 8.5.3), the two principal meridians display different amounts of defocus, so each has a different retinal image size, which may contribute to meridional distortions.

Example ☞: Maese Pedro is an astigmat wearing this Rx OD −1.00 −0.50×180 and OS −1.00 −3.00×180 at 15 mm vertex distance. If we consider only the power factor magnification, what is the difference in spectacle magnification experienced between Pedro's two eyes?

First, we convert both prescriptions to lens cross. OD is −1.00 @ 180° and −1.50 @ 90°. OS is −1.00 @ 180° and −4.00 @ 90°. It is clear that the magnification differences affect the vertical 90° meridian.

Using the simplified version for the power factor, Eq. (9.17):
OD eye, vertical meridian d_v [cm]·Rx = 1.5·(−1.5) = 2.25% minification.
OS eye, vertical meridian d_v [cm]·Rx = 1.5·(−4.0) = 6.00% minification.
These results are illustrated in the astigmatism chapter, Figure 8-54 (although rather exaggerated, indeed).

The **relative spectacle magnification** (*RSM*) describes the ratio of the clear, corrected image size to the (hypothetical) image size <u>if the eye were emmetropic</u> (usually, per the standard $F_{\text{emmetropic eye}}$ = +60 D eye model). RSM is important because the ratio of right-eye RSM to left-eye RSM indicates the relative sizes of the retinal images in the two eyes, i.e., the potential degree of aniseikonia. Several models can be used to express *RSM*. In the simplest form, *RSM* can be approximated by the ratio of the refractive power of the emmetropic eye to that of the corrected eye.

Relative Spectacle Magnification:
$$RSM = \frac{F_{\text{emmetropic eye}}}{F_{\text{corrected eye}}}$$
(9.18)

Example ☞: What is the relative spectacle magnification for an aphakic eye left with +45.0 D uncorrected power, when corrected with an ophthalmic lens Rx = +10.00 D placed at vertex distance 12 mm?

First, we use Gullstrand's formula: $F_{\text{corrected}} = F_{\text{uncorrected}} + F_{\text{lens}} - \dfrac{d_v}{1} F_{\text{eye}} \cdot F_{\text{lens}}$ = +45 +10−0.012·45·10 = +49.6 D.

We use this value in relationship (9.18): $RSM = F_{\text{emmetropic eye}}/F_{\text{corrected eye}}$ = 60 D / 49.6 D = 1.2 ≈ +20%.

Plus spectacle lens:	Minus spectacle lens	Contact lens
• retinal image magnification (greater than 1.0).	• retinal image minification (less than 1.0)	• no magnification (or minification)

9.3.2 Apparent Eye Size

The rules of optics do not depend on the direction of light propagation; symmetry is the general rule. Therefore, when the object through the spectacles is magnified or minified, the eye of the spectacle wearer also appears to an outside viewer as magnified or minified. The eyes of a myope appear smaller, while the eyes of a hyperope appear larger.

This is the **apparent eye size**, which is often considered a cosmetic flaw associated with spectacles. It does not affect contact lens correction, as the vertex distance is zero in this case. The approximate relationship that expresses the apparent eye size in terms of lens power F_{BVP} placed a distance d_v from the pupil is a version of relationship (9.13).

Apparent Eye Size:

$$\frac{1}{1 - \left(\underbrace{d_v}_{\text{vertex distance}} \cdot \underbrace{F_{BVP}}_{\text{lens vertex power}} \right)}$$

(9.19)

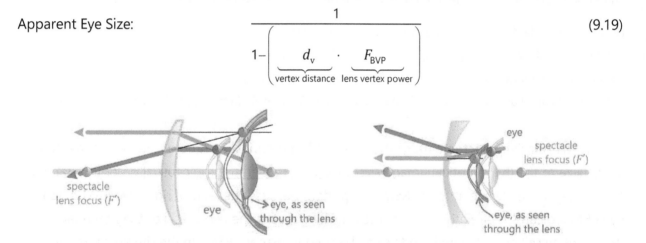

Figure 9-28: *Apparent eye, as seen through (left) a positive (plus) lens and (right) a negative (minus) lens.*

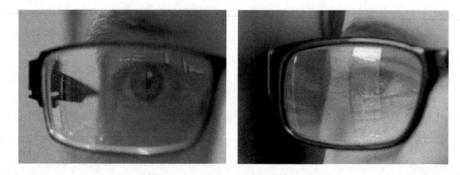

Figure 9-29: *Apparent eye size for (left) myopic spectacles and (right) hyperopic spectacles.*

Relationship (9.19) can be deduced by simple geometrical imaging considerations for a lens placed at a distance d_v. If an anatomical eye feature such as the pupil is the 'object,' then the spectacle lens makes a virtual image of this object, and that image is what we see when we look at someone through (from the outside of) that person's spectacles. With a plus lens, the image is farther away, so it appears larger; with a minus lens, the image is closer, so it appears smaller.

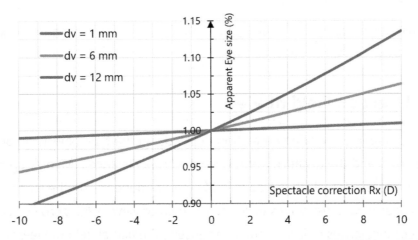

Figure 9-30: Dependence of apparent eye size (%) on spectacle correction power for various vertex distances.

As shown in Figure 9-31, the 'eye,' serving as a real object, is situated at a distance d_v from the lens. Since the typical vertex distance is drawn from the lens to the eye, the 'object' distance is $x = -d_v$, so the object vergence is $L = 1/(-d_v)$. This is added to lens power, F_{BVP}, to produce the image vergence, which is $L' = F_{BVP} + 1/(-d_v)$. The location of the image is now the reciprocal of image vergence, so $x' = 1/[F_{BVP} + 1/(-d_v)] = -d_v/(1-d_v F_{BVP})$. To calculate image magnification, all we need is the vergence ratio relationship developed in *Geometrical Optics*[919] $m = L/L' = 1/(1-d_v F_{BVP})$, which proves relationship (9.19).

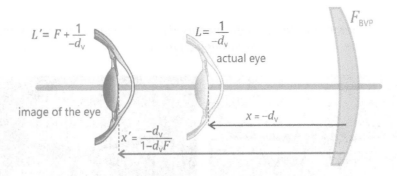

Figure 9-31: Apparent eye size considerations.

---

[919] *Geometrical Optics* § 4.1.2 Image Magnification.

Example ☞: What is the apparent eye size magnification for Mme Huchloup, a −10.00 D myope, wearing her spectacle lens at 15 mm vertex distance?

We use relationship (9.19): The apparent eye size is $1/[1-d_v \cdot F_{BVP}] = 1 / [1- 0.0015\ m \cdot (-10.00\ D)] = 0.8695$. Mme Huchloup's eye appears about (0.8695 − 1.0) = 13% smaller.

Example ☞: What is the apparent eye size magnification for Azelma, a +5.00 D hyperope, wearing her spectacle lens at 15 mm vertex distance?

We use relationship (9.19): The apparent eye size is $1/[1-d_v \cdot F_{BVP}] = 1 / [1- 0.0015\ m \cdot (+5.00\ D)] = 1.08$. Azelma's eye appears about (1.08 − 1.0) = 8% larger.

9.3.3 Lens Effect on Field of View

The field of view of a person wearing correction depends on the type (spectacle or contact lenses, myopic or hyperopic) and the distance from the eye (vertex distance). Myopic spectacles offer a larger actual field of view, for which the degree of increase depends on the lens power. Hyperopic spectacles lend a distinctly smaller actual field of view. With zero correction or correction with contact lenses or laser refractive surgery, the actual field of view is limited only by the extent to which the eyes move and possible facial anatomic limitations (e.g., a deep orbit).

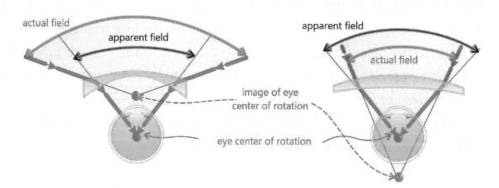

Figure 9-32: Field of view with spectacles: (left) increased field through a minus lens and (right) reduced field through a plus lens.

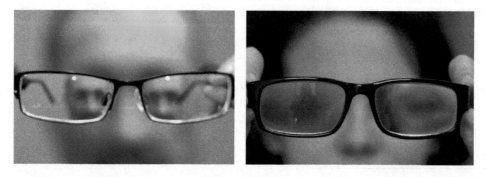

Figure 9-33: Effect of (left) myopic spectacles and (right) hyperopic spectacles on the field of view.

In addition to the field-of-view modification, hyperopic and myopic spectacles have several other unfavorable effects. Due to the prismatic effects (§ 10.4), blind angles (called scotoma rings) and double vision can be produced. In myopia, scotoma rings are seen where the physical edges of a frame interact with the visible visual field. In hyperopia, there is also the Jack-in-the-box phenomenon: Images seem to suddenly appear within a spectacle field of view as a person moves their head around due to the smaller field offered by hyperopic correction. This phenomenon is particularly troublesome in cases of high hyperopic correction, such as in aphakia.

The most interesting aspect of lens effects is the relationship between field of view and spectacle magnification. In a minus lens, the reduced spectacle magnification correlates with an increased field of view, and in a plus lens, the increased spectacle magnification correlates with a decreased field of view. The calculation of the field of view involves the concept of a field stop, whose semi-diameter is a; the angular field of view (aFoV) is computed as the angular subtense of the field stop from the center of the entrance pupil, which is a distance d_p from the field stop per the discussion in *Geometrical Optics*,[920] using the following relationship:

Field of View:
$$\text{aFoV} = 2 \cdot \tan^{-1}\left(\frac{a}{d_p}\right)$$
(9.20)

Example ☞: Consider a circular frame fitted with a plano correction lens (which is often the case in commercial movies). The frames allow a 2-inch clear diameter and are worn at a vertex distance of 15 mm. What is the monocular field of view through these frames?

In this case, the field stop is determined by the rim of the circular spectacle plano lens, and its semi-diameter is a = 2.54 cm. The entrance pupil is the physical pupil of the eye, situated approximately at the position of the vertex distance $d_p = d_v = 0.015$ m.
We now use relationship (9.20): The aFoV is $2 \cdot \tan^{-1}(2.54/1.5) = 2 \cdot \tan^{-1}(1.69) = 2 \cdot 59.43 \approx 119°$.

The following examples explore the change in field of view as it is affected by the placement of a myopic (minus) and a hyperopic (plus) spectacle lens on the frame. As a reminder, the field of view increases with the minus lens and decreases with the plus lens.

Example ☞: Mme Huchloup's circular frame (2-inch diameter) is fitted with a −10.00 D lens. The frames are worn at a vertex distance of 15 mm. What is the monocular field of view through these frames?

As in the previous example, the field stop is the rim of the circular lens frame (semi-diameter a = 2.54 cm). The difference here is that the placement of the minus lens affects the location and size of the entrance

---

[920] *Geometrical Optics* § 7.3.4.1 Definition and Computation of the aFoV.

pupil. The entrance pupil of this system is now not the physical pupil but the image of the eye's pupil via the lens. The field of view is affected because the entrance pupil is situated at a different location.

To find the new location, we employ techniques developed in geometrical optics for the location of the entrance pupil.[921] The vergence of the eye's pupil serving as the real object for the lens is $L = 1/(-0.015$ m$)$ $= -66.66$ D. This is added to the lens power, $F = -10.00$ D. Then the image vergence is $L' = L + F =$ -76.66 D, and the image location is $x' = 1/(-76.66$ D$) = -0.013$ m. This is the location of the entrance pupil for the system 'minus corrective lens + eye': 13 mm from the lens. It is a minified image of the pupil— reduced by the ratio $1.3/1.5 = 0.8695$.

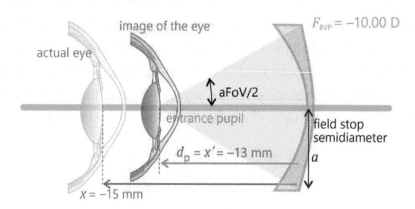

Figure 9-34: A minus correcting lens in front of the eye results in a change in the entrance pupil of the system 'eye + corrective lens.' This results in an increased field of view.

We now have the numerical data to calculate the field of view. The distance from the entrance pupil to the field stop is $d_p = 0.013$ m, and the semi-diameter is $a = 2.54$ cm.
We use relationship (9.20): The aFoV is $2 \cdot \tan^{-1}(2.54/1.3) = 2 \cdot \tan^{-1}(1.95) = 2 \cdot 62.89 \approx 125.6°$.
The field of view with this minus lens is increased by about 7° compared to the plano lens frame.

Food for thought ☻☻: The entrance pupil of the system 'minus corrective lens + eye' represents a minified version of the physical pupil by the amount ... you guessed right—the amount of relative spectacle magnification. If we use relationship (9.13), the thin lens approximation to spectacle magnification, we get $1/[1 - d_v \cdot F_{BVP}] = 1/[1 - (0.0015$ m$) \cdot (-10.00$ D$)] = 0.8695$.

Example ☞: Azelma's circular frame is fitted with a +5.00 D lens. The frames have a 2-inch diameter and are worn at a vertex distance of 15 mm. What is the monocular field of view through these frames?

The plus lens alters the location of the entrance pupil of the system 'corrective lens + eye.' The vergence of the physical pupil serving as the real object for the lens is $L = 1/(-0.015$ m$) = -66.66$ D. This is added to

---

[921] *Geometrical Optics* § 7.1.3.3 Locating the Entrance Pupil: the Aperture Stop Image in Object Space.

the lens power, which in this case is $F = +5.00$ D. The image vergence is $L' = L + F = -61.66$ D, and the image location is $x' = 1/(-61.66$ D$) = -0.0162$ m. The entrance pupil for the system 'plus corrective lens + eye' is situated 16.2 mm from the lens. It is a magnified image of the pupil—increased by the ratio 1.62/1.5 = 1.08.

We now have the numerical data to calculate the field of view. The distance from the entrance pupil to the field stop is $d_p = 0.0162$ m, and the semi-diameter is $a = 2.54$ cm.

We use relationship (9.20): The aFoV is $2 \cdot \tan^{-1}(2.54/1.62) = 2 \cdot \tan^{-1}(1.567) = 2 \cdot 57.47 \approx 114.9°$.

The field of view with this plus lens is decreased by about 4° compared to the plano lens frame.

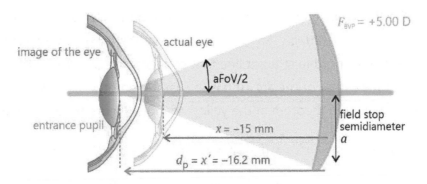

Figure 9-35: A plus correcting lens in front of the eye results in a change in the entrance pupil of the system 'eye + corrective lens.' This results in a reduced field of view.

Practice examples with answers ⚒ monocular Field of View (aFoV) with spectacles:

Frame diameter 40 mm, vertex distance 12 mm.
Plano lens, aFoV = 118°; −12.0 D lens, aFoV = 125°; +12 D lens, aFoV = 110°.

Frame diameter 35 mm, vertex distance 16 mm.
Plano lens, aFoV = 95°; −10.0 D lens, aFoV = 103.5°; +10 D lens, aFoV = 85°.

9.4 OPHTHALMIC LENS GEOMETRY

9.4.1 Optical Center

The **optical center** in a lens is a reference point on a system's optical axis through which incoming light rays are not bent by the lens or the optical surface, so no prism effect (§ 10.4.3) is observed. In a symmetrical, spherical surface lens, the optical center should be its geometrical center as well.

The optical center is an important landmark in cut ophthalmic lenses since the cut center may be displaced from the geometrical center. In ophthalmic lenses, in most cases, the optical center is the part of the lens that the wearer looks through. It is the line-of-sight intercept with the lens, known as the major reference point (MRP), and is also where we measure lens power.

9.4.2 Sagitta

The **sag**, **sagitta**, or sagittal depth s (mathematically, the versine or versed sine), is a geometric characteristic of a lens surface—a line drawn from a chord to a cross-section of a lens surface. This cross-section is shaped like an arc along the surface, and the spoke of this arc is the radius of curvature r for that piece of surface. Sagitta s is therefore the maximum separation between a point at the center of the chord (a straight line that connects the two points of the base of the arc) and the vertex, at the center of the arc. If h is the semi-diameter of the lens chord, then, application of the Pythagorean theorem in the yellow triangle (Figure 9-36) leads to

$$h^2 + (r-s)^2 = r^2 \text{ so } (r-s)^2 = r^2 - h^2 \Rightarrow r - s = \sqrt{(r^2 - h^2)}$$

Lens Sagitta: $s = r - \sqrt{(r^2 - h^2)}$ or $h^2 + s^2 = 2r \cdot s$ (9.21)

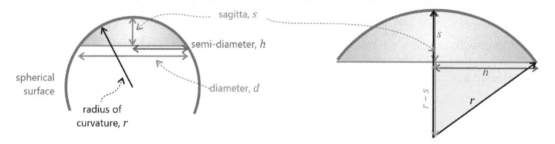

Figure 9-36: Sagitta on a spherical surface.

This formula can be used to compute the sagittal depth of a spherical mirror, a single spherical refracting interface, or a contact lens (whose diameter is referred to as the optical zone). In a thin lens approximate version, the sagitta s is significantly less than the semi-diameter h ($s \ll h \Rightarrow s^2 + h^2 \approx h^2$), and Eq. (9.21) produces two useful approximate relationships:

Finding s / Sag Formula (approximate): $s = (h^2)/2r$ (9.22)

Finding r / Sag Formula (approximate): $r = (h^2)/2s$ (9.23)

Note 💡 : These formulas can be used with any units; it is important, however that all length variables are expressed by the same unit, for example, all in millimeters or all in centimeters.

Examples ☞:

Marius Pontmercy, in addition to studying law, is an avid lens maker. He is designing a 1-inch diameter lens blank (h = 1.27 cm) with radius of curvature 8 cm (r = 8 cm). What is the sagittal depth?

The exact formula (9.21) gives s = 0.1 cm (1 mm); the approximate formula (9.22) gives s = 0.1 cm (1 mm). Next, Marius makes is a 2-inch diameter lens blank (h = 2.54 cm) with radius of curvature 6 cm (r = 6 cm). What is the sagittal depth of this lens?

The exact formula (9.21) gives s = 0.56 cm (5.6 mm); the approximate formula (9.22) gives s = 0.54 cm or 5.4 mm (it is still okay to just use the approximate formula).

The **lens clock** (or spherometer) is a mechanical device (sag gauge) used to measure a lens curve. It has three branched legs (pins), which are brought in contact with the lens surface. The two outer pins are fixed, while the center pin can be moved to match the surface curvature. The center pin directly measures the vertical difference between the outer and inner pins as the sagittal depth s. A fixed variable is the semi-diameter h, which is the horizontal distance between the outer stationary pin and the moveable center pin. Thus, the lens clock measures s for a fixed h. The radius of curvature r is then given by Eq. (9.23).

The lens clock therefore computes the geometric radius of curvature; the dioptric surface power is indirectly calculated assuming a fixed value of the lens refractive index. Most (but not all) lens clocks convert radius to dioptric surface power using a glass refractive index of 1.53. This practice dates back to early lens fabrication times during which most, if not all, ophthalmic lenses were made from glass with an index of refraction of 1.53.

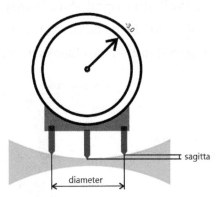

Figure 9-37: Lens clock used to measure surface curvature.

Then, using relationship (9.1), the surface power $F_{measured}$ is calculated using n_{air} = 1.0.

Measured Surface Power: $$F_{measured} \, [\text{D}] = \frac{n' - 1}{r \, [\text{m}]} = \frac{1.53 - 1}{r \, [\text{m}]} = \frac{0.53}{r \, [\text{m}]}$$ (9.24)

If the true lens material is not $n' = 1.53$, we can simply use the exact (true) n'_{glass} from relationship (9.1). Alternatively, to find the true surface power F_{true},

True Surface Power: $F_{true} = F_{measured} \cdot (n'_{glass} - 1.0)/(1.53 - 1.0) = F_{measured} \cdot (n'_{glass} - 1.0)/0.53$ (9.25)

Example ☞: A lens clock measures a lens surface power as –4.00 D. The lens material is glass with refractive index $n'_{glass} = 1.66$. What is the true surface power?

Per relationship (9.1), the true surface power should be $(n'_{glass} - 1.0)/r$. The lens clock reports $(1.53 - 1.0)/r$. Therefore, the true power should be $-4.00 \cdot (n'_{glass} - 1.0)/(1.53 - 1.0) = -4.00 \cdot 0.66/0.53 = -5.00$ D.

9.4.3 Surface Power Curves

The fact that the lens prescription power is derived by adding two separate surface powers leaves open the possibility that a given lens power may be obtained by unlimited combinations of surfaces (i.e., curvature), as long as the algebraic sum of the front and back surface powers produces the net desired power. For example, according to the **nominal lens formula** (§ 9.2.2.1), a +4.00 D lens can be produced with surface power combinations such as +4.00 D front and plano back, +6.00 D front and –2.00 D back, +8.00 D front and –4.00 D back, or +10.00 D front and –6.00 D back. Although these lenses might have the same power and focal length, they differ, perhaps even significantly, in other aspects, mainly in the peripheral image quality.

To optimize quality, lens fabricators gradually developed a series of lens shapes. First, owing to the work of William Hyde Wollaston, ophthalmic lenses were meniscus. Later work led to the grouping of lens powers. This helped lens fabrication workshops to reduce inventory and tooling, as many shops only stock semi-finished lens blanks in certain, fixed, base curve values.

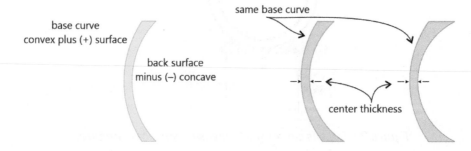

Figure 9-38: *Minus meniscus ophthalmic lens with the same base curve and center thickness and increased back surface power.*

To produce the prescription power, the lens needs to be processed on both the anterior (front) and the posterior (back) surfaces. The lens blanks have their front surface polished to a certain, few, curvatures. Upon ordering the lens prescription, the lens is produced by grinding into the back surface of the lens blank. The **base curve** is defined as the standard or reference surface. Its concept extends to the curvature of this surface, with which all other curvatures are compared. In spherical ophthalmic lenses, the base curve refers to the front surface power.

A simplified rule, known as **Vogel's rule** or Vogel's formula, named after Irwin Vogel, (then an opticianry instructor at New York City Community College and later at the Cañada College in Redwood City, California) states that the typical value for a base curve in low-power ophthalmic lenses is close to +6.00 D. Plus corrections move to steeper base curves: the base curve should be the prescription spherical equivalent (SE, § 8.2.2) (or, simply, the spherical correction in simple lenses) plus 6.00 D. Minus corrections move to flatter base curves. The base curve should be half the prescription spherical equivalent plus 6.00 D.

Vogel's rule for base curve	• For a plus prescription: Base curve = Rx spherical equivalent + 6.00 D. • For a minus prescription: Base curve = ½ Rx spherical equivalent + 6.00 D.

Note ∞: Vogel's formula is an approximation that produces average base curve values, not necessarily the actual values, which may depend on manufacturing constraints and material properties, but mainly depend on the material refractive index—lenses made of a higher refractive index may be flatter. Also, the formula may fail to produce accurate predictions for high corrections.

Other formulas, such as the Boddy formula, state values for base curves for plus and minus digital progressive lenses. The production of substantial quality lenses involves complicated computations to determine which base curve gives the optimal result of a given prescription.

Example ☞: Cousin Théodule Gillenormand wants to use Marius' blanks to make a +2.00 D lens. What powers should he use for the base curve and the back surface power?

The spherical equivalent is +2.00 D. By Vogel's rule, the base curve is $F_1 = +2.00 +6.00 =+8.00$ D. The back surface power F_2 is then –6.00 D.

Théodule checks this with the nominal lens formula: $F_1 + F_2 = +8.00 -6.00 = +2.00 = $ Rx [Figure 9-39 (left)].

$F_1 = +8.00$ D

$F_2 = -6.00$ D

$F_1 = +5.00$ D

$F_2 = -7.00$ D

Figure 9-39: Application of the nominal lens formula: The simple addition of the front and back surface powers produces the lens refractive power for (left) a +2.00 D lens and (right) a –2.00 D lens.

Example ☞: If Théodule wants to make a –2.00 D lens, what base curve and back power should he use?

Half of the SE is ½·(–2.00 D) = –1.00 D; by Vogel's rule, the base curve is F_1 = –1.00+6.00 =+5.00 D. The back surface power F_2 is –7.00 D. Sanity check: +5.00 –7.00 = –2.00 = Rx [Figure 9-39 (right)].

Note 📷: The base curve front power F_1 and the back surface power F_2 should not be confused with the vertex powers, which are the front vertex power F_{FVP} and the back vertex power F_{BVP}. The surface powers F_1 and F_2 are single-surface curve powers that are meaningful only in theory—in the case where the lens medium extends indefinitely—and are governed by the SSRI power rules. The vertex powers refer to the powers of the lens as a whole, as effected by the surface orientation, surface powers, and lens thickness.

In a flat-front-surface lens like the very early ophthalmic lens, the base curve is flat with zero power. Today, ophthalmic lenses almost always have a convex plus (+) base curve, with the very rare exception of very high minus lenses. The back surface is most often a minus (–) concave shape surface. Engineering and fabrication tolerances allow for a certain amount of power error (0.24 D) and/or cylinder error (0.12 D) in the peripheral field. For powers above 6.50 D, the standard is ±2%. These tolerances can be accepted and understood considering (a) the ability of the eye to perform nearly well within small power variations, (b) the depth of focus, and (c) the precision in determining the refractive power in an eye exam, which can be no finer than 0.12 D.

9.4.3.1 Tscherning's Ellipse

The **Tscherning ellipse** is a graphical representation on an elliptically curved line displaying the base curve powers that optimize optical performance, thus eliminating oblique astigmatism, for a given lens prescription (back vertex power Rx).

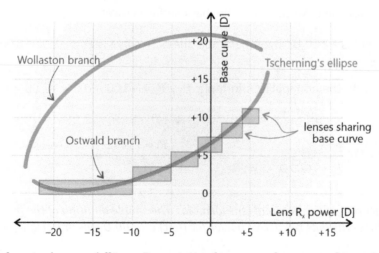

Figure 9-40: Tscherning's curve/ellipse. Prescription lenses can be grouped to a similar base curve.

This ellipse has two branches: The lower branch represents flatter curves, attributed to Frantz Oswalt, while the upper branch represents steeper curves (only used for very high wrap frames), attributed to Wollaston. The exact shape and the position of the Tscherning ellipse on the graph depend on the lens refractive index n and the distance from the lens to the center of rotation (CoR) of the eye (i.e., vertex distance + corneal plane to CoR; recall that the CoR is about 13.5 mm in the eye, see § 2.4.3).[922]

The Tscherning ellipse provides a guide for which to select base curve; effectively, Vogel's rule is a simplified version of the Oswald branch of this ellipse and is <u>most often used for ophthalmic lenses</u>. Note that for very low powers the recommended base curve is +6.00 D.

9.4.4 Lens Thickness

The axial separation between the two refracting surfaces is the **lens thickness** t. Lens thickness is measured at the center of the lens along the optical axis (i.e., the lens is not tilted), regardless of the type of lens—plus or minus. Lens thickness relates to center thickness and is distinguished from the edge thickness et, the separation between the two edge points. In plus lenses, the center thickness t has the greater value, while thickness is minimal at the edges. In minus lenses, the center thickness t has the smallest value, and the edge thickness is the maximum thickness encountered in that type of lenses, as illustrated in Figure 9-41.

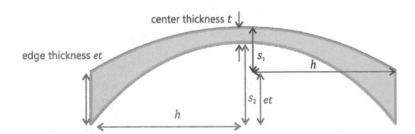

Figure 9-41: Center thickness (t) and edge thickness (et) in a minus meniscus ophthalmic lens.

The radii of curvature and the lens diameter determine the sagitta and center lens thickness. In the minus lenses, the thickness is minimal at the center, and edge thickness is determined by the radii of curvature and lens diameter ($d = 2h$). Center thickness t is dependent on the sagitta (s_1 and s_2) of the two surfaces. Figure 9-41 illustrates the case of a minus meniscus lens, and Figure 9-42 shows the case of a plus meniscus lens. In these meniscus lenses, the center thickness t can be derived from the difference between the two sagittas and the edge thickness:

---

[922] Schwiegerling J. *Field Guide to Visual and Ophthalmic Optics*. SPIE Press, Bellingham, Washington (2004). Retrieved from https://spie.org/publications/fg04_p26-27_spectacles?SSO=1.

Center Lens Thickness: $t = (s_1 - s_2) + \text{edge thickness}$ (9.26)

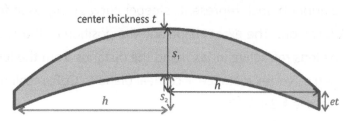

Figure 9-42: Center thickness (t) and edge thickness (et) in a plus meniscus ophthalmic lens.

While a minimum lens thickness is not officially mandated by the United States Food and Drug Administration (US FDA), the American National Standards Institute (ANSI) advocates for a minimum lens thickness of 2.0 mm as a standard. This applies particularly to minus-powered meniscus lenses; a lens thinner than 1.0 mm at its center may have an increased risk of breakage and may result in a potentially severe eye injury.[923]

Note 👓: Eyeglasses and sunglasses are medical devices.[924] As such, they are subject to medical device regulations under the Food, Drug, and Cosmetic Act 201(h). While eyeglass lenses do not have a specified minimum thickness, they do have performance-related standards and must meet the US FDA requirements for impact resistance.[925] Glass lenses, plastic lenses, or laminated glass lenses can be made impact resistant by special treatment, which may be heat or chemical tempering. Devices sold as safety glasses have to meet a specified minimum of no less than 3.0 mm at the thinnest point.

Compliance with the resistance standards can be verified by the impact test described under 21 CFR Part 801.410(d). For glass lenses, testing is verified by a 'referee' or 'drop ball' test, which, in a lab setting, uses a 5/8″ steel ball weighing 0.56 ounce dropped from 50 inches onto the horizontal upper surface of the lens.[926]

While there is no requirement for plastic lenses such as CR-39—the most populous material in use—lens manufacturers must state under what conditions their lenses meet FDA impact standards. Some high-index and polycarbonate lenses are certified to meet impact requirements at 1.5 mm center thickness and, in some cases (very high minus powers), even as thin as 1.0 mm center thickness.

In planoconvex or planoconcave lenses, the sagitta associated with the plano surface is zero. In a <u>biconvex lens</u>, the thickness is the <u>sum of the two sagittas</u> plus the edge thickness [Figure 9-43 (left)]; in a <u>biconcave lens</u>, the center lens thickness is the <u>edge thickness minus the sum of the two sagittas</u> [Figure 9-43 (right)].

---

[923] American National Standards Institute. Recommendations for Prescription Ophthalmic Lenses. ANSI Z80.1, New York (1979).
[924] US FDA information. Retrieved from www.fda.gov/MedicalDevices/ucm150001.htm.
[925] Snesko WM, Stigi JF. Impact resistant lenses: questions and answers. HHS Publication (FDA) 87 4002 (September 1987) (27 pp). Retrieved from www.opticalheritagemuseum.org/Industry/Pdfs/FDAImpactHist/FDA%20Q&A.doc.
[926] Specs retrieved from www.fda.gov/MedicalDevices/DeviceRegulationandGuidance/GuidanceDocuments/ucm150003.htm.

Figure 9-43: Lens thickness and sagitta in (left) a biconvex lens and (right) a biconcave lens.

Example ☞: Mᴵˡᵉ Gillenormand works on fabricating an $F = +10.00$ D symmetric, 1-inch diameter, biconvex glass lens using low-index glass ($n = 1.4$). What would be the center thickness (zero edge thickness)?

In this thin lens, each surface has a refractive power of +5.00 D. The fact that this surface power is $F = +5.00$ D indicates that the radii of curvature must be 8 cm each. To calculate this, we use Eq. (2.1):

$$F_{surface,\ lens\ A} = \frac{n_{lens} - n_{air}}{r\ (m)} \implies +5.0\ D = \frac{1.4 - 1.0}{r\ (m)} \implies r\ (m) = \frac{1.4 - 1.0}{+5.0\ D} = 0.08\ m = 8\ cm$$

The lens semi-diameter is $h = 1.27$ cm. The approximate sagitta formula (9.22) gives $s = 0.1$ cm or 1 mm. This sagitta is identical for both surfaces, i.e., $s_1 = s_2 = 1$ mm.

In this symmetric biconvex, zero edge lens, the thickness is the sum of the two sagittas: $t = s_1 + s_2 = 2$ mm.

Example ☞: The next lens fabricated by Mᴵˡᵉ Gillenormand has the same power and glass type as the first but with a 2-inch diameter (5.08 cm). What is the center thickness of this lens (zero edge thickness)?

Everything else being equal, the only difference is that the semi-diameter h now equals 2.54 cm. The new sagitta would be $s_1 = s_2 = 0.41$ cm = 4.1 mm (exact formula) or 4 mm (approximate). The lens thickness in this symmetric, biconvex, zero-edge-thickness lens is $t = s_1 + s_2 = 8.2$ mm.

Example ☞: Monsieur Gillenormand works to fabricate a symmetric biconcave 2-inch-diameter $F = -10.00$ D lens ($n = 1.4$). What should be the minimum edge thickness if the center thickness is $t = 2$ mm?

Radii of curvature are 8 cm, and lens semi-diameter is $h = 2.54$ cm. For each surface, the sagittas are $s_1 = s_2 = 0.41$ cm = 4.1 mm (exact formula) or 4 mm (approximate formula).

The edge thickness is the sum of the two sagittas plus the center thickness. M. Gillenormand chooses $t = 2$ mm for the center thickness; the edge thickness should be 4.1 mm + 2 mm + 4.1 mm = 10.2 mm.

9.5 CYLINDER AND TORIC LENS

9.5.1 The Cylinder Lens

A cylindrical or cylinder lens has power only along one meridian, called the **refractive** or **power meridian**. Perpendicular to this is the **cylinder axis** (×), along which the optical power is zero.

A plane that includes the refractive (power) meridian focuses at the familiar cross-section of a focal point [blue dot in Figure 9-44 (left)], as in a spherical lens. A plane that includes the cylinder axis, when at the same focus point, produces a rectangular focal line [shown as the orange line in Figure 9-44 (right)]. In other words, this beam does not come to focus.

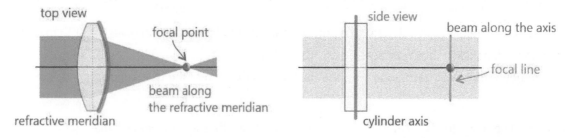

Figure 9-44: (left) View along the refractive meridian. (right) View along the axis.

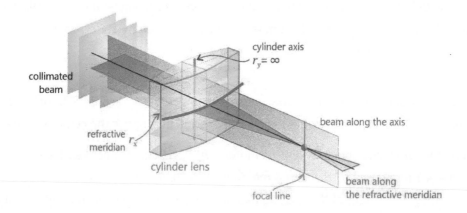

Figure 9-45: A plus cylinder lens focuses a collimated beam to a focal line in front of the lens.

Therefore, when a collimated beam is focused by a cylinder lens (Figure 9-45), there is no focal point, as in a spherical lens. Instead, there is a succession of points that line up along a line parallel to the cylinder axis and produce the 'focal line,' which is also called the stigmatic line. A minus cylinder lens [Figure 9-46 (left)] diverges a collimated beam that appears to be originating from a virtual focal line situated before the lens. A plus cylinder lens converges a collimated beam on this focal line, which is situated in front of the lens [Figure 9-46 (right)].

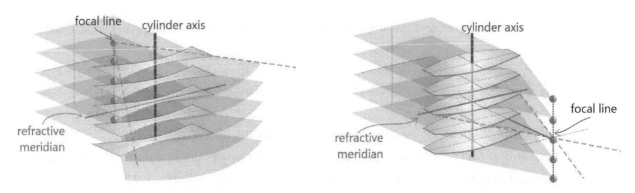

Figure 9-46: Focusing in (left) a minus cylinder lens and (right) a plus cylinder lens. The cylinder axis is parallel to the meridian with zero optical power. The largest optical power lies perpendicular to the meridian with zero optical power, which means that it is parallel to the refractive meridian.

The cylinder is denoted by its dioptric power and its axis (×, for example ×090). Both lenses shown in Figure 9-46 are ×090. The refractive power of a cylinder lens is always along the refractive (power) meridian. Assuming a 1.00 D in each lens, we can denote the plus cylinder as +1.00×090 with refractive power as +1.00 @ 180°, and the minus cylinder as −1.00×090 with refractive power as −1.00 @ 180°. Frequently used in keratometry, @ is used to denote the power and/or the meridian, and can be read as 'at' or 'along.'

Example ☞: Gribier digs a cylinder lens with a prescription form +3.00×045. What are the principal powers of this lens?
This cylinder lens is plano 0.00 @ 45° and has power +3.00 @ 135°. If a collimated light reaches this lens, a focal line is formed at 45°, perpendicular to the meridian power, at 1/(+3.00 D) = 33.3 cm.

The distribution of power in a cylinder lens varies from maximum (along the power meridian) to zero (along the axis angle α). The **cylinder effect**, which is defined as the projection of cylinder power, is maximum at right angles from the axis $(\vartheta - \alpha) = 90°$. By rule, at the axis the cylinder power is 0%; at right angles (90°) from the axis, 100% of the cylinder power is in effect. There is a very basic formula to calculate the distribution of power in meridians other than the two principals: The cylinder power is the squared sine ($\sin^2$) of the <u>relative angle</u> $(\vartheta - \alpha)$ from the axis:

Cylinder Power at Angle ϑ (α = axis): $\qquad\qquad F_{c\vartheta} = F_c \cdot \sin^2(\vartheta - \alpha),$ $\qquad\qquad$ (9.27) where F_c is the cylinder power, and α is the axis meridian. Thus, $(\vartheta - \alpha)$ is the angle away from the axis.

Note ◆: This meridional power formula is described in the literature as curvital power,[927] as opposed to the power perpendicular to the meridian, which is referred to as torsional power.[928]

For 0°, sin0° = 0 and for 90°, sin90° = 1. Thus, the on-axis ($\vartheta = \alpha$, $\vartheta - \alpha = 0°$) cylinder power is zero, and at right angles ($\vartheta - \alpha = 90°$), the cylinder power is maximum. Other angles that are relatively easy to remember include 30° (sin30° = ½), 45° (sin45° = √2/2), and 60° (sin60° = √3/2). Hence, the percentage of cylinder power that is in effect 30° from the axis is sin²30° = (½)² = ¼ = 25%; 45° from the axis, this value is sin²45° = (√2/2)² = ½ = 50%, and 60° from the axis, it is sin²60° = (√3/2)² = ¾ = 75%.

Example ☞: Gribier digs another cylinder lens, –6.00×090. What is its power at the 0° and at the 45° meridians of this lens?

This cylinder has axis ×090; the power along the 90° meridian is therefore zero. The refractive meridian is along the 180° meridian; the power along the 180° (0°) meridian is –6.00 D.

At 45° away from the axis, the power is proportional to (sin45°)² = (√2/2)² = ½, or 50%.

So, at 45°, $F_{c45} = F_c \cdot \sin^2(\vartheta - \alpha) = -6.00 \cdot ½ = -3.00$ D of the cylinder power is in effect.

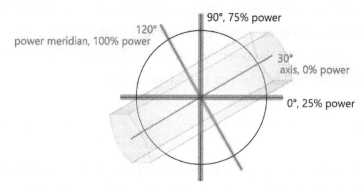

Figure 9-47: Distribution of power in a cylinder lens whose axis is ×030. Along the 90° meridian (60° from the axis), cylinder power is 75%. Along the 0° meridian (30° from the axis), cylinder power in effect is 25%.

9.5.2 The Toric Lens

The **toric lens** is a combined form of spherical and cylinder lens. Along its axis, the lens power equals the spherical power alone, while along the refractive meridian, the power equals the algebraic sum of the spherical and the cylindrical power. In Figure 9-48, the component corresponding to the cylindrical power has axis ×090, which is also the toric lens axis.

---

[927] Harris F. Dioptric power: its nature and its representation in three- and four-dimensional space. Optom Vis Sci.1997; 74(6):349-66.
[928] Keating MP. Dioptric power in an off-axis meridian: the torsional component. Am J Optom Physiol Opt. 1986; 63(10):830-8.

Toric lenses are meniscus, like most lenses in spectacle vision correction. A toric lens needs just one of the two surfaces to carry toric features, while the other can simply be spherical. Thus, the cylinder power may be ground on the front or the back surface of the lens.

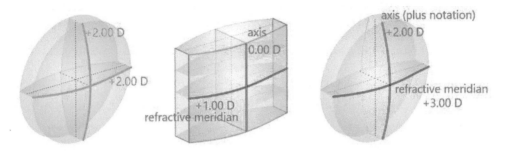

Figure 9-48: (left) A spherical lens, (center) a cylindrical lens, and (right) a toric lens. The toric lens may be considered as a superposition of a +2.00 spherical and a +1.00×090 cylinder lens. The toric lens axis is parallel to the cylinder axis, and the refractive meridian is parallel to the cylinder refractive meridian.

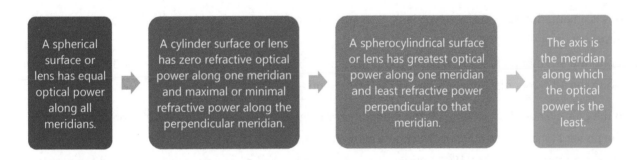

Based on the surface curvature and toricity, toric lenses are distinguished by type: the plus type and the minus type. The plus toric and the minus toric monikers refer to the anterior or posterior surface of the lens being toric. In the plus type, the front (anterior) surface is toric and the back (posterior) surface is spherical. In the minus type, the front (anterior) surface is spherical and the back (posterior) surface is ground to a toric shape.

This 'plus' and minus' distinction dates back to the historical origins of toric lens fabrication, rather than referring to their power or corrective prescription (Rx) sign. An astigmatic Rx can be implemented on either a plus or minus toric lens, regardless of the sphere or cylinder power.

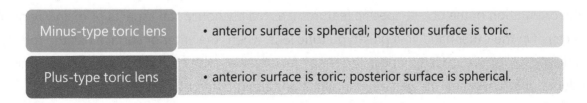

Note 📋 : The historic origin of the plus or minus cylinder monikers dates back to the time when lenses were actually fabricated and ground that way.

To produce a Rx −6.00 −2.00×090 (plus Rx −8.00 +2.00×180), spectacle makers in the Imperial UK could manufacture both forms. To produce the minus form, a −2.00 cylinder lens would be attached, with optically clear glue, to the back surface of a −6.00 D spherical lens. This could result, for example, in a toric lens with a +3.00 D base curve and with a −6.00 D @ 90° / −8.00 D @ 180° posterior surface.

To produce the plus form, a +2.00 cylinder lens would be attached to the front surface of a −8.00 D spherical lens. This could result, for example, in a +5.00 D @ 90° / +3.00 D @ 180° anterior surface and a −11.00 D posterior surface toric lens.

Example ☞: Gribier has a lens with front surface power +6.00 D @ 90° / +7.00 D @ 180° and a spherical back power of −5.00 D. Describe the lens shape and its power distribution. What is the prescription form?

This is an anterior-toric-surface-type lens: The anterior (front) surface is toric, while the posterior (back) is spherical.
Along the 90° meridian, the lens has +6.00 D front and −5.00 D back surface power = +1.00 D total.
Along the 180° meridian, the lens has +7.00 D front and −5.00 D back surface power = +2.00 D total.

In the plus cylinder form, the axis is the meridian of the lesser power, which is the 90° meridian, +1.00 D. The power along this meridian is the sphere element (+1.00 D).
At right angles, which is the 180° meridian, the cylinder has 100% of its power (+1.00 D), and the power along this meridian is +1.00 D. In the plus prescription form, this lens is written as +1.00 +1.00×090.

Today, the vast majority of ophthalmic toric lenses are the minus type, with a posterior toric surface. The major advantage of the posterior-toric-surface-type lenses pertains to the retinal image magnification or minification (§ 9.3.1).

The shape factor is one aspect that determines whether an image is magnified or minified by a thick spectacle lens, where the main parameters leading to an increased retinal image are lens thickness and base curve. In a minus-type toric lens, where the posterior surface bears the toric grinding and the anterior surface is spherical, the shape factor is constant along all meridians, meaning that the lens produces the same retinal image magnification regardless of the orientation of the object-specific features (i.e., mainly horizontal aspects or mainly vertical aspects). On the other hand, in a plus-type toric lens, where the anterior surface has the toricity and the posterior surface is spherical, the shape factor varies with each different meridian; this produces different retinal image size magnifications along different orientations of object-specific features—an undesirable effect.

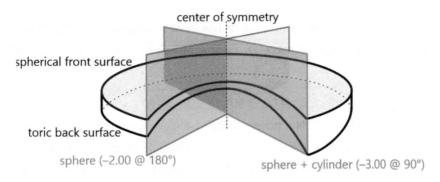

center of symmetry

spherical front surface

toric back surface

sphere (−2.00 @ 180°)

sphere + cylinder (−3.00 @ 90°)

Figure 9-49: Cross-section of a posterior toric lens with prescription −2.00 −1.00×180. The largest peripheral thickness is along the plane that includes the sphere and the cylinder.

In toric lenses, we need to be careful with the use of the term **base curve**. In minus toric lenses, the front surface is spherical, and just like in spherical lenses, the anterior power is still called the base curve. The back surface has two curves called **tool curves**; the one corresponding to the lesser power is the toric base curve, while the one corresponding to the greater power is the cross curve. In plus toric lenses, there are two curves on the front surface. The flatter of the two is designated as the base curve, while the steeper is designated as the cross curve. The back surface has one curve, known as the sphere curve.

Example ☞: Father Mestienne holds a lens with front surface power (base curve) +6.00 D. The lens back surface measures −8.00 D @ 90° and −6.00 D @ 180°. Describe the lens shape and its power distribution as the lens cross and the Rx.

We may help Father Mestienne by drawing the optical lens cross for each surface and then adding front and back powers along each principal meridian.

The lens cross for the anterior surface is +6.00 @ 90° / +6.00 @ 180°, while the lens cross for the posterior surface is −8.00 @ 90° / −6.00 @ 180°. Net power @ 90° is −2.00 D, and net power @ 180° is 0.00 D. The optical lens cross of the lens is −2.00 @ 90° / 0.00 @ 180°. The Rx form is (plano) −2.00×180; the lens cross is represented in Figure 9-50 (left).

This is a minus-toric-type lens because the front surface is spherical, while the back surface is toric.

−2.00

0.00

−2.00×180

0.00

+1.00

+1.00×090

Figure 9-50: Lens cross representation for cylinder lenses: (left) −2.00×180 and (right) +1.00×090.

Example ☞: The next lens in Père Mestienne's hands has front surface power +4.00 D @ 90° / +5.00 D @ 180° and a sphere curve (back power) of −4.00 D. Describe the lens shape and its power distribution. What is the lens cross and the Rx?

The lens cross for the anterior surface is +4.00 @ 90° / +5.00 @ 180°, while the lens cross for the posterior surface is −4.00 @ 90° / −4.00 @ 180°. Net power @ 90° is zero, and net power @ 180° is +1.00 D. The optical lens cross of the lens is 0.00 @ 90° / +1.00 @ 180°. The lens cross is represented in Figure 9-50 (right); the prescription form is (plano) +1.00×090. This is a plus toric lens because the toric surface is the anterior one, while the back (posterior surface) is spherical.

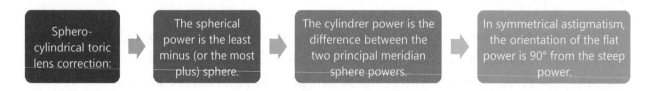

Example ☞: Father Lenoir would like to fabricate a toric lens for this Rx: +4.50 −1.00×180. What should be the base curve?

The spherical equivalent is +4.50 +½·(−1.00) = +4.50+(−0.50) = +4.00 D.
We use Vogel's rule: The spherical equivalent is +4.00 and base curve is F_1 = +4.00+6.00 = +10.00 D.
A minus toric lens can be fabricated to this Rx with an anterior spherical surface (base curve) +10.0D and a toric posterior surface −6.50 @ 90° / −5.50 @ 180°. This results in a lens cross +3.50 @ 90° / +4.50 @ 180°.

Example ☞: P. Lenoir is now studying a toric lens with front surface power (base curve) +6.00 D and back surface powers of −7.00 D @ 180° and −9.00 D @ 90°. Describe the lens shape, the power distribution (as a thin lens), and the lens prescription.

This is a posterior toric (minus) lens: The cylinder is on the back surface.
Along the 180° meridian, the lens has +6.00 D base curve and −7.00 D back surface power = −1.00 D total.
Along the 90° meridian, the lens has +6.00 D base curve and −9.00 D back surface power = −3.00 D total.
Thus, the lens cross is −3.00 @ 90° / −1.00 @ 180°. The Rx form is −1.00 −2.00×180.

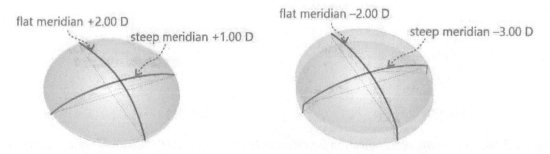

Figure 9-51: Toric lenses can be either converging (plus lenses) or diverging (minus lenses).

Example ☞: P. Lenoir will grind this lens prescription +3.00 −2.00×180 in a minus-type toric lens. If the base curve is +6.00 D, what will be the power distribution on the front (anterior) and back lens surfaces?

At the 180° meridian, sphere power is +3.00 D. At right angles (the 90° meridian) power is +3.00 + (−2.00) = +1.00 D. Thus, the net lens cross is +3.00 @ 180° / +1.00 @ 90°. In this minus-type, front-surface-toric lens, the base curve is +6.00 D. The anterior lens cross is +6.00 @ 180° / +6.00 @ 90°. To produce the net lens cross, along the 180° meridian, the back surface lens cross needs to be −3.00 @ 180° / −5.00 @ 90°.

Example ☞: Boulatruelle clocks a lens with an anterior surface power +6.00 D and posterior surface powers −8.00 @ 90° and −7.00 @ 180°. What type of lens is it, and what is its prescription form?

This is a posterior-surface, minus-type toric lens. The anterior surface lens cross is +6.00 @ 90° / +6.00 @ 180°. The posterior surface lens cross is −8.00 @ 90° / −7.00 @ 180°. The net lens cross is −2.00 @ 90° / −1.00 @ 180°. Its prescription form is −1.00 −1.00×180.

Example ☞: Sœur Simplicity plans to produce a toric lens for this Rx +1.00 +2.00×090 using +6.00 D along the 90° anterior meridian. That does not seem simple! Please help Sr. Simplicity design this lens.

The lens cross is +1.00 @ 90° / +3.00 @ 180°. This will be a plus, anterior-surface toric lens. Regarding the toric curvatures, +6.00 D is along the 90° meridian and +8.00 D is along the 180° meridian. Hence, the anterior lens cross is +6.00 @ 90° / +8.00 @ 180°. The posterior surface has one sphere curve that resembles the lens cross: −5.00 @ 90° / −5.00 @ 180°.

Cylinder and toric lenses have all of the optical characteristics of an astigmatic lens. In other words, they produce astigmatism in order to ...correct astigmatism. They also have **Sturm's interval**, which is determined by the amount of cylinder. Just as in regular astigmatism, there is the dioptric interval and the linear interval. The dioptric interval is the difference in power between the two meridians, which is the cylinder power. The linear expanse of Sturm's interval is the difference between the axial positions of the two focal lines.

Example ☞: Another problem for Sr. Simplicity: What is Sturm's interval for a +4.00 −2.00×180 lens?

First, we convert to lens cross: +2.00 @ 90° / +4.00 @ 180°. The dioptric Sturm interval is simply the difference between these two powers, which is 2.00 D. The linear expanse of Sturm's interval is the difference between the two focal lines/points. The +4.00 @ 180° power forms a vertical line at +0.25 m, and the +2.00 @ 90° power forms a horizontal line at +0.50 m. The linear Sturm interval is the span between the two lines, which is 0.25 m (= 0.50 m − 0.25 m).

Note ⚠ : The linear Sturm interval in this example (0.25 m) is not the reciprocal of the dioptric Sturm interval (2.00 D)—and never is, in principle. We should not convert the dioptric Sturm interval to a linear Sturm interval by simply taking the reciprocal value!

9.5.3 Toric Formulas

The **toric formula** is a form of a **fraction** that communicates the powers of the lens to be ground. The numerator is the front curve(s) and the denominator is the back curve(s) of the lens. To express this fraction, the astigmatic prescription is transposed (if necessary) in order to have the same sign (minus or plus form) as the type of toric lens to be used. A minus toric lens is expressed in the minus Rx and a plus toric lens is expressed in the plus Rx.

In the minus, posterior toric form, the front curve is a single, spherical surface power F_1 and the denominator is the lens cross description of the two tool curves (F_{MIN} and F_{MAX}). Then, the numerator is the selected base curve F_1 (anterior power). The denominator describes the two powers, called tool curves, F_{MIN} and F_{MAX} as follows:

i. F_{MIN} is obtained by subtracting the base curve from the spherical component F_s in the astigmatic Rx prescription: $F_{MIN} = F_s - F_1$.

ii. Add to that value the cylinder power to obtain $F_{MAX} = F_{MIN} + F_c$.

Note 🔍 : The base curve in toric lenses may have a different use in spherical (i.e., non-toric) lenses. In minus-type toric lenses, the base curve is still the front surface curvature F_1. Some textbooks use the back 'base curve' to describe the weaker tool curve F_{MIN}, which is along the refractive meridian.

Note 💡 : The toric formula fraction in the far-less-used plus (anterior surface) toric lens has the two tool curves in the numerator and the single, spherical power of the posterior surface in the denominator.

Example ☞: Soeur Simplicity is looking for the toric formula for astigmatic Rx prescription +2.00 +1.00×090. She plans to grind a posterior toric lens with a base curve (BC) of +9.00 D.

This is a posterior-toric-surface-type lens—the cylinder is on the back surface.

(a): Because the Rx is in the plus form, we rewrite it in the minus form, becoming +3.00 −1.00×180.

(b): The numerator is the selected base curve of F_1 = +9.00 D.

(c): The back base curve is $F_{MIN} = F_s - F_1 = (+3.00) - (+9.00) = -6.00$ D along the 180° meridian. The tool cross curve is $F_{MAX} = F_{MIN} + F_c = (-6.00) + (-1.00) = -7.00$ D along the 90° meridian.

Toric formula fraction:

$$\dfrac{\underset{\text{Base Curve}}{+9.00\ D}}{\underset{\text{Back Surface Toric Curvatures}}{-6.00\ /\ -7.00}}$$

(9.28)

Example ☞: Boulatruelle is seeking the Rx form for a lens with front surface power +6.00 D @ 90° / +7.00 D @ 180° and spherical back power –5.00 D.

This is an anterior-toric-surface-type lens—the cylinder is on the <u>front surface</u>. To produce the toric formula, the prescription should be expressed in the plus cylinder form.
At the 90° meridian, the lens has +6.00 front surface power and –5.00 back surface power = +1.00 total.
At the 180° meridian, the lens has +7.00 front surface power and –5.00 back surface power = +2.00 total.
In the lens cross representation, along the 90° meridian, the power is +1.00 D. At right angles, which is the 180° meridian, the power is +2.00 D. The plus prescription form is +1.00 +1.00×090.

Practice examples with answers ⚒ Toric Formulas:

Rx: +2.50 –0.50×010 with +6.00 base curve. Minus toric lens formula: +6.00 / –3.50 (@ 10°) –4.00 (@ 10°).
Rx: –2.00 +3.00×090 with +6.00 base curve. Minus toric lens formula: +6.00 / –8.00 (@ 90°) –5.00 (@ 180°).
Rx: +2.00 –1.00×170 with +8.00 base curve. Minus toric lens formula: +8.00 / –6.00 (@ 170°) –7.00 (@ 80°).

9.5.4 Toric Power Vector Representation

Just like a cylinder lens, the distribution of power in a toric lens varies from maximum (along the power meridian) to minimum (along the axis). In a fashion similar to relationship (9.27), the astigmatic power distribution can be represented by a harmonic function:

Toric Power at angle ϑ: $\qquad\qquad F_{\text{toric lens}} = F_s + F_c \cdot \sin^2(\vartheta - \alpha)$ (9.29)

where F_s is the sphere power, F_c is the cylinder power, α is the axis, and $\vartheta - \alpha$ is the angle <u>relative</u> to the axis.

Example ☞: Monsieur Leblanc is studying a lens for this Rx: –2.00 +4.00×045. What is its power along the 45°, 90°, and 135° meridians?

Cylinder power: At the 45° meridian (the cylinder axis), cylinder power in effect is 0% of +4.00 D = 0.00 D.
At the 90° meridian (45° relative to the axis), cylinder power in effect is 50% of +4.00 D = +2.00 D.
At the 135° meridian (90° relative to the axis), cylinder power in effect is 100% of +4.00 D = +4.00 D.

The spherical lens has the same power for any meridian = –2.00 D. We now add the powers:
At the 45° meridian, the lens has 0.00 D cylinder power and –2.00 D sphere power; total power is –2.00 D.

At the 90° meridian, the lens has +2.00 D cylinder power and –2.00 D sphere power; total power is 0.00 D. At the 135° meridian, the lens has +4.00 D cylinder power and –2.00 D sphere power; total power is +2.00 D.

With some help from trigonometry, relationship (9.29) is re-written as

$$F_{toric} = F_s + F_c \left[\frac{1}{2} - \frac{1}{2}\cos 2(\vartheta - \alpha) \right] = \underbrace{F_s + \frac{F_c}{2}}_{\text{spherical equivalent}} \underbrace{- \frac{F_c}{2}\cos(2\vartheta - 2\alpha)}_{\text{pure cylinder phasor power}} =$$

$$= \underbrace{F_s + \frac{F_c}{2}}_{\text{spherical equivalent}} \underbrace{- \frac{F_c}{2}\left[\cos 2\vartheta \cdot \cos 2\alpha\right]}_{\text{Stokes component } J_0} \underbrace{- \frac{F_c}{2}\left[\sin 2\vartheta \cdot \sin 2\alpha\right]}_{\text{Stokes component } J_{45}}$$

(9.30)

We recognize two parts. The first part is the familiar **spherical equivalent**[929] (SE, § 8.2.2), which represents a fixed spherical component per relationship (8.1). The second part consists of harmonic functions similar to the cylinder function introduced in relationship (9.27). This part describes the pure cylinder whose magnitude is F_c and whose axis is along the meridian oriented at angle α. It is represented as phasors of amplitude $F_c/2$ and harmonic function with phase 2α. This is drawn as a combination of two orthogonal power vector components[930, 931] (Figure 9-52):

J power vectors: Horizontal: $J_0 = -\frac{1}{2}F_c \cos 2\alpha$ Vertical: $J_{45} = -\frac{1}{2}F_c \sin 2\alpha$ (9.31)

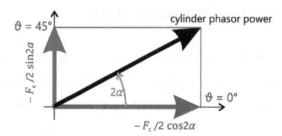

Figure 9-52: Phasor diagram for astigmatic decomposition. The magnitude of the phasor vector is ½F_c.

With this approach, astigmatic power is specified via three **power vectors**: the spherical equivalent, vector J_0, and vector J_{45}. Vector J_0 corresponds to a Jackson cross cylinder with its axis at 180°/90°, and vector J_{45} corresponds to a Jackson cross cylinder with its axis at 45°/135°.[927] In spectacular similarity to the description originally provided by George Gabriel Stokes [Eq. (8.2)], astigmatism can be described with power vectors as

---

[929] Most literature that presents the power vectors adopts the letter M to denote the spherical equivalent. On the other hand, most of the optometric applications use the letters SE to denote spherical equivalent. We will avoid the use of the letter M here.

[930] Deal FC Jr, Toop J. Recommended coordinate systems for thin spherocylindrical lenses. Optom Vis Sci. 1993; 70(5):409-13.

[931] Thibos LN, Wheeler W, Horner D. Power vectors: an application of Fourier analysis to the description and statistical analysis of refractive error. Optom Vis Sci. 1997; 74(6):367-75.

Spherocylindrical error = Spherical equivalent (SE) + Stokes lens components ($J_0 + J_{45}$):

$$(F_s + \tfrac{1}{2} F_c) + (-\tfrac{1}{2} F_c \cos 2\alpha) \times \cos 2\vartheta + (-\tfrac{1}{2} F_c \sin 2\alpha) \times \sin 2\vartheta \qquad (9.32)$$

The **blur strength** B is the cartesian diagonal (norm modulus) of the three power vectors:[932]

Blur Strength (using J power vectors): $\qquad B = \sqrt{(SE)^2 + J_0^{\,2} + J_{45}^{\,2}} \qquad (9.33)$

We can <u>convert back</u> from the power vectors to the (negative form of) the spherocylindrical Rx:

Sphere $F_s = SE + \sqrt{J_0^{\,2} + J_{45}^{\,2}}$ $\quad$ Cylinder $F_c = -2\sqrt{J_0^{\,2} + J_{45}^{\,2}}$ $\quad$ Axis $\alpha = \dfrac{1}{2} \times \tan^{-1}\left(\dfrac{J_{45}}{J_0}\right)$ $\quad (9.34)$

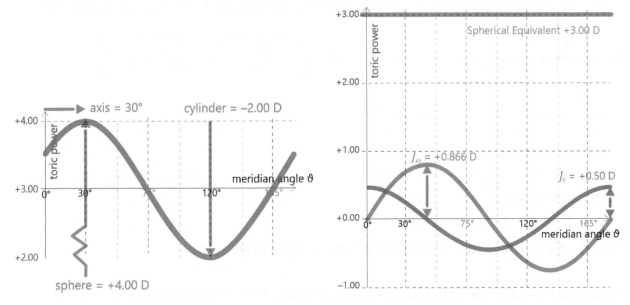

Figure 9-53: (left): Meridional power variation for the +4.00 –2.00×030 toric lens according to formula (9.29): $F_{toric\,lens} = F_s + F_c \cdot \sin^2(\vartheta - \alpha)$. (right): Power vectors according to formula (9.32) for the same toric power as displayed is on the left. The power of the spherocylindrical lens is the sum of the spherical equivalent (=+3.00 D), a cos(2ϑ) function scaled by J_0 (=+0.50 D), and a sin(2ϑ) function scaled by J_{45} (=+0.866 D).

Example ☞: Urbain Fabre calculates the power vectors for the astigmatic prescription +4.00 –2.00×030:

Spherical equivalent: $SE = F_s + \tfrac{1}{2} \cdot F_c = +4.00 + \tfrac{1}{2} \cdot (-2.00) = +3.00$ D.

Stokes lens components: $J_0 = -\tfrac{1}{2} \cdot F_c \cos 2\alpha = -\tfrac{1}{2} \cdot (-2.00) \cdot \cos 2\alpha = +1.0 \cdot \cos 60° = +0.50$ D.

$J_{45} = -F_c/2 \, \sin 2\alpha = -\tfrac{1}{2} \cdot (-2.00) \cdot \sin 2\alpha = +1.0 \cdot \sin 60° = +0.866$ D.

---

[932] Thibos LN, Wheeler W, Horner D. A vector method for the analysis of astigmatic refractive errors. In: Vision Science and its Applications, Vol 2. 1994 Technical Digest Series. Washington, DC: Optical Society of America; 1994, 14-17.

Note 💡 : Because the set of formulas in Eq. (9.34) defaults to the minus cylinder prescription form, if the plus form is desired, the minus form can be transposed back using the standard power transposition technique (§ 8.2.1).

Example ☞:   The mayor of Montreuil-sur-Mer wants to calculate the spherocylindrical Rx if SE $= +3.00$ D, $J_0 = +0.50$ D, and $J_{45} = +0.866$ D. Let us help him.

We use formulas (9.34) as follows:
Sphere power $F_s = +3.00 + \sqrt{(0.5^2 + 0.866^2)} = +3.00 + 1.00 = +4.00$ D.
Cylinder power $F_c = -2\sqrt{(0.5^2 + 0.866^2)} = -2.00$ D.
Axis $a = \frac{1}{2} \cdot \tan^{-1}(0.866/0.5) = \frac{1}{2} \cdot \tan^{-1}(\sqrt{3}) = \frac{1}{2} \cdot 60° = 30°$.
The spherocylindrical prescription is $+4.00\ -2.00 \times 030$ (note that it is the reverse of the example above).

Again, the blur strength B can be calculated from the spherocylindrical prescription components:

Blur Strength (using spherocylindrical Rx): $$B = \sqrt{\frac{F_s^2 + (F_s + F_c)^2}{2}} = \sqrt{F_s^2 + F_s F_c + \frac{F_c^2}{2}} \qquad (9.35)$$

Note 🔍 : The blur strength is a very accurate metric (pertaining to the retinal image) for describing the blur projected onto the retina and provides a better predictor of visual acuity than the spherical equivalent.[874]

Example ☞:   The blur strength B in the mayor's lens is 3.16 D. The result is the same using either relationship (9.33) or relationship (9.35).

9.5.5 Combination of Oblique Cross Cylinders

When the axes of two prescriptions are the same or are 90° from each other, obtaining the power is simple: We add the cylinders together. Often, however, the axes differ, for example, when one component has its axis at 15° and the other component has its axis at 25°. These are called **obliquely crossed cylinders**. Their powers <u>cannot</u> be directly added or subtracted. Clinically, this occurs when the axes of anterior and posterior corneal astigmatism do not line up, or when a toric lens is not oriented properly with respect to the subject's astigmatic axis.

One might be tempted to think that cylinders can be treated as vectors that we can simply add together. However, unless the cylinders share the same axis, this is not the case, particularly if the 180° axis, or one near it, is involved. Here is a simple, but intriguing case: Take a -1.00×180 cylinder and a -1.00×001 cylinder. Vector analysis gives zero, but we know this is not the case! Clinically, the sum should be -2.00×180 or -2.00×001. (Or, more realistically, what would be the simple vector sum of -1.00×178 and -1.00×003?) This example showcases that we cannot combine cylinders by treating them as vectors whose phasor is the axis. The solution uses analysis into power vectors. The steps are:

1. The cylinder is decomposed into SE and J power vectors, per relationship (9.31).
2. The SE and J power vectors are summed individually.
3. The net spherocylindrical (Rx) representation is recomposed per relationship (9.34).

This technique has important applications in wavefront analysis of the refractive error: The three second-order Zernike terms correspond to the three power vectors, J_{45}, SE, and J_0.[933, 934] In addition, the technique facilitates statistical analysis of refractive errors, and it can be particularly useful when there is need to combine cylinder powers whose axes are not parallel.[935]

Example ☞: Monsieur Leblanc wants to add two cross cylinders: plano −1.00×180 and plano −1.00×090. Let us guide him in doing it correctly.

Both prescriptions are in the negative form. We now convert the individual Rx expressions into power vectors:
plano −1.00×180 converts to $SE_1 = -0.50$, $J_{0\,1} = 0.50$ D, $J_{45\,1} = 0.00$ D
plano −1.00×090 converts to $SE_2 = -0.50$, $J_{0\,2} = -0.50$ D, $J_{45\,2} = 0.00$ D
Next, the summation: $SE = -1.00$, $J_0 = 0.00$ D, and $J_{45} = 0.00$ D. The Rx form is a simple sphere −1.00 D.

Note ◎: This case is trivial and does not need power vectors. We can simply transpose one cross cylinder or the other to the same axis: plano −1.00×180 and −1.00 +1.00×180. Now we add sphere and cylinder powers to produce the simple sphere power −1.00 D since the cylinders are along the same axis and their magnitudes cancel out.
Likewise, if +1.00 −2.00×180 is combined with −1.00 +1.00×180, their sum is plano −1.00×180.

Example ☞: Champmathieu is attempting to add two cross cylinders: plano −2.00×180 and plano −2.00×000 (please accept this slight rule violation for an axis designated as 000).

Both prescriptions are in the negative form. We now convert the individual Rx expressions into power vectors:
plano −2.00×180 converts to $SE_1 = -1.00$, $J_{0\,1} = 1.00$ D, $J_{45\,1} = 0.00$ D
plano −2.00×0 converts to $SE_2 = -1.00$, $J_{0\,2} = 1.00$ D, $J_{45\,2} = 0.00$ D
Next, the summation: $SE = -2.00$, $J_0 = 2.00$ D, $J_{45} = 0.00$ D. The Rx is plano −4.00×180.

Example ☞: Champmathieu is now adding these two JCC lenses: +0.50 −1.00×180 and flipped +0.50 −1.00×090. Let us follow the process to see if he's doing it right.

---

[933] Thibos LN, Horner D. Power vector analysis of the optical outcome of refractive surgery. J Cataract Refract Surg. 2001; 27(1):80-5.
[934] *Ocular Imaging* § 5.6.2 Low Order Aberrations & Vision.
[935] Remón L, Benlloch J, Furlan WD. Corneal and refractive astigmatism in adults: a power vectors analysis. Optom Vis Sci. 2009; 86:1182-6.

The power vectors are: SE 0.00, J_0 = 0.50 D, J_{45} = 0.00 D, and SE 0.00, J_0 = –0.50 D, and J_{45} = 0.00 D. Naturally, this leads to a plano combination—no surprise here, right? We could reach this result by simply expressing the flipped spherocylindrical form to minus: –0.50 +1.00×180, which gives the net plano result.

Example ☞: What is the net spherocylindrical prescription that derives from anterior corneal astigmatism –2.75 –1.00×010 combined with posterior corneal astigmatism –0.75 +0.50×022?

We use the obliquely crossed cylinders technique. First, we convert to power vectors:
–2.75 –1.00×010 converts to SE = –3.25, J_0 = 0.47 D, and J_{45} = 0.17 D.
–0.75 +0.50×022 converts to SE = –0.50, J_0 = –0.18 D, and J_{45} = –0.17 D.
The sum of the above yields the net power vectors: SE = –3.75 D, J_0 = 0.29 D, and J_{45} = 0.00 D.
Net spherocylindrical prescription (approximated to the nearest 0.25 D): –3.50 –0.50×180.

Note 🖥: The mean spherical equivalent of the net prescription (–3.75 D) is the sum of the individual spherical equivalents (–3.25 and –0.50 D). This is a general rule but applies only to the spherical equivalent. The individual sphere, cylinder, and axis values cannot be simply added!

Example ☞: Fauchelevent is adding these two obliquely crossed cylinders: +1.00 –1.00×180 and –1.00 +1.00×135. What is the resultant prescription form?

Fauchelevent is tempted to simply add sphere and cylinder values for a net zero result. But this does not happen (and rightly so!). He instead implements the obliquely crossed-cylinder technique.

+1.00 –1.00×180 converts to SE = +0.50, J_0 = 0.50, J_{45} = 0.00.
–1.00 +1.00×135 converts to SE = –0.50, J_0 = 0.00 J_{45} = 0.50.
The sum of the above yields the net power vectors: SE 0.00, J_0 = 0.50 D, and J_{45} = 0.50 D.

Net spherocylindrical prescription (approximated to the nearest 0.25 D): 0.75 –1.50×22.5. Not zero! And we ended up with a greater cylinder than what we started with.

Here is an important final correction regarding the axis: The axis formula in Eq. (9.34) may lead to unpredicted results. Specifically,

- If J_{45} =0, the axis is zero if J_0 > 0 and can be reported as α = 180 or becomes α = 90 if J_0 < 0.
- If J_0 =0, the axis returns an error result. so it is suggested to enter a near-zero J_0 value, or to follow the rubric stating that if J_{45} <0, α = 135, and if J_{45} > 0, α = 45.

Depending on the sign of J_0 and J_{45}, a negative value of axis is produced. This happens when:

- J_0 < 0 and J_{45} > 0. In this case, 90 is added to place the axis in the second quadrant.
- J_0 < 0 and J_{45} < 0. In this case, 90 is added to place the axis in the third quadrant.

- $J_0 > 0$ and $J_{45} < 0$. In this case, 180 is added to place the axis in the fourth quadrant.

Examples ☞:

$J_0 = -0.50$ D and $J_{45} = +0.50$ D. Formula produces axis $\alpha = -22.5°$. Add 90 to get the correct axis 67.5°.

$J_0 = -0.50$ D and $J_{45} = -0.50$ D. Formula produces axis $\alpha = +22.5°$. Add 90 to get the correct axis 112.5°.

$J_0 = +0.50$ D and $J_{45} = -0.50$ D. Formula produces axis $\alpha = -22.5°$. Add 180 to get the correct axis 157.5°.

Note ⊡: When adding oblique cross cylinders, i.e., having different axes, the resultant axis lies between the two axes, closer to the cylinder with the larger magnitude (ensure that the Rx forms are the same, either both minus or both plus). The resultant axis is exactly halfway only if the cylinder powers are equal.

Example ☞: Fauchelevent is adding the following obliquely crossed cylinders: +0.50 –3.00×010 and +3.00 –1.00×040. What is the resultant prescription form?

Both prescriptions are in the minus form. The final axis is 020, between 010 and 040.

Conversion to power vectors:

+0.50 –3.00×010 converts to SE = –1.00, J_0 = 1.41, J_{45} = 0.51.

+3.00 –1.00×040 converts to SE = +2.50, J_0 = 0.09, J_{45} = 0.49.

The sum of the above yields the net power vectors: SE +1.50, J_0 = 1.50 D, and J_{45} = 1.00 D.

Net spherocylindrical prescription (approximated to the nearest 0.25 D): 3.25 –3.50×020.

Practice examples with answers ⚒ Adding Obliquely Crossed Cylinders:

Obliquely crossed cylinders: –1.25 –2.25×010 and –2.75 –1.50×060.

Power vectors: SE = –2.50 D, J_0 = 0.94 D, J_{45} = 0.34 D and SE = –3.50 D, J_0 = 0.38 D, J_{45} = 0.65 D.

Combination of the above: SE = –6.00 D, J_0 = 0.56 D, J_{45} = 0.99 D.

Spherocylindrical Rx form: –4.86 –2.28×030, rounded to –5.00 –2.25×030.

Obliquely crossed cylinders: –1.50 +1.00×025 and 3.00 –1.50×075.

Power vectors: SE = –1.00 D, J_0 = –0.32 D, J_{45} = –0.38 D and SE = 2.25 D, J_0 = –0.65 D, J_{45} = 0.38 D.

Combination of the above: SE = 1.25 D, J_0 = –0.97 D, J_{45} = 0.00 D.

Spherocylindrical Rx form: 2.22 –1.94×090, rounded to 2.25 –2.00×090.

Obliquely crossed cylinders: –4.00 –1.00×030 and –2.00 –1.00×070.

Power vectors: SE = –4.50 D, J_0 = 0.25 D, J_{45} = 0.43 D and SE = –2.50 D, J_0 = –0.38 D, J_{45} = 0.32 D.

Combination of the above: SE = –7.00 D, J_0 = –0.13 D, J_{45} = 0.75 D.

Spherocylindrical Rx form: –6.23 –1.53×050, rounded to –6.25 –1.50×050.

9.6 LIGHT TRANSMISSION IN OPHTHALMIC LENSES

9.6.1 Transmissivity and Reflectivity

As light passes through an ophthalmic lens, part of its intensity is lost. Reflection and absorption are the key mechanisms associated with decreased light intensity.

Losses due to reflection occur at the interfaces. When light strikes any surface, part of it is reflected and the rest of it propagates through that interface. Just as on ocular surfaces, the transmissivity T can be calculated indirectly from the reflectivity R (both expressed as fractions with values ranging from 0 to 1):

Transmissivity at a Surface (losses due to reflection): $\qquad T = 1 - R \qquad$ (9.36)

where T expresses the fraction of transmitted light intensity through an interface by a combination of refraction and/or forward scatter. In this case, R is the fraction of light intensity that is lost due to reflection / backward scatter. In most cases, R is calculated for normal incidence, using relationships (2.12), as introduced in § 2.5.2.1:

Reflection Loss (at an interface): $\qquad R = \left(\dfrac{1 - n_{21}}{1 + n_{21}}\right)^2 \qquad$ (9.37)

where n_{21} is the ratio of the two values of the refractive index (n_2/n_1) that straddle the interface.

Example ☞: For normal incidence from air ($n_1 = 1.0$) to high-index glass ($n_2 = 1.73$), the ratio of the two indices is $n_{21} = 1.73$, and reflectivity is:

$$R = \left(\frac{1 - 1.73}{1 + 1.73}\right)^2 = \left(\frac{-0.73}{2.73}\right)^2 = (-0.267)^2 = 0.0715 = 7.15\%$$

Thus, the percentage of reflected intensity from this air–glass interface is about 7%.

Losses due to absorption occur in the volume between the interfaces:

Bulk Transmissivity (losses due to absorption): $\qquad T = 1 - A \qquad$ (9.38)

where T is the fraction of transmitted light intensity through the bulk volume of a lens material by absorption and/or forward scatter. In this case, A is the fraction of light intensity that is lost due to absorption. In most cases, A is calculated for a standard optical length of that material along the direction of propagation and is often reported as the percent or fraction lost per unit length.

In summary: The total transmissivity through any interface and any bulk volume of optical material is computed by multiplying all successive transmissivities, up to the final one (T_F):

Total Transmissivity: $$T_{TOT} = T_1 \cdot T_2 \cdot T_3 \cdot \, ... \, \cdot T_F \qquad\qquad (9.39)$$

Example ☞: What percent of the incident light can be transmitted through a perfectly clear lens made of high-index glass (n_{glass} = 1.73) if the lens is surrounded by air (n_{air} = 1)?

The 'perfectly clear' suggests no absorption. We now have the following effects to consider:
Reflection losses at the air–glass interface (R = 0.07): T_1 = 1 − R = 0.93.
Reflection losses at the glass–air interface (R also equals 0.07): T_2 = 1 − R = 0.93.
The total transmissivity is the product of the two consecutive transmissivities:
T_{TOT} = $T_1 \cdot T_2$ = 0.93·0.93 = 0.86. This can be expressed as 86% of the transmitted light.

Example ☞: Inspector Javert is holding a 2 mm thick glass (n_{glass} = 1.5) lens. The lens absorbs 20% of the incident light. What is the total amount of light transmitted through the lens held by Javert in air?

Reflection losses at the air–glass interface (R = 0.04): T_1 = 1 − R = 0.96.
Propagation through the 2 mm length of the lens material (A = 0.20): T_2 = 1 − A = 0.80.
Reflection losses at the glass–air interface (R = 0.04): T_3 = 1 − R = 0.96.
The total transmissivity is the product of the three consecutive transmissivities:
T_{TOT} = $T_1 \cdot T_2 \cdot T_3$ = 0.96·0.80·0.96 = 0.737. This can be expressed as 73.7% of the transmitted light.

In a system, to calculate total transmission we multiply individual and consecutive transmissivity values.	At any interface, transmissivity is what is not reflected: $T = 1 - R$. R depends on the relative ratio of the refractive indices.	At any thickness, transmissivity is what is not absorbed: $T = 1 - A$. A depends on the material type and thickness.

As discussed in *Wave Optics* § 3.4.2, absorption in glass has two notable characteristics. The first is that it increases appreciably for shorter wavelengths. Absorption in the blue (λ = 400 nm) is far stronger than absorption in the red (λ = 700 nm); absorption peaks in the near UV for most ophthalmic glasses. Certain elements present in the glass composition also affect absorption in other parts of the spectrum, such as the infrared (λ > 800 nm).

The second characteristic is the exponential dependence on thickness: The Beer–Lambert law of absorption clearly states that absorption increases exponentially with thickness. To facilitate calculations, we use the transmittance factor q, which is the fraction of light transmitted per unit length of optical material. Due to the exponential dependence of absorption on thickness, transmissivity is calculated by the transmittance factor raised to the power of the fractional length for which the transmittance factor is quoted (glass thickness/unit length of transmittance factor).

Example ☞: A given glass material has transmittance factor $q = 0.8$ per 1 mm of material. What is the transmissivity for 1 mm of lens thickness? For 2 mm of thickness?   For 4 mm of thickness?

For the 1 mm lens thickness, we simply need q: $T = q^1 = 0.8$.
For the 2 mm lens thickness, we raise q to the power of 2: $T = q^2 = 0.64$.
For the 4 mm lens thickness, we raise q to the power of 4: $T = q^4 = 0.41$.

Example ☞: Dumont wants to know the total transmittance for a lens whose center thickness is 6 mm if $n_{glass} = 1.523$ and the lens material has transmittance factor $q = 0.70$ per 2 mm.

The absorption-related transmittance within the lens is $T_2 = 0.76^{/2} = 0.7^3 = 0.343$.
An alternative approach is to convert the $q = 0.70$ per 2 mm to the equivalent per 1 mm. It is not the same as $q = 0.35$ per 1 mm, but it is 0.8366 (the square root of 0.7) per 1 mm. Then, we raise this value to the power of 6: $T_2 = 0.83666^6 = 0.343$.

Reflection losses are calculated using relationship (2.12): $R = [(1.532–1)/(1.532+1)]^2 = 0.043$. Thus, the reflection-related transmittance at the interfaces are $T_1 = T_3 = 1 – R = 0.957$.
The total transmissivity is the product of the three consecutive transmissivities:
$T_{TOT} = T_1 \cdot T_2 \cdot T_3 = 0.957 \cdot 0.343 \cdot 0.957 = 0.314$, or 31.4% of the transmitted light.

| In tandem systems, | we first compute individual system transmissivity, | then multiply the individual transmissivities. |

Example ☞: Monseigneur Myriel is holding two lenses stacked back-to-back, with a thin layer of air between them. In the first lens, transmissivity is 70%; in the second, transmissivity is 80%. What is the total transmissivity?

Given the two values of transmissivity $T_{TOT} = T_1 \cdot T_2 = 0.7 \cdot 0.8 = 0.56$, or 56%.

9.6.2 Spectacles of Higher Refractive Index

Aside from cost considerations, (being generally more expensive) spectacles made of a higher refractive index material (larger than 1.6) tend on average to be thinner and therefore offer several advantages: a reduction in spectacle magnification, a reduction in the physical weight of the lenses, and a reduction in the optical absorption of light. All of these are beneficial attributes that also help to create a better cosmetic appearance. However, one striking disadvantage is that the higher the index of refraction the higher the reflectance, so this may necessitate applying an antireflective treatment to the lenses.

Example ☞: Mgr Myriel is building a symmetric, 1-inch diameter biconvex glass spectacle lens that needs to have a power of $F = 10.0$ D. What would be the center thickness and reflectivity difference if lens A is made of low-index material $n_A = 1.4$ versus lens B, which is made of high-index glass $n_B = 1.8$?

As in § 9.4.4, each surface power, which is $F = +5.0$ D, is associated with the following radii of curvature:

Lens A: $F_{surface,\ lens\ A} = \dfrac{n_{lens\ A} - n_{air}}{r_A\ [m]} \Rightarrow +5.0\ D = \dfrac{1.4 - 1.0}{r_A\ [m]} \Rightarrow r_A\ [m] = \dfrac{1.4 - 1.0}{+5.0\ D} = 0.08\ m = 8\ cm$

Lens B: $F_{surface,\ lens\ B} = \dfrac{n_{lens\ B} - n_{air}}{r_B\ [m]} \Rightarrow +5.0\ D = \dfrac{1.8 - 1.0}{r_B\ [m]} \Rightarrow r_B\ [m] = \dfrac{1.8 - 1.0}{+5.0\ D} = 0.16\ m = 16\ cm$

The lens semi-diameter h is 1.27 cm in both lenses. We now calculate the sagitta and thickness:

Lens A: $s_A = h^2/2 \cdot r_A = 1.27^2/2 \cdot 8 = 0.10$ cm = 1.0 mm; thickness: $t_A = s_{1A} + s_{2A} = 1.0 + 1.0$ mm = 2.0 mm.

Lens B: $s_B = h^2/2 \cdot r_B = 1.27^2/2 \cdot 16 = 0.05$ cm = 0.5 mm; thickness: $t_B = s_{1B} + s_{2B} = 0.5 + 0.5$ mm = 1.0 mm.

The high-index lens B has about half the thickness of the low-index lens A for the same prescription and size (diameter). There is a clear advantage to the high-index glass lens in this respect.

However, reflectivity and transmissivity are notably different:

Lens A: $n_{21\ A} = 1.4$, and reflectivity is $R_A = \left(\dfrac{1 - 1.4}{1 + 1.4}\right)^2 = \left(\dfrac{-0.4}{2.4}\right)^2 = (-0.1667)^2 = 0.0277 = 2.78\%$

Reflectivity from this interface is ≈ 3%, and single-surface transmissivity is $T_{1A} = 1 - 0.0278 = 0.9722$. Total lens A transmissivity (two surfaces) with zero absorption is $T_{TOT\ A} = T_{1A} \cdot T_{2A} = 0.9722 \cdot 0.9722 = 0.945 \approx 94\%$.

Lens B: $n_{21\ B} = 1.8$, and reflectivity is $R_B = \left(\dfrac{1 - 1.8}{1 + 1.8}\right)^2 = \left(\dfrac{-0.8}{2.8}\right)^2 = (-0.285)^2 = 0.0816 = 8.16\%$

Reflectivity from this interface is ≈ 8%, and single-surface transmissivity is $T_{1B} = 1 - 0.0816 = 0.9184$. Total lens B transmissivity (two surfaces) with zero absorption is $T_{TOT\ B} = T_{1B} \cdot T_{2B} = 0.9184 \cdot 0.9184 = 0.843 \approx 84\%$.

9.7 HAND NEUTRALIZATION AND LENSOMETRY

9.7.1 Hand Neutralization in Spherical Lenses

Hand neutralization is a simple technique that allows one to determine the type of lens (plus or minus or astigmatic) and its power by moving or rotating the lens across a field while observing a fixed target through it. In essence, the technique employs a combination of vergence and prismatic effects such as those discussed in § 10.4.

9.7.1.1 Hand Motion Effects

When a minus lens moves in one direction while the gaze is fixed upon a target, the image through the lens appears to move in the same direction: If the lens moves up, the image appears to move up as well. This is the **with-the-motion movement**—the image moves in the same direction as the lens moves, maintaining the same speed as well.

A plus lens exhibits the opposite effect: The image of the target through the plus lens appears to move in the opposite direction, so plus lenses demonstrate **against-the-motion movement**. For example, if the lens moves up, the image of the target through the lens appears to move down.

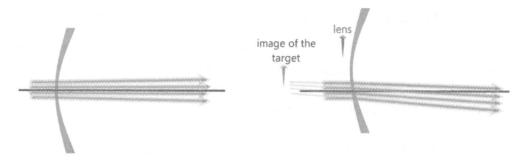

Figure 9-54: With-the-lens movement of a target when a minus lens moves laterally.

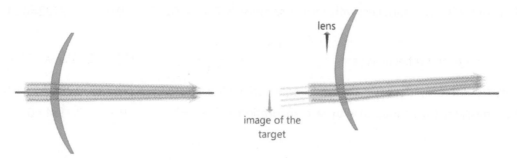

Figure 9-55: Against-the-lens movement of a target when a plus lens is moved laterally.

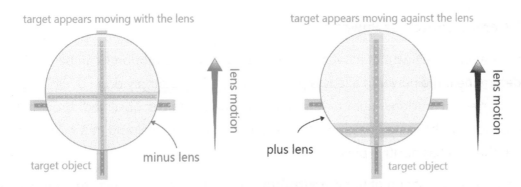

Figure 9-56: (left) With-the motion movement and (right) against-the-motion movement of a target image with(left) a minus lens and (right) a plus lens. The observed target is a green cross.

The effects are not restricted when the lens moves in only one direction. If the lens is spherical, having the same power regardless of the meridian, the movement of the lens along any direction displays the corresponding target move; for example, if a minus lens moves down and to the right, the image of the target through the lens appears to move down and to the right as well.

In order for these effects to manifest as described, the lens is held close to the observer's eye so that the possible aerial image of the target through the lens is not formed between the lens and the observer's eye; otherwise, there may be an image inversion with high plus lenses.

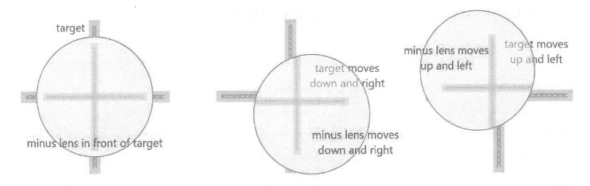

Figure 9-57: When a minus lens moves diagonally, a target cross appears to move in the same direction.

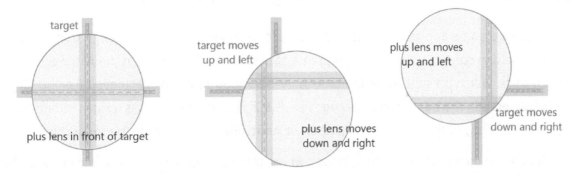

Figure 9-58: When a plus lens moves diagonally, a target cross appears to move in the opposite direction.

9.7.1.2 Determination of Power

The manifestation of the type of movement—with or against the motion—can be used to rapidly determine if the power in a lens is plus or minus. This is simply done by holding the lens close to the eye and moving it right or left, or up or down. A target observed through the lens appears to move in the same direction if the lens has negative power and in the opposite direction if the lens has positive power.

This is the foundation of **hand neutralization**, which is a simple way to determine the power of a lens. The thinking is that, if the lens has no power, when it moves up, down, right or left, the target does not move, regardless of the direction the lens moved; thus, if we use a known-power trial lens in contact with the unknown (power) lens to be examined, the net effect is zero, or neutralized, only if the trial lens is of equal and opposite power to the unknown lens.

If the trial lens does not match the power of the unknown lens, the combined lens may be a net minus (i.e., if the unknown lens is plus and the trial lens has less power) or a net plus (i.e., when the unknown lens is plus and the trial lens has more power). Neutralization is demonstrated by the target movement—the combination of the two lenses gives rise to no target motion, so the dioptric power is zero. The unknown-lens power is thus determined to be equal in magnitude and opposite in sign to that of the trial lens. For instance, if the trial lens was –2.00 D, then the power in the unknown lens is +2.00 D.

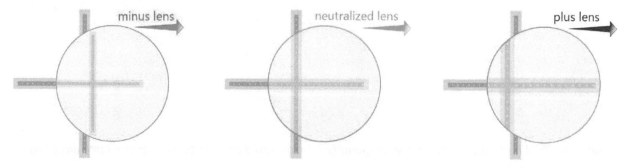

Figure 9-59: Right horizontal movements viewed through a minus lens, a neutralized lens, and a plus lens.

There are some approximations in this simple technique. It applies well to thin lenses that can be held in contact without resulting in a considerable thickness. In the real world, all lenses are thick, which present some limitations. When neutralization is achieved (i.e., no target motion is observed), the **back vertex power** F_{BVP} (§ 9.2.5) of the first lens is equal (in magnitude but opposite in sign) to the front vertex power, or **neutralizing power**, of the second lens.

Specific to meniscus ophthalmic lenses, where the front surface is most often convex while the back surface is concave, when placing a plus trial lens in contact with a minus unknown lens, the air gap can be minimal. Peripheral image distortion can be an issue when the two lenses held together result in a lens combination with a notable air gap and lens thickness.

Figure 9-60: In neutralization, a trial lens is placed against the front surface of the unknown lens. In this case, the unknown lens parameter that can be determined is the neutralizing (front vertex) power.

9.7.2 Hand Neutralization in Astigmatic and Cylinder Lenses

We mentioned the translation of the lens against a target. The use of a cross target allows for the determination of power along a given meridian. When using a simple, spherical power lens, the rotation of the lens does not result in any apparent target rotation seen through the lens. This is no longer true if the lens is toric or cylindrical.

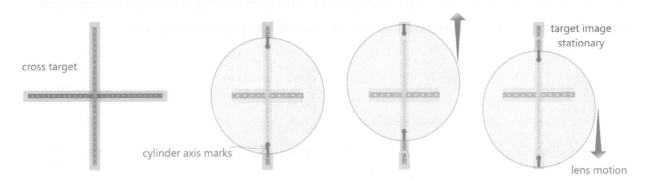

Figure 9-61: (left) Cross target. (right) A minus cylinder trial lens with its vertical axis placed against the target. If the lens is moved vertically, the cross target does not move, regardless of any lens movement.

Consider a toric lens whose vertical cylinder axis is placed against a cross target, with the target and lens centers perfectly aligned. The lens is held so that the cylinder axis is lined vertically such that the most minus power is along the horizontal meridian. In a purely cylindrical lens, there is no power along the axis (it is aligned with the vertical meridian) at all. What is interesting is that we observe a distorted cross; the target appears squeezed along the horizontal meridian (are you wondering why?—because there is minus power along this meridian!). We can verify this further by simply moving the lens strictly up and down. This lens motion does not produce any target movement.

If the lens is moved horizontally, a **with-the-motion movement** is noted. This is a clear indication that the power along the horizontal meridian is a minus power (recall we assumed a minus cylinder lens).

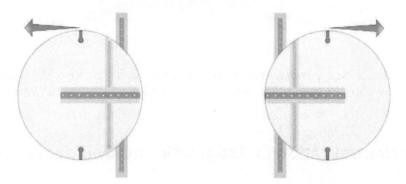

Figure 9-62: A minus cylinder trial lens with its axis oriented vertically is moved horizontally. The vertical part of the cross target exhibits with-the-motion movement.

If we turn the lens 90°, the axis is horizontal. Now the cross is squeezed along the vertical meridian (this time because there is minus power along this meridian). If we move the lens to the right or left, this lens motion does not produce any target movement regardless of the movement. A vertical lens movement will show with-the-motion movement.

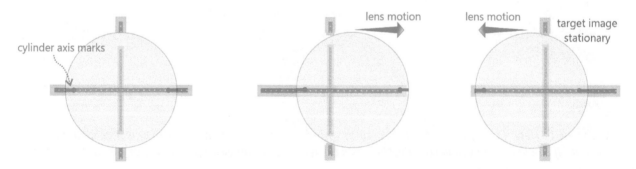

Figure 9-63: A minus cylinder trial lens with its axis oriented horizontally is placed against that target. If the lens is moved horizontally, the cross target does not move, regardless of the lens movement.

Toric and cylinder lenses exhibit a different effect when the lens is rotated. The target appears to rotate and/or skew; this is referred to as **scissors-motion movement**.

Consider a minus cylinder trial lens. Start by placing the cylinder axis oriented vertically such that the lens is rotated clockwise. The vertical limb of the target (cross) appears to rotate in the same (clockwise) direction until it reaches an extreme orientation at about 45° of lens rotation. At the same time, the horizontal limb of the cross appears to rotate in the opposite direction (counter-clockwise), and the scissors appear to be closing (with-the-scissors-motion movement).

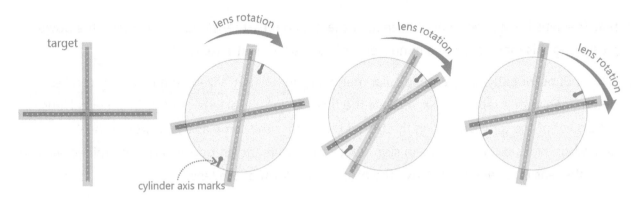

Figure 9-64: The scissors effect as observed when a cross is viewed through a minus cylinder lens.

The opposite trend is observed when the cylinder is plus. Again, starting with the axis oriented vertically, as the lens is rotated clockwise, the vertical limb of the cross rotates in the opposite direction (counter-clockwise), while the horizontal limb rotates in the same direction, so the scissors appear to be opening (against-the-scissors-motion movement).

The maximum of the scissors closing or opening is seen when the cylinder axis (whether plus or minus) makes a 45° angle with the target lines. The amount of 'scissors' either closing or opening is dependent on the cylinder magnitude as well. In other words, a –6.00 D cylinder will produce a greater effect than a –3.00 D cylinder.

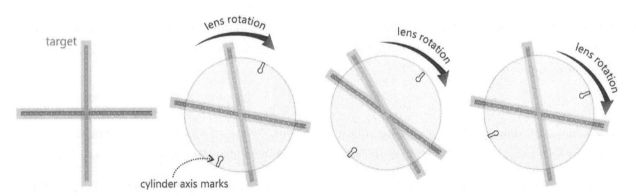

Figure 9-65: The scissors effect as observed when a cross is viewed through a plus cylinder lens.

The above effects can be used to determine the refractive power in a toric lens. The principal meridians correspond to the orientation at which the cross lines appear perpendicular, i.e., there is no scissors effect. Once the meridians are identified, we seek the power along the principal meridian. For example, whether the power along that meridian is plus or minus can be determined by holding the lens in the orientation of its principal meridian and moving it <u>along the direction of that meridian</u>. We then selectively neutralize this meridian and determine its power. If there is with-the-motion movement, the power is minus along this meridian, and a plus trial lens is required to neutralize it. If there is against-the-motion movement, the power is plus along this meridian, and a minus lens is required to neutralize it.

Subsequently, the perpendicular meridian can be neutralized, and its power can be determined with a separate (i.e., remove the first trial lens) trial lens. Just as in spherical lenses, the power of the toric lens along the tested meridian is the same as the power of the neutralizing lens but is opposite in sign. Once the two meridian powers are determined, we can write the lens cross and then derive the prescription form of the lens.

Hand neutralization Practice ⏱ :

1. Find a rectangular frame (picture or door frame) or draw a cross on a board or a piece of paper. The farther away the cross is from the eye the better; each arm of the cross should be at least 5 inch long.

2. Identify the principal meridians: Rotate the lens to determine if there is astigmatism by checking for scissor movements of the target. If no scissor movement is observed, the lens is spherical. If scissor movements are observed, rotate the lens so that the target cross lines are perpendicular; i.e., they line up with the cross lines of the object cross.
Congratulations, you determined the orientation of the lens principal meridians (you may want to mark these on the lens). Also, the point at which the target cross lines intersect on the lens is the optical center of the lens (you may want to mark this with a felt tip pen on the lens as well).

3. Neutralize each meridian separately by moving the lens that is in orientation with the principal meridian along the direction of that meridian. Once this meridian is neutralized, the power of the other meridian is determined separately.

Example ☞: Mlle Baptistine is trying to neutralize a toric lens. She used +3.00 D lens to neutralize the vertical meridian and +1.00 D lens to neutralize the horizontal meridian. What is the lens prescription?

The power along the vertical meridian (90°) is –3.00 D, and the power along the horizontal meridian (180°) is –1.00. The lens cross is –1.00 @ 180° / –3.00 @ 90°. The spherocylindrical formula is –1.00 –2.00×180 or –3.00 +2.00×090.

9.7.3   Hand Neutralization in a Prism

Hand neutralization can be used to detect the presence of prisms in an ophthalmic lens. To detect the presence of a prism, we hold the lens over an object (cross line). The cross appears as broken through the lens and displaced toward the apex of the prism. In a fashion similar to power neutralization, a prism of known power is stacked against and alongside the unknown prism until the combined element brings the target to the optical center.

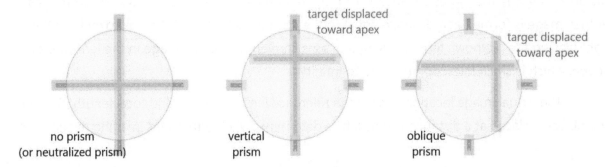

no prism
(or neutralized prism)

target displaced
toward apex

vertical
prism

target displaced
toward apex

oblique
prism

Figure 9-66: Prism effects as seen using hand neutralization. The trial lens is stationery, and the target shifts toward the apex of the prism. (In real cases, there are also lens effects associated with the prism that manifest as target magnification or minification—for simplicity, these effects are not drawn.)

9.7.4 Lensometry

Hand neutralization can quickly determine if a lens is plus or minus and can determine the presence of astigmatic correction; however, hand neutralization entails poor accuracy. The **lensometer**, which is the basis of the lensometry technique, is an optical bench instrument that determines the power of a spectacle or contact lens. The lensometer is also known in various countries by trade names, such as lensmeter (by American Optical since 1921), focimeter (by Rodenstock), vertometer (by Bausch + Lomb and later by Reichert), and the Humphry Lens Analyzer (by Humphrey). In addition to power, the lensometer also measures (if present) cylinder power and axis, add power(s), and the amount of prism in a lens.

In the simplified lensometer layout shown in Figure 9-67, a light source illuminates the target (a green cross), which is at a distance x from a strong plus reference lens with power F_s (focal length f_s) of between 20 and 25 D; this value determines the highest value of a plus lens that can be measured, which cannot exceed that of the reference lens.

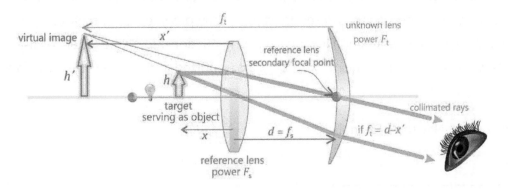

Figure 9-67: The lensometer principle of operation.

The object viewed through the unknown lens is the virtual image of the target created by the reference lens at a location x'. Given a reference lens-to-unknown-lens separation distance of $d = f_s$, the target distance x from the reference lens is varied via a knob so that its virtual image is formed at a distance equal to the back focal length of the unknown lens; then light leaving the unknown lens is collimated, as is verified by a clear image in the lensometer scope, which is small telescope focused to infinity.

The virtual image location x' from the reference lens (power F_s and focal length f_s), when the object is placed at a distance x to its left, is determined via the thin-lens imaging relationship:

$$\frac{1}{x} + \frac{1}{f_s} = \frac{1}{x'} \tag{9.40}$$

Note that x and x' are negative since they are drawn against the direction of light propagation. The unknown-lens focal length f_t is related to the reference-lens focal length and image location:

$$f_t = f_s - x' \tag{9.41}$$

We eliminate x' from the above two equations by transforming Eq. (9.40) into

$$x' = \frac{x \cdot f_s}{x + f_s} \tag{9.42}$$

Subsequently, Eq. (9.41) becomes

Unknown-Lens Focal Length: $$f_t = f_s - \frac{x \cdot f_s}{x + f_s} = \frac{f_s^2}{x + f_s} \tag{9.43}$$

Lens Power: $$F_t = F_s + F_s^2 x \tag{9.44}$$

Thus, the unknown-lens power F_t has a linear dependence on the target location if the movable target location x is measured and the reference lens power F_s is known. Most lensometers are graduated on the power drum to directly provide power measurement. In some other analysis, implementing Newton's imaging relationship,[936] the letter x is used to denote the distance that the target is moved (again, reported in m). Then, the formula appears as

Lens Power using Newton's Formula: $$x = f_s^2 \cdot F_t \tag{9.45}$$

---

[936] *Geometrical Optics* § 4.1.4 Newton's Imaging Relationship.

where f_s is the focal length of the reference/standard lens, and F_t is the power of the unknown test lens, and (as mentioned above) x is the distance that the target is moved.

Yet one more advantage of this layout is that image magnification is fixed and independent of the unknown-lens power measured. This is achieved by implementing the **Badal principle**, a principle similar to Knapp's rule (§ 6.6.5). The principle is named after the French ophthalmologist Antoine Jules Badal and implements a positive lens placed so that its posterior focal plane is coincident with the anterior focal plane of the eye.[937]

The consequence is that an object viewed through the optometer appears to always be the same size (the angular subtense of the image is unaltered) and the scale in diopters is linear with distance from the lens. This is why the unknown lens is placed at the secondary focal point of the reference lens, which means that $d = f_s = 1/F_s$. Then, the equivalent power of the two-lens system (reference and unknown) using relationship (1.4) is found to equal that of the reference lens alone:

$$F_{equiv} = F_s + F_t - dF_s \cdot F_t = F_s + F_t - \frac{1}{F_s}F_s \cdot F_t = F_s \qquad (9.46)$$

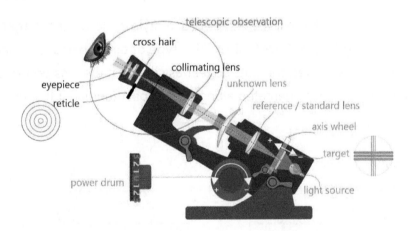

Figure 9-68: Schematic of a manual lensometer.

In a fashion similar to hand neutralization, the unknown lens power measured by the lensometer is the back vertex power F_{BVP}, or its reciprocal value, the back focal length. More generally, the lensometer measures the vertex power associated with the surface of the unknown lens facing the reference lens. Thus, to measure the back vertex power, the spectacle

---

[937] Badal J. Optomètre métrique international Pour la mesure simultanée de la réfraction et de l'acuité visuelle même chez les illettrés. Annales d'Oculistique. 1876; 75:101-17.

lens is placed on the lensometer stop, in contact with the back (ocular) surface, with the temples facing away from the instrument eyepiece, akin to the instrument 'wearing' the spectacle lens.

The measurement of front vertex power is also desired, particularly when the add power in bifocal lenses is to be determined, assuming that the add segment is 'added' on the front surface. To measure the front vertex power, the spectacle lens is placed on the lensometer stop, touching the front surface (usually the convex), with the temples facing toward the instrument eyepiece, akin to the examiner 'wearing' the spectacle lens.

9.7.4.1 Power Measurement Examples

The **reticle** is a visual guide that projects concentric ('bull's eye'), numbered rings to form the graticule scale, which is often accompanied by a protractor scale. Through the reticle, the examiner views the **target** (more accurately, the image of the target through the lens), which, in most types, is a cross line comprising widely spaced lines (a triplet line) that represent the cylinder power and a closely spaced triplet line, which appears as a single line when focused and represents the sphere power [Figure 9-69 (left)]. The target color is either a greenish 546.074 nm (mercury e-line) or a yellowish 587.6 nm (helium d line).

Another less-common target type is the corona-style circle-of-dots target, a circle of 12 small dots that form a ring [Figure 9-69 (right)]. This type of target helps to visualize the power orientation—when the lens rotates, the dots appear as circular if the lens power is spherical and appear to be stretched into lines orientated along a principal meridian if the lens is toric.

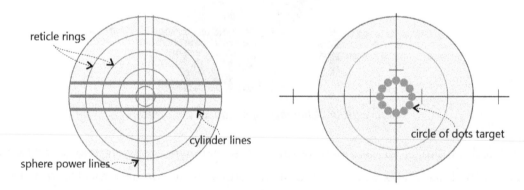

Figure 9-69: Lensometry target views: (left) cross-target type and (right) circle-of-dots-target type.

The reticle allows the correct placement of the lens optical center. When the two sets of target lines cross each other within the center small circle, the lens is correctly positioned at its optical center. As the two sets of lines are not clear initially, the power drum is turned to a high plus reading and then is decreased until the target lines start to become clear. Then, the power drum is slowly turned and the lens (or the cylinder axis wheel, which rotates the target) is rotated to bring the closely spaced power lines (called a single line to distinguish them from the perpendicular, widely spaced lines) into sharp focus, as they may initially appear broken at the center.

If the target lines are not in the proper axis orientation, they appear broken, running diagonally to their intended course. Rotation of the axis wheel can straighten the broken single lines [Figure 9-70 (left)] or the triple lines [Figure 9-70 (right)]. The triple lines, when focused, still form three distinct lines, whereas the 'single' lines, when focused, appear as a single line.

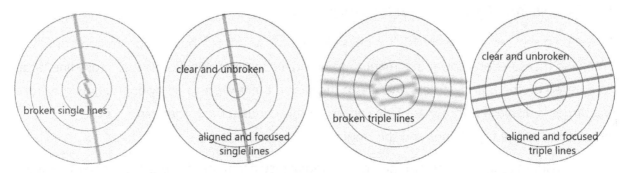

Figure 9-70: (left) Alignment and focusing of single spherical-power single lines. (right) Alignment and focusing of cylinder-power triple lines.

If the lens has a spherical power, all target lines can be brought into focus at the same time [Figure 9-71 (left)]. If the lens is toric, only one set of lines can be clear and focused at a given power and axis setting; either the sphere-power lines (Figure 9-71 center) or the cylinder-power lines [Figure 9-71 (right)] can be brought to focus, but not both concurrently.

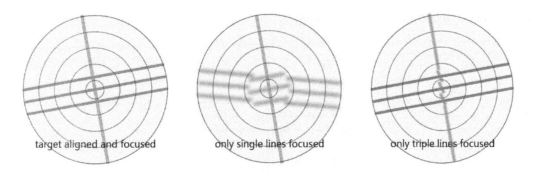

Figure 9-71: (left) In simple spherical lenses, the entire target can be aligned and focused concurrently. In a toric lens, depending on the lens power distribution, it is possible that (center) only the single (sphere power) lines or (right) only the triple (cylinder power) lines are focused.

In order to measure **toric lens power**, the target is rotated (or the axis wheel is adjusted) and moved forward or backward (by means of the power drum rotation) until the sphere-power single lines are first brought to focus, appearing clear and unbroken. Then the reading on the power wheel is the most positive power meridian (least negative) of the lens and corresponds to the sphere in the minus form astigmatic prescription, e.g., −3.00 ×180. Next, a slow turn of the power wheel toward decreased power brings the three cylinder lines into focus (and the single line is now blurry), appearing clear and unbroken (the axis wheel is turned 90° as well). The reading on the power wheel is the least positive (most negative) meridian power of the lens, e.g., −4.00 D. The cylinder is the difference in powers between the two readings, e.g., −1.00 D. The axis of astigmatism is the orientation of the meridian with the sphere power, e.g., 180°.

9.7.4.2 Lensometry and Prism Measurement

As will be discussed in Chapter 10, it is possible that the lens has a build-in prism component. When we measure lens power in a manual-focusing lensometer, the illuminated cross-line target is centered on the reticle center. This is not the case if there is prism component; now the cross-line target is displaced from the reticle center. In this context, the target center is the intersection of the triplet lines and the single lines.

Prism magnitude is determined by the radial displacement of the target center relative to the reticle center; displacement by one concentric circle equals one prism diopter ($^\Delta$). The reading is facilitated because the rings are labeled in prism diopters. For example, if the target is overlaid on the number 3 line, then prism magnitude is 3^Δ. Most lensometers are graduated for up to 5^Δ of prism; it is thus possible that one set of lines is not visible if the lens has more than 5^Δ of prism.

The base direction is determined by coordinate placement of the cross-line target. For example, if the target is displaced downward, a base-down prism is present, and if the target is displaced upward, a base-up prism is present.

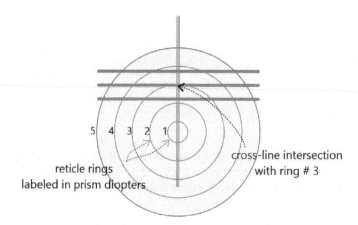

Figure 9-72: Presence of a prism identified using lensometry. The cross-line target is displaced by three in the upward direction, indicating a 3^Δ base-up prism.

Finding the horizontal displacement follows the same rules; however, we need to know if the lens is meant for the OD or the OS eye to determine whether the prism is base-in or base-out. For example, if the cross-line target is displaced to the right of the center of the reticle, the prism is base-in if the lens is for the right eye, and the prism is base-out if the lens is for the left eye [Figure 9-73 (left)].

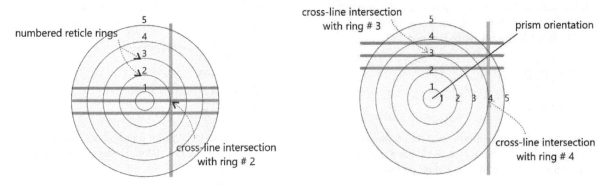

Figure 9-73: Presence of a prism identified using lensometry. (left) The cross-line target is displaced two rings to the right, indicating the presence of a 2ᐃ base-in prism if the spectacle lens is for the right eye or a base-out prism if the lens is for the left eye. (right) The cross-line target is displaced three rings up (this makes a 3ᐃ base-up prism) and four rings to the right (this makes a of 4ᐃ base-in prism if the spectacle lens is for the right eye). Using polar coordinates (§ 10.6), this is a 5ᐃ prism oriented at 36.8°.

In oblique prisms, the intersection of the sphere lines (single) and the (center of the triplet) cylinder lines provides the location of the prism base [Figure 9-73 (right)].

9.8 OPHTHALMIC OPTICS QUIZ

Lens Power and Vergence; Vertex Distance

1) A crown glass spherical surface (n_{crown} = 1.523) placed in air has power F = +4.00 D. Marius fabricates, using the same grinding and curvature parameters, another glass surface with $n_{high\ index}$ = 1.74. What is the power of this surface?

   a) +2.82 D
   b) +4.00 D
   c) +4.57 D
   d) +5.66 D

2) Two glass spherical interfaces A and B ($n_{high\ index}$ = 1.74) are surrounded by air. Both have radius of curvature of 10 cm. What is their power?

   a) F_A = +7.4 D, F_B = +7.4 D
   b) F_A = +7.4 D, F_B = −7.4 D
   c) F_A = +17.4 D, F_B = +17.4 D
   d) F_A = +17.4 D, F_B = −17.4 D

3) Brevet is using these two interfaces to make a thin lens (thickness = 0 cm) using the interfaces in Q 2. The lens is _____ and has power _____.

   a) biconvex, F = +0.0 D
   b) biconvex, F = +7.4.0 D
   c) biconvex, F = +14.8 D
   d) meniscus, F = +7.4 D

4) Brevet realizes that there is no zero-thickness lens. The lens he made has a center thickness of 6.5 mm. The effective lens power for this lens is ...

   a) +7.35 D
   b) +14.0 D
   c) +14.6 D
   d) +15.0 D

5) Brevet is still experimenting. He places this lens on the lensometer he measures the back vertex power of his lens. What is the reading?

   a) +7.35 D
   b) +14.0 D
   c) +14.6 D
   d) +15.0 D

6) Bamatabois is planning to fabricate a lens using standard glass of n = 1.5. This lens has a front surface power +10.00 D and back surface power −5.00 D. What is the nominal lens power?

   a) +10.00 D
   b) +7.50 D
   c) +6.00 D
   d) +5.00 D
   e) −5.00 D

7) The lens fabricated by Bamatabois has center thickness t = 3 cm. What is the effective power?

   a) +10.00 D
   b) +7.50 D
   c) +6.00 D
   d) +5.00 D
   e) −5.00 D

8) What is the Rx power of Bamatabois' lens?

   a) +10.00 D
   b) +7.50 D
   c) +6.00 D
   d) +5.00 D
   e) −5.00 D

9) If a +2.00 D add power segment is to be used on Bamatabois' lens front surface, what front vertex power should this segment have?

   a) +2.00 D
   b) +5.45 D
   c) +7.45 D
   d) +8.00 D
   e) +9.50 D

10) Babet fabricates an ophthalmic lens (n=1.6) with base curve +8.00 D and back surface power −3.85 D. Thickness is 2.5 mm. What is the prescription power?

   a) +3.95 D
   b) +4.05 D
   c) +4.10 D
   d) +4.15 D
   e) +4.20 D
   f) +4.25 D

11) Gavroche wants to know vergence like he knows the streets. He measures light vergence at point A

= –20.0 D. How far <u>from point A</u> does he have to move so that light vergence becomes = –2.0 D?

a) 5 cm upstream
b) 5 cm downstream
c) 45 cm upstream
d) 45 cm downstream
e) 50 cm upstream
f) 50 cm downstream

12) Where is the source (in relation to point A) whose vergence was measured as –20.0 D?

a) 5 cm upstream
b) 5 cm downstream
c) 45 cm upstream
d) 45 cm downstream
e) 50 cm upstream
f) 50 cm downstream

13) In a second experiment, Gavroche measures light vergence at point C = +10.0 D. What will light vergence be at a point that is 35 cm downstream from point C?

a) +2.22 D
b) +2.86 D
c) –2.86 D
d) –4.00 D

14) In his third and final experiment, Gavroche measures light vergence at point E = –5.0 D. How far <u>from point E</u> does he have to move such that light vergence becomes = –2.5 D?

a) 5 cm upstream
b) 5 cm downstream
c) 20 cm upstream
d) 20 cm downstream
e) 40 cm upstream
f) 40 cm downstream

15) How far from the final point of –2.5 D vergence is the point source?

a) 5 cm upstream
b) 5 cm downstream
c) 20 cm upstream
d) 20 cm downstream
e) 40 cm upstream
f) 40 cm downstream

16) At point A, 5.0 cm to the left of a lens, vergence is +4.0 D. At a point B, 10.0 cm to the right of this lens, vergence is +25.0 D. What is the power of the lens?

a) +24.0 D
b) +16.0 D

c) +15.0 D
d) +13.33 D
e) +10.0 D

17) Fantine wears spectacle lenses +3.75 D @ 15 mm vertex. What would be the contact lens (CL) power?

a) +3.50 D
b) +3.75 D
c) +4.00 D
d) +4.25 D
e) +4.50 D

18) Cosette's Rx is –4.25 D @ 15 mm vertex. Rather unhappy (it must runn in the family!), she, too, wants to switch to contact lenses. What should be the contact lens (CL) power?

a) –3.75 D
b) –4.00 D
c) –4.25 D
d) –4.50 D
e) –4.75 D

19) Which <u>two</u> of the following spectacle Rx's will produce the same refractive effect as Cosette's original spectacle Rx –4.25 D @ 15 mm?

a) –4.15 D @ 12 mm
b) –4.20 D @ 12 mm
c) –4.29 D @ 14 mm
d) –4.35 D @ 20 mm

20) Jean Valjean is wearing a +8.25 D contact lens distance Rx. The streets in Paris are rather dusty and he is uncomfortable wearing his CLs, wishing to switch back to his spectacle Rx. Can we help him pick up the correct Rx?

a) +7.50 @ 12 mm vertex
b) +7.50 @ 15 mm vertex
c) +8.50 @ 12 mm vertex
d) +9.00 @ 10 mm vertex

21) Monsieur Madeleine wears a spectacle of Rx +7.50 @ 12 mm vertex. Had he been wearing contact lenses (CL), what would their power be?

a) +7.00 D
b) +7.50 D
c) +7.75 D
d) +8.00 D
e) +8.25 D

22) Prisoner 24601 is undecided between a couple of frames to wear. Can you help him choose the two that produce the same CL equivalent power?

a) +7.50 @ 12 mm and +7.25 @ 16.5 mm
b) +7.75 @ 7.5 mm and +7.50 @ 15 mm
c) +8.50 @ 7.0 mm and +7.25 @ 17 mm
d) +8.00 @ 12 mm and +7.50 @ 15.5 mm

23) Mme Huchloup wants to use a pince-nez lens (5 mm vertex) to replace a frame-mounted Rx of −10.00 D (15 mm vertex). What pince-nez Rx should she pick?

a) −11.00 D
b) −10.00 D
c) −9.00 D
d) −5.00 D

24) Feuilly, during a heated debate at the ABC Café, drops his pince-nez and has to go back to frame-mounted Rx. His pince-nez was +9.00 D, worn @ 5 mm vertex. What Rx spectacle power would Feuilly need if the frame-imposed vertex distance is 12 mm?

a) +8.12 D
b) +8.50 D
c) +9.60 D
d) +10.00 D

25) Combeferre fabricates a lens with +6.00 D base curve and −2.00 D back surface power. The nominal lens power is ...

a) −2.00 D
b) +2.00 D
c) +4.00 D
d) +6.00 D

26) Combeferre realizes that his lens must have a center thickness. As lens thickness increases, what is the effect on prescription power?

a) less plus power
b) no change
c) more plus power

27) Combeferre has an inquisitive mind. If the lens ($n = 1.6$) thickness becomes 4 cm, the Rx power of this unusually thick lens becomes ...

a) +3.70 D
b) +3.90 D
c) +4.10 D
d) +4.30 D
e) +5.00 D

28) Les amis de l'ABC Café are busy fabricating lenses. Courfeyrac is using a +5.00 D base curve and −7.00 D back surface power. The nominal lens power is ...
a) −7.00 D
b) −2.00 D

c) +2.00 D
d) +5.00 D

29) Courfeyrac realizes that his lens must have a center thickness. As lens thickness increases, what is the effect on prescription power?

a) less minus power
b) no change
c) more minus power

30) Courfeyrac wants to know what becomes of the prescription power if his lens is 1.6 cm thick (material $n = 1.7$).

a) −2.50 D
b) −2.33 D
c) −2.22 D
d) −1.75 D
e) −1.67 D
f) −1.57 D

31) Montparnasse can make a −3.00 D Rx lens using any combination of a plano or a concave −3.00 D surface. If the desired Rx is −3.00 D, what surface should be the base curve and what is the back surface power?

a) base curve plano, back −3.00 D
b) base curve plano, back plano
c) base curve −3.00 D, back −3.00 D
d) base curve −3.00 D, back plano

32) The lens Montparnasse fabricates has thickness 15 mm and is made of material with $n = 1.5$. If the lens is oriented with the plano surface as the base curve, the neutralizing and the prescription powers are ...

a) neutralizing −3.00 D; prescription −3.14 D
b) neutralizing plano; prescription −3.14 D
c) neutralizing −2.91 D; prescription −3.00 D
d) neutralizing −3.00 D; prescription −2.91 D

33) Joly is an astigmat. His Rx is −6.00 −4.00×180 @ 15 mm vertex. Please help Joly pick the proper contact lens Rx (round to the nearest 0.25).

a) −5.50 −3.50×180
b) −5.50 −3.25×180
c) −6.50 −2.25×180
d) −5.25 −3.50×180

34) Prouvaire is another astigmat member of the ABC Café. His Rx is +3.50 +2.50×090 @ 12 mm vertex. Help Prouvaire pick the proper contact lens Rx (round to the nearest 0.25).

a) +3.50 +2.50×090

b)   +3.50 +3.00×090
c)   +3.00 +2.50×090
d)   +3.50 +3.00×090

35) Lègle drops his contact lenses (Rx −7.25 +2.50×180) on the floor of the Rue Saint-Hyacinthe Café. Help Lègle order his spectacle Rx (vertex 10.50 mm - two correct answers).

a)   −4.50 −2.25×090
b)   −5.00 −2.85×180
c)   −5.00 −2.85×090
d)   −6.75 +2.25×180
e)   −7.85 +2.50×180
f)   −7.25 +2.85×090

Spectacle Magnification / the Sergeant de Waterloo section

36) Monsieur Thénardier wears a +12.00 D, 5 mm thick spectacle lens. If the lens central thickness increases to 10 mm, what change occurs?

a)   shape factor decreases
b)   shape factor increases
c)   power factor increases
d)   power factor decreases

37) Somehow, experimentation has led M. Thénardier to create a 4.5 cm thick, +12.00 D lens. What is the power factor (%) (d_v = 15 mm, F_1 = +6.00 D, n = 1.5)?

a)   2.195%
b)   4.872%
c)   21.95%
d)   43.90%
e)   48.72%

38) Still working with this monstrous lens made by M. Thénardier, what is the shape factor (%)?

a)   2.195%
b)   4.872%
c)   21.95%
d)   43.90%
e)   48.72%

39) Still working with this monstrous lens made by M. Thénardier, what is the spectacle magnification (%)?

a)   2.195%
b)   4.872%
c)   21.95%
d)   43.90%
e)   48.72%

40) M. Thénardier, realizing how impractical his monstrous lens is, finally fabricates the correct +12.00 D, 5 mm thick spectacle lens with no other change. The new shape factor is 2.04%. What is the new power factor?

a)   2.04%

b)   21.95%
c)   23.99%
d)   24.44%

41) Still working with the new lens made by M. Thénardier. what is the new spectacle magnification (%)?

a)   2.04%
b)   21.95%
c)   23.99%
d)   24.44%

42) Madame Thénardier wears −12.00 spectacles (t = 7 mm, F_1 = +2.00 D, n = 1.5) at 13 mm vertex distance. What change is expected to the power factor if the thickness increases to 15 mm?

a)   increase
b)   no change
c)   decrease

43) What is the biggest contributor to spectacle magnification in Mme Thénardier's lens?

a)   The shape factor is the most important.
b)   The shape factor and power factor are equally important.
c)   The power factor is the most important.

44) What is the power factor in Mme Thénardier's lens (negative sign indicating minification)?

a)   +0.94%
b)   −12.68%
c)   −13.49%
d)   −26.17%

45) What is the spectacle magnification in Mme Thénardier's lens?

a)   +0.94%
b)   −12.68%
c)   −13.49%
d)   −26.17%

46) What would be the spectacle magnification if Mme Thénardier would switch to contact lens Rx (allow a 3 mm corneal plane to principal plane separation, CL thickness 3 mm, base curve 2.00 D, n = 1.5)?

   a) +0.40%
   b) −2.63%
   c) −3.02%
   d) −3.42%

47) Gavroche is quite proficient with spectacle magnification. He claims that a reduced base curve affects _____ , specifically, _____.

   a) the shape factor, it decreases
   b) the shape factor, it increases
   c) the power factor, it increases
   d) the power factor, it decreases

48) Éponine claims that a higher refractive index in her father's spectacle lens affects _____ , specifically, _____.

   a) the shape factor, it decreases
   b) the shape factor, it increases
   c) the power factor, it increases
   d) the power factor, it decreases

49) Azelma disagrees with all that. She claims that a notable change will be possible by decreasing the vertex distance. In this case, ...

   a) the shape factor decreases
   b) the shape factor increases
   c) the power factor increases

d) the power factor decreases

50) Éponine wears a −3.00 D lens at 12 mm vertex. Lens thickness t = 2.5 mm, base curve +4.50 D, n = 1.5. What is the spectacle magnification (%)?

   a) +0.50%
   b) +0.75%
   c) −2.75%
   d) −3.00%
   e) −3.50%
   f) −3.75%

51) Éponine switches to a lens with +3.00 D base curve (from +4.50 D). Which <u>two</u> parameters change?

   a) shape factor becomes +0.50%
   b) shape factor becomes +1.00%
   c) spectacle magnification becomes −3.00%
   d) spectacle magnification becomes −3.25%
   e) power factor becomes −3.75%
   f) power factor becomes −2.75%

52) Magnon steps in for a final consideration: What if the lens is plano? What is the shape factor and what is the power factor (vertex distance 12 mm, thickness 2.5 mm, base curve +6.00 D, refractive index 1.5)?

   a) shape factor +1%, power factor +1%
   b) shape factor 0%, power factor +1%
   c) shape factor +1%, power factor 0%
   d) shape factor 0%, power factor 0%

Ophthalmic Lens Geometry and Properties

53) What determines the field of view when Marius Pontmercy wears a frame fitted with plano power lenses (two correct answers)?

   a) the frame size (diameter)
   b) the distance between frame and pupil (vertex)
   c) the pupil size (diameter)
   d) Marius's refraction (in diopters)

54) Marius is still wearing the same 'plano' frame, bringing it closer to his eyes. The field of view ...

   a) increases
   b) remains the same
   c) decreases

55) What is the field of view (aFoV) if Marius' frame (still plano) is 30 mm in diameter, worn at 14 mm vertex distance?

   a) 12.2°
   b) 84.4°
   c) 94°
   d) 102°
   e) 130°

56) Marius now starts true experimentation. He fits a +11.0 D lens on the frames. What parameter affecting the aFoV changes?

   a) location of the entrance pupil
   b) field stop size (diameter)
   c) pupil size (diameter)
   d) vertex distance

57) Help Marius determine the field stop in this case. It is the ...

   a) frame of the ...frame

b) pupil diameter
c) entrance pupil diameter
d) cornea

58) OK, we got it. The plus lens affects the location of the entrance pupil. How?

a) The entrance pupil has a fixed location.
b) The entrance pupil is now farther from the frame.
c) The entrance pupil is now closer to the frame.

59) Marius is fitting a plus lens on the frames, so the aFoV is now smaller because it is dependent on the ratio of ...

a) field stop diameter to its separation from the entrance pupil
b) pupil diameter to its separation from the frame
c) field stop diameter to vertex distance
d) pupil diameter to separation of field stop to entrance pupil

60) Time for some math now. What is the aFoV for the frame that Marius has fit with a +11.0 D lens (vertex distance 14 mm)?

a) 12.2°
b) 84.4°
c) 94°
d) 102°
e) 130°

61) To reach the correct answer to Q 60, we first need to calculate the location of the entrance pupil in this system. It is ...

a) 16.55 mm
b) 14.00 mm
c) 12.13 mm

62) Marius continues with his experimentation. He now has fitted a –11.0 D lens (vertex distance is still 14 mm). What is the new aFoV?

a) 12.2°
b) 84.4°
c) 94°
d) 102°
e) 130°

63) To reach the correct answer to Q 62, we first need to calculate the location of the entrance pupil in this system. It is ...

a) 16.55 mm
b) 14.00 mm
c) 12.13 mm

64) Lieutenant Théodule Gillenormand is working on sag formulas. What happens to the sagittal depth if he reduces the radius of curvature by half?

a) It nearly halves.
b) It remains the same.
c) It nearly doubles.
d) It nearly quadruples.

65) What happens to the sagittal depth if Gillenormand doubles the lens blank diameter?

a) It nearly halves.
b) It remains the same.
c) It nearly doubles.
d) It nearly quadruples.

66) Gillenormand is working on the approximate formula for sag. He has a 2-inch diameter lens blank with 16 cm radius of curvature. What is the sag if it is calculated with the exact formula and with the approximate formula?

a) exact 0.2 cm; approximate 0.18 cm
b) exact 0.2 cm; approximate 0.2 cm
c) exact 0.1 cm; approximate 0.1 cm
d) exact 0.05 cm; approximate 0.05 cm

67) Gillenormand has a 2-inch diameter lens blank with a radius of curvature of 4 cm. What is the sag if it is calculated with the exact formula and with the approximate formula?

a) exact 0.9 cm; approximate 0.8 cm
b) exact 0.8 cm; approximate 0.8 cm
c) exact 0.9 cm; approximate 0.9 cm
d) exact 0.8 cm; approximate 0.9 cm

68) Colonel Georges Pontmercy is helping his son measure some lens blank curves. Their Geneva clock is graduated to the 1.53 refractive index. The lens blank has $n = 1.666$. What is the true curve if the measured curve was +8.00 D?

a) +6.42 D
b) +8.00 D
c) +9.00 D
d) +10.0 D

69) In Pontmercy's lens clock, the distance between the moveable (center) pin and the stationery pin is 20 mm. What is the radius of curvature of a convex lens surface if the sag is 2.52 mm?

a) 0.44 cm
b) 0.88 cm
c) 4.4 cm
d) 8.8 cm

70) What is the power of this lens blank (Q 69), if the standard refractive index ($n = 1.53$) is used?

a)   +3.00 D
b)   +6.00 D
c)   +9.00 D
d)   +12.00 D

71) The scale in Monsieur Mabeuf's lens clock is in diopters, units invented by the famed French ophthalmologist Ferdinand Monoyer. This clock truly measures the ...

a)   refractive power of a lens
b)   back vertex power of a lens
c)   front vertex power of a lens
d)   surface power of a lens

72) Monsieur Mabeuf is about to reveal to Marius that he should be paying attention to the base curves. If the desired Rx is +6.00, for example, what should the base curve be (Vogel's rule)?

a)   +2.0 D
b)   +3.0 D
c)   +6.0 D
d)   +9.0 D
e)   +12.0 D

73) Using the nominal formula, what should be the second (back) surface power for the lens in Q 72?

a)   0.0 D
b)   −3.0 D
c)   −6.0 D
d)   −9.0 D
e)   −12.0 D

74) Lesson deux: If the desired Rx is −6.00, what should the base curve be?

a)   0.0 D
b)   +3.0 D
c)   +6.0 D
d)   +9.0 D
e)   +12.0 D

75) Using the nominal formula, what should be the second (back) surface power for the lens in Q 74?

a)   0.0 D
b)   −3.0 D
c)   −6.0 D
d)   −9.0 D
e)   −12.0 D

76) Which is the best choice for a base curve if the desired Rx is −8.00?

a)   +2.0 D
b)   +3.0 D
c)   +6.0 D
d)   +9.0 D
e)   +12.0 D

77) What is the most likely value of the back surface power F_2 in a plus lens per Vogel's rule?

a)   0.0 D
b)   −3.0 D
c)   −6.0 D
d)   −9.0 D
e)   −12.0 D

78) The back lens surface power F_2 is −10.00 D. What is the Rx and the base curve F_1 per Vogel's rule?

a)   Rx = −12.00 D; F_1 = −2.00D
b)   Rx = −6.00 D; F_1 = −2.00D
c)   Rx = −8.00 D; F_1 = +2.00D
d)   Rx = −9.00 D; F_1 = +1.00D

79) Mother Plutarch needs a lens with base curve +14.0 D and back surface power −6.0 D. She wants to keep the center thickness to a minimum of 2 mm. Her frame is round and 40 mm in diameter. What is the radius of curvature of the base curve?

a)   2.4 mm
b)   5.6 mm
c)   3.57 cm
d)   8.33 cm

80) What is the radius of curvature of the back surface in Mother Plutarch's lens?

a)   2.4 mm
b)   5.6 mm
c)   3.57 cm
d)   8.33 cm

81) Seems like we have all available info to calculate sagitta values. Es-tu prêt? What is the sagittal depth for the base curve?

a)   2.4 mm
b)   5.6 mm
c)   3.57 cm
d)   8.33 cm

82) Good. We are making progress. What is the sagittal depth for the back surface?

a)   2.4 mm
b)   5.6 mm
c)   3.57 cm
d)   8.33 cm

83) Almost there. If the minimum edge lens thickness for Mother Plutarch's lens is 1 mm, what should the center lens thickness be?

a) 3.2 mm
b) 4.2 mm
c) 5.6 mm
d) 9.0 mm

84) Gribier digs a cylinder lens of +2.00×020. What is the meridian with the maximum power in this lens?

a) 20°
b) 70°
c) 90°
d) 110°

85) What is the lens cross for Gribier's lens?

a) plano @ 20°; +2.00 @ 70°
b) +2.00 @ 20°; plano @ 110°
c) plano @ 20°; +2.00 @ 110°
d) plano @ 110°; +2.00 @ 20°

86) Gribier shines a collimated light beam on his lens. What is the focused light formation?

a) spot, 20 cm away
b) spot, 50 cm away
c) line, 50 cm away, horizontally (180°) oriented
d) line, 20 cm away, obliquely (20°) oriented
e) line, 50 cm away, obliquely (110°) oriented
f) line, 50 cm away, obliquely (20°) oriented

87) What is the power along the horizontal meridian in Gribier's lens?

a) +0.234 D
b) +0.342 D
c) +0.684 D
d) +2.0 D

88) Mestienne dug another lens from a nearby site (base curve +6.00 D, back surface −7.00 D @ 90° / −6.00 D @ 180°). What is the Rx of this lens?

a) plano −7.00×180
b) plano −1.00×180
c) plano −1.00×090
d) −6.00 −1.00×180

89) What is the lens cross for Mestienne's lens?

a) plano @ 180° / −1.00 @ 90°
b) plano @ 180° / −7.00 @ 90°
c) −6.00 @ 180° / −7.00 @ 90°
d) −6.00 @ 180° / −1.00 @ 90°

90) Still on P. Mestienne's lens. This lens is a _____ toric lens because _____.

a) minus; the Rx is plano −1.00×180
b) minus; the back surface is toric
c) plus; the Rx is −1.00 +1.00×090
d) plus; the front surface is spherical

91) Sœur Simplicity is given a rather complex lens. The front surface is +5.00 D @ 90° / +7.00 D @ 180°, and the back surface is spherical −5.00 D. What is the Rx for this lens?

a) plano −2.00×090
b) −5.00 +2.00×090
c) +2.00 −2.00×180
d) +2.00 +2.00×180

92) What is the lens cross for Sr. Simplicity's lens?

a) plano @ 180° / +2.00 @ 90°
b) +2.00 @ 180° / plano @ 90°
c) plano @ 180° / +5.00 @ 90°
d) +2.00 @ 180° / −5.00 @ 90°

93) Still on Sr. Simplicity's lens. This lens is a _____ toric lens because _____.

a) minus; the back surface is spherical
b) minus; the Rx is +2.00 −2.00×180
c) plus; the Rx is plano +2.00×090
d) plus; the front surface is toric

94) Sr. Simplicity shines a collimated light beam on her lens. What is the focused light formation?

a) spot, 20 cm away
b) spot, 50 cm away
c) line, 20 cm away, horizontally (180°) oriented
d) line, 20 cm away, vertically (90°) oriented
e) line, 50 cm away, horizontally (180°) oriented
f) line, 50 cm away, vertically (90°) oriented

95) Boulatruelle is holding a toric lens made to prescription +5.00 −2.50×090 up to the sunlight. What is the focused formation off this lens?

a) vertical line 40 cm; horizontal line 20 cm
b) vertical line 20 cm; horizontal line 40 cm
c) vertical line 40 cm; horizontal line 40 cm
d) vertical line 20 cm; horizontal line 20 cm

96) The treasure trove is full of toric lenses. Boulatruelle finds a second lens, marked (base curve) +10.00 D, while its back surface is −6.00 D @ 90° / −2.00 D @ 180°. What is the Rx of this lens?

a) +8.00 −4.00×090
b) +8.00 +4.00×180

c) +4.00 +4.00×180
d) +4.00 +4.00×090

97) Still on Boulatruelle's second lens. This lens is a _____ toric lens because _____.

a) minus; the Rx is +8.00 –4.00×180
b) minus; the back surface is toric
c) plus; the Rx is +4.00 +4.00×090
d) plus; the front surface is spherical

98) Boulatruelle holds a pen light 25 m in front of his second lens. What is the formation at the focus?

a) a vertical line of 50 cm
b) a vertical line of 25 cm
c) a vertical line of 12.5 cm
d) a horizontal line of 50 cm
e) a horizontal line of 25 cm
f) a horizontal line of 12.5 cm

99) Cochepaille is holding this Rx lens: +3.00 –6.00×180. Where is the lens the thickest (two correct)?

a) top edge
b) bottom edge
c) center
d) nasal edge
e) temporal edge

100) Monsieur Leblanc is studying this lens Rx: –2.00 +2.00×030. What is its power along the 180° and the 90° meridians?

a) –1.50 D @ 180°; –0.50 D @ 90°
b) –1.50 D @ 90°; –0.50 D @ 180°
c) –1.00 D @ 90°; –3.00 D @ 180°
d) –3.00 D @ 90°; –1.00 D @ 180°

101) Which meridian orientation corresponds to the most and which to the least power in M. Leblanc's lens?

a) –4.00 D @ 120°; –2.00 @ 30°
b) –4.00 D @ 30°; –2.00 @ 120°
c) –2.00 D @ 120°; plano @ 30°
d) –2.00 D @ 30°; plano @ 120°

102) M. Leblanc's second lens is built to this Rx: +3.00 –5.00×060. What is the total power along the 60° and the 150° meridians?

a) –2.00 D @ 60°; –2.00 @ 150°
b) –2.00 D @ 60°; +3.00 @ 150°
c) +3.00 D @ 60°; –2.00 @ 150°
d) –3.00 D @ 60°; –2.00 @ 150°

103) Still on M. Leblanc's second lens. What is the total power along the 120° and 180° meridians?

a) –0.75 D @ 120°; –0.75 @ 180°
b) +1.75 D @ 120°; –0.75 @ 180°
c) –0.75 D @ 120°; +1.75 @ 180°
d) +1.75 D @ 120°; –1.75 @ 180°

104) Champmathieu will be exonerated if he properly states which J power vectors are zero (two correct).

a) J_0 is zero if the axis is 180 or 045.
b) J_0 is zero if the axis is 045 or 135.
c) J_{45} is zero if the axis is 180 or 045.
d) J_{45} is zero if the axis is 180 or 090.

105) Satisfied with his exoneration, Champmathieu is now examining a couple of lenses. Lens A has this Rx: +5.00 –2.50×045. Lens B has this Rx: +3.00 +1.50×090. What are the spherical equivalent values of these lenses?

a) lens A SE = +3.75; lens B SE = +3.75
b) lens A SE = +6.25; lens B SE = +3.75
c) lens A SE = +3.75; lens B SE = +2.25
d) lens A SE = +6.25; lens B SE = +2.25

106) What are the power vectors (J_0 and J_{45}) for lens A?

a) J_0 = 0.00 D; J_{45} = +1.25 D
b) J_0 = 0.00 D; J_{45} = –1.25 D
c) J_0 = +1.25 D; J_{45} = –1.25 D
d) J_0 = +1.25 D; J_{45} = 0.00 D

107) What are the power vectors (J_0 and J_{45}) for lens B?

a) J_0 = 0.00 D; J_{45} = +0.75 D
b) J_0 = 0.00 D; J_{45} = –0.75 D
c) J_0 = –0.75 D; J_{45} = 0.00 D
d) J_0 = +0.75 D; J_{45} = 0.00 D

108) Treating the two lenses A & B as oblique cross cylinders, what is the net CE, J_0 and J_{45}?

a) CE = +7.50 D; J_0 = +0.75 D; J_{45} = +1.25 D
b) CE = +3.75 D; J_0 = +0.75 D; J_{45} = +1.25 D
c) CE = +3.75 D; J_0 = +0.75 D; J_{45} = –1.25 D
d) CE = +7.50 D; J_0 = +0.375 D; J_{45} = +1.25 D

109) After successfully adding the oblique cross cylinders, Champmathieu wants the combined Rx (rounded to the nearest 0.25 D).

a) +6.00 +3.00×030
b) +6.00 –3.00×120
c) +9.00 –3.00×030
d) +9.00 +3.00×030

110) Fauchelevent's lens A is –3.00 +1.50×045 and lens B is the same lens rotated a further 45°, with Rx –3.00

+1.50×090. If J_0 and J_{45} are 0.00 D and –0.75 D for lens A, then the J_0 and J_{45} vectors for lens B are ...

a) J_0 = 0.00 D; J_{45} = +0.75 D
b) J_0 = +0.75 D; J_{45} = +0.00 D
c) J_0 = +0.75 D; J_{45} = +0.75 D
d) J_0 = –0.75 D; J_{45} = +0.00 D

111) The two orientations of Fauchelevent's lenses produce a similar (two correct answers) ...

a) spherical equivalent
b) J_0 and J_{45} vectors
c) astigmatic axis
d) blur strength

112) Petit Gervais looks at his image formed by a flat glass window at a Parisian bakery. What percent of light is reflected in this image (nearly normal incidence) if the window's glass has n = 1.48?

a) 0.48%
b) 1.48%
c) 2.48%
d) 3.75%

113) A certain air–glass interface reflects 6% of incident light (nearly normal incidence). What is the refractive index of the glass?

a) 1.06
b) 1.50
c) 1.60
d) 1.65

114) Gervais shines light through two thin blocks of glass (n = 1.5), each with negligible absorption. What percent of light leaves the second block?

a) 84.9%
b) 88.5%
c) 92.2%
d) 96.0%

115) Inspector Javert uses a glass plate with a transmittance factor q = 0.8 per 1 mm of material. What is the total transmittance when light shines through a 1 mm glass plate (n = 1.5)?

a) 96.0%
b) 92.2%
c) 80.0%
d) 76.8%
e) 73.7%

116) Dumont is holding a glass plate whose transmittance factor is q = 0.9 per 1 mm. What is

the total transmittance when light shines through a 2 mm thick glass plate (n = 1.5)?

a) 74.6%
b) 77.8%
c) 81.0%
d) 90.0%
e) 92.2%

117) Petit Gervais compares two lenses with the same Rx power. Lens A is made of crown glass (n = 1.523); lens B is made of flint glass (n = 1.666). Both lenses have same diameter and are to be fit at same vertex distance. The two properties that differ between the two lenses are:

a) lens A is thicker
b) lens B is thicker
c) surface reflectivity in lens A is higher
d) surface reflectivity in lens B is higher

118) What lenses does Mlle Baptistine need to neutralize this toric lens: –2.00 –1.00×180.

a) –2.00 @ 180° and –3.00 @ 90°
b) +2.00 @ 180° and –3.00 @ 90°
c) +2.00 @ 180° and +3.00 @ 90°
d) –2.00 @ 180° and +3.00 @ 90°

119) Mme Magloire wants to hand neutralize this lens: – 2.00 +2.00×090. When she observes a cross through the lens, the horizontal movement is ...

a) with-the-motion
b) there is no movement
c) against-the-motion

120) Mme Magloire's observation through the lens cross along a vertical direction is ...

a) with-the-motion
b) there is no movement
c) against-the-motion

121) Claquesous is rather rushed during a lensmeter test. He flips the lens, placing the concave side on the stop as if he were wearing the spectacle lens. That is the measured power?

a) back vertex
b) front vertex
c) equivalent
d) base curve
e) back surface power

9.9 OPHTHALMIC OPTICS SUMMARY

Lens Powers and Focal Length(s)

The **optical power** F for a <u>single</u> spherical interface with radius of curvature r, medium after the interface refractive index n', and medium before the interface refractive index n is

SSRI Optical Power:
$$\underbrace{F}_{\text{optical power, expressed in D}} = \frac{\overbrace{n'}^{\text{refractive index after the interface}} - \overbrace{n}^{\text{refractive index before the interface}}}{\underbrace{r}_{\text{radius of curvature, expressed in m}}}$$

Any physical lens has two distinct surface powers. In a lens of refractive index n_{lens}, with radii of curvature r_1 and r_2, surrounded by a medium with refractive index n_{ext}, the surface powers are

Surface Powers in a Lens:
$$F_1 = \frac{n_{lens} - n_{ext}}{r_1} \quad \text{and} \quad F_2 = \frac{n_{ext} - n_{lens}}{r_2}$$

If the lens is surrounded by air, the surface powers are

$$F_1 = \frac{n_{lens} - 1}{r_1} \quad \text{and} \quad F_2 = \frac{1 - n_{lens}}{r_2}$$

In a thin lens, the simple addition of the front and back surface powers produces the lens refractive power. This is described by the **nominal lens formula**:

Thin Lens Power:
$$F = F_1 + F_2$$

In a lens of thickness t, the **equivalent power** is described by the Gullstrand relationship. The concept of equivalent power answers the question: If the lens was ideally thin, what would be the power of this (equivalent) lens?

Thick Lens Equivalent Power:
$$F_e = F_1 + F_2 - \frac{t}{n_{lens}} F_1 \cdot F_2$$

In a thick lens, there are two **vertex powers** and two vertex focal lengths:

Back Vertex Power: $F_{BVP} = \dfrac{F_1}{1 - \dfrac{t}{n_{lens}} \cdot F_1} + F_2$ Front Vertex Power: $F_{FVP} = F_1 + \dfrac{F_2}{1 - \dfrac{t}{n_{lens}} \cdot F_2}$

These powers are measured with the use of a lensmeter.

Front Surface Power F_1

- The beam vergence that leaves front (first) lens surface if a collimated beam (object at infinity) is incident on the lens.
- Is calculated using the SSRI power formula.
- Referenced at the front (object-space) vertex point V.

Equivalent Power F_e

- The beam vergence that leaves the image-space principal plane H' of a thick lens if a collimated beam (object at infinity) is incident on the lens.
- Is the sum of the front surface power F_1, back surface power F_2, and the third term introduced by Gullstrand's formula.
- Referenced at the back (image-space) principal plane H'.

Front Vertex Power (also known as neutralizing power) F_{FVP}

- The beam vergence leaving the object-space front surface of a thick lens if a collimated beam is incident on the lens from the back side
- Is the sum of the front surface power F_1 and the downstream-adjusted back surface power F'_2.
- Referenced at the front (object-space) vertex point V.

Back Vertex Power (also known as prescription power) F_{BVP}

- The beam vergence leaving the image-space back surface of a thick lens if a collimated beam (object at infinity) is incident on the lens.
- Is the sum of the downstream-adjusted front surface power F'_1 and the back surface power F_2.
- Referenced at the back (image-space) vertex point V'.

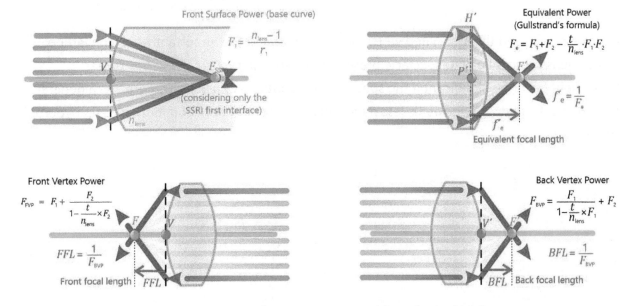

Figure 9-74: Summary of power concepts and formulas in thick lenses.

The reciprocal of the equivalent power (in air) is the equivalent focal length f'_e, measured from the principal plane H'. The reciprocal of the back vertex power (in air) is the back focal length BFL or f_{BFL}, measured from the back vertex point V'; likewise, the reciprocal of the front vertex power is the front focal length FFL or f_{FFL}, measured from the front vertex point V.

Vergence

Downstream vergence is the value of vergence along the propagation of light. When vergence L is known at a certain point, then at a point that is located d [m] downstream of the initial (known) vergence, the (unknown) vergence L' is

Downstream Vergence (in air): $$\underbrace{L'}_{\text{downstream vergence [D]}} = \frac{L}{1 - \underbrace{d}_{\text{downstream distance [m]}} \cdot \underbrace{L}_{\text{initial vergence [D]}}}$$

Distance $\underline{d\ is\ positive}$ since <u>downstream</u> means along the direction of light propagation. The <u>same formula</u> is used for the <u>upstream</u> vergence, in which case the <u>distance d is negative</u>.

Because the spectacle lens is placed a finite distance in front of the eye (the vertex distance, usually 12 to 15 mm), a corrective lens mounted on a frame at the vertex distance has a different power than a contact lens in … contact with the eye. The contact lens has a downstream power:

Vertex Power Adjustment: $$\underbrace{F_d}_{\text{effective downstream power [D]}} = \frac{F}{1 - \underbrace{d_v}_{\text{vertex distance [m]}} \cdot \underbrace{F}_{\text{spectacle lens power [D]}}}$$

Vertex distance and the associated vertex power adjustment are important when converting contact lens prescriptions to spectacle prescriptions (and vice versa); the vertex power adjustment becomes significant if the spectacle prescription is ±4.00 D or more. As a general rule, the contact lens (CL) power is less minus (in myopic correction) and more plus (in hyperopic correction).

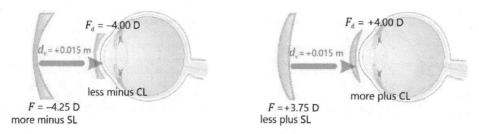

Figure 9-75: Examples of vertex power adjustment between spectacle lens (SL) and contact lens (CL) prescriptions for a vertex distance of d_v = 15 mm in (left) myopic correction and (right) hyperopic correction.

Corrective Spectacle Lens Effects

A corrective spectacle lens worn in front of the eye leads to:

- Retinal images being minified (in myopia) or magnified (in hyperopia). The descriptor is called relative spectacle magnification (RSM). The greater the lens power the more it magnifies for a plus lens or minifies for a minus lens. Vertex distance influences magnification; away from the eye, magnification increases, while closer to the eye, it decreases.

Spectacle Magnification (thin lens/power factor only): $M = \dfrac{1}{1 - \left(\underbrace{d_v}_{\text{vertex distance}} \cdot \underbrace{F_{\text{BVP}}}_{\text{lens vertex power}} \right)}$

In a thick lens, there is also the shape factor, which involves lens thickness t, refractive index n, and base curve F_1. Then, spectacle magnification becomes

Spectacle Magnification (thick lens): $M = \underbrace{\dfrac{1}{1 - \left(\dfrac{t \cdot F_1}{n} \right)}}_{\text{shape factor}} \cdot \underbrace{\dfrac{1}{1 - \left(d_v \cdot F_{\text{BVP}} \right)}}_{\text{power factor}}$

- The eye appears as minified by the amount of the apparent eye size. The dependencies are similar to those of the RSM.
- The field of view increases (in myopia) or decreases (in hyperopia).

Ophthalmic Lens Geometry

The majority of spectacle lenses are meniscus. The lens front surface is convex, and its power is termed the base curve or front lens surface (F_1). Vogel's formula is an <u>approximate formula</u> that helps determine the base curve. For very low prescription power, the recommended base curve is about +6.00 D.

Vogel's rule for the base curve	• For a plus prescription: Base curve = Rx spherical equivalent + 6.00 D. • For a minus prescription: Base curve = ½ Rx spherical equivalent + 6.00 D.

The optical center in an ophthalmic lens is where the wearer looks through the lens (the line of sight) and where we measure lens powers.

Sagitta s is the maximum separation of the lens chord at the center of the base and the vertex at the center of the arc. For a lens semi-diameter h, the relationship between sagitta s and radius of curvature r is

Lens Sagitta:
$$s = r - \sqrt{r^2 - h^2}$$

Sagitta is a property of a single surface. The combination of two sagitta with the edge thickness relates to the center lens thickness t:

Center Lens Thickness: $\qquad t = (s_1 - s_2) + \text{edge thickness}$

Cylinder and Toric Lens Geometry

A cylindrical or **cylinder lens** has optical power only along a meridian, called the refractive or power meridian. Perpendicular to this is the cylinder axis (×), along which the optical power is zero. The distribution of power in a cylinder lens varies from maximum (along the power meridian) to zero (along the axis). The **cylinder effect**, which is defined as the projection of cylinder power, is maximum at right angles from the axis $(\vartheta - \alpha) = 90°$.

The **toric lens** is a combined form of spherical and cylinder lenses. Along its axis, the lens power equals the spherical power alone, while along the refractive meridian, the power equals the sum of the spherical power and the cylindrical power. In a 'minus'-type toric lens, the anterior surface is spherical and the posterior surface is toric; in a 'plus'-type toric lens, the anterior surface is toric and the posterior surface is spherical.

Just like the cylinder lens, the distribution of power in a toric lens varies from maximum (along the power meridian) to minimum (along the axis). The power distribution is

Toric Power at angle ϑ: $\qquad F_{\text{toric lens}} = F_s + F_c \cdot \sin^2(\vartheta - \alpha)$

When the axes of two prescriptions are either the same or 90° away from each other, we can simply add the cylinders together. Often the axes differ, for example, when one component has its axis at 15° and the other component has its axis at 25°. These are called **oblique crossed cylinders**.

In oblique crossed cylinders, power cannot be directly added or subtracted. The proper procedure involves analysis into spherical equivalent (SE) and J power vectors. The addition of oblique crossed cylinders involves the following steps:

1. Ensure that both individual prescriptions are either positive or negative forms.
2. Decompose the cylinder into SE and J power vectors.

3. Sum the SE and J power vectors.

4. Recompose the net spherocylindrical (Rx) representation.

J power vectors:　　　　Horizontal: $J_0 = -\frac{1}{2}F_c \cos 2\alpha$　　Vertical: $J_{45} = -\frac{1}{2}F_c \sin 2\alpha$

Light Transmission in Ophthalmic Lenses

Light loss can be attributed to either reflection at a surface (described by reflectivity R) or absorption A (and, also, scatter) as light transcends a medium. A is the fraction of light intensity that is lost. Transmissivity T is the property describing the opposite of light loss.

Transmissivity at a Surface (losses due to reflection):　　　　$T = 1 - R$

Bulk Transmissivity (losses due to absorption):　　　　$T = 1 - A$

Total transmissivity through any interface and any bulk volume of optical material is computed by multiplying all successive transmissivities.

Total Transmissivity:　　　　$T_{TOT} = T_1 \cdot T_2 \cdot T_3 \cdot \ldots \cdot T_F$

Neutralization and Lensometry

Hand neutralization is a simple technique that allows one to determine the type of lens (plus or minus or astigmatic) and its power by moving or rotating the lens across a field while observing a fixed target through it.

- The image through a minus lens moving in one direction moves <u>with</u> the lens (with-the-motion movement).
- The image through a plus lens moving in one direction moves <u>against</u> the lens (against-the-motion movement).
- Toric and cylinder lenses also exhibit a <u>scissors effect</u>, which manifests when the lens is rotated.

The lensometer, which uses the lensometry technique, is an optical bench instrument that determines the power of a spectacle or contact lens. Decentration of the cross-line target from the reticle center is indicatory of a prism.

CHAPTER 10
PRISMATIC EFFECTS

10.1 THIN PRISM OPTICS AND GEOMETRY

10.1.1 Prism Deviation Angle

A **prism** is a transparent optical element with two non-parallel refracting sides that form the **apical angle** A. A prism deviates rays without affecting their vergence; a collimated beam of light emerges collimated but in a different direction. The more powerful the prism the larger the deviation angle ϑ_E formed between the emerging ray and the ray that is incident on the first surface (ϑ_{i1}). If the angle of refraction at the second interface is ϑ_{t2}, then (see Figure 10-1):

Prism Deviation Angle: $$\vartheta_E = \vartheta_{i1} + \vartheta_{t2} - A \qquad\qquad (10.1)$$

The deviation angle is dependent on the prism's refractive index (which is dependent on the incident light wavelength and the prism material), the apical angle (prism geometry), and the angle of the incident ray. This can be particularly complicated, especially if the apical angle is greater than 30° (what we call a large angle).[938] To accurately calculate the deviation angle, we need the details about four angles: the incident angle ϑ_{i1} and refraction angle ϑ_{t1} at interface 1, and the incident angle ϑ_{i2} and refraction angle ϑ_{t2} at interface 2, as shown in Figure 10-1. In

---

[938] *Introduction to Optics* § 3.3.2 Minimum Angle of Deviation.

other words, prism deviation depends on 'how one looks at the prism' because it changes significantly with the angle of incidence.

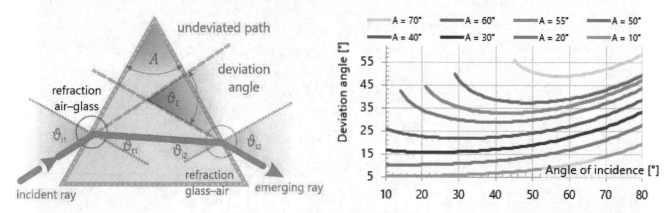

Figure 10-1: (left) Schematic for the detailed calculation of the prism deviation angle. (right) Dependence of deviation angle on angle of incidence for various values of the apical angle A for refractive index n = 1.5.

In ophthalmic optics, two aspects are particularly important: First, the deviation angle is fairly constant over a large range of values for the angle of incidence. Second, the prism is thin to minimize aesthetic effects and discomfort.

These two important aspects are both met in thin prisms (broadly defined as a prism with an apical angle less than 30°), as they are thin *and* provide constant deviation regardless of the angle of incidence under certain conditions. The data plotted in Figure 10-1 (right) suggest that the deviation angle for the prisms with small apical angles (shown in shades of green, $A = 30°, 20°,$ and $10°$) have a near-constant value of minimum deviation, particularly for angles close to normal incidence (less than 30° along the horizontal axis).

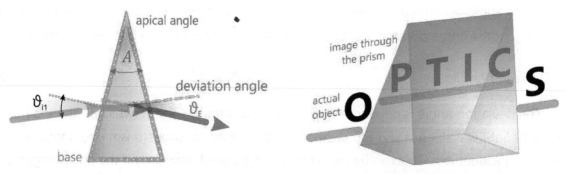

Figure 10-2: (left) A thin prism. (right) The image through the prism is displaced toward the apex. The ray deflection toward the base results in a shift of the viewed image toward the apex.

Thus, we define the **thin**, or **wedge prism** as being one whose apical angle A is small (again, less than 30°) and whose incident rays are nearly normal. This prism deviates light by a fixed angle. If the prism is surrounded by air and its material has refractive index n, then the thin prism deviation angle is written as[939]

Thin Prism Deviation Angle: $\quad\quad\quad\quad\quad\quad\quad \vartheta_E = (n-1)\cdot A \quad\quad\quad\quad\quad\quad$ (10.2)

The utility of this simple relationship lies in the fact that the deviation angle in a thin prism is not dependent on the angle of incidence (as long as the deviation angle is small).

10.1.2 Prism Power

The ability of a prism to produce a linear deviation of a ray at a given distance is quantified by the **prism power** $P\,[^\Delta]$:

$$\text{Prism power } P\,[^\Delta] \;=\; \frac{\text{ray deviation [cm]}}{\text{distance away [m]}} \;=\; 100\cdot\frac{\text{ray deviation [cm]}}{\text{distance away [cm]}} \quad\quad (10.3)$$

Prism power is expressed in **prism diopter** $[^\Delta]$ units denoted by the uppercase Greek letter $\delta\acute{\varepsilon}\lambda\tau\alpha$ Δ; other textbooks use the PD notation. 1^Δ deviates a ray by 1 cm over 1 m. Thus, the prism diopter is a simple expression of the one in one-hundred rule; the two lengths in the numerator and the denominator simply must be expressed in the same unit!

We can draw prism power in a vector format along the bisector of the apical angle, in the direction from the apex to the base, since ray deviation always points towards the base of a prism. The prism deviation angle $\vartheta_E\,[°]$ relates to the prism power $P\,[^\Delta]$ via the formulas

$$\text{Prism power } P\,[^\Delta] = 100\cdot\tan\vartheta_E \quad\text{or}\quad \tan\vartheta_E = P\,[^\Delta]\,/\,100 \quad\quad (10.4)$$

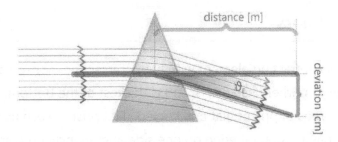

Figure 10-3: Prism power and beam deviation (using monochromatic light).

Example ☞: What is the prism power if it deviates light by 10°?

Since $\vartheta_E = 10°$, $\tan(\vartheta_E) = \tan(10°) = 0.1763$. Prism power $P = 100\cdot0.1763 = 17.63^\Delta$.

---

[939] *Introduction to Optics* § 3.3.4 Thin Prism.

Example ☞: What is the prism power of a thin prism of apical angle 10°, made of material with n = 1.5? This prism has a deviation angle, per Eq. (10.2), ϑ_E = (1.5 − 1) · 10°= 5°. Then, tan(ϑ_E) = tan(5°) = 0.0875. Prism power P = 100·0.0875 = 8.7$^\Delta$.

Approximation $\Big\{$ • For angles less than 45° (or 100$^\Delta$), a degree (°) of angular deviation equals about 2$^\Delta$.

Example ☞: At what distance does a prism 5$^\Delta$ deviate a ray by 10 cm? The distance [m] is found by the deviation ray formula (cm) ÷ P[$^\Delta$]: distance = 10 cm/5$^\Delta$ = 2 m.

Figure 10-4: Prisms are available as loose prisms in a glass trial set. The two here are ophthalmic prisms 10$^\Delta$ and 8$^\Delta$ from a trial frame set. Prisms are also available as prism bars.

There are several ways to create or induce a prism. In general, a prism in an ophthalmic lens can be induced by grinding, decentering (§ 10.4), or tilting (§ 10.7) a lens.

Prism by **grinding** describes the prismatic effect induced in an ophthalmic lens by grinding an edge thickness difference across the base-apex meridian (see also § 10.1.3 and § 10.4.2). Effectively, this creates a prism by forming an apical angle toward the thinnest of the two ends of that meridian; it also moves the lens optical center away from its geometric center.

10.1.3 Prism Thickness

By definition, a prism is a refracting element with two intersecting, non-parallel sides. Thus, the prism is thinnest at the top, where its apex is, and is thickest at the bottom, where its base is. In general, there are two types of prisms: flat and curved. Flat prisms, such as those in an ophthalmic prism bar, have a straight edge on one side and an inclined plane on the other side, and curved prisms are like menisci in shape, with both sides exhibiting a curve.

The often-used trial lens types of prisms tend to be circular (Figure 10-5), so we can describe them geometrically as having thickness-difference peaks along the base-apex line. The length of this base-apex line corresponds with the circular diameter of the prism (d, usually expressed in millimeters).

Figure 10-5: Lateral profile of a 10ᐃ trial-lens round prism showing the thickest part toward the base (close to the handle) and the thinnest toward the apex (away from the handle).

Hence, prism thickness t is the difference between the thinnest part (the apex) and the thickest part (the base). If the prism is 1 mm at the apex and 6 mm at the base, its thickness t is 5 mm. Prism thickness can be approximated by the apical angle A [rad] and prism diameter d [mm]:

Prism Thickness t:
$$A = t/d \ \Rightarrow \ t = A \cdot d \qquad (10.5)$$

Combining Eq. (10.2) and Eq. (10.4), prism thickness expressed in millimeters is given by

Prism Thickness t [mm]:
$$t\,[\text{mm}] = \frac{P\,[^\Delta]}{100 \cdot (n-1)} \cdot d\,[\text{mm}] \qquad (10.6)$$

where P is the prism power [ᐃ], d is the diameter [mm], and n is the refractive index of the material.

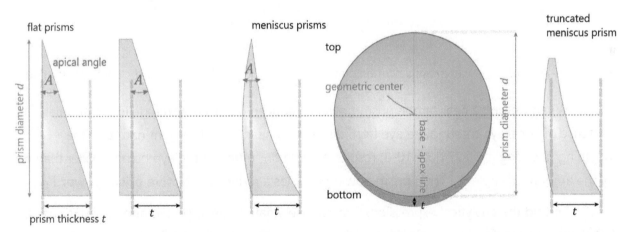

Figure 10-6: Various shapes of ophthalmic prisms. The truncated meniscus prism can be considered an offset part of a round ophthalmic spectacle lens.

Prism power P can be predicted from prism thickness, diameter, and refractive index as follows:

Prism Power and Prism Thickness:
$$P\,[^\Delta] = t[\text{mm}] \cdot \frac{100 \cdot (n-1)}{d[\text{mm}]} \qquad (10.7)$$

These prism power relationships apply to all prism types, flat or meniscus. However, in significantly bent meniscus prisms, these relationships are applicable only at the prism center.

Example ☞: What is the prism power [△] at the center of a 5-cm diameter prism made of glass of refractive index n = 1.5 if the difference between the thickest and thinnest parts of the prism is 4 mm?

We use relationship (10.7) with n = 1.5, t = 4 mm, and d = 50 mm: P [△]= 100·(1.5 – 1)·4 / 50 = 4.0△.

10.2 EFFECTIVE PRISM POWER

Prism power is typically discussed under the assumption that the eye is viewing a distant object. For an object at infinity (Figure 10-7), the prism angularly displaces the image by ϑ_E, as described by relationship (10.4), which equals the angle ϑ_{EFF} that the ray forms on entering the eye. Thus, the prism power P corresponding to an object at infinity for the angle formed $\vartheta_{EFF} = \vartheta_E$ is exactly equal to the prism power corresponding to $\vartheta_E = \tan^{-1}[P[△] / 100]$.

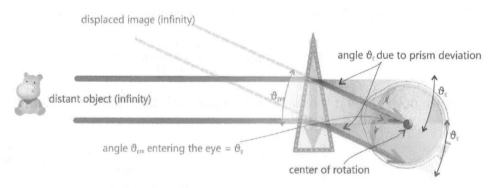

Figure 10-7: Angle ϑ_E due to prism deviation and angle ϑ_{EFF} entering the eye when the object is at infinity.

When viewing a near target, <u>prism power is reduced</u> due to the change in the angular subtense of light rays entering the eye from distance to near. The divergent nature of the incoming rays (angle ϑ_c in Figure 10-8) results in angle ϑ_{EFF} entering the eye being smaller than ϑ_E by the amount of angle ϑ_c. Thus, prism power becomes a reduced **effective prism power** P_{EFF}.

To find the analytical expression, first, we use small-angle approximation in relationship (10.4), which simplifies to $\vartheta_E = P/100$, and $\vartheta_{EFF} = P_{EFF}/100$, when ϑ_E and ϑ_{EFF} are expressed in radians. Geometrical analysis leads to $\vartheta_{EFF} = \vartheta_E - \vartheta_c$, $\vartheta_{EFF} = h/PC$, and $\vartheta_c = h/PN$; again, the small angles ϑ_{EFF} and ϑ_c are expressed in radians. As shown in Figure 10-8, h is the ray height intercept at the prism, PC is the distance from the prism to the eye's center of rotation (COR, itself being 13.5 mm from the corneal plane, § 2.4.3), and PN is the distance from the prism to the near object. Note that all distances are positive.[940] We now write:

---

[940] In several textbooks, the distance PN (prism to near object) is taken as <u>negative</u>, as it should, if we keep consistency with the Cartesian sign convention. Then, in relationship (10.8), the denominator is 1—the fraction of PC / PN. Owing to the fact that the near object is always a real object in front of the prism, we simplified the process by considering this distance as positive.

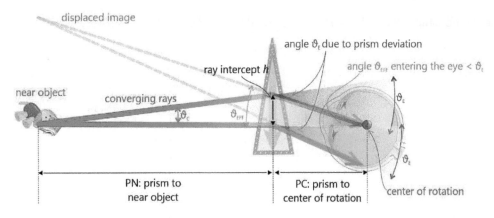

Figure 10-8: Angle ϑ_E due to prism deviation and angle ϑ_{EFF} entering the eye when object is nearby.

$\vartheta_{EFF} = \vartheta_E - \vartheta_c \Rightarrow P_{EFF}/100 = (P/100) - (h/PN)$ and $P_{EFF}/100 = h/PC \Rightarrow h = PC \cdot P_{EFF}/100$

Combination of the above yields: $P_{EFF}/100 = P/100 - (PC/PN) \cdot P_{EFF}/100 \Rightarrow$

Effective Prism Power: $$P_{EFF}[^\Delta] = \frac{P[^\Delta]}{1 + \dfrac{\text{distance from prism to COR}}{\text{distance from prism to near object}}}$$ (10.8)

Example ☞: What is the effective prism power for a prescription prism of $P = 3.0^\Delta$, set at vertex distance 11.5 mm, when Aeneas views a near object at 25 cm from his eye (the distance from the corneal plane)?

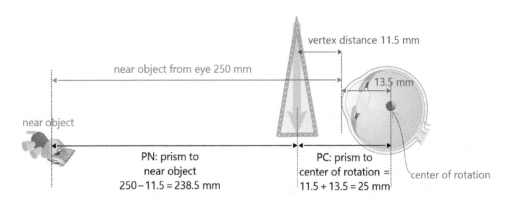

Figure 10-9: Calculation of effective prism power in the presence of a near object.

Step one is to determine the distance PC from the prism to the center of rotation of the eye. In an average-sized eye, the center of rotation is 13.5 mm behind the anterior pole of the cornea (§ 2.4.3). Thus, the distance from prism to the center of rotation is 11.5 + 13.5 = 25 mm.

Step two is to determine the distance PN from the prism to the near object. Since the object is 250 mm from 'the eye,' it is 250 – 11.5 = 238.5 mm from the prism (all distances use the same distance unit, millimeters).

We now use relationship (10.8): $P_{EFF} = P / (1 + 25/238.5) = +3.0^{\Delta}/1.104 = +2.715^{\Delta}$.

Note ⚏ : Relationship (10.8) works under the condition that all mentioned distances are expressed with the same unit (both in centimeters, for example) AND are positive. The effective prism power can also be presented in some alternative forms that conform to the Cartesian convention, in which the distance from the prism to the near object is negative. In this case, the correct formula to use has a minus sign in the denominator. Thus, an alternative to relationship (10.8) is the following:

Effective Prism Power:
$$P_{EFF}[^{\Delta}] = \frac{P\lfloor^{\Delta}\rfloor}{1 - \dfrac{\text{distance from prism to COR}}{\text{distance from prism to near object}}} \qquad (10.9)$$

and
$$P_{EFF}[^{\Delta}] = \frac{P\lfloor^{\Delta}\rfloor}{1 - \text{distance from prism to COR [m]} \cdot \text{near point vergence [D]}} \qquad (10.10)$$

in which all distances follow the cartesian sign convention. All three relationships, (10.8), (10.9), and (10.10), are interchangeable and produce the same result, provided that their respective conventions are followed.

Notes 🧠 :

• The effective prism power P_{EFF} is <u>always less</u> than the distance prism power P. There is no such thing as a negative prism. Thus, the prism has just a bit less power for any object location other than infinity.

• When calculating the effective prism, the base is not affected. A base-up (BU) prism remains base-up, a base-in (BI) prism remains base-in, and so on.

Practice examples with answers ⚒ Effective Prism Power:

Prism $P = 7^{\Delta}$, placed 20 cm from the center of rotation, near object 2 m from the prism: $P_{EFF} = 6.36^{\Delta}$.
Prism $P = 5^{\Delta}$, placed 15 mm from the eye, near object 40 cm from the eye: $P_{EFF} = 4.65^{\Delta}$.
Prism $P = 10^{\Delta}$, placed 11.5 mm from the eye, near object 10 cm from the eye: $P_{EFF} = 7.79^{\Delta}$.

Practical note 🧠 : A rule of thumb is that, when observing an object at the near point, the effective prism power is about 90% of the prism power when observing at infinity. The closer the object the less the effective prism power (prism power is reduced more)—perhaps closer to 80% of the distance prism power. The farther the object the greater the effective prism power (prism power is reduced less).

10.3 FRESNEL AND RISLEY PRISMS

The **wafer** or **Fresnel prism**, named after the French physicist Augustin-Jean Fresnel, is a compact prism compared to conventional prisms because the prism is divided into a set of parallel sections. The apical angle of each section is the same as the equivalent conventional prism. Creating a Fresnel prism is like cutting off the tops of a large number of equally powered prisms and placing them together, side by side.

A Fresnel prism is significantly thinner (and thus, more lightweight) than a conventional prism. A high-power Fresnel prism can be much thinner, for example, a simple, transparent, 1-mm-thick adhesive membrane sheet (with a comparable prism power) that can easily be outfitted on regular prescription glasses.

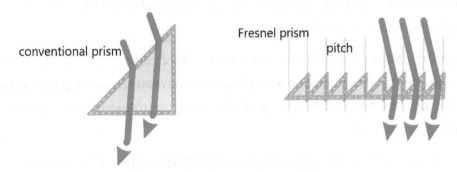

Figure 10-10: (left) Conventional prism versus (right) Fresnel-type prism.

Fresnel prisms are commonly used for individuals who are affected with nerve palsies or head trauma and experience sudden-onset diplopia. Because these prisms are easily adhered to a pair of spectacle lenses, they are easy to change when the demands for fusion change.

For example, if a subject affected with sudden-onset diplopia from a cranial nerve 6 palsy experiences resolution of their diplopia with 20^Δ BO (base-out) applied over the eye with the palsy, with time, as the palsy resolves, a clinician can also reduce the prismatic correction by using a Fresnel prism of a different power. The disadvantages of Fresnel prisms are the striated appearance of the grooves to observers and the difficulty in keeping them clean. The presence of the grooves also contributes to diffraction effects, which reduce contrast sensitivity.[941, 942]

---

[941] Veronneau-Troutman S. Fresnel prisms and their effects on visual acuity and binocularity. Trans Am Ophthalmol Soc. 1978; 76:610-53.

[942] Katz M. Visual acuity through Fresnel, refractive, and hybrid diffractive/refractive prisms. Optometry. 2004; 75(8):503-8.

Figure 10-11: Application of a vertical Fresnel prism on spectacle glass over the OS eye (yes, COVID-19 era!). The prism is 2Δ base-down. The material is ultrathin, 1 mm Fresnel prisms pressed onto the prescription spectacle habitually worn by the subject.

A combination of obliquely crossed prisms forms a **rotary** or **Risley prism**, named after the American ophthalmologist Samuel Doty Risley.[943] In a Risley prism, two identical thin prisms can be counter-rotated in opposite directions such that a variable net deviation—hence, prism power—along a select direction is produced.

These prisms are often used in the evaluation of binocular accommodation, which is the ability of the two eyes to converge their line of sight for viewing nearby objects. In the two extreme orientations, the two prisms are placed base to base (maximum prism power) or base to apex (minimum prism power).

For example, two 5Δ prisms placed base to base form a prism of a total power of 10Δ; when stacked base to apex, they form a prism of a total power of 0Δ. This is because, when the two prisms are placed base to apex, they resemble a parallel slab; the emerging ray is parallel to the incident ray (just a bit displaced). The deviation, and therefore the prism power, is zero [Figure 10-12 (left)]. To the contrary, two identical prisms stacked base to base produce twice the deviation and contribute to double the prism power [Figure 10-12 (right)].

---

[943] The name is attributed to Risley, as he was the first to make the prism known when he published a paper entitled "A new rotary prism," presented orally at the 25th Annual Meeting of the American Ophthalmological Society in New London, Connecticut, and subsequently published as Risley, S. D. Discussion of partial tenotomies in neurasthenia. Trans Am Ophthalmol Soc. 1889; 5:404-5. In this paper, Risley writes, …"*I present herewith … a new, and I think more convenient, form of revolving prisms than those heretofore in use. Adopting the principle first put in practice by Volkmann [German ophthalmologist Alfred Wilhelm Volkmann, 1801–1877] … two prisms … are mounted in a delicately milled edge… The prisms are caused to rotate in opposite directions by means of a milled head screw … The strength of the successive prisms, resulting from the rotation, is read off on the graduated scale engraved on the front plate of the containing cell.*" Despite Risley's modestly, the real genius of his rotary prism is that the two prisms are mounted in a cell with the same diameter as that of the cells employed in the Nachet trial glasses, meaning that the prism readily fits into an ordinary trial frame.
In some textbooks this prism is also called the Herschel prism, named after the English astronomer John Herschel (1792–1871), son of the famous astronomer William Herschel.

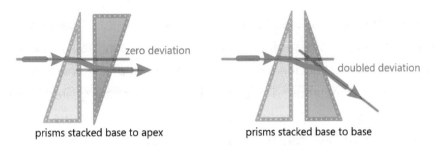

zero deviation

doubled deviation

prisms stacked base to apex

prisms stacked base to base

Figure 10-12: Risley prisms stacked (left) base to apex and (right) base to base.

Food for thought 🍕: The air gap between the two stacked prisms can be ignored. Assuming parallel surfaces and an identical refractive index, the space between acts as a parallel slab. The ray path inside the first prism is simply parallel to the ray path inside the second prism. If the air gap is thin enough, we may simply ignore this space and consider the two prisms as a continuity. No ray path changes are noted at that point.

When the two prisms are stacked base-to-base, we can also assume that the parallel surfaces (if there are any) form an air gap that simply acts to produce a small, and therefore, dismissed, displacement. We can thus assume a continuity at that interface, resulting in a prism whose apical angle is twice that of the single prism. Thus, the deviation doubles; just think of Eq. (10.2) describing the thin prism deviation.

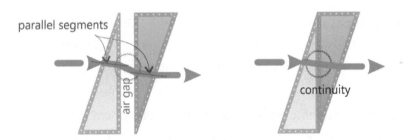

parallel segments

air gap

continuity

Figure 10-13: The air gap between the two parallel prism surfaces only introduces a parallel displacement between the in-prism segments.

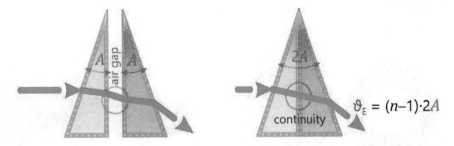

A A

air gap

$2A$

continuity

$\vartheta_E = (n-1) \cdot 2A$

Figure 10-14: Two (thin) prisms stacked base-to-base produce a prism that doubles the deviation.

Time for practice ⏰: Given prisms with $A = 30°$ and $n = 1.5$, identify the ray path and estimate the deviation angle when the initial incidence is normal to the surface with (a) just one prism present, (b) two identical prisms stacked base to base, and (c) two identical prisms stacked base to apex.

In addition to the extreme base-to-base (2× prism power) and base-to-apex (zero prism power) positions, the Risley prism is rotated at any angle between them (usually by a knurled rotating knob), consistently producing a controlled amount of prism along the same direction, noted as the Risley prism orientation. The two individual prisms are geared to move in tandem at equal but opposite angles; thus, the two components moving along the Risley prism orientation add up, while the two components perpendicular to that orientation cancel each other out. This is why the net prism power is always along the direction of the Risley prism orientation and varies only in magnitude.

Example ☞: A vertically oriented 5^Δ Risley prism is turned in a 30° rotation. This means that each prism component is rotated by this amount but in opposite directions. To find the produced prism effect:

- components of the 5^Δ prism at +30°: vertical $5^\Delta \cdot \cos(30°) = 4.33^\Delta$, horizontal $5^\Delta \cdot \sin(30°) = 2.5^\Delta$, and
- component of the 5^Δ prism at –30°: vertical $5^\Delta \cdot \cos(-30°) = 4.33^\Delta$, horizontal $5^\Delta \cdot \sin(-30°) = -2.5^\Delta$.

The combined (rotated Risley) prism has 8.66^Δ vertical prism power and zero horizontal prism power.

Example ☞: A vertically oriented 5^Δ Risley prism is turned in a 45° rotation. This means that each prism component is rotated by this amount but in opposite directions. To find the produced prism effect:

- components of the 5^Δ prism at +45°: vertical $5^\Delta \cdot \cos(45°) = 3.53^\Delta$, horizontal $5^\Delta \cdot \sin(45°) = 3.53^\Delta$, and
- component of the 5^Δ prism at –45°: vertical $5^\Delta \cdot \cos(-45°) = 3.53^\Delta$, horizontal $5^\Delta \cdot \sin(-45°) = -3.53^\Delta$.

The combined (rotated Risley) prism has 7.07^Δ vertical prism power and zero horizontal prism power.

The above examples demonstrate that, as the Risley prism rotates, the net prism power varies in magnitude but is always along the same direction, which is vertical in these two examples. This ability of a Risley prism to produce a variable prismatic power by simply turning a knob has been the basis for its use in ocular diagnostics, such as for the measurement of vergence abilities.

Figure 10-15: (left) Phoropter-mounted Risley prisms and (right) a handheld Risley prism.

10.4 THE LENS AS A PRISM

Lenses can be considered as a series of small prisms put together with slightly different angles, as this produces a controlled ray deviation. Effectively, a lens is a step-like, MesoAmerican pyramid-style, prism. At first glance, plus lenses are like two prisms with their bases placed against each other on the optical axis, while minus lenses are like two prisms with their apices placed together at the optical axis and their bases along the lens edge (Figure 10-16).

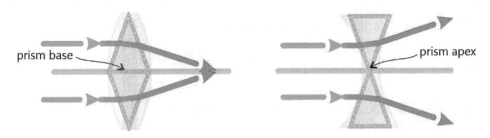

Figure 10-16: A lens can be considered as a combination of two prisms. (left) In positive (plus-powered) lenses, the prism base is on the optical axis, which is the center of the lens and (right) in negative (minus-powered) lenses, the prism base is at the edge of the lens.

Lenses are placed with their optical center in front of the wearer such that, within the center zone, there is no lateral displacement of the image, only an image magnification or minification. The optical center of a lens (§ 9.4.1) can be redefined as the area (point, ideally) of the lens that has no prismatic effect. However, this precise alignment requiring the center of the lens to be placed directly in front of the center of the eye is rarely achieved.

Lens decentration pertains to the shift of the optical center of the lens away from the line of sight of the spectacle wearer. For example, when we view at a distance, the line of sight of the wearer may coincide directly with the optical center of the lens, but when we view a target at close range, due to convergence of the eyes, the line of sight of the eyes shifts laterally from the optical center of the lens (and slightly inferiorly as well). In an optical shop, lens decentration is a common problem caused by the improper fitting of a lens within a spectacle frame. The optical center of the lens never changes; instead, the **major reference point** (MRP) becomes the new position where the line of sight intersects a lens.

Note 👤📷 : The pupil center should directly <u>intercept the line of sight</u>. If the line of sight crosses the lens optical center, the two elements (eye and lens) are aligned; however, it is a simplification to state that the lens optical center is in front of the pupil center, and it is even less accurate to state that the lens optical center is the center of the eye.

10.4.1 Prentice's Rule

Decentering a lens induces a prismatic effect that is dependent on the lateral decentration (from the axis), the lens power, and whether power is positive or negative. This way, a prism can be introduced by simply decentering a finished lens, thereby avoiding the time and associated expense of having to grind the required prism on a semi-finished lens blank.

This induced prism is described by the **Prentice's rule**, named after the 'founding father' of American Optometry, Charles Frederick Prentice.[944] The rule states that one centimeter of decentration (10 mm = 1 cm) between the optical axis (lens center) and the major reference point induces one prism diopter (1^Δ) per one diopter (1 D) of lens optical power:

Prentice Rule:
$$\text{induced prism } [^\Delta] = \frac{\text{lens power [D]} \cdot \text{decentration [mm]}}{10} \qquad (10.11)$$

Alternatively, the Prentice rule induced prism can be expressed as [945]

$$\text{Induced prism } [^\Delta] = \text{lens power [D]} \cdot \text{decentration [cm]} \qquad (10.12)$$

This relationship expresses a progressive increase in prism power as one moves away from the center of the lens. For example (Figure 10-17), a +8.00D lens has zero prismatic power at its optical center (as does any lens at its center), whereas 1 mm away from the optical center the prism power is $= 1 \cdot 8/10 = 0.8^\Delta$, and at 5 mm away, the prism power is 4.0^Δ, etc.

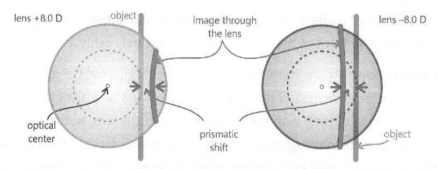

Figure 10-17: Prismatic image shift when looking through (left) a +8.00 D lens and (right) a –8.00 D lens at a distance of 20 mm from the lens center.

In a lens at any given radius from the optical center, the points along a circumferential circle all have the same fixed prismatic power (Figure 10-18). At 20 mm from the lens optical center, the prism power is 16^Δ. This affects the way the image shifts if the gaze is 20 mm from the optical axis. The answer is provided by prismatic deviation and the Prentice rule: The image

---

[944] Prentice CF. A metric system of numbering and measuring prisms. Arch of Ophth. 1890; XiX(1).

[945] Cox M. The passing scene in optometry and optics—a 50-year review. Opt J Rev Optom. 1969; 106(1):29-37.

is offset from the optical axis (farther for a positive lens and closer for a negative lens) by 0.16×
the actual shift of the object ray from the lens center. This is the **prismatic image offset**.

Example ☞: What prism is induced at distances of 1, 5, 10, and 20 mm from the optical center of a +8.00
D lens?

We can use relationship (10.11) or (10.12) if we convert the distances to centimeters. Then,
* 1 mm from the center, prism power is +8.00 D · 0.1 cm = 0.8$^\Delta$.
* 5 mm from the center, prism power is +8.00 D · 0.5 cm = 4.0$^\Delta$.
* 10 mm from the center, prism power is +8.00 D · 1.0 cm = 8.0$^\Delta$.
* 20 mm from the center, prism power is +8.00 D · 2.0 cm = 16.0$^\Delta$.

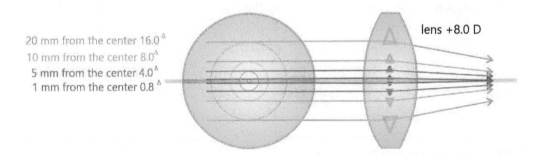

Figure 10-18: Lens prism power as a function of distance from the optical axis (lens center).

The original definition of a prism diopter, as developed by Prentice, requires that all
refraction must occur at a single surface; alternatively, this implies that the first refracting surface
must be perpendicular to a collimated incident light beam (object at distance). For the precise
derivation of Prentice's rule by a thin lens, we consider the flat (zero surface power) surface of a
planoconvex lens facing a collimated beam.

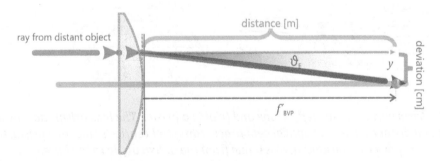

*Figure 10-19: Derivation of Prentice's rule using a plus-powered planoconvex lens with its flat surface
facing a collimated incident beam.*

In this lens, the entire lens power, hence all refraction, takes place at the second surface—
the convex surface. Also, the power of the lens equals the power of the single (second) surface

power, so the back vertex power also equals the 'simple' lens power F, and its reciprocal is the back focal length f. Now, the deviation angle ϑ_E exerted by the prismatic action of this lens for a ray that is decentered by a distance y can be expressed by its tangent as $\tan\vartheta_E = y/f = y \cdot F$.

Recall Eq. (10.4): Prism power $P\,[^\Delta] = 100 \cdot \tan\vartheta_E$. Then, induced prism $= 100 \cdot y \cdot F$, so induced prism $= 100 \cdot$ decentration [m] $\cdot$ lens power [D], which is the expression of the Prentice rule!

Notes 📷: Due to the definition of the Prentice rule and the associated prism diopters, the flat surfaces of the prism bars are held perpendicular to the direction of the fixation object. The implication is that often, particularly in low-power lenses, the results obtained by the Prentice rule deviate from the accurate prism power. Recall, that, for example, to produce a nearly plano ophthalmic lens (say, for example, +0.25 D), the base curve is notably convex, usually, +6.00 D, and the back surface is about −6.00 D, too (see § 9.2.5.1). Thus, the results for a prism from lens decentration obtained by the Prentice rule can be erroneous, considering the very low equivalent power value of this lens, while neither surface of the lens is flat. In high-power lenses, the discrepancy is also present but represents a far smaller component of the resulting prism due to the large prism induced by the high-power lens.

10.4.2 Prism Ground on a Lens

The lens prismatic power varies with increasing radial distance from the optical center according to Prentice's rule; in a prism, the prismatic power is constant across a line from the apical angle to the base.

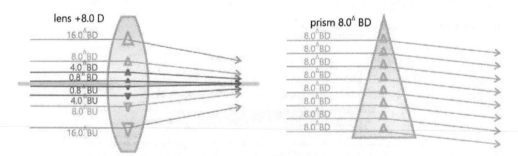

Figure 10-20: Prism variation for (left) a lens and (right) a prism. The lens prismatic power varies with increasing radial distance from the optical center according to Prentice's rule; in a prism, the prismatic power is constant across a line from the apical angle to the base.

Prism by grinding describes the prismatic effect induced in an ophthalmic lens by grinding an edge thickness difference across the base-apex meridian. In this case, the geometrical center of the lens is no longer its optical center.

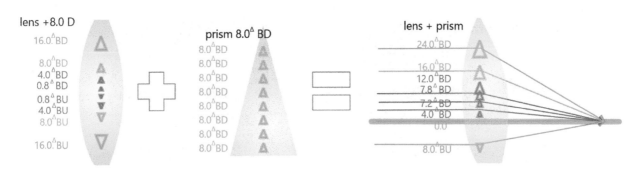

Figure 10-21: A prismatic effect can be ground into a lens to produce a combined lens and prism effect.

10.4.3 Prismatic Effects in Cylinder Decentration

In a properly centered spherical lens, the optical center (§ 9.4.1) coincides with the geometrical center. By rule, the optical center is associated with zero prism effect. In a spherical lens, the induced prism base directions point radially, as if radiating from that center. In a plus-powered lens, the base points toward the optical center [Figure 10-22 (left)], while in a minus powered lens, the base points away from the center [Figure 10-22 (right)]. For this reason, the prism effect due to decentration, as described by Prentice's rule, is simply proportional to the radial displacement from the center; i.e., it has the same magnitude for a fixed displacement, regardless of the orientation of the displacement.

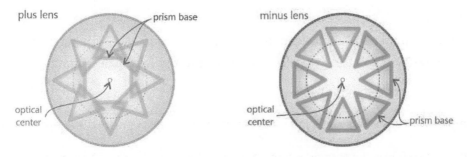

Figure 10-22: The base directions for a spherical lens point in a radial fashion either toward the optical center, as in a plus-powered lens (left), or away from the optical center, as in a minus-powered lens (right).

The cylinder lens (§ 9.5.1) has zero power along its axis and maximum power along the power meridian, which sits at right angles to the axis. The optical center in a cylinder lens lies along the axis; it is therefore not a point center but a line. As in spherical lenses, a decentered cylinder lens induces prismatic effects; the Prentice rule applies to cylinder decentration as well. The difference is that the prism effect due to decentration is proportional to the perpendicular translation about the axis; the prism base directions are always perpendicular to the axis (i.e., they are parallel to the power meridian, as shown in Figure 10-23.

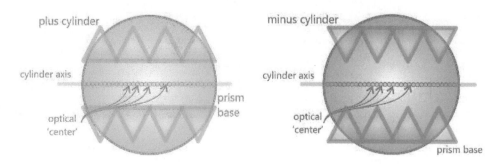

Figure 10-23: The base directions for a cylindrical lens point either toward the optical center (the axis), as in a plus-powered cylinder lens (left), or away from the axis, as in a minus-powered cylinder lens (right).

If the decentration is along the axis or perpendicular to it, then the math is rather simple. No prism is induced if the decentration is parallel to the axis. The maximum amount of induced prism occurs if the decentration is along the power meridian.

Example ☞: What is the induced prism if a –3.00×180 cylinder lens is decentered 10 mm horizontally and 10 mm vertically?

The axis is horizonal; no prism is induced if this cylinder is decentered horizontally. The power is –3.00 D along the vertical. We use Eq. (10.12) with decentration = 1 cm. Then, $P = -3.00 \text{ D} \cdot 1 \text{ cm} = -3.0^{\Delta}$.

Example ☞: What is the induced prism if a –3.00×090 cylinder lens is decentered 3 mm horizontally and 5 mm vertically?

The axis is vertical, so power is –3.00 D along the horizontal direction. A 0.3 cm horizontal decentration induces $P = -3.00 \text{ D} \cdot 0.3 \text{ cm} = -0.9^{\Delta}$. There is no prism due to the vertical decentration.

Practice examples with answers ⚒: Cylinder decentration (Hint: first construct the optical lens cross!)

A cylinder lens +3.00×090 is decentered 6 mm upward and 2 mm laterally (horizontally):
The upward movement has no prism effect. The horizontal movement creates a 0.6^{Δ} prism.

A toric lens +1.00 +2.00×180 is decentered 5 mm horizontally and 2 mm vertically:
The vertical decentration results in a 0.6^{Δ} prism effect. The horizontal results in a 0.5^{Δ} prism.
A horizontal decentration of a ×090 cylinder lens induces a prism along the horizontal power meridian and zero prism power along the vertical axis meridian.
The decentration of a ×045 cylinder lens induces a prism along the 135° power meridian and zero prism power along the 45° axis meridian.

The more complex case involves a cylinder decentered in a direction other than the axis direction (zero effect) or the direction perpendicular to the axis (maximum effect). The simplest approach is to seek the <u>decentration component that is parallel to the power meridian</u>. This distance, converted to cm and multiplied by the cylinder power, yields the induced prism [Δ].

This technique applies to any orientation of the axis and any orientation of decentration (as in all previous examples). The resultant prism has its base aligned along the power meridian (facing inward or outward, depending on the cylinder power), and it can be resolved in the two horizontal and vertical components utilizing prism resolution (§ 10.6).

Example ☞: What is the induced prism power if a –2.00×030 cylinder lens is decentered 3 mm to the left?

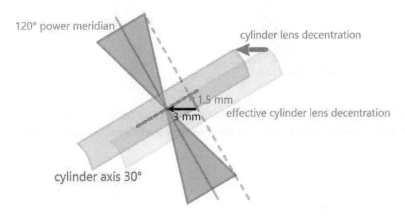

Figure 10-24: Oblique cylinder decentration and related prism effects.

The decentration along the power meridian is (0.3 cm) · sin(120°) = –0.15 cm. The induced prism is P = –2.00 D · (–0.15 cm) = +0.3^Δ, which deploys along the power meridian (120°). Its components are along the horizontal = +0.3^Δ · cos(120°) = –0.15^Δ, and along the vertical = +0.3^Δ · sin(120°) = +0.26^Δ.

Practice examples with answers ⚒: Oblique cylinder decentration (Hint: first determine decentration along the power meridian.)

A cylinder lens +6.00×060 is decentered 8 mm downward. Decentration along the power meridian (150°) is 0.40 cm. Induced prism is –2.4^Δ along 150°, which resolves as 2.0^Δ horizontal and –1.2^Δ vertical prism.

A cylinder lens –4.00×045 is decentered 8 mm laterally to the left. Decentration along the power meridian (135°) is 0.56 cm. Induced prism is –2.263^Δ along 135°, which resolves as –1.6^Δ horizontal and +1.6^Δ vertical.

A cylinder lens 5.00×070 is decentered 8 mm along the 120°. Decentration along the power meridian (160°) is 0.61 cm. Induced prism is 3.0^Δ along 160°, which resolves as –2.88^Δ horizontal and +1.0^Δ vertical.

10.5 PRISMS IN VISION COMPENSATION

10.5.1 Specifying Prism Base

Prism base orientation is defined with reference to the <u>wearer's face</u>. Along the vertical direction, the prism is **base-up** (BU) if the base is superior (S) and **base-down** (BD) if the base is inferior (I) (Figure 10-25). Along the horizontal lateral direction, the **base-in** (BI) prism has a nasal (N) base orientation, while the **base-out** (BO) prism has a temporal (T) base (Figure 10-26).

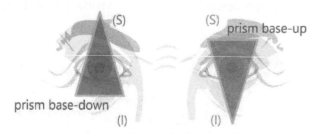

Figure 10-25: (left) Prism base-down (OD eye) and (right) prism base-up (OS eye). The 'triangle' prism is illustrates the prism profile, not what is facing the eye, and used is to indicate the base orientation only.

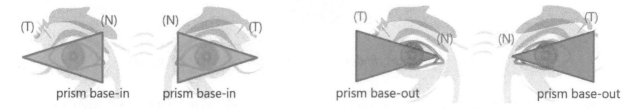

Figure 10-26: (left) Prism base-in in both OD and OS. (right) Prism base-out in both OD and OS.

In the eye examination, prisms can be used a variety of ways, such as in the phoropter, in a handheld trial lens, as free-space prisms (Figure 10-27), or as handheld prism bars.

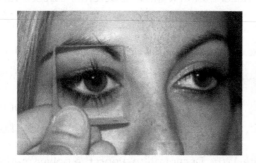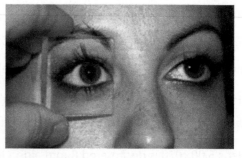

Figure 10-27: A handheld loose prism held in front of the right eye during a sensorimotor evaluation. (Left) A BD (base-down) prism measures hyperphoria, and (right) a BO (base-out) prism measures esophoria. Images by Costas Katsoulos used with permission.

A prism is often incorporated into a spectacle prescription via decentration of the lens. This way, the prism base depends on the plus or minus power of the lens and the direction of the displacement. The amount of induced prism depends on the lens power and the magnitude of the displacement, per the Prentice rule (10.12). In a plus lens, a downward decentration results in a base-down (BD) prism, and an upward decentration results in a base-up (BU) prism (Figure 10-28).

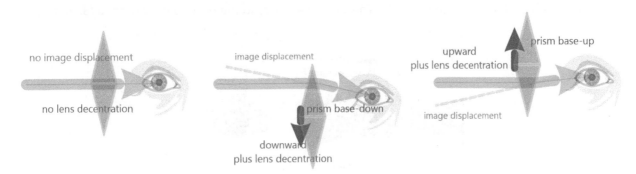

Figure 10-28: Image displacement and prism effect in the decentration of a plus lens.

Thus, the prism base is along the direction of the lens displacement in plus-powered lenses (stated differently, the prism base is oriented the same as the direction of displacement in plus lenses; for example, it is base-down in an inferior displacement).

A minus-powered lens decentered in a downward direction results in a base-up (BU) prism and an upward decentration in a base-down (BD) prism (Figure 10-29). Thus, the prism base is against lens displacement in minus lenses (stated differently, the prism base is oriented in a direction opposite to the displacement in minus lenses; for example, it is base-down in a superior displacement, or base-in for a temporal displacement).

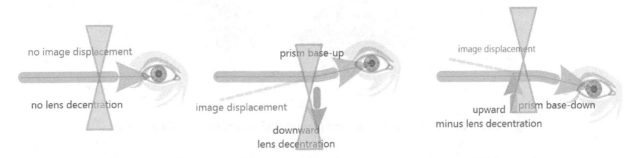

Figure 10-29: Image displacement and prism effect in the decentration of a minus lens.

Example ☞: What prism is induced from a +7.75 D lens if its optical center is decentered 4 mm inferiorly?

Prismatic deviation is (+7.75 D)·(0.4 cm) = +3.10$^\Delta$. The lens is plus, so the prism base is down (BD).

Note 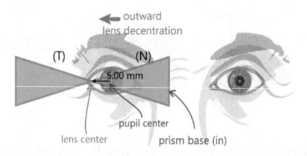: Remember to convert lens displacement/decentration into centimeters if you are using relationship (10.12). Often, lens decentration is reported in millimeters.

Example ☞: What is the induced prism when a –2.00 D lens is decentered 5 mm temporally in front of Lavinia's right eye (OD)?

Induced prism is (–2.00 D)·(0.5 cm) = –1.0$^\Delta$. The lens is negative, so the prism base is base-in (BI, nasally).

Figure 10-30: Prism effect by lateral (temporal) decentration of a minus lens.

Note 📖: The algebraic sign appearing in the calculation of induced prism by the Prentice rule indicates a prism base in relation to the lens displacement if the lens power is properly signed. The negative sign in this example indicates that the prism base is in the direction opposite to the lens decentration in minus lenses.

Example ☞: Determine the decentration of a +4.00 D lens that produces a +1.00$^\Delta$ prism BO for the OD eye.

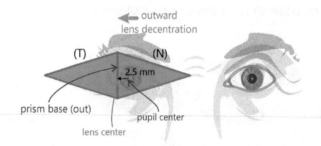

Figure 10-31: Prism effect by lateral (temporal) decentration of a plus lens.

The induced prism (+1.00$^\Delta$) is proportional to the lens power (+4.00 D) and distance [cm] from the optical axis. Therefore, the desired displacement is prism/lens power: 1.00$^\Delta$ / 4.00 D = +0.25 cm = +2.5 mm. The plus lens is before the right eye (Figure 10-31), which means that, to induce base-out, the lens should be displaced in the temporal direction; in the plus-powered lens, decentration is in the same direction as the base. Thus, the lens should be decentered outward (temporally) by 2.5 mm.

Example ☞: What is the induced prism when a –2.00×035 cylinder lens placed in front of the right eye of Francisco's eyes is decentered temporally by 4 mm?

A 4 mm temporal decentration results in an effective 2.294 mm upward decentration along the power meridian (125°). This induces a prism of (–2.00 D)·(0.294 cm) = –0.459$^\Delta$, deployed along the 125° power meridian. This prism resolves into two components along the horizontal and the vertical as follows: horizontal –0.459$^\Delta$· cos(125°) = 0.263$^\Delta$ (BI) and vertical –0.459$^\Delta$· sin(125°) = –0.376$^\Delta$ (BD).

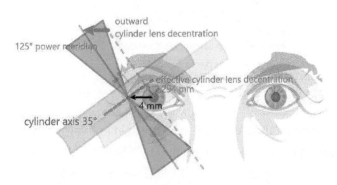

Figure 10-32: Prism effect by lateral displacement of an oblique minus cylinder.

Prism due to lens decentration practice examples with answers ⚒:

Rx lens +3.00 D, decentered 2 mm temporally on the right eye. The prism induced is = 0.6$^\Delta$ BO.

A 0.6$^\Delta$ BU is induced when a lens is decentered by 3 mm inferiorly on the left eye. Then lens Rx is –2.00 D.

Rx lens +3.00 –2.00×180 is decentered 2 mm superiorly on the right eye. Prism induced = 0.2$^\Delta$ BU.

Rx lens +3.00 –2.00×180 is decentered 2 mm nasally on the right eye. Prism induced = 0.6$^\Delta$ BI.

10.5.2 Prisms in front of Both Eyes

10.5.2.1 Interpupillary Distance Disparity

It is possible that the lens optical center spacing (due to frame limitations) is different from the wearer's interpupillary distance (abbreviated as PD or IPD); the average human PD is 64 mm, ranging between 60 and 65 mm, while some frames may impose a lens spacing of up to 70 mm.

In interpupillary distance disparity, the lens decentration can be calculated as being half of the difference between the lens center spacing and the wearer's PD. If the lens center ('frame' PD) is larger than the wearer's PD, the lenses have a temporal displacement, and if the frame PD is smaller than the wearer's PD, the lenses have a nasal displacement. Therefore, the amount of induced prism depends on the amount of displacement, the direction of displacement, and the lens power. Assuming that the lenses are symmetrical, this effect is the same for each lens; the type of prism is the same, and the total prism is the compound effect from each lens.

Example ☞: Adriana is playing with her new toy, a virtual reality cardboard fitted with +10.00 D lenses spaced by 68 mm. Her PD is 64 mm. How much and what type of prism is induced per eye?

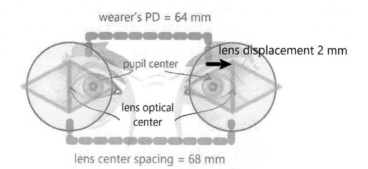

Figure 10-33: *When the pupil centers are displaced with respect to the lens, there is a prismatic effect.*

Here, the plus lenses, both shifted outward, create a BO prism in both eyes. The difference between Adriana's PD and the lens center spacing is 4 mm, which is divided by 2 between the two eyes; thus, each lens is displaced temporally by 0.20 cm. The prism for a +10.00 D lens displaced by 0.20 cm is (+10.0 D)·(0.2 cm) = 2.0^Δ BO per eye. The total prism is 4.0^Δ calculated by the compound effect, so this is a 4.0^Δ BO prism.

Example ☞: Orlando's frames are not as he likes. They are fitted with a set of –5.00 D spectacles, and there is a 3 mm outward, horizontal decentration per lens. What amount and what type of prism is induced?

Per eye, the induced prism is (–5.00 D)·(0.3 cm) = $–1.5^\Delta$; the – sign indicates a direction opposite to the lens decentration (Figure 10-34). This is a 1.5^Δ BI prism for each eye; collectively, it is a 3.0^Δ BI prism.

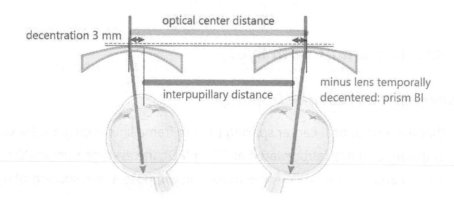

Figure 10-34: *Minus lens shifted outward results in a base-in prism in both eyes.*

Practice examples with answers ⚒ Prism due to interpupillary distance disparity:

Rx OD –3.00 D / OS –4.00 D. Wearer PD is 66 mm, frame-imposed lens centers are 62 mm apart. Prism induced is 0.6^Δ BO for the right eye and 0.8^Δ BO for the left eye. Total prism is 1.4^Δ BO.

Rx OD –3.00 –2.00×180 OS –2.00 –2.00×180. Wearer PD is 68 mm, frame-imposed lens centers are 60 mm apart. Prism induced is 1.2^Δ BO for the right eye and 0.8^Δ BO for the left eye. Total prism is 2.0^Δ BO.

Rx OD +2.00 –2.00×090 OS +3.00 –2.00×090. Wearer PD is 68 mm, frame-imposed lens centers are 58 mm apart. No prism is induced for the right eye, and 0.5^Δ BI is induced for the left eye.

10.5.2.2 Distance and Near Vision; Convergence

In addition to decentration imposed by frame size, other aspects can contribute to the lens center not aligning with the pupils. An infrequently discussed finding is the centroid shift—the shifting of the pupillary center during dilation.[172, 173] The most common decentration is due to near-viewing convergence. Shifting from distance viewing (the two lines of sight are parallel when viewing infinity) to near viewing causes the lines of sight to move nasally and to converge, shifting the MRP nasally on each lens such that it is closer than the lens center spacing. This 'inward' pupillary decentration for near vision leads to a physiologically smaller interpupillary distance compared to the anatomical PD measured at a distance, by about 3 mm[157, 946, 947] (Figure 10-35). Again, here it is assumed that the pupils move downward as well, although the pupil movement would depend on the position of the near object; however, this movement is not associated with convergence effects.

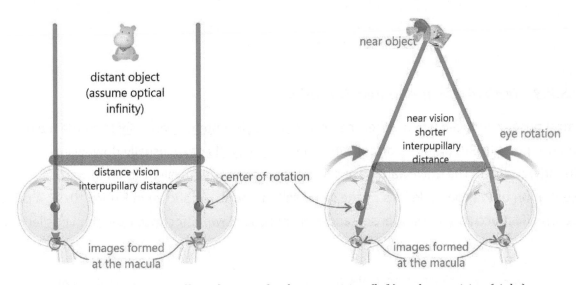

Figure 10-35: Interpupillary distance for distance vision (left) and near vision (right).

If the pupils are in perfect alignment with the lens centers, there is no prism effect [Figure 10-36(a)]. The effect of the pupils moving inward is equivalent to an outward lens decentration of the same amount; this induces prism. Thus, convergence induces prism because the two lenses are effectively decentered in opposite directions, i.e., temporally. When viewing a near object, a person

[946] Leffler CT, Davenport B, Rentz J, Miller A, Benson W. Clinical predictors of the optimal spectacle correction for comfort performing desktop tasks. Clin Exp Optom. 2008; 91(6):530-7.

[947] Jiang B, Ramamirtham R. The adaptive effect of narrowing the interocular separation on the AC/A ratio. Vision Res. 2005; 45(20):2704–09.

with myopia wearing spectacles is subject to a base-in prism [Figure 10-36(b) versus (c)], and a person with hyperopia wearing spectacles is subject to a base-out prism [Figure 10-36(d) versus (e)].

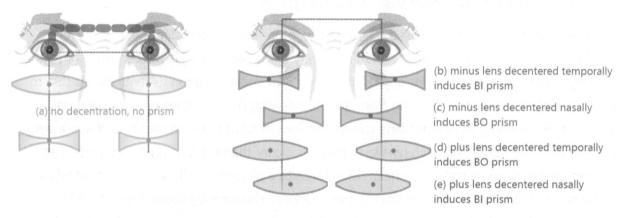

(b) minus lens decentered temporally induces BI prism

(c) minus lens decentered nasally induces BO prism

(d) plus lens decentered temporally induces BO prism

(e) plus lens decentered nasally induces BI prism

Figure 10-36: Prism effects induced by a disparity between the frame/lens optical center spacing and the wearer's interpupillary distance.

Note ☞ : Often, the lenses for near vision are plus powered, so the induced horizontal prism when fixating on a near target is base-out. To avoid inducing this prism, the add power segment in a bifocal lens must be properly placed according to the PD for near distance.[948]

10.5.2.3 Vertical Prism and Vertical Imbalance

Vertical prism is induced when either the <u>lens center is decentered vertically</u> from the major reference point (MRP) or (more often!) when the <u>wearer shifts gaze</u>, usually downward (inferiorly) to read. The downward gaze shift of the wearer is equivalent to an upward decentration of the spectacle lens by the same shift amount. As shown in Figure 10-37, a prism base-up effect occurs with plus lenses, and a prism base-down effect occurs with minus lenses.

prism base-up   gaze shifts downward   gaze shifts downward

prism base-down

Figure 10-37: Prism effects with the gaze shifting downward.

Example ☞: Macbeth wears a Rx +3.00 OU (both eyes viewing); what is the induced vertical prism when he shifts his gaze downward by 5 mm to read the playscript?

---

[948] Fonda G. Spectacle correction for aphakia. The prismatic effect. Surv Ophthalmol. 1981; 26(3):154-6.

The induced prism is 1.5^Δ BU per eye, with the same magnitude and orientation for both eyes because his gaze shifts by the same amount (5 mm) and the two lenses have the same power (not always the case!).

For the vertical direction, unless the lenses have opposing power signs (one plus and one minus, as in the rare case of antimetropia[949]), the prism effect is yoked, in the sense it has the same direction (i.e., both eyes BU or BD). However, having the same direction does not mean having the same magnitude; if the two lenses in front of the eyes have different powers (for example, two different spherical powers or two different meridional cylindrical powers), then the two prisms will have different magnitudes, and the <u>difference between those two prisms</u> is a **vertical imbalance**.

Note ☵ : Prism imbalance is an important <u>clinical consideration</u>. The reason is none other than it leads to disjunctive eye movements that are, by nature, not well tolerated by the visual system: Prism imbalance increases the fusional vergence demands (§ 10.5.3.1) of the eye system, perhaps exceeding its capacity to sustain comfortable binocular vision. Thus, it is the prism imbalance and not the prism per eye that is more detrimental to vision and therefore attracts more clinical attention.

The vertical imbalance is reported (as a single value) on the most affected eye as the prism power difference between the two eyes. In the rare case where the two prisms are oriented along opposing directions (one BU and the other BD or one BI and the other BO), the net prism effect is compounded, and the vertical (or horizontal, if the differences are along the horizontal direction!) imbalance is the numerical sum of the simple magnitudes of the two prisms.

Examples ☞: Lady Macbeth's right (OD) eye experiences 2.5^Δ BU and her left (OS) eye experiences 1.0^Δ BU prism. What is the prismatic imbalance between her two eyes?

Both vertical prisms are along the same direction (BU), causing conjugate eye moments. Their difference is $2.5^\Delta - 1.0^\Delta = 1.5^\Delta$ BU, reported in front of the most-affected right eye.

Examples ☞: Iago's right (OD) eye has 2.0^Δ BO and his left (OS) eye has 1.5^Δ BO prism. What is the net effect?

These two horizontal prisms are facing opposite directions (yes, although—or better yet, <u>because</u>—they are both BO!), so they lead to disjunctive eye movements, compounding each other. The net effect is the sum, not the difference: $2.0^\Delta + 1.5^\Delta = 3.5^\Delta$ BO.

---

[949] Vincent SJ, Read SA. Progressive adult antimetropia. Clin Exp Optom. 2014; 97(4):375-8.

Examples ☞: The following Rx's produce vertical imbalance:

+2.00 OD / +4.00 OS; the difference of the magnitudes of the two prisms.

+2.00 OD / –1.00 OS; the sum of the magnitudes of the two prisms.

–1.00 +2.00×180 OD / –1.00 –1.00×180 OS; the sum of the magnitudes of two prisms (draw the lens cross!)

Example ☞: Othello's Rx is OD –6.00 D / OS –2.00 D. What is the induced vertical imbalance when his gaze shifts 5 mm downward from the lens optical centers?

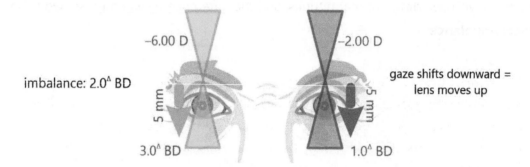

Figure 10-38: Vertical imbalance in Othello's eyes. The downward gaze shift is simulated with an upward lens movement.

We calculate separately the decentration-induced prism due to Othello looking downward by 0.5 cm. A downward shift in the gaze is equivalent to an upward lens decentration by the same amount.
OD prism is (–6.00 D)·(0.5 cm) = –3.0$^\Delta$, or 3.0$^\Delta$ BD. OS prism is (–2.00 D)·(0.5 cm) = –1.0$^\Delta$, or 1.0$^\Delta$ BD. The vertical imbalance is 2.0$^\Delta$, reported on the most-affected eye as 2.0$^\Delta$ BD OD.

Vertical Imbalance Practice examples with answers ⚒ :

Valeria's Rx is OD –2.00 / OS +1.00. Her gaze shifts downward by 1 cm. Vertical imbalance is 3.0$^\Delta$ BD OD.

Miranda's Rx is OD –3.00 –2.00×180 / OS –2.00 –1.00×180. When her eyes shift downward by 3 mm, a 0.6$^\Delta$ BD vertical imbalance is induced, noted on the most affected OD eye (hint: draw the lens cross!).

When Prospero gazes downward 5 mm, a 1.5$^\Delta$ BD vertical imbalance is noted in his OS eye. What is the cylinder in his OS eye if the Rx is OD –3.00 +2.00×180 and the sphere in OS is –4.00 D? (Answer: plano.)

Reynaldo's Rx is OD +3.00 –2.00×180 / OS –2.00 –2.00×090. His gaze shifts downward by 5 mm through the optical centers of the lenses. Vertical imbalance induced is 1.5$^\Delta$ BD noted on the most affected OS eye.

Note 🏮 : In some textbooks, vertical imbalance is reported on the most affected eye as the prism power <u>required to compensate for this imbalance</u>. In this case, the prism direction is opposite to what was introduced here. Attention is therefore warranted to the proper definition of 'imbalance.'

10.5.3 Prisms for Binocular Vision Dysfunction

10.5.3.1 Fusional Vergence

To maintain binocularity, the visual system uses fusional vergence, accommodative vergence, proximal vergence, and tonic vergence.[950] Proximal vergence is a convergence movement generated by object proximity; accommodative vergence is a convergence movement initiated by accommodation; tonic vergence is related to the baseline normal resting posture of the eye; and fusional vergence is the act of moving the eyes in response to disparity.[951] In particular, fusional vergence can be subdivided into positive fusional vergence, which is the act of convergence (mimicked by the introduction of a base-out prism), and negative fusional vergence, which is the act of divergence (mimicked by the introduction of a base-in prism).

The placement of prisms in front of the eyes interacts with the fusional vergence system. A prism can place considerable strain on fusional vergence reserves. However, if properly implemented, prisms may help in conditions such as divergence insufficiency, which may cause double vision because of excess convergence and reduced reserves to diverge for fusing targets. For example, in the case of a myopic spectacle wearer, the BI prism effect that occurs when switching to near vision reduces the demand for convergence [Figure 10-39 (left)].

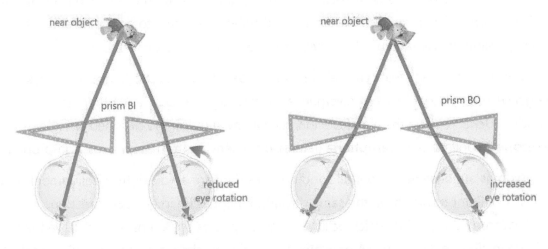

Figure 10-39: (left) Base-in prism results in a reduced need for eye rotation. (right) Base-out prism results in an increased need for eye rotation.

The opposite is true in spectacle lenses for hyperopia, which, when looking at a near object, creates a BO prism. This prism increases the demand for convergence [Figure 10-39

---

[950] Maddox EE. The clinical use of prisms and the decentering of lenses. 2nd ed. Bristol: John Wright and Co; 1893.

[951] Fogt N, Toole A, Rogers D. A review of proximal inputs to the near response. Clin Exp Optom. 2016; 99(1):30-8.

(right)]. The condition is more common in near-vision spectacle Rx's.[952] In general, a BI prism reduces convergence demand, while a BO prism increases convergence demand.

Similarly, there is a vertical fusion vergence ability that relates to the applicability of (up to certain tolerance limits) a vertical prism. In general, a healthy individual has a range of normal vergence reserves. The largest reserves are the positive vergences, followed by the negative vergences, and then by the vertical ones.[953] However, in fusional vergence dysfunction, these reserves are reduced, so the tolerance to prism is reduced.

Clinical note 👁 : How much is too much?

Prism tolerance depends on the fusional vergence reserves. A healthy individual has a range of vergence reserve—the capacity to move the eyes inward, outward, or in a vertical direction. The vertical vergence system has the smallest reserve.[954] An individual with fusional vergence dysfunction has overall reduced reserves and therefore lower tolerance to any type of prism.

10.5.3.2 Ocular Misalignments

Prisms can be introduced to manage clinically relevant departures from an **orthophoric**, or **orthovergence**, position of the eyes. **Orthophoria** (ορϑό, for proper) is the normal alignment of the eyes, where there exists no associated or dissociated deviation of the two lines of sight when fixating on a distant target.[955] Although orthophoria appears to be the ideal ocular alignment, a slight misalignment of the eyes, especially at near vision, is the norm.

Deviations from an ideal ocular alignment can be attributed conditions such as nystagmus, convergence insufficiency or excess, divergence insufficiency or excess, and other binocular vision deficiencies. Depending on the manifestation, such a deviation can be classified as either **heterotropia** (manifest) or **heterophoria** (latent), both deriving from έτερο-, for 'non-proper.'

Tropias are observed under all conditions, as they are an outright misalignment of the two eyes. Comitant tropias have the same deviation magnitude in all gaze directions. In contrast, concomitant tropias, which occur with nerve palsies or trauma, do not have the same magnitude in all gaze directions. A noncomitant tropia can show a greater misalignment when looking to the right compared to when looking to the left, for example.

---

[952] Fischer LG. Analytical aids for determining induced vertical prism imbalances in anisometropia. Am J Optom Physiol Opt. 1976; 53(5):249-58.

[953] London RF, Wick BR. Vertical fixation disparity correction: effect on the horizontal forced-vergence fixation disparity curve. Am J Optom Physiol Opt. 1987; 64(9):653-6.

[954] Du Toit R, Ramke J, Brian G. Tolerance to prism induced by readymade spectacles: setting and using a standard. Optom Vis Sci. 2007; 84(11):1053-9.

[955] Owens DA, Tyrrell RA. Lateral phoria at distance: contributions of accommodation. Invest Ophthalmol Vis Sci. 1992; 33(9):2733-43.

Phorias are observed when binocular vision is suspended. Thus, phoria is the eyes' misalignment when they are dissociated from each other and are not viewing the same target. Under normal binocular conditions, however, the two eyes are associated with each other; they are both open and fixated on the same target, and no misalignment is observed.

The phoria deviation is latent, hidden from observation by fusional mechanisms[956, 957] and are uncovered when the fusional vergence is interrupted.[958] Thus, phoria is evaluated when the stimuli for fusion are eliminated, for example, with the cover–uncover test, the alternate-cover test, the use of a dissociating prism, etc.

Clinical note about measuring phorias 🗋 :

Dissociated phoria is measured when fusion is present (both eyes are open and fixating on the target). This includes objective tests such as the alternate-cover test or subjective tests such as the Maddox rod, the von Graefe, the modified Thorington, and the Hess–Lancaster tests.

Associated phoria involves fixation disparity and is measured in the absence of fusion—either one eye is occluded (alternate-cover test) or each eye is shown a different target.

Lateral deviations are distinguished as either eso- (ἔσω-) or exo- (ἔξω-), indicating inward and outward misalignment, respectively. **Esophoria**/esotropia is an inward, converging deviation, and **exophoria**/exotropia is an outward, diverging deviation (Figure 10-40 top).

Phorias and tropias are reported in the necessary prism power [$^{\Delta}$] to compensate for them. They depend on whether fixation is at distance (6 m) or near (40 cm). Even an individual without any binocular vision dysfunction may still display a slight phoria posture, often exophoria. Normative tropia values are between 0.0^{Δ} and 2.0^{Δ} of exophoria for distance and between 0.0^{Δ} and 6.0^{Δ} of exophoria for near.[959, 960]

The prefixes used in vertical deviations are hyper- (ὑπέρ-) and hypo- (ὑπό-) for the upward and downward deviation, respectively. **Hyperphoria**/hypertropia is an upward deviation of the affected eye, and **hypophoria**/hypotropia is a downward deviation (Figure 10-40 bottom). Vertical phorias are typically between 0.0^{Δ} and 1.0^{Δ} in either direction.[961]

---

956 Dowley D. Heterophoria. Optom Vis Sci. 1990; 67(6):456-60.

957 Goss DA, Jackson TW. Clinical findings before the onset of myopia in youth: 3. Heterophoria. Optom Vis Sci. 1996; 73(4):269-78.

958 Leone JF, Cornell E, Morgan IG, Mitchell P, Kifley A, Wang JJ, Rose KA. Prevalence of heterophoria and associations with refractive error, heterotropia, and ethnicity in Australian school children. Br J Ophthalmol. 2010; 94(5):542-6.

959 Schmitt EP. The Skeffington perspective of the behavioral model of optometric data analysis and vision care. Bloomington, Indiana: AuthorHouse; 2010: p 375.

960 Morgan MW. The analysis of clinical data. Optom Weekly. 1964; 55:27-34.

961 Abraham NG, Srinivasan K, Thomas J. Normative data for near point of convergence, accommodation, and phoria. Oman J Ophthalmol. 2015; 8(1):14-8.

Finally, there is **cyclophoria**, the tendency of the eyes to rotate (κύκλος, for circle) around their anteroposterior axis. If the rotation of the 12 o'clock mark is nasal, cyclophoria is called incyclophoria, while if the rotation of the 12 o'clock mark is temporal, it is exocyclophoria.

We can use the Hirschberg test (§ 2.3.1) to clinically estimate the approximate size of tropia by observing the locations of the P_1 reflexes in each of the eyes when the examinee views a penlight binocularly. These reflex locations are compared to the locations when the penlight is viewed monocularly with each eye (Figure 10-40). The P_1 reflexes of the penlight are observed unhindered, as opposed to the cover-uncover test, where a cover paddle is used to occlude one eye at a time. In exotropia, the reflex of the deviating eye is displaced nasally, whereas, in esotropia, the reflex of the deviating eye is displaced temporally.

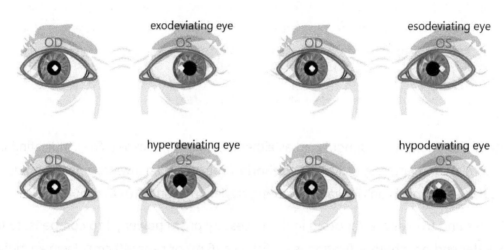

Figure 10-40: The four major ocular alignment deviations as illustrated on the left (OS) eye under binocular fixation. (top) Lateral exo- and esodeviations. (bottom) Vertical hyper- and hypodeviations.

The established conversion rule is that 1 mm of reflex displacement represents about 22^Δ of deviation.[962, 963] Typically, both reflexes are situated about 0.5 mm nasally, indicating symmetry or absence of tropia. This is a reminder of the compensation rule stated in § 2.3.1: To obtain the true deviation value, if the reflex is nasal, we subtract 0.5 mm, and if the reflex is temporal, we add 0.5 mm to the measured deviation to obtain the true deviation values, which are then multiplied by $22^\Delta/1$ mm to obtain the deviation measure in prism diopters.

---

[962] Eskridge JB, Wick BR, Perrigin DA. The Hirschberg test: a double-masked clinical evaluation. Am J Optom Physiol Opt. 1988; 65(9):745-50.

[963] While the conversion factor of 1 mm = 22^Δ of deviation is generally accepted, German ophthalmologist Jean-Cyriaque Barry suggests that in the Hirschberg test the correct value might be 1 mm = 12^Δ of deviation. The difference could be due to the poor accuracy of the test (at best, accuracy is $\pm 5^\Delta$). To produce a more accurate measurement, tropia can be measured with dissociated prisms or the cover-uncover test—techniques that afford accuracy down to $\pm 0.5\Delta$. Reference: Barry JC. Hirschberg erred here: the correct angle factor is 12 degrees pro mm corneal reflex decentration. Geometric optical analysis of various methods in strabismometry. Klin Monbl Augenheilkd. 1999; 215(2):104-13.

Example ☞: Alonso's Hirschberg test reveals P_1 reflections as follows: OD 2.0 mm nasally; OS 0.5 mm nasally (Figure 10-41). What is his lateral deviation?

We implement the compensation rule: Because each reflex is nasal, we subtract 0.5 mm from each measured value. The true deviations are 1.5 mm nasally for OD and no deviation for OS. We then multiply the 1.5 mm value by 22^Δ/1 mm. The result is 1.5 mm × 22^Δ/1 mm = 33^Δ of exotropia (OD).

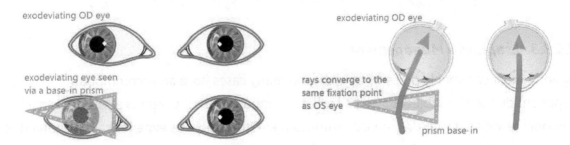

Figure 10-41: Base-in prism compensating for OD exotropia. The prism can be implemented with a round plus lens decentered nasally or a minus lens decentered temporally. The image of the affected eye through the prism shifts toward the apex of the prism.

Example ☞:: Othello's Hirschberg test reveals that P_1 is displaced 1.5 mm temporally on the OS eye. What is the type and the amount of deviation in this eye?

We implement the compensation rule: For the temporal displacement, we add 0.5 mm. The true deviation is a temporal displacement by 2.0 mm, which becomes 2.0 mm × 22^Δ/1 mm = 44^Δ of esotropia (OS).

Clinical note 👁👁: Suppresion under strabismus

In strabismus (στραβός, for obliquely distorted) there is a manifest deviation, and binocular vision cannot be maintained by fusional mechanisms.[964] To avoid double vision resulting from this manifest misalignment, the deviating eye undergoes suppression. Thus, the distinction between heterophoria and strabismus may be said to rest on one's ability to maintain binocular vision.

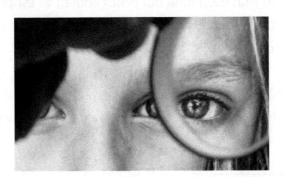

Figure 10-42: A BI prism (base oriented nasally, hence BI) from a trial lens set placed in front of the OS eye. Note the deviation of the image of the eye seen through the prism, which is toward the apex (temporal).

---

[964] Millodot M. Dictionary of Optometry and Visual Science. Oxford: Butterworth-Heinemann; 1997:1-29.

Note 👥 : A mnemonic device that helps when selecting the desired base direction in ocular misalignment is to remember that, when placing a prism in front of the eye, the compensating action comes from ray deviation, which is always toward the base of the prism; the image through the lens is toward the apex. Thus, to 'correct' exodeviation, we need to compensate inwardly, using a base-in prism. For esodeviation, we use a base-out prism. To correct hyperdeviation, we need to move 'the eye' downward, hence we use a base-down prism, and for hypodeviation, we use a base-up prism.

10.5.3.3 Esophoria Management

Esophoria most commonly presents at near, and many cases have an accommodative component due to the subject having a high AC/A ratio. When it presents at distance, it is commonly associated with divergence insufficiency. Other subjects experience esophoria due to undercorrected hyperopia. To provide visual comfort in non-hyperopic esophoria, a BO prism can be prescribed to move the image to where the subject's eyes naturally tend to point, thereby reducing the effort needed to see near targets comfortably and clearly.

The minimum amount of prism power required to relieve symptoms should be utilized, but there are no set rules that dictate this. **Percival's criterion** is one method commonly used to prescribe for esophoria and states that a subject should be functioning in the middle third of their fusional vergence ranges.[965] This criterion is named after the English ophthalmologist Archibald Stanley Percival,[966] who is renowned for his contributions to the understanding of spectacle prescription.[910]

Percival's Criterion: Prism = ⅓·(greater of lateral limits) − ⅔·(lesser of lateral limits)   (10.13)

or   Prism = (greater of lateral limits − 2 · lesser of lateral limits) / 3

This criterion does not take into consideration either the magnitude or direction of the deviation (it is primarily used with esophoria but is not limited to esophoria). When using this criterion, if a negative number is found (suggesting a BI prism) after performing the calculation, then no prism needs to be prescribed.[967]

Example ☞: Bianca shows 6.00^Δ of esophoria and has, as her positive fusional vergence findings, a diplopia break of 24^Δ and, as her negative fusional vergence findings, a diplopia break of 9^Δ. What prism should be prescribed according to Percival's criterion?

---

[965] Conway ML, Thomas J, Subramanian A. Is the aligning prism measured with the Mallett unit correlated with fusional vergence reserves? PloS One. 2012; 7(8):e42832.

[966] Percival AS. The relation of convergence to accommodation and its practical bearing. Ophthal Rev. 1892; 11:313-28.

[967] Saladin JJ. Horizontal prism prescription. In: Cotter SA, ed. Clinical uses of prism: a spectrum of applications. St Louis: Mosby; 1995: 109-48.

Prism needed to help reduce Bianca's symptoms = ⅓·(24) − ⅔·(9) = 8 − 6 = 2.00$^\Delta$. Since Bianca is showing esophoria, this would translate to 2.00$^\Delta$ BO.

Another common prism prescribing calculation for esophoria is the **1:1 rule**, which states that there should be one prism diopter of negative fusional vergence (NFV) base-in recovery for each prism diopter or esophoria measured;[968] if this condition is not met, a prism can be prescribed to help balance fusional ranges.

1:1 rule: Prism = ½·(esophoria − NFV recovery) (10.14)

The 1:1 rule, also known as Saladin's rule, named after Professor James Saladin, can be conceptualized as stating that base-in recovery should be at least as great as the amount of the esophoria.

Example ☞: Valeria has 8.00$^\Delta$ of esophoria and shows a 6.00$^\Delta$ recovery when measuring negative fusional vergence values. What prism should she be prescribed, according to the 1:1 rule?

Prism needed: ½·(8 − 6) = 1.00$^\Delta$ BO would be beneficial to help keep Valeria symptom-free.

Example ☞: Claudius has 5.00$^\Delta$ of esophoria and shows a −1.00$^\Delta$ BI recovery. What prism should be prescribed according to the 1:1 rule?

Prism needed: ½·[5 − (−1)] = 3.00$^\Delta$ BO would be beneficial to help relieve Claudius' symptoms.

10.5.3.4 Exophoria Management

Exophoria may either present at distance in the cases of divergence excess, or at near in the cases of convergence insufficiency. In cases with convergence insufficiency, particularly in adults or presbyopic individuals, the use of a BI prism can be explored.[969] As with for esophoria, there are no rules that state the amount of prism that should be prescribed. A commonly used rule is **Sheard's criterion**,[970] named after the American biophysicist Charles Sheard, Professor of physics and applied optics, and founder of the American Academy of Optometry.

Sheard's criterion: Prism = ⅔·(exophoria) − ⅓·(compensating fusional vergence) (10.15)

or Prism = (2·exophoria − compensating fusional vergence)/3

[968] Birnbaum MH. Optometric management of nearpoint vision disorders. Oxford: Butterworth-Heinemann; 1995.

[969] Scheiman M, Gwiazda J, Li T. Non-surgical interventions for convergence insufficiency. Cochrane Database Syst Rev. 2011; (3):CD006768

[970] Sheard C. Zones of ocular comfort. Am J Ophthalmol. 1930; 7:9-25.

We can better understand Sheard's criterion by stating it as follows: The prism to be prescribed should be ⅔ of the demand (exophoria) minus ⅓ of the reserve (compensating fusional vergence).

Example ☞: Demetrius has 9.00^Δ of exophoria, measures as having 6.00^Δ of positive fusional vergence before the diplopia break (BO to blur). What prism should be prescribed, according to Sheard's criterion?

Prism prescribed to help Demetrius: $⅔ \cdot (9) - ⅓ \cdot (6) = 4.00^\Delta$ BI.

Example ☞: Cordelia has 6.00^Δ of exophoria, measures as having 6.00^Δ of positive fusional vergence before diplopia break. What prism should be prescribed, according to Sheard's criterion?

Prism needed to help Cordelia: $⅔ \cdot (6) - ⅓ \cdot (6) = 2.00^\Delta$ BI should be prescribed.

Prismatic compensation (by <u>deliberate</u> lens decentration or by grinding) is prescribed to alleviate the effects of these conditions in symptomatic subjects because these conditions are associated with diplopia, asthenopia, headaches, dizziness, blurred vision, and near-vision convergence issues. A well-balanced relieving prism prescription must be preceded by a thorough evaluation of the patient's needs based on a comprehensive diagnosis. A prism may offer a significant improvement in the symptomatic binocular vision conditions.

Prism prescription can be implemented on the most affected eye or can be split between the two eyes, depending on the clinical determination and the pathology. It is emphasized that the optical management with prisms does not treat these conditions, but it simply provides compensation for symptom relief. Only vision therapy, or surgical management in the case of a tropia, addresses these conditions from the perspective of 'fixing' the problem.

Example ☞: The following prism prescriptions are possible when a $+5.0^\Delta$ is desired:

OD $+2.5^\Delta$ and OS $+2.5^\Delta$, achieved by a <u>symmetric</u> <u>temporal</u> displacement of the plus lenses;
OD $+1.5^\Delta$ and OS $+3.5^\Delta$, or OD $+0.5^\Delta$ and OS $+4.5^\Delta$, which can be achieved by an <u>asymmetric temporal</u> displacement of the plus lenses. The combined effect is numerically the same (both provide a net $+5.0^\Delta$), but the prescription may not have the same clinical outcome if the pathology between the two eyes is different.

Percival's and Sheard's criteria provide formulas for prescribing prism that help to restore comfortable and efficient binocular vision. These criteria are derived based on an idea called the 'zone of clear single binocular vision' (ZCSBV), which is defined as the set of vergence and focal stimuli that an individual can see clearly while maintaining binocular fusion. The prescribed prism maintains vision within the ZCSBV.

Simply put, these criteria help one to select the minimum amount of prism that allows for fusion and most effectively reduces the demand for vergence effort. Specifically, Sheard's criterion is based on the dissociated phoria and the compensating vergence, which states that the prescribed prism should be twice the fusional reserve for the phoria.[971] Percival's criterion is based on the determination that the comfort zone should be the middle third of the ZCSBV.

Clinical note 🖻: The multitude of available formulas on the determination of relief prism prescriptions indicates that there is no one (singular) way to prescribe.
Prism prescription is ultimately determined following extensive interaction with the patient. This interaction entails trialing an amount of prism, observing patient responses, and modifying the prism used, all the while, seeking an improvement in the patient's responses.

There are several other ways that a prism can be applied. Some clinicians prescribe prisms for therapeutic purposes, where the prescription is for another reason than what is expected (called a compensatory prism)—to train their patients out of their condition. This is one way that prisms can be utilized in cases of strabismus, for example.[972] If a patient with esotropia has anomalous correspondence,[973] some clinicians may prescribe an overcompensating BO prism to help the eyes to learn to diverge. In cases of traumatic or paralytic strabismus, on the other hand, compensatory prisms are usually prescribed to provide diplopia relief.

In cases of retinal pathologies, such as macular degeneration, prisms may be used to physically move an image to a functional portion of the retina. In cases of neurological pathologies, such as in visual field defects (hemianopsias),[974] prisms may be used to shift images into the 'seeing' portions of the visual field to help improve ambulation.[975]

Prisms may also be utilized in special ways, such as for head injuries. **Yoked prisms** (a binocular prism prescription with the bases pointing in the same direction, such as two prisms with their bases oriented towards the right, or two prisms oriented with their bases pointed downwards) may be prescribed to reorient one's sense of balance and posture.[976]

---

[971] Freier BE, Pickwell LD. Physiological exophoria. Ophthalmic Physiol Opt. 1983; 3(3):267-72.

[972] Farnè A, Rossetti Y, Toniolo S, Làdavas E. Ameliorating neglect with prism adaptation: visuo-manual and visuo-verbal measures. Neuropsychologia. 2002; 40(7):718-29.

[973] London RF, Wick BR. Patients with amblyopia and strabismus. In: Borish, I. Clinical refraction. Oxford: Butterworth-Heinemann; 2006; 1461-78.

[974] Redding GM, Wallace B. Prism adaptation and unilateral neglect: review and analysis. Neuropsychologia. 2006; 44(1):1-20.

[975] O'Neill EC, Connell PP, O'Connor JC, Brady J, Reid I, Logan P. Prism therapy and visual rehabilitation in homonymous visual field loss. Optom Vis Sci. 2011; 88(2):263-8.

[976] Ward M, Yamamoto T, McDowell K. The postural effects of yoked prism. (1993). Pacific University College of Optometry.

10.6 COMBINATIONS OF THIN PRISMS

In cases where the necessary compensation has an orientation at an oblique angle (that is not along the 180° or 90° meridian), the **oblique** prism corresponds to a vector on the *x-y* plane, with the –*x* axis along the $\vartheta = 0° - 180°$ meridian and the –*y* axis along the $\vartheta = 270° - 90°$ meridian. An oblique prism is implemented by an oblique lens decentration along the same meridian. The base direction is also along the same meridian, either along the direction of lens displacement if the lens is plus, or against this direction if the lens is minus.

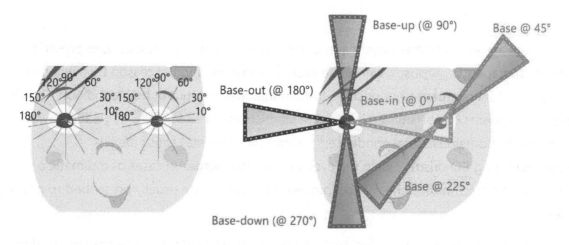

Figure 10-43: A prismatic correction prescription lists prism diopters [△] with the abbreviations BI (base-in, nasally), BO (base-out, temporally), BU (base-up, superiorly), and BD (base-down, inferiorly).

Example ☞: What is the induced prism and the base direction if a +10.00 D lens is displaced from Ariel's pupil center by 2.5 mm along the 30° meridian?

We simply implement Prentice's rule [Eq. (10.12)]: Induced prism is $(+10.00 \text{ D}) \cdot (0.25 \text{ cm}) = +2.5^{\triangle}$. The prism base direction is along the 30° meridian.

In oblique prisms, we follow the parallelogram law; graphically we draw a rectangle and apply the Pythagorean theorem. The **combination of thin prisms** employs a vector analysis of two individual prisms. The opposite calculations may involve the breaking down or **resolution of the oblique prism** into its horizontal and vertical components. The mathematics for the combination is simple. The net deviation vector is the vector sum of the two individual component vectors.

Net Deviation Vector:	$\boldsymbol{\Delta} = \boldsymbol{\Delta}_x + \boldsymbol{\Delta}_y$	(10.16)
Net Prism Magnitude:	$\Delta = \sqrt{(\Delta^2_x + \Delta^2_y)}$	(10.17)

Net Deviation Angle: $$\tan\vartheta = \frac{\Delta_y}{\Delta_x}$$ (10.18)

For prism resolution, we apply trigonometry to calculate the projections on each axis.

Prism Resolution: $\Delta_x = \Delta\cdot\cos\vartheta$ and $\Delta_y = \Delta\cdot\sin\vartheta$ (10.19)

We can then simply add the prisms. To calculate their combined power, we follow these steps:

- Apply prism resolution to each of them to find the individual Δ_x and Δ_y.
- Add the components (Σ denoting summation) along each axis to find the components along each axis $\Delta_{xTOT} = (\Sigma\,\Delta_x)$ and $\Delta_{yTOT} = (\Sigma\,\Delta_y)$.
- Apply vector combination for Δ_{xTOT} and Δ_{yTOT}.

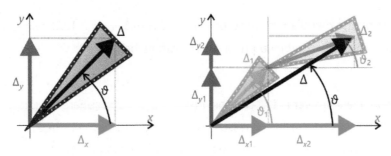

Figure 10-44: (left) Resolution and (right) vector combination in oblique prisms.

Example ☞: What is the net prism if Othello's prescription requires a 4.0$^\Delta$ BI prism and a 3.0$^\Delta$ BU prism over his OD (right) eye?

The prisms are represented by vectors in Figure 10-44 (left).

The horizontal component is $\Delta_x = +4.0^\Delta$ and the vertical component is $\Delta_y = +3.0^\Delta$.

The net prism has magnitude: $\Delta = \sqrt{(\Delta^2_x + \Delta^2_y)} = \sqrt{(4^2 + 3^2)} = 5.0^\Delta$.

Base orientation is along the meridian specified by $\tan\vartheta = \Delta_y/\Delta_x = \frac{3}{4} = 0.75$, so $\vartheta = \tan^{-1}(0.75) = 36.87°$.

Thus, the combined prism is 5.0$^\Delta$ with its base @ 36.87°.

Example ☞: Find the horizontal and vertical components of a prism 1.3$^\Delta$ with base @ 22.62° placed over Oliver's OD eye.

Resolving the prism into two components,

Horizontal $\Delta_x = \Delta\cdot\cos\vartheta = 1.3\cdot\cos(22.62°) = 1.3\cdot0.923 = 1.2^\Delta$ BI.

Vertical $\Delta_y = \Delta\cdot\sin\vartheta = 1.3\cdot\sin(22.62°) = 1.3\cdot0.38 = 0.5^\Delta$ BU.

Food for thought 🍲: What would be different if this prism were to be placed over Oliver's OS eye? (hint: start with one of the two components!).

Example ☞: What is the net prism magnitude if Ariel's prescription requires a $\Delta_1 = +2.0^\Delta$ base at 30° prism and a $\Delta_2 = +3.0^\Delta$ base at 45° prism over Ariel's right eye?

In this more complex problem, we first resolve each prism into horizontal and vertical components:
$\Delta_{1x} = \Delta_1 \cdot \cos\vartheta_1 = 2.0 \cdot \cos(30°) = 2.0 \cdot 0.866 = 1.73^\Delta$ BI; $\Delta_{1y} = \Delta_1 \cdot \sin\vartheta_1 = 2.0 \cdot \sin(30°) = 2.0 \cdot 0.50 = 1.0^\Delta$ BU.
$\Delta_{2x} = \Delta_2 \cdot \cos\vartheta_2 = 3.0 \cdot \cos(45°) = 3.0 \cdot 0.707 = 2.12^\Delta$ BI; $\Delta_{2y} = \Delta_2 \cdot \sin\vartheta_2 = 3.0 \cdot \sin(45°) = 3.0 \cdot 0.707 = 2.12^\Delta$ BU.

We now sum up and apply vector combination (Σ stands for sum):
$\Delta_{xTOT} = \Sigma \, \Delta_x = +1.73 + 2.12 = 3.85^\Delta$ BI and $\Delta_{yTOT} = \Sigma \, \Delta_y = +1.0 + 2.12 = 3.12^\Delta$ BU.
$\Delta_{TOT} = \sqrt{(\Delta^2_{xTOT} + \Delta^2_{yTOT})} = \sqrt{(3.85^2 + 3.21^2)} \approx 5.0^\Delta$.

Base orientation is along the meridian specified by $\tan\vartheta = \Delta_{yTOT}/\Delta_{xTOT} = 3.12/3.85 = 0.81$; therefore, $\vartheta = \tan^{-1}(0.81) = 39°$. Thus, the combined prism is 5.0^Δ with its base at 39°.

Note ✐: When using a lensometer (§ 9.7.4.2), the intersection of the sphere ('single' lines) and cylinder lines (triplet lines) provides the location of the prism base. The displacement of this intersection point along the x and y axes indicates the horizontal and vertical prism components.

10.7 LENS TILT AND SHIFT EFFECTS

10.7.1 Wrap Tilt and Pantoscopic Tilt

Lens **tilting** is what is referred to when the lens is oblique (as opposed to the lens being exactly at right angles) with the line of sight of the wearer [Figure 10-45 (left) and Figure 10-46 (left)]. Tilt is often desired for aesthetic purposes because it helps to reduce direct light reflections and is influenced by the frame geometry as it sits on the face.

Wrap tilt, also known as the **faceform tilt**, is the lens tilt about the vertical axis / 90° meridian with respect to primary gaze [Figure 10-45 (right)]; it is simply the rotation of the lens (angling of the side rim) toward the temple, away from the nose.

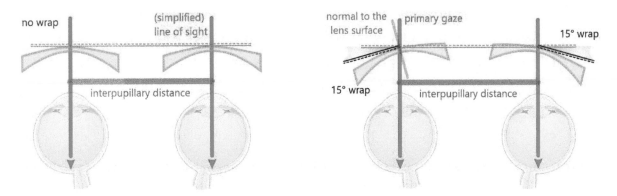

Figure 10-45: (left) No wrap in spectacle lenses. (right) Wrap tilt in a frame with a total of 30° wrap; each lens is rotated 15°. In both cases, the interpupillary distance remains unaltered.

Pantoscopic tilt occurs when the lens rotates about the horizontal axis / 180° meridian [Figure 10-46 (right)], for example, when the lens is leaning down toward the cheeks. A tilt (either wrap or pantoscopic) of up to 3° to 7° is within the normal range, whereas a tilt of 15° may be considered significant. The opposite of pantoscopic tilt is retroscopic tilt, where the lens is angled <u>away</u> from the cheeks (not used in actual fitting).

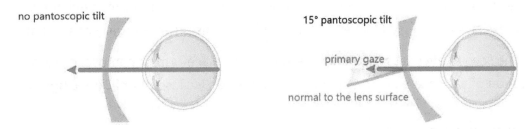

Figure 10-46: (left) No pantoscopic tilt in spectacle lenses. (right) A 15° pantoscopic tilt.

The tilt of the faceform or wrapped frame can determine the tilt angle α; however, the lens base curve F_1 and center thickness t may also affect angle α. Two sets of effects are associated with lens tilt: prism induction and an effective change to the power of the lens, whether it is sphere, cylinder, or axis power.

The first effect associated with lens tilt is the induced prism.

Induced Prism (due to tilt by angle $\alpha[°]$): $\qquad P\,[^\Delta] = 100 \cdot \tan\alpha \cdot (t/n) \cdot F_1$ $\qquad$ (10.20)

where α is the tilt angle, t [m] is the lens center thickness, F_1 [D] is the lens front (base) curve power, and n is the index of refraction of the lens material.[977] If the angle α is small (most likely it is) and expressed in radians, then the above relationship can be simplified as

Induced Prism (due to tilt, when α is small [rad]): $\quad P\,[^\Delta] = 100 \cdot \alpha \cdot (t/n) \cdot F_1$ $\qquad$ (10.21)

Note 🔋 : The prism induced by either type of lens tilt is dependent on the base curve power F_1 and not on the lens prescription power Rx (F_{BVP})—more prism is induced in a lens with a steep base curve. At the limit of a lens with a plano front surface (zero base curve), zero prism is generated upon tilt.

Most ophthalmic lenses have little variation in the base curve (see Vogel's rule, § 9.4.3), and most minus lenses have relatively thin center thickness; the induced prism upon tilt depends mostly on tilt angle α.

Example ☞: A +6.00 base curve in a glass lens (n = 1.5 and t = 2.5 mm) with a tilt α = 6° induces a 0.10^Δ prism.

In pantoscopic tilt, because the lenses rotate in a yoked fashion (both toward the cheeks), the prism effect is similar in both lenses. The prism base and the amount of prism, which is typically of small magnitude, are usually the same in both eyes. However, if the two (right and left) lens base curves are of unequal values, differing more than 1.50 D, a slight vertical prism effect may develop. In general, **vertical imbalance** may be induced if there is a difference in vertical prism effects caused by lens pantoscopic tilt or vertical displacement as the gaze shifts down.

Lens wrap tilt is always in opposite (non-yoked) directions, with one lens turning clockwise and the other counter-clockwise. This creates a base-out prism in either eye since the base curve is always positive (convex anterior surface). This prism is usually of small magnitude.

The second effect associated with lens tilt (either faceform or pantoscopic) is a modification of the sphere and cylinder Rx components. Because of **oblique astigmatism**,

---

[977] Landgrave JE, Moya-Cessa JR. Generalized Coddington equations in ophthalmic lens design. J Opt Soc Am A. 1996; 13(8):1637-44.

sphere power is increased, and cylinder is induced, with its sign the same as that of the sphere power and its axis the same as the axis of rotation.[978] According to the terminology of oblique astigmatism, the axis (plane) of tilt is termed the sagittal axis (plane),[907] while the tangential plane is perpendicular to the sagittal plane. The amounts of effective dioptric power induced by tilting a lens (with refractive index n) about a degrees are described by Coddington's equations, named after the English natural philosopher Henry Coddington.[979, 980]

Coddington's Equation for Power: New sphere power = sphere $\cdot [1 + (\sin^2\alpha)/2n]$ (10.22)

This is the new sphere power along the sagittal plane (90° for pantoscopic tilt and 180° for faceform tilt). There is also a new sphere power along the tangential plane (180° for pantoscopic tilt and 90° for faceform tilt). The difference between the two new spheres is the induced cylinder, which, in spherical lenses is approximated by

Coddington's Equation for Cylinder: Induced cylinder = (new sphere) $\cdot (\tan^2\alpha)$ (10.23)

The axis of the induced cylinder is the axis of rotation: faceform tilt at 90° and pantoscopic tilt at 180°. Due to the relatively small amounts of change in the sphere power, often the induced cylinder is simply calculated using the 'old' sphere $\times (\tan^2\alpha)$.

For a minus lens:	• pantoscopic tilt induces more –sphere and induces –cylinder @ 180° • faceform tilt induces more –sphere and induces –cylinder @ 90°
For a plus lens:	• pantoscopic tilt induces more +sphere and induces +cylinder @ 180° • faceform tilt induces more +sphere and induces +cylinder @ 90°

These relationships become important when relatively large lens powers are placed in a frame that has a significant tilt. In this case, if the fitted lens is placed exactly at the correct positioning, the frame-induced tilt may have detrimental effects on both the induced sphere and the induced cylindrical powers. Thus, in high-tilt frames, a modified Rx should be fitted that takes into account and compensates for the dioptric changes due to lens tilt.

Cylinder power is induced in the meridian that is tilted, so the cylinder axis is the axis of tilt rotation. In pantoscopic tilt, relationships (10.22) and (10.23) use the sphere power along the

[978] Keating MP. Oblique central refraction in spherocylindrical lenses tilted around an off-axis meridian. Optom Vis Sci. 1993; 70:785-91.
[979] Keating MP. Oblique central refraction in spherocylindrical corrections with both faceform and pantoscopic tilt. Optom Vis Sci. 1995; 72:258-65.
[980] Blendowske R. Oblique central refraction in tilted spherocylindrical lenses. Optom Vis Sci. 2002; 79(1):68-73.

90° meridian, while the induced cylinder is along the 180° meridian. In faceform tilt, the formulas use the sphere power along the 180° meridian, while the induced cylinder is along the 90° meridian.[981, 982] When the cylinder is oblique or there is both pantoscopic and faceform tilt, the required mathematical approach becomes more complex.

Note 🈂: Often, the denominator $2n$ appearing in Coddington's equation for power is replaced by the numeral 3 simply because most lenses have a refractive index very close to 1.5.

Example ☞: A lens with prescription power +8.00 D, made of a material with $n = 1.5$, whose optical center is placed before the eye, has 10° of pantoscopic tilt. What is the effective Rx of this lens?

New sphere power = sphere · [1 + ($\sin^2 10$)/3] = +8.00 · [1 + 0.03015/3] = +8.00 · [1 + 0.01] = +8.08 D.
The pantoscopically tilted plus lens has a slightly stronger plus power from +8.00 D to +8.08 D.
The induced cylinder power is on the 180° meridian = (+8.08 D) · ($\tan^2 10$) = +8.08 · 0.0311 = +0.25 D.
Thus, the +8.00 D lens, when pantoscopically tilted by 10°, will be an effective +8.08 +0.25×180.

Example ☞: A −8.00 −4.00×090 lens made of a material with $n = 1.5$ has 12° of pantoscopic tilt when its optical center is placed directly in front of Polonius' pupil. What is the effective Rx of this lens?

A key challenge here is that <u>we must express the lens power on the 180° meridian</u>, the axis of rotation in a <u>pantoscopic tilt</u>. The power transposition is −12.00 +4.00×180.
New sphere power = sphere · [1 + ($\sin^2 12$)/3] = −12.00 · [1 + 0.0432/3] = −12.00 · [1 + 0.0144] = −12.50 D.
The pantoscopically tilted minus lens has a slightly stronger minus power (from −12.00 to −12.50).

The induced cylinder power is on the 180° meridian: (−12.50 D) · ($\tan^2 12$) = −12.50 · 0.045 = −0.56 D ≈ −0.50 D. The lens already had a +4.00 cylinder on the 180° meridian, so the net effect will be to reduce the +cylinder to +3.50. The effective Rx for the tilted spectacles is −12.50 +3.50×180, or −9.00 −3.50×090.

Example ☞: A lens with prescription +7.00 −1.00×180, made of a material with $n = 1.5$ and whose optical center is placed before the eye, has 15° of faceform tilt. What is the effective Rx of this lens?

We pay attention to the fact that the tilt is faceform: The lens is rotated along the vertical meridian. Thus, we consider in relationships (10.22) and (10.23) the power along the horizontal meridian, while the induced cylinder is along the 90° meridian. Initial lens cross powers: +7.00 D @ 180° and +6.00 D @ 90°.

New sphere power = sphere · [1 + ($\sin^2 15$)/3] = +7.15 D (@ 180°).

[981] Fannin T, Grosvenor T. Clinical Optics, 2nd edition, Butterworth-Heinemann, 1996; 48-50.
[982] Dowaliby M. Practical Aspects of Ophthalmic Optics. New York: Professional Press, 1988.

The induced cylinder power is on the 90° meridian = $(+7.15\ D)\cdot(\tan^2 15) = +0.51\ D$ (@ 90°).

Thus, the +7.00 D (@ 180°) power, when faceform-tilted by 15°, will be an effective +7.15 D (@ 180°) with an additional +0.51 D (@ 90°). The latter is added to the initial (@ 90°) power of +6.00 D.

Lens cross powers: +7.15 D @ 180° and +6.51 D @ 90°.

Effective Rx = +7.15 −0.65×180 or +6.50 +0.65×090.

Practice examples with answers ⚒ Prism and Rx effects of tilt

Common to all, lens thickness t = 3.5 mm, n = 1.5, base curve according to Vogel's rule.

Low correction, pantoscopic tilt 10°:

Rx: +2.00 with +8.00 base curve. Induced prism $P = 0.32^\Delta$, new sphere +2.02, induced cylinder +0.06×180.

Rx: −2.00 with +5.00 base curve. Induced prism $P = 0.20^\Delta$, new sphere −2.02, induced cylinder −0.06×180.

Low correction, high pantoscopic tilt 22°:

Rx: +2.00 with +8.00 base curve. Induced prism $P = 0.75^\Delta$, new sphere +2.09, induced cylinder +0.34×180.

Rx: −2.00 with +5.00 base curve. Induced prism $P = 0.47^\Delta$, new sphere −2.09, induced cylinder −0.34×180.

High correction, high pantoscopic tilt 22°:

Rx: +6.00 with +12.00 base curve. Induced prism $P = 1.13^\Delta$, new sphere +6.28, induced cylinder +1.00×180.

Rx: −6.00 with +3.00 base curve. Induced prism $P = 0.28^\Delta$, new sphere −6.28, induced cylinder −1.00×180.

10.7.2 Compensation: Martin's Rule of Tilt

To keep the optical axis of the lens passing through the eye's center of rotation, a drop of the lens' optical center can also compensate for the induced cylinder due to pantoscopic tilt. The rule that governs this compensation, known as **Martin's rule of tilt**, states that a single-vision lens can be lowered by 1 mm for every 2° of pantoscopic tilt.

A simple proof of Martin's rule can be provided if we consider that, for a lens at about 13.5 mm vertex distance, the center of rotation of the eye (itself being about 13.5 mm to the right of the cornea, § 2.4.3) is 27 mm inward. Then, one degree of rotation runs about (27 mm · tan 1° = 0.5) 0.5 mm across the lens surface. So, a drop of the optical center of the lens by 1 mm for every 2° keeps the axis passing through the center of rotation of the eye.[184, 983]

This rule has practical purposes. The pupil is not typically centered vertically with the center of the lens, but it is typically about 5 mm above the frame (and lens) midpoint. Thus, a

---

[983] Meister D, Sheedy JE. In: Introduction to Ophthalmic Optics. Petaluma, CA: SOLA Optical 1999:99-100.

pantoscopic tilt of about 10° serves to bring the intersection of the lens optical axis to the eye's center of rotation.

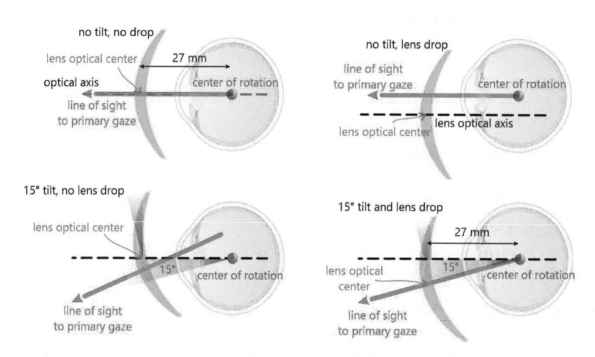

Figure 10-47: A drop of the lens optical center to maintain the line of sight passing through the center of rotation of the eye.

Martin's rule in pantoscopic tilt:	• To ensure that the optical axis of the lens passes through the center of rotation of the eye, the optical center of the lens should be dropped by 1 mm for every 2° of pantoscopic tilt.

The problem is (just as you may be thinking that we have said it all) that this lens drop is effectively a decentration that induces prism (§ 9.6.2.1)! The question becomes more complicated as it may lead to a prism imbalance for horizontal displacements considering that the tilt of the lens also induces prism. Compensating for the effective Rx would be preferred when necessary in significantly high corrections.

Example ☞: The induced cylinder with a 10° pantoscopic tilt of a lens with +2.00 D prescription is +0.06 D. What lens drop balances this tilt according to Martin's rule?

Balancing of this tilt requires a 5 mm drop, which in turn induces 1^Δ prism. This is perhaps a high price for just a 0.06 D cylinder. If desired, the best option would be to subtract this cylinder power from the original Rx to obtain the most accurate power correction.

10.8 PRISMATIC EFFECTS QUIZ

Prism Optics

1) The prism deviation angle equals the angle ...

   a) between the emerging ray and the ray incident on the first surface
   b) of reflection at the second prism surface
   c) of refraction at the second prism surface
   d) between the emerging ray and the second prism surface

2) For a thin glass (n = 1.5) prism, the deviation angle ϑ_E is approximately (A = apical angle) ...

   a) $0.5 \cdot A$
   b) $1 \cdot A$
   c) $1.5 \cdot A$
   d) $2 \cdot A$
   e) $2.5 \cdot A$

3) In a thin glass (n = 1.5) prism, the deviation angle ϑ_E is 5°. The apical angle A is ...

   a) 5°
   b) 10°
   c) 15°
   d) 20°
   e) 40°

4) What is the power of a thin prism made of n =1.5 glass that has a deviation angle ϑ_E = 6°?

   a) 4.0^Δ
   b) 6.0^Δ
   c) 8.0^Δ
   d) 10.5^Δ
   e) 12.0^Δ

5) What is the power of a thin prism made of n =1.5 glass if the apical angle is A = 12°?

   a) 4.0^Δ
   b) 6.3^Δ
   c) 8.0^Δ
   d) 10.5^Δ
   e) 12.0^Δ

6) A prism of prism power 4^Δ at a distance of 0.5 m causes a deviation equal to ...

   a) 0.2 cm
   b) 1 cm
   c) 2 cm

   d) 4 cm
   e) 8 cm

7) What is the deviation caused by a 4^Δ prism at 3 m?

   a) 1.2 cm
   b) 3 cm
   c) 6 cm
   d) 12 cm
   e) 18 cm

8) What is the prism power $P(^\Delta)$ when a prism deviates a ray by 1 cm over a distance of 50 cm?

   a) 0.1^Δ
   b) 0.2^Δ
   c) 0.5^Δ
   d) 1.0^Δ
   e) 2.0^Δ
   f) 20.0^Δ

9) At what distance does a 10^Δ prism deviate a ray by 5 cm?

   a) 0.05 m
   b) 0.5 m
   c) 5 m
   d) 50 m

10) What is 'wrong' with thick prisms (select the two most important drawbacks to their use in vision compensation)?

    a) the aesthetic appearance due to significant thickness and weight
    b) the deviation angle is too small
    c) the deviation angle is too large
    d) the deviation angle is dependent on the angle of incidence
    e) they disperse light

11) In a glass prism surrounded by air, the ray deviation is always ...

    a) toward the prism base
    b) toward the prism apex
    c) perpendicular to the first refracting surface
    d) parallel to the first refracting prism surface
    e) parallel to the second refracting prism surface
    f) perpendicular to the second refracting surface

12) If everything else remains the same, prism power is greater when the viewed object is at the ...

   a) far point of the eye
   b) secondary focal point of the corrective lens
   c) primary focal point of the eye
   d) near point of the eye

13) A prism has 10^Δ power. What is the effective prism power when viewing a near object 5 cm in front of the eye (COR = 13.5 mm from cornea, vertex distance is 11.5 mm)?

   a) 14^Δ
   b) 12^Δ
   c) 10^Δ
   d) 9^Δ
   e) 6^Δ

14) Back to Q 13. The near object is now 25 cm in front of the eye. What is the effective prism power?

   a) 14^Δ
   b) 12^Δ
   c) 10^Δ
   d) 9^Δ
   e) 6^Δ

15) When a 10^Δ prism (for distance) views a near object at 25 cm, its effective power becomes 9^Δ. If the (distance) prism power is switched to 6^Δ, what would the new effective prism power be?

   a) 9^Δ
   b) 6^Δ
   c) 5.4^Δ
   d) 3.6^Δ

16) What near object viewing distance (from the eye) is required to bring a 5% difference between the distance and the effective prism power?

   a) 5 cm
   b) 10 cm
   c) 25 cm
   d) 50 cm
   e) 100 cm

17) A 4^Δ (distance) prism with vertex 12.5 mm, when viewing a near object at 25 cm, has effective power 3.6^Δ. If the vertex is 10 mm, the effective power is ...

   a) only moderately affected, 3.56^Δ

   b) not affected at all, 3.6^Δ
   c) only moderately affected, 3.64^Δ
   d) somehow affected, 3.75^Δ

18) A prism is ground on its vertical orientation onto a meniscus lens of d = 2 inch / 5.08 cm (n = 1.5). What edge thickness t difference is required to fabricate a prism whose center power is 10^Δ?

   a) 1.5 mm
   b) 5 mm
   c) 10 mm
   d) 15 mm

19) Back to Q 18. What happens to the prism power if the ground lens blank is cut to fit a frame of 3 cm along the vertical direction?

   a) 6^Δ (less prism)
   b) 8^Δ (less prism)
   c) 10^Δ (remains the same)
   d) 16^Δ (more prism)

20) A prism is fabricated to a center power 10.0^Δ using n_1 = 1.5 material. Ariel accidentally picks up a lens blank whose index is n_2 = 1.7 and executes the grinding design with no other change. The prism Ariel fabricates has power ...

   a) 8.8^Δ
   b) 10.0^Δ
   c) 11.3^Δ
   d) 14.0^Δ

21) What is the prism effect when a vertically oriented 5^Δ Risley prism is rotated 60°?

   a) vertical 10.0^Δ; horizontal zero
   b) vertical 8.66^Δ; horizontal zero
   c) vertical 5.0^Δ; horizontal zero
   d) vertical zero; horizontal 5.0^Δ
   e) vertical zero; horizontal 8.66^Δ
   f) vertical zero; horizontal 10.0^Δ

22) The maximum prism power produced by a pair of 5^Δ Risley prisms is ...

   a) 5^Δ
   b) 10^Δ
   c) 15^Δ
   d) 20^Δ

Prism Application

23) Minimum prism in front of the lens is achieved at the (select two) ...

   a) center of a minus lens
   b) periphery of a minus lens

c) center of a plus lens
d) periphery of a plus lens

24) A spherical lens induces a 4.0^Δ prism when decentered 5 mm vertically. If, <u>instead</u>, the lens were to be decentered 5 mm laterally, what would the induced prism be?

a) 0.0^Δ
b) 4.0^Δ
c) 5.65^Δ
d) 8.0^Δ

25) Back to Q 24. What is the power of this lens?

a) 2.0 D
b) 4.0 D
c) 5.65 D
d) 8.0 D

26) A spherical lens induces a 4.0^Δ prism when decentered 5 mm upwards. If, <u>subsequently</u>, the lens were to be decentered another 5 mm upwards, what would the induced prism be?

a) 0.0^Δ
b) 4.0^Δ
c) 5.65^Δ
d) 8.0^Δ

27) A -2.00×180 cylinder lens induces a 2.0^Δ prism when decentered 10 mm upwards. If, <u>instead</u>, the lens were to be decentered 10 mm laterally, what would the induced prism be?

a) 0.0^Δ
b) 1.0^Δ
c) 2.0^Δ
d) 4.0^Δ

28) The induced prism when a -2.50×090 cylinder lens is decentered 0.4 cm horizontally is …

a) 0.0^Δ
b) 1.0^Δ
c) 2.5^Δ
d) 4.0^Δ

29) The induced prism when a -2.50×180 cylinder lens is decentered 2 mm vertically is …

a) 0.0^Δ
b) 0.5^Δ
c) 1.0^Δ
d) 2.5^Δ

30) A lens made for the Rx $+2.00 -2.00 \times 180$ creates prism when decentered … (two correct)

a) horizontally to the right
b) horizontally to the left
c) vertically up
d) vertically down

31) A lens with Rx $+1.50 -1.00 \times 090$ develops 0.75^Δ prism when decentered by … (two correct)

a) 15 mm horizontally
b) 5 mm horizontally
c) 15 mm vertically
d) 5 mm vertically

32) Benvolio's new frame imposes a 68 mm lens center distance; his PD is 60 mm. What is the magnitude and direction of each lens decentration?

a) 8 mm temporally
b) 4 mm temporally
c) 4 mm nasally
d) 8 mm nasally

33) Benvolio's frames are now fitted with -2.00 D myopic lenses. What is the magnitude and base direction of the induced prism per eye?

a) 0.4^Δ BI
b) 0.8^Δ BI
c) 4.0^Δ BI
d) 0.4^Δ BO
e) 0.8^Δ BO
f) 4.0^Δ BO

34) Octavia is fitted with an OU $+2.50$ D Rx on a frame that has 66 mm lens center spacing, while her PD is 62 mm. What is the magnitude and base direction of the induced prism per eye?

a) 0.5^Δ BI
b) 1.0^Δ BI
c) 2.5^Δ BI
d) 0.5^Δ BO
e) 1.0^Δ BO
f) 2.5^Δ BO

35) Prince Escalus' eyes converge to view a near object while wearing his $+5.00$ D prescription glasses, and his PD is reduced from 64 mm to 62 mm. How much and what type of prism does Escalus experience per eye?

a) 0.5^Δ BI
b) 1.0^Δ BI
c) 2.5^Δ BI
d) 0.5^Δ BO
e) 1.0^Δ BO
f) 2.5^Δ BO

36) Rosaline is wearing the Rx OD −2.50 / OS −3.50 D fitted on a frame-imposed lens center of 56 mm. However, her PD is 62 mm. What is the <u>total</u> prism experienced by Rosaline?

   a) 0.9^Δ BO
   b) 1.5^Δ BO
   c) 1.8^Δ BO
   d) 2.1^Δ BO

37) Titania, with an PD of 58 mm, wears a spectacle Rx of OD +2.00 / OS −1.00 +4.00×090 fitted on a frame with an optical center separation of 64 mm. What is the <u>total</u> prism experienced by Titania?

   a) 1.0^Δ BO
   b) 1.5^Δ BO
   c) 1.5^Δ BI
   d) 2.5^Δ BI

38) Ophelia, with a PD of 58 mm, wears spectacle Rx OD −1.00 −1.00×090/ OS −2.00 fitted on a frame with an optical center separation of 62 mm. What is the <u>total</u> prism experienced?

   a) 0.4^Δ BO
   b) 0.4^Δ BO
   c) 0.4^Δ BI
   d) 0.8^Δ BI
   e) 2.0^Δ BO

39) Macbeth, wearing his spectacle Rx OU +3.00, looks down 3.3 mm from the lens center to read the script of the play. What is the induced prism?

   a) 1.0^Δ BU
   b) 1.5^Δ BU
   c) 3.0^Δ BU
   d) 4.5^Δ BD

40) Leonato wears this spectacle Rx OU +3.00 −4.00×180. What is the prismatic effect as he shifts his gaze 10 mm inferiorly?

   a) 1.0^Δ BD
   b) 3.0^Δ BU
   c) 4.0^Δ BU
   d) 10.0^Δ BD

41) Beatrice wears her spectacle Rx OU −3.00 +1.00×180. What is the prismatic effect as she shifts her gaze down by 5 mm?

   a) 1.0^Δ BD
   b) 3.0^Δ BU
   c) 4.0^Δ BU
   d) 10.0^Δ BD

42) What is the likely OU Rx that Benedick is wearing if he experiences a 2.0^Δ BD prism when he shifts his gaze 5 mm inferiorly?

   a) −2.00 +2.00×180
   b) +2.00 +2.00×180
   c) +2.00 −2.00×090
   d) −2.00 −2.00×180

43) Viola's Rx is −2.00 +2.00×180 OU. What prism (per eye) does she experience when she shifts her gaze 5 mm <u>inferiorly</u>?

   a) no prism
   b) 1.0^Δ BU
   c) 1.0^Δ BD
   d) 2.0^Δ BU
   e) 2.0^Δ BD

44) Viola (again). What is the prism experienced on her right eye when she shifts her gaze 5 mm <u>temporally</u>?

   a) no prism
   b) 1.0^Δ BO
   c) 1.0^Δ BI
   d) 2.0^Δ BO
   e) 2.0^Δ BI

45) To shift, or not to shift? That is the question. Hamlet's Rx is OD +1.75 D/ OS +2.25 D. He experiences a vertical imbalance of 0.2^Δ BU OS (most affected). By what amount and in which direction does Hamlet's gaze shift?

   a) 2 mm superiorly
   b) 2 mm inferiorly
   c) 4 mm superiorly
   d) 4 mm inferiorly
   e) 8 mm superiorly
   f) 8 mm inferiorly

46) Sir John Falstaff wears the Rx OD +4.00 −3.00×180 / OS +2.00 −4.00×180. What is the induced prism when he shifts his gaze down 5 mm?

   a) 0.5^Δ BU OD; 1.0^Δ BD OS
   b) 0.5^Δ BD OD; 1.0^Δ BD OS
   c) 0.5^Δ BD OD; 1.0^Δ BU OS
   d) 0.5^Δ BU OD; 1.0^Δ BU OS

47) What is the vertical imbalance experienced by Sir John Falstaff in this case?

   a) 0.5^Δ BU OD
   b) 0.5^Δ BU OS
   c) 1.0^Δ BD OS
   d) 1.5^Δ BD OS

48) Iago's Rx is +3.50 D. What is the induced prism when the lens is decentered 2.75 mm temporally?

   a) 0.9625^Δ BO
   b) 0.9625^Δ BI
   c) 9.625^Δ BO
   d) 9.625^Δ BI

49) What is the induced prism when Iago's lens is decentered 5 mm inferiorly?

   a) 1.75^Δ BU
   b) 1.75^Δ BD
   c) 17.5^Δ BU
   d) 17.5^Δ BD

50) What are the magnitude and direction of the total (single) prism when Iago's lens is decentered 2.75 mm temporally and 5 mm inferiorly?

   a) 0.7875^Δ; base @ 241°
   b) 2.7125^Δ; base @ 61°
   c) 2.0^Δ; base @ 61°
   d) 2.0^Δ; base @ 241°

51) What is the single prism combination of a 3.0^Δ BI with a 2.0^Δ BU placed in front of Gertrude's <u>left</u> eye?

   a) 3.6^Δ, base @ 56.3°
   b) 3.6^Δ, base @ 33.7°
   c) 1.0^Δ, base @ 56.3°
   d) 5.0^Δ, base @ 33.7°

52) What is the single prism equivalent to a 5.0^Δ BO combined with a 2.25^Δ BU placed in front of Juliet's right (OD) eye?

   a) 5.25^Δ; base @ 24.23°
   b) 2.75^Δ; base @ 155.77°
   c) 5.5^Δ; base @ 24.23°
   d) 5.5^Δ; base @ 155.77°

53) A prism of 3.6^Δ, base @45° placed in front of Viola's left (OS) eye resolves into ...

   a) 2.5^Δ BO; 2.5^Δ BU
   b) 2.5^Δ BI; 2.5^Δ BU
   c) 2.5^Δ BO; 2.5^Δ BD
   d) 2.5^Δ BI; 2.5^Δ BD

54) A 4.0^Δ; base @165° prism is placed in front of Olivia's left (OS) eye. This prism resolves into ...

   a) 3.86^Δ BO; 1.0^Δ BU
   b) 1.0^Δ BI; 3.86^Δ BD
   c) 3.86^Δ BI; 1.0^Δ BU
   d) 1.0^Δ BO; 3.86^Δ BD

55) Mark Antony is a myope spectacle wearer. Assuming that the placement of his lenses is perfectly matched to his MRP(s), what effects take place when as Antony's eyes converge to view a near object (select <u>three</u> correct)?

   a) a BI prism effect
   b) a BO prism effect
   c) effectively, lens moves temporally
   d) effectively, lens moves nasally
   e) IPD is shorter
   f) IPD is larger

56) Alonso has an exodeviating OD eye. What type of relief prism is prescribed (two choices)?

   a) a BO prism on the OD eye
   b) a BI prism on the OD eye
   c) a combination of BI prisms on the OD and the OS eye
   d) a combination of BO prisms on the OD and the OS eye

57) Claudius has non-hyperopic OD esophoria. It is suggested to prescribe (two choices) ...

   a) a BO prism on the OD eye
   b) a BI prism on the OD eye
   c) a combination of BI prisms on the OD and the OS eye
   d) a combination of BO prisms on the OD and the OS eye

58) Malvolio has 5.00^Δ of non-hyperopic esophoria. The prescribed prism has a magnitude and base of ...

   a) probably more than 5.00^Δ BO
   b) exactly 5.00^Δ BO
   c) probably less than 5.00^Δ BO

59) Malvolio's positive fusional vergence findings indicate a diplopia break of 18^Δ, and his negative fusional vergence findings indicate a diplopia break of 9^Δ. What prism should be prescribed according to Percival's criterion?

   a) no prism is needed
   b) 1.0^Δ BO
   c) 2.0^Δ BO
   d) 5.0^Δ BO
   e) 9.0^Δ BO

60) Cesario's has 8.0^Δ of esophoria and a 2.0^Δ of NFV recovery BI. What prism should be prescribed according to Saladin's 1:1 rule?

   a) no prism is needed
   b) 1.0^Δ BO

c) 2.0$^\Delta$ BO
d) 3.0$^\Delta$ BO
e) 5.0$^\Delta$ BO

61) When Cesario is measured through a 3.0$^\Delta$ BO, his phoria becomes ...

a) 2.0$^\Delta$ exophoria
b) 3.0$^\Delta$ exophoria
c) 5.0$^\Delta$ esophoria
d) 8.0$^\Delta$ esophoria
e) 11.0$^\Delta$ esophoria

62) Prince Hal has 16.0$^\Delta$ of near exophoria and 17.0$^\Delta$ of near compensating fusional vergence. Using Sheard's criterion, what prism should be prescribed?

a) 1.0$^\Delta$ BO
b) 2.0$^\Delta$ BI
c) 3.0$^\Delta$ BO

d) 5.0$^\Delta$ BI

63) When Prince Hal is fixating in the distance, he has 12.0$^\Delta$ of distance exophoria and 15.0$^\Delta$ of distance compensating fusional vergence. What prism should be prescribed for distance?

a) 1.0$^\Delta$ BI
b) 2.0$^\Delta$ BO
c) 3.0$^\Delta$ BI
d) 5.0$^\Delta$ BO

64) Using a lens clock, Prince Escalus measures two different lens thicknesses from the lens MRP: 15 mm temporally, 5 mm, and 15 mm nasally, 6.5 mm. If $n = 1.5$, what is the prismatic effect?

a) 2.5$^\Delta$ BI
b) 2.5$^\Delta$ BO
c) 5.0$^\Delta$ BI
d) 5.0$^\Delta$ BO

Tilt and Shift Effects

Unless specified otherwise, the lens material has a refractive index $n = 1.5$.

65) Enobarbus is worried that the wrap tilt of his spectacles will induce a ____ prism.

a) base-out
b) base-in
c) base-up
d) base-down

66) Enobarbus decides to dive into the math (as you should) to find the total affected prism for wrap angle 10°. Lenses have thickness $t = 3.5$ mm, and base curve $F_1 = +5.00$ D. Total prism will be ...

a) 0.2 BO
b) 0.2 BI
c) 0.4 BO
d) 0.4 BI

67) Rosalind just bought a new frame that has a faceform tilt of 25°. The corrective power of these lenses is a sphere –8.00 D. What is the effective corrective power that Rosalind experiences along the vertical meridian (@ 90°)?

a) –7.00 D
b) –7.50 D
c) –8.00 D
d) –8.50 D

68) Which of the following changes will bring Rosalind's effective corrective lens power along the vertical meridian close to –8.00 D?

a) reduce faceform tilt to 10°
b) increase faceform tilt to 30°
c) select lenses of refractive index $n = 1.9$
d) select lenses of refractive index $n = 1.4$

69) What is the cylinder experienced by Rosalind because of the faceform tilt of 25°?

a) –1.50×090
b) –1.75×090
c) –1.50×180
d) –1.75×180

70) What is the effective corrective lens power along the horizontal meridian (@ 180°) that Rosalind experiences with the faceform tilt of 25°?

a) –7.00 D
b) –8.00 D
c) –9.75 D
d) –10.25 D

71) Rosalind decides to buy another frame that has a faceform tilt of 10°. What is the cylinder she now experiences?

a) –0.25×090
b) –0.50×090
c) –1.00×090
d) –1.50×090
e) –1.75×090

72) Celia is a –9.00 D myope. Her new frame imposes a pantoscopic tilt. Effectively, Celia will experience a lens that is ...
   a) more minus
   b) no change in power
   c) less minus

73) Celia's new frame imposes a pantoscopic tilt of 18.5°. The new sphere power along the horizontal meridian (@ 180°) will be ...
   a) –8.70 D
   b) –9.00 D
   c) –9.30 D
   d) –10.30 D

74) Because of the pantoscopic tilt of 18.5°, Celia will experience along the vertical meridian (@ 90°) a sphere power of ...
   a) –8.70 D
   b) –9.00 D
   c) –9.30 D
   d) –10.30 D

75) Because of the pantoscopic tilt of 18.5°, Celia will experience a cylinder of ...
   a) –0.25×180
   b) –0.50×180
   c) –1.00×090
   d) –1.00×180
   e) –1.75×090

76) Celia tries another frame for her –9.00 D spectacle glasses that impose a pantoscopic tilt of 9.5°. The cylinder now experienced is ...
   a) –0.25×180
   b) –0.50×180
   c) –1.00×090
   d) –1.00×180
   e) –1.75×090

77) Cleopatra, in order to impress Mark Antony, orders her optician to fabricate a lens to fit Antony's Rx, which is an ATR myopic astigmatism –5.25 –1.00×090. Her Majesty's optician, however, back in the day, has only sphere power lenses with n = 1.8 available. To save the day, he proposes to fit these lenses on a frame with some tilt. Which tilt will produce the desired Rx for Mark Antony?
   a) a –5.25 D lens; faceform tilt of 25°
   b) a –5.00 D lens; faceform tilt of 25°

   c) a –4.75 D lens; pantoscopic tilt of 25°
   d) a –5.00 D lens; pantoscopic tilt of 25°

78) Rosencrantz tilts his new +2.00 spectacles 15° downwards. He experiences some changes (two correct) ...
   a) +cylinder ×180
   b) –cylinder ×180
   c) increased plus power
   d) decreased plus power

79) What is the Rx that Rosencrantz is most likely experiencing?
   a) +2.05 +0.14×180
   b) +2.05 –0.14×180
   c) +1.95 –0.14×180
   d) +1.95 +0.14×180

80) Guildenstern wants to fit a pair of +3.00 D spherical lenses on a frame that has a faceform tilt of 15°. What prescription will Guildenstern experience?
   a) +3.15 –0.50×090
   b) +3.15 +0.50×090
   c) +3.65 –0.50×090
   d) +3.65 +0.50×090

81) Horatio's –2.00 spectacles are fitted on a frame that imposes a 10° pantoscopic tilt. According to Martin's rule, what should the compensating drop be?
   a) 0.5 mm
   b) 1 mm
   c) 2 mm
   d) 5 mm

82) The suggested drop in Horatio's spectacles is going to induce a prism ...
   a) 0.5$^\Delta$ BU
   b) 1$^\Delta$ BU
   c) 2$^\Delta$ BU
   d) 5$^\Delta$ BD

83) Elsinore is a –5.00 myope. Her new spectacle glasses have a +3.50 D base curve, are made of 2.5 mm thick lens, and have a pantoscopic tilt of 12°. The induced prism due to this tilt is ...
   a) 0.125$^\Delta$ BU
   b) 0.25$^\Delta$ BU
   c) 0.5$^\Delta$ BU
   d) 0.5$^\Delta$ BD

10.9 PRISMATIC EFFECTS SUMMARY

Prism Optics

A **prism** is a transparent optical element with at least two non-parallel refracting sides, forming the **apical angle** A. A thin prism (apical angle < 30°) has a prism deviation angle ϑ_E independent of other parameters, depending only on material refracting index and apical angle.

Thin Prism Deviation Angle: $\qquad\qquad\qquad \vartheta_E = (n-1) \cdot A$ $\qquad\qquad\qquad$ (10.24)

The ability of a prism to produce a linear deviation of a ray at a given distance is quantified by the **prism power** $P[^\Delta]$:

$$\text{prism power } P[^\Delta] = \frac{\text{ray deviation [cm]}}{\text{distance away [m]}} = 100 \cdot \frac{\text{ray deviation [cm]}}{\text{distance away [cm]}} \qquad (10.25)$$

Prism power is expressed in **prism diopter** $[^\Delta]$ units; the unit is denoted by the Greek letter $\delta\acute{\epsilon}\lambda\tau\alpha$ Δ, often in uppercase. 1^Δ deviates a ray by 1 cm over a distance of 1 m. The prism deviation angle ϑ_E can be expressed in prism power diopters:

$$\text{prism power } P[^\Delta] = 100 \cdot \tan\vartheta_E \quad \text{or} \quad \tan\vartheta_E = P[^\Delta] / 100 \qquad (10.26)$$

The above equations are applicable to an object at a distance (optical infinity). For a near object, we use the effective prism power, with all distances as positive; COR = center of rotation of the eye (13.5 mm from the corneal plane):

Effective Prism Power: $\qquad P_{EFF}[^\Delta] = \dfrac{P[^\Delta]}{1 + \dfrac{\text{distance from prism to COR}}{\text{distance from prism to near object}}}$ $\qquad$ (10.27)

When the lens is decentered (the lens optical center is not aligned with the pupil center), a prismatic effect is induced. According to **Prentice's rule**, one centimeter of decentration (10 mm = 1 cm) induces one prism diopter (1^Δ) per one diopter (1 D) of lens power.

Prentice's Rule: $\qquad\qquad \text{induced prism } [^\Delta] = \dfrac{\text{lens power [D]} \cdot \text{decentration [mm]}}{10}$ $\qquad$ (10.28)

Alternatively, a Prentice's-rule-induced prism can be expressed as

$$\text{induced prism } P[^\Delta] = \text{lens power [D]} \cdot \text{decentration [cm]} \qquad (10.29)$$

To implement Prentice's rule in a spherocylindrical lens, convert the Rx prescription to lens cross.

Prisms in Vision Correction

Prism base orientation is referenced with respect to the <u>wearer's face</u>.

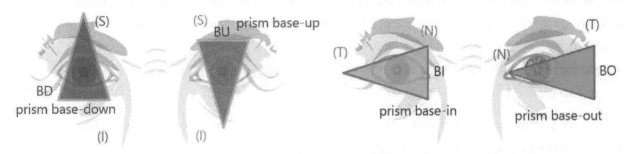

Figure 10-48: The four major prism base orientations.

Prism can be induced by lens decentration in front of the pupil. This can be due to interpupillary distance mismatch from a shorter or wider frame, or due to near vision convergence.

Horizontal prism can be induced by **disparity** (mismatch) between the interpupillary distance (IPD or PD) and the distance separating the two lens centers. The effect is bilateral, i.e., in both eyes, it is either BI or BO. The disparity is usually split between the two eyes, i.e., a 68 mm lens center distance for a 62 mm PD means that each lens is shifted 3 mm temporally.

Vertical imbalance is the difference in vertical prism due to unequal sphere powers (along the vertical meridian) present in front of the two eyes. It is reported (as a single value) on the most affected eye as the difference (if conjunctive) or the sum (if disjunctive) prisms.

Depending on the type of deviation, the prism can be **prescribed** to alleviate the symptoms. In exodeviation, we need to compensate inwardly, using a base-in prism. For esodeviation, we use a base-out prism. For hyperdeviation, we need to move 'the eye' downward, so we use a base-down prism, and for hypodeviation, we use a base-up prism. Depending on the clinical judgment, the following empirical rules are in use.

Empirical Rules for Esophoria:

Percival's Criterion: prism = ⅓·(greater of lateral limits) − ⅔·(lesser of lateral limits)   (10.30)

1:1 rule: prism = ½·(phoria − NFV recovery)   (10.31)

Empirical rules for exophoria:

Sheard's criterion: prism = ⅔·(phoria) − ⅓·(compensating fusional vergence)   (10.32)

Tilt and Shift Effects

Tilting with respect to the line of sight of the wearer can be:

- **wrap tilt** (faceform tilt): the lens tilt about the vertical axis / 90 meridian with respect to primary gaze—simply put, the rotation of the lens (angling of the side rim) toward the temple, away from the nose.
- **pantoscopic tilt**: the lens tilt about the horizontal axis / 180° meridian when the lens leans down toward the cheeks.

Two effects are associated with lens tilt: the induction of prism and the effective change of the three Rx components: sphere, cylinder, and axis.

Induced Prism due to tilt α: $$P[^\Delta] = 100 \cdot \alpha \cdot (t/n) \cdot F_1 \qquad (10.33)$$

where α is the tilt angle [rad], which is considered as small. Note that the effect is dependent on the base curve power F_1.

The amounts of effective dioptric power induced by a lens tilt of about a degrees are described by Coddington's equations:

$$\text{New (effective) sphere power} = \text{sphere} \cdot [1 + (\sin^2\alpha)/2n] \qquad (10.34)$$
$$\text{Induced cylinder} = (\text{new sphere}) \cdot (\tan^2\alpha) \qquad (10.35)$$

For a minus lens:	• pantoscopic tilt induces more –sphere and –cylinder on the 180°. • faceform tilt induces more –sphere and –cylinder on the 90°.
For a plus lens:	• pantoscopic tilt induces more +sphere and +cylinder on the 180°. • faceform tilt induces more +sphere and +cylinder on the 90°.

In order to keep the optical axis of the lens passing through the eye's center of rotation, a drop of the lens optical center can also compensate for the induced cylinder due to pantoscopic tilt. The rule that governs this compensation, known as **Martin's rule of tilt**, states that a single-vision lens can be lowered 1 mm for every 2° of pantoscopic tilt.

Martin's rule in pantoscopic tilt:	• To ensure that the optical axis of the lens passes through the center of rotation of the eye, the optical center of the lens should be dropped by 1 mm for every 2° of pantoscopic tilt.

(a) Lens at vertex distance

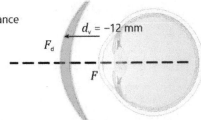

Vertex power transposition:

$$F_d\,[D] = \frac{F\,[D]}{1 - d_v\,[m] \cdot F\,[D]}$$

Typical vertex distance is 12 mm.
Is positive if to the right, negative if to the left.
Minus contact lens correction becomes less negative,
Plus contact lens correction becomes more positive.

(b) Lens is decentered

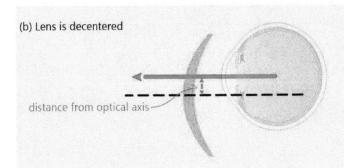

Decentered lens / Prentice's rule

Induced prism:
$P\,[^\Delta]$ = lens power [D] · distance from optical axis [cm]

(c) Lens is tilted, no lens drop

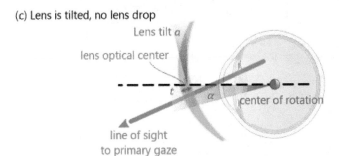

Two effects associated with lens tilt by angle a [rad]:

(i) Prism is induced: $P\,[^\Delta] = 100 \cdot a \cdot (t/n) \cdot F$,

(ii) Sphere and cyl are affected, per Coddington's rules:

New sphere power = sphere $\cdot [1 + (\sin^2 a)/2n]$
Induced cylinder = (new sphere) $\cdot (\tan^2 a)$

New sphere and induced cylinder same sign as sphere.
Cylinder axis is the axis of rotation, 90 for tilt and 180 for panto.

(d) Lens tilt and drop

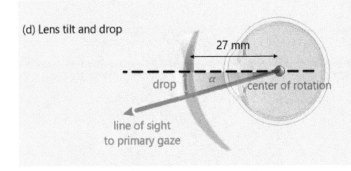

Martin's rule describes the compensation required to offset the effects of lens tilt.

Drop of the optical center of the lens by 1 mm for every 2° of lens tilt

Figure 10-49: Summary of power and prism effects associated with lens position and rotation.
(a) Power compensation when lens is positioned at a vertex distance d_v along the optical axis.
(b) Prism when lens is decentered (shifted laterally) as described by Prentice's rule.
(c) Prism and Rx components when a lens is tilted (either faceform or pantoscopic).
(d) Lens is titled and dropped. To maintain the intersection of the line of sight with the eye's center of rotation, the lens is dropped by 1 mm for every 2° of tilt (Martin's rule).

APPENDIX

CONVENTIONS AND NOTATIONS

Conventions

The 2003 General Conference on Weights and Measures convention is followed.

- o The period (.) is used as decimal marker symbol.
- o A comma is used as grouping symbol in order to facilitate reading of numbers having more than four digits.
- o The fundamental unit for length is the meter (m).

Example: 1.50 m indicates one meter and 50 centimeters.

Length	Divisions		
1 m	1 cm (centimeter)	$=10^{-2}$ m	1 m = 100 cm
	1 mm (millimeter)	$=10^{-3}$ m	1 m = 1000 mm
	1 µm (micrometer)	$=10^{-6}$ m	1 m = 1,000,000 µm
	1 nm (nanometer)	$=10^{-9}$ m	1 m = 1,000,000,000 nm

Conversion factors from the English linear measurements:

- o 1 m = 39.37 in
- o 1 cm = 0.394 in
- o 1 in = 2.45 cm

Object-Space versus Image-Space Notation

Quantities such as distances or height, points such as focal, principal or nodal points, planes such as the focal or the principal are denoted as

- o non-primed if they correspond to the object space.
- o primed if they correspond to the image space.

Examples:

x indicates object location, *h* indicates object height, *x'* indicates image location, and *h'* indicates image height.

$L = 1/x$ indicates object vergence: Object vergence is the reciprocal of object distance, when the latter is expressed in meters. Likewise, $L' = 1/x'$ indicates image beam vergence.

The Cartesian Sign Convention

- o This convention is also known as the English System.
- o The origin of the coordinate system is at the intersection of the wavefront vertex or of the optical component with the optical axis. Examples: center of the lens, vertex of the mirror.
- o Directed distances refer to distances along the optical axis and are vectorial in nature. Examples: Focal length, radius of curvature, object and image distances. These distances are all measured from the origin.
- o Positive sign is assigned for any distance that is along the direction of light. Negative sign is assigned for any distance that points opposite to the direction of light.
- o Height refers to normal to the optical axis. An upward height is positive, and a downward height is negative.
- o Unless otherwise noted, light travels from left to right.

Examples:

An object:

- o If it is (as is typical) placed before (to the left of) an optical interface, it has a negative location and negative vergence. It corresponds to a real object.
- o If it is (to be) formed after (to the right of) an optical interface, it has a positive location and positive vergence. It corresponds to a virtual object.

An image:

- o If it is formed to the right of a lens or refractive surface, it has a positive location and positive vergence. It is therefore real.
- o If it is formed to the left of a lens or refractive surface, it has a negative location and negative vergence. It is therefore virtual.

In mirrors, light reverses direction after reflection. Any directional distance associated with reflected light (focal length, radius of curvature, and image location) is positive if it is in front (to the left of) the mirror and negative if it is after (to the right of) the mirror. Object location is unaffected, as it is associated with the initial light direction of propagation to the right.

- o In a concave mirror, focal length and radius of curvature are positive.
- o In a convex mirror, focal length and radius of curvature are negative.
- o Image location is positive if it is formed before the mirror (real) and negative if it is formed after the mirror (virtual).
- o Object location is negative if it is placed before the mirror (real) and positive if it is to be formed after the mirror (virtual).

Frequently used Notation

Description	Notation	Units	Alternate Notation
Curvature	C	D (diopter)	
Radius of Curvature	r	m (meter)	
Optical Power	F	D	P
Focal length (distance)	f / f'	m	f_1 / f_2
Vergence	L / L'	D	U / V
Object / image location	x / x'	m	u / v
Object / image height	h / h'	m	
Magnification	m (linear) M (angular)	-	
Focal points	F / F'	-	F_1 / F_2
Principal points	P / P'	-	P_1 / P_2
Principal planes	H / H'	-	H_1 / H_2
Nodal points	N / N'	-	N_1 / N_2
Index of refraction	n	-	
Wavelength	λ	nm or μm	
Frequency	ν	Hz (hertz)	f

Note 👤: In the notation followed in this series, unless otherwise stated, non-primed quantities correspond to object space, and primed quantities correspond to image space. Alternative notation is followed by other textbooks in optics and is provided here in order to facilitate the use of material from these other sources.

Useful Notes

Angle units

Angle	Divisions			
1° (degree)	1′ (minute, arcmin)	= 1°/60		1° = 60′
	1″ (second, arcsec)	= 1′/60 = 1°/3600	1° = 3660″	
1 rad (radian)	1 rad ≈ 57.3°			1° = 0.0175 rad

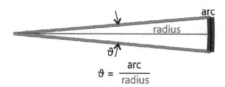

$$\vartheta = \frac{arc}{radius}$$

Trigonometry

Name	Noted as	definition
sine	sin	= opposite / hypotenuse
cosine	cos	= adjacent / hypotenuse
tangent	tan	= opposite / adjacent
cotangent	ctan	= adjacent / opposite

Useful Trigonometric Numbers

angle (°)	angle (rad)	$\sin(\vartheta)$	$\cos(\vartheta)$	$\tan(\vartheta)$
0	0	0	1	0
30	$\frac{\pi}{6}$	$\frac{1}{2}$	$\frac{\sqrt{3}}{2}$	$\frac{\sqrt{3}}{3}$
45	$\frac{\pi}{4}$	$\frac{\sqrt{2}}{2}$	$\frac{\sqrt{2}}{2}$	1
60	$\frac{\pi}{3}$	$\frac{\sqrt{3}}{2}$	$\frac{1}{2}$	$\sqrt{3}$
90	$\frac{\pi}{2}$	1	2	not defined

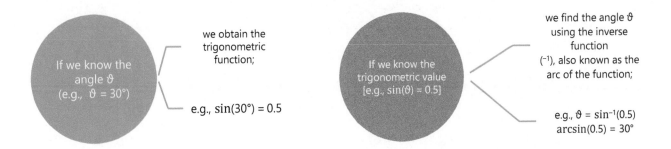

If we know the angle ϑ
(e.g., ϑ = 30°)

we obtain the trigonometric function;

e.g., sin(30°) = 0.5

If we know the trigonometric value
[e.g., sin(ϑ) = 0.5]

we find the angle ϑ using the inverse function
($^{-1}$), also known as the arc of the function;

e.g., $\vartheta = \sin^{-1}(0.5)$
$\arcsin(0.5) = 30°$

ANSWERS TO QUIZ QUESTIONS

(Answers are provided only to odd-numbered questions.)

Chapter 1 Optics of the Eye

1) b		11) b		21) a
	7) g	13) d	17) a and b	
3) d	9) c		19) a	
5) c		15) a and c		

Chapter 2 Refractive Elements of the Eye

1) e	19) b	37) b	55) d and f	73) d
3) a	21) c	39) a	57) b and c	75) a
5) b and f	23) e	41) e	59) f	77) d
7) a	25) b	43) d	61) c	79) c
9) a	27) b	45) c	63) c	81) b
11) e	29) b	47) b and f	65) c	83) d
13) b and c	31) a	49) c	67) a	85) c
15) a	33) a	51) d	69) a	87) a, c, and f
17) c	35) a	53) a, b, and c	71) d	89) a

Chapter 3 Visual Acuity

1) e	13) c	25) d	37) a and c	49) e
3) a	15) d	27) e	39) b	51) b
5) a	17) c	29) a	41) d	53) e
7) b	19) a	31) b	43) c	55) a
9) c	21) a	33) c	45) d	57) d
11) d	23) d	35) a	47) d	59) d

Chapter 4 Optics of the Retina

1) e		23) b		45) b
	13) a	25) b	35) c and d	47) b
3) c	15) c	27) c	37) c	49) a
5) b	17) c	29) d	39) a	51) b
7) a	19) a	31) a	41) b	53) c
9) b	21) c	33) c	43) c	55) c
11) b				

57) c	59) c	61) e	63) a

Chapter 5 Color Perception

1) c and d	17) c	33) c	49) d	65) a and f
3) c	19) b	35) d	51) a	67) a
5) d	21) a	37) b and d	53) b and c	69) a
7) c	23) b	39) b	55) a and d	71) d
9) d	25) d	41) a	57) d	73) a
11) a	27) d	43) b	59) d	75) d
13) f	29) d	45) e	61) c	77) a
15) b	31) a	47) a and b	63) b and c	79) a

Chapter 6 Ametropias

1) c		35) c		69) a and c
3) d	19) a	37) a	53) c	71) b
5) b	21) a and d	39) a	55) b	73) b
7) a	23) b and c	41) d	57) a	75) c
9) c	25) a and d	43) c	59) a	77) a
11) b	27) a	45) a	61) d	79) b and d
13) c and e	29) c	47) a	63) d	81) b
15) b	31) d	49) b	65) a	83) a
17) c	33) d	51) b	67) b	

Chapter 7 Accommodation and Presbyopia

1) d	15) d	29) b	43) b	57) a
3) d	17) a	31) c	45) c	59) d
5) a and d	19) b	33) b	47) a	61) d
7) b	21) b	35) c	48) 49) c	63) b
9) c	23) c	37) c	51) a	65) b
11) a	25) d	39) a	53) b	67) a
13) d	27) c	41) d	55) c	

Chapter 8 Astigmatism

1) c		15) b		29) e
3) a	9) c	17) a and b	23) b	31) e
5) d	11) d	19) b	25) a	33) c
7) a	13) a	21) a, d, and e	27) c	35) b

37) d

39) a

41) b

43) b

45) f

47) e

49) a and d

51) c

53) b

55) b

57) b

59) b

61) e

63) b

65) b and c

67) b

69) b

71) b and d

73) d

75) a

77) a

79) b

81) c

83) b

85) b

87) b

Chapter 9 Ophthalmic Lens Optics

1) d

3) c

5) d

7) c

9) c

11) d

13) d

15) e

17) c

19) b and d

21) e

23) c

25) c

27) e

29) a

31) a

33) b

35) a and d

37) c

39) e

41) d

43) c

45) b

47) a

49) d

51) a and c

53) a and b

55) c

57) a

59) a

61) a

63) c

65) d

67) a

69) d

71) d

73) c

75) d

77) c

79) c

81) b

83) b

85) c

87) a

89) a

91) c

93) d

95) a

97) b

99) a and b

101) d

103) a

105) a

107) d

109) c

111) a and d

113) d

115) e

117) a and d

119) b

121) b

Chapter 10 Prismatic Effects

1) a

3) b

5) d

7) d

9) b

11) a

13) e

15) c

17) c

19) c

21) c

23) a and c

25) d

27) a

29) b

31) a and d

33) b

35) d

37) b

39) a

41) a

43) a

45) d

47) d

49) b

51) b

53) a

55) a, d, and e

57) a and d

59) a

61) c

63) c

65) a

67) d

69) b

71) a

73) c

75) d

77) b

79) a

81) d

83) a

INDEX

B

C

N

O

T

 **George Asimellis**, PhD, MBA, serves as Professor of Vision Science at the New England College of Optometry (Boston, Massachusetts). He oversees the development and coordination of the Geometric Optics and Vision Science Courses and the development of the Advanced Optometry at NECO.

In the past, he served as Associate Professor of Optics and Research Director at the Kentucky College of Optometry (Pikeville, Kentucky), which he joined as Founding Faculty. Other positions include: Research Director at the LaserVision.gr Institute, Athens, Greece, and faculty at the Physics Department, Aristotle University, Greece; Medical School, Democritus University, Greece; and Electrical Engineering Department, George Mason University, Virginia. His doctorate research involved advanced optical signal processing and pattern recognition techniques (PhD, Tufts University, Massachusetts), and optical coherence tomography (Fellowship, Harvard University, Massachusetts). He then worked on the research and development of optoelectronic devices in a number of research centers in the USA. He has authored more than 75 peer-reviewed research publications, 8 scholarly books on optics and optical imaging, and a large number of presentations at international conferences and meetings.

He is on the Editorial Board of eight peer-reviewed journals, including the *Journal of Refractive Surgery*, for which he serves as Associate Editor. He received the 2017 Emerging Vision Scientist Award from the National Alliance for Eye and Vision Research (NAEVR).

His research interests include optoelectronic devices, anterior-segment (corneal and epithelial) imaging, keratoconus screening, ocular optics, and ophthalmological lasers. His recent contributions involve publications in clinical *in vivo* epithelial imaging and corneal cross-linking interventions.